Prealgebra for College Students

Santa Rosa Junior College

2nd Edition

Matthew P. Greaney

CENGAGE
Learning™

Australia • Brazil • Japan • Korea • Mexico • Singapore • Spain • United Kingdom • United States

CENGAGE
Learning™

Prealgebra for College Students: Santa Rosa Junior College, 2nd Edition

Matthew P. Greaney

Executive Editors:
Michele Baird
Maureen Staudt
Michael Stranz

Project Development Manager:
Linda deStefano

Senior Marketing Coordinators:
Sara Mercurio
Lindsay Shapiro

Senior Production / Manufacturing Manager:
Donna M. Brown

PreMedia Services Supervisor:
Rebecca A. Walker

Rights & Permissions Specialist:
Kalina Hintz

Cover Image:
Getty Images*

For product information and technology assistance, contact us at
Cengage Learning Customer & Sales Support, 1-800-354-9706

For permission to use material from this text or product,
submit all requests online at **cengage.com/permissions**
Further permissions questions can be emailed to
permissionrequest@cengage.com

ISBN-13: 978-0-7593-5515-6

ISBN-10: 0-7593-5515-0

Cengage Learning
5191 Natorp Boulevard
Mason, Ohio 45040
USA

Cengage Learning is a leading provider of customized learning solutions with office locations around the globe, including Singapore, the United Kingdom, Australia, Mexico, Brazil, and Japan. Locate your local office at:
international.cengage.com/region

Cengage Learning products are represented in Canada by Nelson Education, Ltd.

For your lifelong learning solutions, visit **custom.cengage.com**

Visit our corporate website at **cengage.com**

Printed in the United States of America

Table of Contents

Prealgebra for College Students

Chapter 3: Signed Numbers

Chapter 4: Exponents

Chapter 5: Geometry

Chapter 6: Algebraic Expressions

Chapter 7: Algebraic Equations

Appendix A

Preface: Understanding How this Math Book Works

This text has been written for the adult student and covers thoroughly arithmetic and prealgebra. Dependent upon an instructor's need, the book may be used for an arithmetic class, a prealgebra course, or over a two-semester period for both arithmetic and prealgebra. The intent of the book's set up is to share with students that arithmetic and algebra share the same mathematical truths and follow the same processes. To understand arithmetic concepts is to understand algebraic problem solving.

The book follows the same sequential format in every section of every unit.

Objectives — At the top of every section are simple short statements regarding the subject matter which should be learned after working through this part of the book.

Application — After the objective is an example problem which one might face in the real world. The student needs to know and use one or more of the skills which will be learned in this section to solve this problem.

Vocabulary — Following the example application are a few math words or symbols which are important to the student in the upcoming section. Basic math truths (i.e. any number times 1 is that number itself) and concepts are also stated here.

How to — The *How to* parts in each section are placed inside boxes and give short easy steps to explain a particular math process. These often give steps for basic math computation.

Examples — After every *How to* in the book an *example* or *examples* are given which show a step-by-step working of a problem that follows the given *How to* process.

Why — This is inserted in some sections in the book to give an explanation of why certain math processes work or why they are needed. This is for the student who isn't content with only the mathematical truth, but is always wanting to know why.

Samples — The samples given in the book are more example problems, but differ from the *Examples* in two ways. First, the explanation is normally not as detailed. Second, its purpose is not to reproduce another explanation of basic step-by-step computation. The samples are usually word problems, or at a minimum are a more complex math problem which may simply challenge a student because of its length or different presentation.

You try it now — Following every *sample*, this part of the book gives 2 problems similar to the sample just explained. Answers to these problems are provided just before that section's *Problem Sets*.

Answers to you try it now and **Answer to Application** The answers to all the *You try it now* problems and the *Application* problem from the beginning of each section are located immediately before the *Problem Sets*. A full explanation to the initial application problem is provided here.

Problem Sets — The Problem Sets do vary in different parts of the books, but are basically composed of groups of problems which separately address five major areas:

(A) Basic computation.

(B) Noncomputational mathematical expressions, equations, and word problems which address the skill of translating words into math statements. Variables are used extensively in this area of the problem sets.

(C) Noncomputational or limited computational problems that require students to fully understand math concepts, math symbols, and important math vocabulary. Students will develop the ability to recognize different forms of the same expressions and equations.

(D) Word problems. An emphasis is put on solving these application problems in two parts. The first answer is **the set up—a <u>single</u> mathematical statement** (expression or equation) **that will solve the entire problem** (not piece by piece solving). This establishes a necessary recognition that problems are often multi-step in nature. The second answer is the actual solution.

(E) Noncomputational or limited computational problems using variables which have students recognizing math truths in the abstract algebraic format.

Skills Check   This part of each section gives a few problems from material covered in the previous section, providing students the opportunity to solidify older material. If the students can't do these problems, it is a siren warning them that they need to review the previous subject matter.

This text is cumulative in its pedagogy. However, as stated earlier, movement forward can be done at different levels. If using this text for the arithmetic level only, Unit #1 and Unit #2 will be your focus. Choose homework problems from the A and B problem-set areas and hand-select appropriate (the initial) translation and word problems from the C and D problem-set areas.

If using this text for the prealgebra level, every instructor and math program needs to decide how much the computational skills need to be addressed (problem-set area A), but of course at this level a greater emphasis needs to be spent on problem-set areas B through E.

Before We Get Started: An Introduction for the Students and Instructors of Prealgebra

To utilize this text most efficiently, and for students to avoid some confusion or frustration from the start, it is important that everyone, that is instructors and students, have a particular and similar understanding of some vocabulary and a few particular math truths.

First, let's look at the vocabulary words which we all need to know so we can communicate with each other effectively. **We need to constantly remind ourselves that math is a language.** We communicate by agreeing upon the meaning of certain words and symbols just as in our common language we know the meaning of certain words and use common gestures to communicate.

Vocabulary

variable—a **variable** is any letter of the alphabet that represents an unknown number value.
Some examples:

$$2 + x = 10 \qquad \text{where x is the variable}$$
$$b - 7 \qquad \text{where b is the variable}$$

expression—A **mathematical expression** is the grammar equivalent of a phrase. It says something, but <u>does not</u> express a complete thought.

Examples: $5 + 7$, $11 - 4$, $8 \bullet 3$, and $20 \div 5$ are four examples of expressions.

equation—An **mathematical equation** is the grammar equivalent of a complete sentence. It differs from an expression in that it has **an equal sign** (the verb of our sentence) <u>and</u> **an answer.**

Compare these examples of equations with the above examples of expressions:

$$5 + 7 = 12 \qquad 11 - 4 = 7 \qquad 8 \bullet 3 = 24 \qquad 20 \div 5 = 4$$

It is important that you know the difference between an **expression** and an **equation**. These two words will be used throughout the book and in many of the directions to your problem exercises.

Two Mathematical Truths

Addition & subtraction are opposites of each other.

Multiplication and division are opposites of each other.

Two Basic Equation Truths

Step #1: We get rid of any number or value in an equation by doing the <u>opposite operation</u>.

Step #2: We must do the <u>same thing</u> to both sides of an equation (meaning both sides of an equal sign) for the equation to stay equal.

***These two steps always work at the same time. Look at the following examples.

Example #1: The given equation is: $5 + 7 = 12$

Step #1: Let's decide to get rid of "plus 7."
We get rid of "plus 7" by doing the opposite
operation. The opposite of "plus 7" is "subtract 7."

Step #2: Do the same thing to both sides of the equation.
"Subtract 7" from both sides of the equation. Our
equation would now look like this: $5 + 7 - 7 = 12 - 7$

We can see that the equation is still true when
we do the same thing to both sides. It is true that: $5 = 5$

Example #2: The given equation is: $11 - 4 = 7$

Step #1: Let's decide to get rid of "subtract 4."
We get rid of "subtract 4" by doing the opposite
operation. The opposite of "subtract 4" is "add 4."

Step #2: Do the same thing to both sides of the
equation. "Add 4" to both sides of the equation.
Our equation would now look like this: $11 - 4 + 4 = 7 + 4$

We can see that the equation is still true when
we do the same thing to both sides. It is true that: $11 = 11$

Example #3: The given equation is: $8 \cdot 3 = 24$

Step #1: Let's decide to get rid of "multiply by 3."
We get rid of "multiply by 3" by doing the opposite
operation. The opposite of "multiply by 3" is
"divide by 3."

Step #2: Do the same thing to both sides of
the equation. Both sides of the equation must
be "divided by 3." Our equation would now
look like this:

$$8 \cdot 3 \div 3 = 24 \div 3$$

We can see that the equation is still true when
we do the same thing to both sides. It is true that: $8 = 8$

Example #4: The given equation is: $20 \div 5 = 4$

Step #1: Let's decide to get rid of "divide by 5."
We get rid of "divide by 5" by doing the opposite
operation. The opposite of "divide by 5" is
"multiply by 5."

Step #2: Do the same thing to both sides of the equation. Both sides of the equation must be "multiplied by 5." Our equation would now look like this:

$$20 \div 5 \bullet 5 = 4 \bullet 5$$

We can see that the equation is still true when we do the same thing to both sides. It is true that:

$$20 = 20$$

We will save most of our equation work for later in the book, but in the very first unit we will start manipulating equations—that is, doing the same thing to both sides of the equation—as shown above.

Remember: Equations are puppets. We are all puppeteers and control what happens to those equations. Our only limitation is that we have to follow the rules.

o

Chapter 1   Whole Numbers and Decimals

Section 1.1 Place Values and Comparisons

Objectives:

• To understand place values of whole numbers and decimals

• To compare number values

Application:

A nursing student is told to draw up 0.5 mg of Demerol for a patient. The Demerol label states that a patient should never receive more than 0.05 mg. Is 0.5 greater than (>), equal to (=), or less than (<) 0.05? Should the nursing student question this order?

Vocabulary:

decimal point—The **decimal point** separates whole number values (to the left of the decimal pt.) from parts or decimal values (to the right of the decimal pt.). When writing numbers, the decimal point is represented by the word "and."

place value—A **place value** is the name given for every digit which tells the worth or value of that digit or place. Whole number digits are to the left of the decimal point; decimal digits are to the right of the decimal point.

place value system—The **place value system** has its foundation in our "base 10" number system (that is, each digit has only ten numbers that can possibly fill its space—0, 1, 2, 3, 4, 5, 6, 7, 8, or 9).   When we get beyond a single digit in value (as in increasing the number 9 to 10), the value of the given number "spills over" into another place value. The decimal point is the center of the place value system. **When finding the name of a particular place value, <u>always</u> begin at the decimal point.**

inequality symbols— The relationship of two number values that are not equal to each other can be expressed using inequality symbols.

> is the symbol meaning "**greater than.**"

< is the symbol meaning "**less than.**"

PLACE-VALUE CHART

WHOLE NUMBERS											Decimal Point	DECIMAL VALUES (parts)					
Billions			Millions			Thousands			Ones			•	$\frac{1}{10}$	$\frac{1}{100}$	$\frac{1}{1,000}$	$\frac{1}{10,000}$	$\frac{1}{100,000}$	$\frac{1}{1,000,000}$
Hundreds	Tens	Ones	Hundreds	Tens	Ones	Hundreds	Tens	Ones	Hundreds	Tens	Ones		Tenths	Hundredths	Thousandths	Ten thousandths	Hundred thousandths	Millionths

Look at the place-value chart above and see the place-value names. It is important that we memorize the place values.

Heading left from the decimal point (that is naming the <u>whole number</u> places), the place values are the ones (1), the tens (10), the hundreds (100), the thousands (1000), the ten thousands (10,000), the hundred thousands (100,000), the millions (1,000,000), etc.

Heading right from the decimal point (that is naming the <u>decimal</u> number places) the place values are the tenths (how many parts out of 10), the hundredths (how many parts out of 100), the thousandths (how many parts out of 1000), the ten-thousandths (how many parts out of 10,000), etc.

Applying place values to money: Think of $5.42

> The 4 is in the tenths place. This represents 4 dimes, or 4 tenths of a dollar. The 2 is in the hundredths place. This represents 2 cents (pennies), or two hundredths of a dollar.

**Remember: The decimal place value names always end in <u>ths</u>.

**Remember: The digits farthest to the left have the greatest value.

How to:

Read/Write a Number:

1. Read the whole number.

2. Say "**and**" if there is a decimal value that follows the whole number.

3. Read the number of parts (the number to the right of the decimal point) out of the place value (the name of the decimal digit farthest to the right).

Example #1 (Reading and writing a number): 8,650,731.49

Step #1: Read the whole number (check the place-value chart above if necessary). Know the values of each number.

The <u>8</u> is in the millions place, so it has a real value of 8 × (1,000,000) or eight million (8,000,000).

The <u>6</u> is in the hundred-thousands place, so it has a real value of 6 × (100,000) or six hundred thousand (600,000).

The <u>5</u> is in the ten-thousands place, so it has a real value of 5 × (10,000) or fifty thousand (50,000).

The <u>0</u> is in the thousands place, so it has a real value of 0 × (1,000) or zero (0).

The <u>7</u> is in the hundreds place, so it has a real value of 7 × (100) or seven hundred (700).

The <u>3</u> is in the tens place, so it has a real value of 3 × (10) or thirty (30).

The <u>1</u> is in the ones place, so it has a real value of 1 × (1) or one (1).

Thus, the whole number value is: Eight million, six hundred fifty thousand, seven hundred thirty-one.

Step #2: Read the decimal point as "and."

Step #3: Read the decimal number.

The number to the right of the decimal point is 49 (parts). The place value name of the digit farthest to the right is the hundredths place. Thus, the decimal value is 49 parts out of 100 (49/100) or forty-nine hundredths (0.49).

Finally, we would read and write the entire number as:
Answer: **Eight million, six hundred fifty thousand, seven hundred thirty-one and forty-nine hundredths.**

Remember: When reading or writing whole numbers, we read them in groups—how many millions, how many thousands, and how many ones (units). **These whole number groupings are set off by commas.

> **How to:**
>
> Compare Numbers
>
> 1. Look at and compare the whole numbers.
>
> 2. If the whole numbers are the same, look at and compare decimal place values from left to right (from tenths to hundredths, etc.).

**Remember: Read inequalities from left to right as English words are read left to right.

$9 > 5$ reads: "Nine is **greater than** five." This is a true statement.

$17 < 10$ reads: "Seventeen is **less than** ten." This is a false statement.

Example #2: Which is larger, 80.24 or 80.226?

Step #1: Compare whole numbers. Both have 80 wholes. They are equal so far.

Step #2: Compare decimal place values from left to right.

Compare the values in each tenths place first. Both numbers have a 2 or two tenths. They are equal.

Compare the values in each hundredths place.

80.24 has a **4** or four hundredths.   80.226 has a **2** or two hundredths.

The 4 is larger than the 2. We can then say that 80.24 is larger than 80.226: Using an inequality symbol we can express this as:
Answer: 80.24 > 80.226

**Remember: When comparing decimals, you can add zeros (there is always "and nothing" more) to the right of the last decimal digit without changing the real value of the number, thus creating the same number of decimal places in both numbers.

In the example above you could add a zero at the end of 80.24, thus making it 80.240, still keeping its exact same value. One can see now that 240 (thousandths) is more than the 226 (thousandths) that exist in the number 80.226.

Sample #1   What are the place-value names for the digits 2, 4, 5, and 7 in the number 2,640,880.507?

Look at the whole numbers first:
        The place value for the 2 is the *millions* .
        The place value for the 4 is the *ten-thousands* .

Look at the decimal numbers second:
        The place value for the 5 is the *tenths* .
        The place value for the 7 is the *thousandths* .

- **You try it now:**
- a) What are the place-value names for the digits 3, 4, 6, and 9 in the number 28,406.0309?
- b) What are the place-value names for the digits 1, 8, and 0 in the number 1,286,753,053?

Sample #2 Write the following words as a number: Twenty-two million, five hundred eight thousand, fifty and sixteen thousandths.

Look at the whole number digits first:
How many millions?   **22 (comma)**
How many thousands? **508 (comma)**
How many ones?   **050**

The whole number is 22,508,050 Now remember that "**and**" is the decimal point.

Look at the decimal number digits second:
What is the number to the right of the decimal point?   16
What is the place value of the last digit? **The thousandths (3 decimal places)**

So we would write sixteen-thousandths as .016

The number written above in standard number form would be: **Answer: 22,508,050.016**

- **You try it now:**
- c) Write the following words as a number: Six million, eighty-five thousand, four hundred and twenty-four hundredths
- d) Write the following words as a number: Forty billion, eighty million, seven hundred and six tenths

Sample #3 Write the following number in words: 37,462.8

Look at the whole number digits first:
How many thousands? **thirty-seven (comma)**
How many ones?   **four hundred sixty-two**

So we write 37,462 wholes as **thirty-seven thousand, four hundred sixty-two**

We would write "**and**" for the decimal point.

Look at the decimal number second:
What is the number to the right of the decimal point? eight
What is the place value of the last digit? **The tenths (1 decimal place)**

So we would write .8 as **eight-tenths**.

The number above would be written as:
Answer: Thirty-seven thousand, four hundred sixty-two and eight-tenths

You try it now:

e) Write the following number in words: 12,205,000

f) Write the following number in words: 340,007.714.

Sample #4: Put the following numbers in order from the smallest value to the largest (put a comma between each number.

    3.8   3.92   3.815   3   3.65

The easiest way to solve this problem is to line up the numbers so their decimal points are lined up:

    3.8

    3.92

    3.815

    3

    3.65

Now we can compare. First we look at the whole numbers. They are all 3. They are the same so far. Now look at the digits in the tenths place. We have a 9, two 8's, a 6, and a 0 (3 is the same as 3.0). The 0 is the smallest; the 6 is the 2nd smallest. Therefore, we know that 3 is the smallest number and 3.65 is the second smallest. 3.92 is the largest number. Now with the 3.8 and 3.815, let's compare the digits in the hundredths place. 3.8 (same as 3.80) has a 0 in the hundredths place. 3.815 has a 1 in the hundredths place. 3.815 is larger than 3.8.

Answer: 3, 3.65, 3.8, 3.815, 3.92

You try it now:

e) Put the following numbers in order from the smallest value to the largest: 6.381, 6.4, 5.95, 6, 6.42

f) Put the following numbers in order from the smallest value to the largest: 4.5, 4.508, 4, 4.51, 4.6

Answers to You try it now: a) 3 is in the hundredths place; 4 is in the hundreds place; 6 is in the ones or units place; 9 is in the ten-thousandths place; b) 1 is in the billions place; 8 is in the ten-millions place; 0 is in the hundreds place; c) 6,085,400.24; d) 40,080,000,700.6; e) Twelve million, two hundred five thousand; f) Three hundred forty thousand, seven and seven hundred fourteen thousandths; (g) 5.95, 6, 6.381, 6.4, 6.42; (h) 4, 4.5, 4.508, 4.51, 4.6.

Answer to Application: 0.5 > 0.05 Read as five tenths is greater than five hundredths. There is a large difference between 0.5 and 0.05 so the nursing student should question the order.

1.1 Place Value Problems

In exercises #1-10, indicate the place value of the digit 6:

1) 63   2) 506   3) 1,633   4) 162,304

5) 36,001   6) 682,993   7) 62,000,000   8) 86,092,354

9) 6,420,200,500   10) 462, 333

In exercises #11-16, indicate the place value of the digit 4:

11) 0.34   12) 203.4   13) 56.004   14) 9.374

15) 27.08524   16) 906.40392

In exercises #17-24, indicate the place value of the digit 1:

17) 8.31   18) 2,103.45   19) 906.201   20) 51,387.33

21) 10,000   22) 497.0931   23) 20.381422   24) 134,827,000

In exercises # 25-34, write each number in words:

25) 75   26) 13,067   27) 0.43   28) 9.5

29) 32.702   30) 600.006   31) $3,300.03   32) 0.0266

33) $8,005.92   34) 12,000.012

In exercises #35-43, write the words in a number form:

35) Seven hundred sixty-four.   36) Eighty-six hundredths.

37) One and six tenths.   38) Seventeen and nine thousandths.

39) Three million, five hundred thirty thousand, seven hundred twenty-two.

40) Two hundred nine thousand, ninety-seven and sixteen hundredths.

41) Forty million and nine hundred-thousandths.

42) Three hundred six and forty-four hundredths.

43) Twelve ten-thousandths.

In exercises #44-57, indicate whether the written statement is True or False.

44) The numbers to the left of the decimal point are whole numbers.

45) The numbers to the right of the decimal point represent parts of a whole.

46) With any given number the digit farthest to the left has the least value.

47) With any given number the digit farthest to the right has the least value.

48) When writing whole numbers, a comma separates the thousands from the millions.

49) When writing whole numbers, a comma separates the thousands from the billions.

50) When writing whole numbers, a comma separates the ones from the millions.

51) Never write commas to the right of the decimal point.

52) $84.6 = 84.60$ 53) $12 = 12.0$ 54) $0.7 = 7.00$

55) $106.20 = 106.020$ 56) $4 = 4.0000$ 57) $0.3 = 0.30$

In exercises #58-62, indicate how many thousands are in each of the given numbers.

58) 84, 672   59) 306,546   60) 5,000,670

61) 8,742   62) 4,097,004

In exercises #63-70, fill in the blank with the appropriate inequality symbol (> or <).

63) 88 ___ 89   64) 0.6 ___ 0.4   65) 800.3 ___ 800.5

66) 0.0008 ___ 0.008   67) 5.063 ___ 5.1   68) 16 ___ 16.0001

69) 4.25 ___ 4.2   70) .22 ___ .217

Solve the following problems.

71) Put the following five numbers in order from the lowest value to the greatest (put a comma between each number).

   a) 8   3.57   3.057   7.92   0.81

   b) 24.2   2.428   24   2.43   2.4

72) Write the following five numbers in order from the greatest to the least by using the greater than symbol (>) as in the form: $8 > 6 > 5 > 2$

   a) 77.7   0.7   7.7   .77   7

   b) 5.36   53   5.036   5.03   53.6

73) Write the following five numbers in order from the least to the greatest by using the less than symbol (<) as in the form: $2 < 5 < 6 < 8$

   a) 1.44   14.4   0.145   14   14.04

   b) 8.58   8.7   8.608   8.6   8.68

In exercises #74-81, write the <u>value</u> or <u>actual worth</u> of the underlined number, not the name of its place value.

74) <u>3</u>,862   75) <u>4</u>01,270   76) 8<u>1</u>2,148,000   77) 206,30<u>5</u>

78) 347.2<u>1</u>5   79) 11.<u>0</u>86   80) 4,563.291<u>7</u>   81) 46.3<u>5</u>8

Using your knowledge of place values, answer the questions asked in exercises #82–89.

82) Abel won a contest to reach into a wind-whipped barrel and grab as much floating money as he could in one minute while blindfolded. He managed to grab 2 $100 dollar bills, then 6 $10 bills, then 4 $1 bills. With 2 last blind grasps he got another $100 bill, 2 $10 bills, a $5 bill, and a single $1000 bill. How much money did Abel win?

83) When expressing a place value, does the <u>ths</u> at the end of a word, such as the <u>ths</u> in the word hundred<u>ths</u>, tell us that we are talking about a whole number or a part of a whole?

84) A bank teller found some errors on a check when he compared the decimal number amount, $3,020.75, with the amount written in words below. Describe the errors.

Three thousand and twenty dollars and 75/100 cents

85) Anisa is making cheesecake using a recipe that calls for 12.5 oz. of cream cheese. At the store there are packages labeled 10.9 oz. and 14.0 oz. Which should she buy?

86) You need a piece of wood that is at least 4.25 feet long. When you go to the lumber yard they have three choices. You can buy boards that are 6 ft., 4.5 ft, or 4.0 ft. in length. Which length piece should you buy?

87) At the bakery you have a choice of a dozen doughnuts for $2.99 or 12 doughnuts for $2.59. Which is the better buy?

88) At the county fair the livestock judges were measuring the lengths of the cows' tails. Cow A had a tail of 2.09 units, Cow B had a tail of length 2.49 units, and Cow C had a tail of length 2.5 units. Which cow had the longest tail?

89) Gordon, the mountain climber, wishes to climb the highest peak on his vacation. He can climb Mount Lithed, listed in the guidebook as being 23,019 feet high, Mount Holontite, listed at 23,910 feet, or Brakaleg Peak listed at 23,190 feet. To climb the highest one which should he climb?

Section 1.2 Add and Subtract Whole Numbers and Decimals

Objectives:

• To add/subtract whole numbers and decimals

• To translate words to addition/subtraction math statements

• To set up/solve application problems

• To manipulate equations with addition and subtraction

Application:

Bob's weekly paycheck is $463.65. His bills this week are $143.21, $36.95, $12.00, and $195.79. Does Bob have any money left over? If so, how much?

Vocabulary:

    sum—The **sum** is the answer to an addition problem. Find the sum of 10 and 6 means to write 10 + 6.

    difference—The **difference** is the answer to a subtraction problem. Find the difference of 10 and 6 means to write 10 - 6.

    carrying—**Carrying** is a process used in addition problems when one adds digits of a particular value and gets an answer that is greater than a single digit. We must write down the one's digit in the answer and carry what remains to the digit to the left.

Example:
$$
\begin{array}{r}
\overset{1}{7\,5\,4} \\
+\ 3\,1\,8 \\
\hline
2
\end{array}
$$

In this problem we add the 4 and the 8 in the ones place and get 12 (2 digits). We put the 2 down in the answer and carry the 1 to the left.

$$
\begin{array}{r}
\overset{1}{}\overset{1}{7}\,5\,4 \\
+\ 3\,1\,8 \\
\hline
1\,0\,7\,2
\end{array}
$$

In the tens place we add the digits (5 + 1 + 1) and get 7. When we add the digits in the hundreds place (7 + 3), we get 10 (2 digits). We put the 0 down in the answer and carry the 1 to the left. Bring down the 1 in the thousands place. The answer is 1072.

borrowing—Borrowing is a process used in subtraction problems when a particular place value digit of the number we are subtracting is larger than the place value digit with which we start.

Example:

$$
\begin{array}{r}
8\ 5\ 2 \\
-\ 1\ 3\ 7 \\
\hline
\end{array}
$$

In this problem the 7 in the ones column of the number we are subtracting is larger than the 2 in our original or top number. We can't take 7 from 2 so we must borrow 1 from the 5 (the tens place)

$$
\begin{array}{r}
8\ \overset{4}{\cancel{5}}\ \overset{1}{2} \\
-\ 1\ 3\ 7 \\
\hline
7\ 1\ \mathbf{5}
\end{array}
$$

In the ones column we can now subtract 7 from 12 to get 5. The final answer is 715

Translation Skills: Changing Words to Math:

Phrases that mean addition:

The **sum** of 21 and 13 means:	$21 + 13$
The **total** of 9 and 8 means:	$9 + 8$
15 **more than** 4 means:	$4 + 15$
8 **increased by** 5 means:	$8 + 5$

Phrases that mean subtraction:

Find the **difference** of 15 and 5 means:	$15 - 5$
20 **decreased by** 5 means:	$20 - 5$
17 is **how much more** than 12 means:	$17 - 12$
**Subtract 3 from 12 means:	$12 - 3$
15 **less than 19 means:	$19 - 15$

**It is important to notice that in our last two subtraction examples the order of the numbers presented was switched. Whatever number comes <u>after</u> the word *from* or the words *less than* is what you start with, what comes first.

Key Concept: Addition and subtraction are opposites of each other. Every addition equation can be rewritten as a subtraction equation; every subtraction equation can be rewritten as an addition equation.

Examples: The addition equation of 12 + 3 = 15 can be rewritten as the subtraction equation of: 12 = 15 - 3 after "subtracting 3" from both sides of the equation.

$$12 + \mathbf{3} = 15$$
$$12 + \mathbf{3} - \mathbf{3} = 15 - \mathbf{3}$$
$$12 = 15 - 3$$

The addition equation of **12** + 3 = 15 can
also be rewritten as the subtraction
equation of 3 = 15 - **12** after
"subtracting 12" from both sides
of the equation.

$$12 + 3 = 15$$
$$12 - 12 + 3 = 15 - 12$$
$$3 = 15 - 12$$

The subtraction equation of 10 - **x** = 6
can be rewritten as the addition
equation of 10 = 6 + x after "adding x"
to both sides of the equation.

$$10 - x = 6$$
$$10 - x + x = 6 + x$$
$$10 = 6 + x$$

Also: If we agree that **10 - x = 6** and
10 = 6 + x are the same, we can take this
one step further to discover the value of x
by changing the addition equation of
10 = 6 + x to the subtraction equation
of 10 - 6 = x after subtracting 6 from
both sides of the equation.

$$10 = 6 + x$$
$$10 - 6 = 6 - 6 + x$$
$$10 - 6 = x$$
$$4 = x$$

By following the basic equation truth that we can always do the same thing to both sides of an
equation, we have proved that: 10 - x = 6 is the same as 10 = 6 + x which is the same as 10 - 6 = x.

How to:

Add Whole Numbers & Decimals

1. Write the numbers in columns so the decimal points line up vertically. Remember we can fill in
   any blank spaces with zeros.

2. Add each column, starting with the column farthest to the right. If the sum of the digits is
   greater than 9, write the ones digit and carry the other digit to the next column to the left.

3. If the numbers we are adding include decimals, bring the decimal point straight down into the
   answer.

Example #1: In its first hour of business, an internet company received three orders for merchandise. The
bills were for $46.27, $212.36, and $82. What was the total amount of merchandise ordered
in the first hour?

To find the total amount, we must add.

Set up: 46.27 + 212.36 + 82

Step #1: Write the numbers in columns so the decimal points line up vertically. We can fill in any blank spaces with zeros.

```
  46.27
 212.36
+ 82.00
```

Step #2: Add each column, starting with the column to the farthest right.

Start with the hundredths column.
7 + 6 = 13 Put down the 3 and carry the 1 to the tenths column.

```
      1
  46.27
 212.36
+ 82.00
      3
```

Add the tenths column. 2 + 3 + 0 + 1 (the carried number) = 6 Put down the 6. There is no carry. Add the ones column. 6 + 2 + 2 = 10. Put down the 0 and carry the 1 to the tens column.

```
      1
  46.27
 212.36
+ 82.00
    0 63
```

Add the tens column. 4 + 1 + 8 + 1 (the carried number) = 14 Put down the 4 and carry the 1 to the hundreds column. Add this 1 to the digit 2 in the hundreds column to get 3.

```
   1  1
   46.27
 1
  212.36
+ 82.00
 340.63
```

Step #3: Finally, bring the decimal point straight down.

Answer: $ 340.63

How to:

Subtract Whole Numbers & Decimals

1. Write the numbers in columns so the decimal points line up vertically. Make sure the number we are subtracting is beneath the number from which we are starting.

2. Subtract each column, starting with the column farthest to the right. If the digit we are subtracting is larger than the number we start with, we must borrow 1 from the digit to the left.

3. If the numbers we are subtracting include decimals, bring the decimal point straight down into the answer.

Example #2: Total sales for the first day of business for this internet company were $2014.84. The costs to the business were $1628.39. How much profit did the company make?

To find the profit we will have to **find the difference** between the money earned by the company and its costs. We must subtract the costs to the business ($1628.39) from the money earned ($2014.84).

Set up: $2014.84 − $1628.39

Step #1:   Write the numbers in columns so the decimal points line up vertically.

$$\begin{array}{r} 2014.84 \\ -\ 1628.39 \\ \hline \end{array}$$

Step #2:   Subtract each column, starting with the column farthest to the right.

We can't subtract 9 from 4 because 9 is more than 4. We must borrow 1 from the digit to the left of the 4. If we take 1 from the 8, we leave 7. The 4 becomes 14. Now subtract: 14 - 9 = 5

$$\begin{array}{r} 2014.8\overset{7}{\cancel{8}}\overset{1}{4} \\ -\ 1628.39 \\ \hline 5 \end{array}$$

Now, in the tens place, 7 - 3 = 4

$$\begin{array}{r} 2014.8\overset{7}{\cancel{8}}\overset{1}{4} \\ -\ 1628.39 \\ \hline 45 \end{array}$$

We can't subtract 8 from 4 because 8 is more than 4. We must borrow 1 from the digit to the left of the 4. If we take 1 from the 1, we leave 0. The 4 becomes 14. Now subtract: 14 - 8 = 6

$$\begin{array}{r} 20\overset{0}{\cancel{1}}4.8\overset{7}{\cancel{8}}\overset{1}{4} \\ -\ 1628.39 \\ \hline 6\ \ 45 \end{array}$$

We can't subtract 2 from 0 because 2 is more than 0. We look to the digit to the left to borrow, but it is a zero. There is nothing to borrow, so we must go over 2 places to borrow from the 2 at the far left. If we borrow 1 from the 2, we leave 1. The 0 to the right of the 2 becomes a 10 momentarily, but we then borrow 1 from that 10 and leave 9. Finally, our 0 in the tens place becomes a 10. We can now subtract: 10 - 2 = 8.

$$\begin{array}{r} \overset{1}{\cancel{2}}\overset{9}{\cancel{0}}\overset{10}{\cancel{1}}4.8\overset{7}{\cancel{8}}\overset{1}{4} \\ -\ 1628.39 \\ \hline 86.45 \end{array}$$

Now in the hundreds place, 9 - 6 = 3
Then, in the thousands place 1 - 1 = 0

$$\begin{array}{r} \overset{1}{\cancel{2}}\overset{9}{\cancel{0}}\overset{10}{\cancel{1}}4.8\overset{7}{\cancel{8}}\overset{1}{4} \\ -\ 1628.39 \\ \hline 0386.45 \end{array}$$

Step #3: Finally, bring the decimal point straight down.   **Answer: $386.45**

Why: Why must the decimal points be lined up?

The decimal points have to be lined up so that we are adding and subtracting similar values. Look at $3.86 minus $1.24. To subtract $1.24 we have to know that the 4 represents pennies, the 2 represents dimes and the 1 represents dollars.

This is very similar to what we looked at earlier (Chapter 1.1)—comparing decimal numbers. We can only compare the same place values (that is those places that represent the same value or amount).

Sample #1:   Four girl scouts sold chocolates for a week. Two of them each earned $48. One of the girls earned $26.75, and the fourth $58.50. How much money did the girls earn altogether?

Add to find the total amount.

Set up: 48 + 48 + 26.75 + 58.50

```
  4 8 . 0 0
  4 8 . 0 0
  2 6 . 7 5
+ 5 8 . 5 0
```

Answer: $ 1 8 1 . 2 5

You try it now:

a) For exercise Martha walked the trails of a state park three days one week. If she walked 3.6 miles on Monday, 2.8 miles on Wednesday, and 5 miles on Friday, how far did she walk that week?

b) Craig was a cashier for Good Food Groceries. He sold $936.26 worth of goods during his morning shift and $2208.96 during the afternoon. What was the total amount of goods he sold that day?

Sample #2:   At a neighborhood garage sale, Alexis earned $308 and Jenny earned $224.45. How much more money did Alexis earn than Jenny?

Subtract the smaller amount from the larger to find the difference.

Set up: 308 − 224.45

```
  3 0 8 . 0 0
− 2 2 4 . 4 5
```

Answer: $ 8 3 . 5 5

You try it now:

c) Patrick earns $1722 every month; his rent and car payments cost him $1026.87. How much money does he have left over every month after he makes these two payments?

d) At a charity event, a neighborhood association collected $1190. After making sure that every family in the neighborhood could eat a wholesome Thanksgiving dinner, the association still had $110. How much money was given to families for Thanksgiving dinners?

Sample #3: A family of three picked strawberries. Dad picked 2 pounds, and Mom picked 2.7 pounds. How many pounds did their three year old daughter Sherri pick if the family picked a total of 5.5 pounds?

We are looking for the amount of strawberries that Sherri picked. This is the difference between the total amount of strawberries picked and the amount picked by her dad and mom. Conceptually we view this as:

Concept Setup: $\left(\begin{array}{c}\text{total amount of}\\ \text{strawberries picked}\end{array}\right) - \left(\begin{array}{c}\text{amount picked by}\\ \text{her dad and mom}\end{array}\right)$

Substitute the numbers that we are given to fit the concepts above. We now have a math expression:

Math Set up: (5.5)   –   (2 + 2.7)

We have a two-step problem.

First, we must find the sum of the amount picked by Dad and Mom. Set up an addition column and solve:

$$\begin{array}{r} 2.0 \\ + 2.7 \\ \hline 4.7 \end{array} \text{ pounds}$$

Our math statement now looks like: (5.5) - (4.7)

Second, find the difference between the total amount and the amount picked by Mom and Dad. Set up a subtraction column:

$$\begin{array}{r} 5.5 \\ - 4.7 \\ \hline \end{array}$$

Answer: 0.8 pounds is the amount of strawberries that Sherri picked.

You try it now:

e) Driving across the country on their way to college, three friends took turns driving. When they started on the trip, the odometer read 44,562 miles. Twenty-four hours later it read 45,827 miles. If Mike drove 400 miles and Terry 350, how far did Reiner drive?

f) The Hernandez family originally budgeted $400 for the month of August to buy school clothes and supplies for their 2 children. This amount was decreased by the cost of a dental bill of $86.25 and a doctor's bill of $57.00. How much money was left for the two children to get school materials?

Answers to You try it now: a) 11.4 miles; b) $3145.22; c) $695.13; d) $1080; e) 515 miles; f) $256.75

Answer to Application: One way to solve this problem is to add up all his bills and then subtract them from his income.

```
        143.21        Concept:   (Total income) – (Total of bills)
         36.95        Set up:       ($463.65)  – ($143.21 + $36.95 + $12 + $195.79)
         12.00                      ($463.65)  – ($387.95)
      + 195.79        Answer:   $75.70 is the money left over
Total Bills: $ 387.95
```

1.2 Addition & Subtraction Problems

In exercises #1-9, add the following numbers.

1) 3074 + 8438

2) 9098 + 1714

3) 64.894 + 36.721

4) 582 + 78.29

5) 908.25 + 97.7

6) 86.9 + 3.25

7) 298.38 + 176 + 5.07

8) 47.309 + .051 + 3.8 + 236

9) 264.88 + 18.9 + .0009 + 4000

In exercises #10-19, subtract the following numbers.

10) 4823 – 313

11) 7805.25 – 926

12) 743 – 97.306

13) 12 – 11.216

14) 537.02 – 243.93

15) 206.81 – 99

16) 9 – 3.005

17) 444.2 – 8.56 – 78

18) 30,000 – 10,800 – 160 – 2.6

19) 82.4 – 7.1 – 33.9 – 6.05

In exercises #20-29, (a) translate the following words into math expressions, and (b) give the solution.

20) The sum of 3.4 and 17

21) The sum of 3.06 and 18

22) 8.5 more than 4

23) 11.3 more than 12

24) The difference of 104.26 and 56.39

25) The difference of 214.25 and 84.17

26) Subtract 18.6 from 47.05

27) Subtract 29.8 from 67.14

28) 18.356 less than 45.8

29) 15.736 less than 52

In exercises #30-39, translate the following words into math expressions.

30) The sum of x and 48

31) The sum of x and 7

32) 8 less than x

33) The difference of 18 and x

34) Subtract 7 from x

35) The difference of x and 3

36) Subtract x from 14

37) x less than 10

38) 5 more than x

39) x more than 40

In exercises #40-47, state whether the following statements are True or False.

40) Addition and subtraction are opposite operations.

41) $6 + 4 = 10$ is the same as $6 = 10 - 4$

42) $11 + 7 = 18$ is the same as $11 = 18 - 11$

43) $7 - 3 = 4$ is the same as $7 = 4 + 3$

44) $12 - x = 8$ is the same as $12 = 8 + x$

45) $4 + x = 10$ is the same as $4 = 10 + x$

46) $25 - x = 14$ is the same as $25 - 14 = x$

47) $8 - x = 3$ is the same as $8 - 3 = x$

In exercises #48-55, write an equivalent equation which changes any given addition statement to a subtraction statement or changes any given subtraction statement to an addition statement. There is nothing to solve here.

48) $8 - 5 = 3$

49) $12 + 7 = 19$

50) $14 - x = 10$

51) $x - 8 = 15$

52) $x + 10 = 25$

53) $7 + x = 12$

54) $20 - x = 8$

55) $x + 4 = 20$

In exercises #56-64, solve for the value of x, the unknown number.

56) $7 + x = 27$

57) $x + 3.9 = 7.7$

58) $4.05 + 12 = x$

59) $25 - x = 14$

60) $127.4 - x = 65.7$

61) $62 - 4.83 = x$

62) $38 + x - 6.4 = 43$

63) $56.2 - x + 7 = 52.8$

64) $18.2 + x + 2.4 = 30$

In exercise #65–84: (a) write a mathematical expression that will solve the problem, and (b) give the solution.

65-66) In the city of Baedeker, the buses in zone A transport 2184 people daily while the buses carry 928 passengers in zone B and 1370 in zone C.

65) How many people ride buses in Baedeker on a typical day?

66) How many more passengers are carried daily in zone A than zone C?

67-68) Ms. Ibarra taught four different classes. The chart below shows the number of male and female students in each class.

Courses	Female Students	Male Students
History 1	16	12
History 2	?	?
World History	9	11
Culture As History	12	12

67) If 52 women attended Ms. Ibarra's classes, how many attended her History 2 course?

68) If a total of 97 students attended her classes, how many men were enrolled in her History 2 class?

69-72) The chart below from a local newspaper reports the known and predicted temperature readings for the town of Forestville. The expected high temperature for today is 67 degrees.

Day	Morning Low Temperture	Daytime High Temperature
Yesterday	Not Reported	74
Today	28	67
Tomorrow	29	?

69) What was the temperature decrease from yesterday's high to today's lowest reading?

70) What increase in temperature is expected from the low reading this morning to today's predicted high?

71) If in fact today's temperature reaches 67 degrees, what will be the difference in high temperatures between yesterday and today?

72) If the daytime high temperatures in Forestville for the listed 3 days would add up to 205 degrees, what would the high temperature be for tomorrow?

73-75) Amy, a first-year college student, earns $700 a month at her job, has a scholarship which pays her $350 a month, and receives $300 a month from her parents. Every month, before she spends any money, Amy budgets for four major monthly necessities—$500 for rent, $200 for a car payment, $110 for her utilities and phone, and $200 for food.

73) What is Amy's monthly income?

74) How much money does Amy still have to spend every month after budgeting for her four major bills?

75) If Amy's parents stopped sending her money, how much money would Amy have left over every month after budgeting for her four major bills?

76-79) Xuan had budgeted $250 to buy Christmas presents for five members of his family. He bought presents for his two younger brothers, spending $38.79 and $43.05 respectively. He bought a single present for his mother and father that cost $82.55. Finally, he spent $85 on a special gift for his older sister.

76) How much money did Xuan spend on Christmas presents for his family?

77) Did he spend more on the gifts for his two brothers or on the gift for his sister? How much more money?

78) Did Xuan spend more or less money than he budgeted for presents? How much?

79) If Xuan had bought his sister a present that cost only $40 instead of $85, how much of his original budgeted $250 would he still have?

80-84) Derrick is on his high school's track team. Last week he ran 8.6 miles on Monday, 12 miles each day on Tuesday, Thursday, and Saturday, 4.5 miles in sprints on Wednesday, and another 6.25 miles on Friday.

80) How many miles did Derrick run last week?

81) How many more miles did he run on Tuesday than Monday?

82) What is the difference between the distances which Derrick ran on Friday and Saturday?

83) Did Derrick run more miles on the three days Monday, Wednesday, and Friday, or the two days Tuesday and Thursday? How many more miles?

84) Take the sum of the miles Derrick ran on Friday and Saturday and subtract this from the sum of the miles he ran on Monday and Tuesday. How many miles more did he run on Monday and Tuesday?

Skills Check

1. Write the value 1234.12 in words.

2. What digit occupies the tens place in the value 796.562?

3. Order the following decimals from smallest to largest: 1.056, 1.5, 1.05

4. True or False? 0.032 > 0.3

Answers to Skills Check: 1) one thousand two hundred thirty-four and twelve hundredths; 2) 9;
3) 1.05, 1.056, 1.5; 4) false.

Section 1.3   Multiply Whole Numbers and Decimals

Objectives:

• To multiply whole numbers and decimals

• To convert common length and time English measurements

• To translate words to multiplication math statements

• To set up/solve multiplication application problems

Application:

A seamstress has an order for 28 shirts for the local cheerleading team. The order specifies 15 large and the rest mediums. If each large shirt requires 2.2 yards of material and each medium requires 1.8 yards of material how much material should she order?

Vocabulary:

> **product**—The product is the answer to a multiplication problem. Find the product of 10 and 7 means to write $10 \cdot 7$.

> **of**—When there is a statement "a number of another number," the "of" means multiply. We often state this when multiplying by a decimal number or a fraction [Examples: 0.5 of 8 means $(0.5) \cdot (8)$ or 1.3 of 15 means $(1.3) \cdot (15)$]

> **twice**—Twice means to double something, to multiply by two.

> **double**—To double something means to multiply by 2 (double a 3 means $2 \cdot 3$ or 6)

> **triple**—To triple means to multiply by 3 (triple a 5 means $3 \cdot 5$ or 15)

**Remember: We know that 5×6 and $5 \cdot 6$ mean multiply, but a parenthesis also means to multiply in the following examples:

$$5 (6) = (5) (6) = (5) 6$$

Note: We will rarely use the "x" for multiplication because in algebra we use the "x" to represent an unknown value. Instead, use either the dot (•) or the parenthesis as shown above.

**Any number multiplied by 1 equals that number.

**Any number multiplied by 0 equals zero.

Measurements to know:

<u>Lengths</u>		<u>Time</u>	
12 inches = 1 foot	60 seconds = 1 minute	7 days = 1 week
3 feet = 1 yard	60 minutes = 1 hour	52 weeks = 1 year
5280 feet = 1 mile	24 hours = 1 day	12 months = 1 year

How to:

Multiply Whole Numbers & Decimals

1. Write the numbers in columns (the decimals points do not need to line up vertically). It is easiest to put the longest number on the top.

2. Multiply the bottom number by the top number, one digit at a time, starting with the digit farthest to the right.

3. Add the products together.

4. Insert the decimal point into the answer (We need to do this step only if decimal numbers are present). First count the number of digits to the right of the decimal points in the numbers you are multiplying. Then, starting from the right end of your answer, count back to the left this number of places and insert the decimal point.

Example #1: Multiply 854 times 8

Step #1: Write the numbers in columns.

$$\begin{array}{r} 8\,5\,4 \\ \times \quad 8 \\ \hline \end{array}$$

Step #2: Multiply the bottom number by the top number, one digit at a time.

8 x 4 = 32   The 2 is put directly beneath the 8, the number by which we are multiplying. The 3 is carried over to the next digit to be added to the next product.

$$\begin{array}{r} ^{3} \\ 8\,5\,4 \\ \times \quad 8 \\ \hline 2 \end{array}$$

8 x 5 = 40   40 plus the carried 3 equals 43. The 3 is written down while the 4 is carried over to the next digit to be added to the next product.

$$\begin{array}{r} ^{4}\ ^{3} \\ 8\,5\,4 \\ \times \quad 8 \\ \hline 3\,2 \end{array}$$

8 x 8 = 64   64 plus the carried 4 equals 68. The 8 is written down while the 6 is carried over to the next digit.

$$\begin{array}{r} ^{6}\ ^{4}\ ^{3} \\ 8\,5\,4 \\ \times \quad 8 \\ \hline 8\,3\,2 \end{array}$$

There is nothing further to multiply so we just bring down the 6.

$$\begin{array}{r} ^{6}\ ^{4}\ ^{3} \\ 8\,5\,4 \\ \times \quad 8 \\ \hline 6\,8\,3\,2 \end{array}$$

Answer: 6832

Example #2: 2.05 multiplied by 98

> Step #1: Write the numbers in columns.

$$
\begin{array}{r}
2.05 \\
\times\ 98 \\
\hline
\end{array}
$$

> Step #2: Multiply the bottom number by the top
> number, one digit at a time.
>
> Start with the 8. Multiply it by the 5, then
> the 0, and then the 2 to get the first product
> of 1640. The first answer (8 x 5) goes directly
> beneath the 8, the number by which we are
> multiplying.

$$
\begin{array}{r}
{}^{1}\ ^{4}\ \\
2.05 \\
\times\ 98 \\
\hline
1640 \\
\end{array}
$$

> Multiply the 9 by the 5, then the 0, and then
> the 2 to get the second product of 1845. The
> first answer (9 x 5) goes directly beneath the 9,
> the number by which we are multiplying.

$$
\begin{array}{r}
{}^{1}\ ^{4}\ \\
2.05 \\
\times\ 98 \\
\hline
1640 \\
+1845 \\
\end{array}
$$

> Step #3: Add the products together.

$$
\begin{array}{r}
2.05 \\
\times\ 98 \\
\hline
1640 \\
+1845 \\
\hline
20090 \\
\end{array}
$$

Step #4: Insert the decimal point in the answer.

2.05   (2 numbers to the right of the decimal point)

x 98   (0 numbers to the right of the decimal point)

1640

1845

200.90   Count back to the left 2 places and insert the decimal point

Answer: 200.90 or, because the last zero has no value it is the same as 200.9

Example #3: Multiply 0.72 by 0.134

Step #1: Write the numbers in columns.

$$\begin{array}{r} .134 \\ \times \ .72 \\ \hline \end{array}$$

Step #2: Multiply the bottom number by the top number, one digit at a time.

Start with the 2. Multiply it by the 4, then the 3, and then the 1 to get the first product of 268. The first answer (2 x 4) goes directly beneath the 2, the number by which we are multiplying.

$$\begin{array}{r} .134 \\ \times \ .72 \\ \hline \mathbf{268} \end{array}$$

Multiply the 7 by the 4, then by the 3, and then the 1 to get the second product of 938. The first answer (7 x 4) goes directly beneath the 7, the number by which we are multiplying.

$$\begin{array}{r} 2\ 2 \\ .134 \\ \times \ .72 \\ \hline 268 \\ \mathbf{938} \end{array}$$

Step. #3: Add the products together.

$$\begin{array}{r} 2\ 2 \\ .134 \\ \times \ .72 \\ \hline 268 \\ 938 \\ \hline \mathbf{9648} \end{array}$$

Step #4: Insert the decimal point in the answer.

.134   (3 numbers to the right of the decimal point)

× .72   (2 numbers to the right of the decimal point)

$$\begin{array}{r} 268 \\ 938 \\ \hline \mathbf{0.09648} \end{array}$$

Count back to the left 5 places and insert the decimal point. To move the decimal point all five places we must fill in an added blank space with a zero.

Answer: 0.09648

Sample #1: Martha started jogging around a local lake to get her weekly exercise. If it is 2.75 miles around the lake, and if she jogs every Monday, Wednesday, and Friday, how many miles does she run each week?

First we need to recognize that there is a **repeated addition** (2.75 + 2.75 + 2.75). Martha does the same thing 3 times a week. A repeated addition tells us to multiply.

$$\begin{array}{r} 2.75 \\ \times \ 3 \\ \hline \mathbf{825} \end{array}$$

Set up : 2.73 (3)

Insert the decimal point.   **Answer: 8.25 miles**

You try it now:

a) Every morning before school, Monday through Friday, Kareem stops in at a cafe and buys a coffee for $1.50. How much money does he spend on coffee every week?

b) The Green Lumber Company reports that it cuts down an average of 2.35 acres of woodland a week. If it does this for a year, how many acres of woodland would be cut?

Sample #2: 15 minutes equals how many seconds?

Here we recognize that 1 minute equals 60 seconds.
Thus 15 minutes equals 60 seconds repeated 15 times.

Set up : 60 (15)   60 x 15 = 900

Answer: 900 seconds

You try it now:

c) 3.5 years is how many months?

d) 6 hours is how many seconds?

Sample #3: In a laboratory a bacterium was measured to be .0037 of an inch in length. When a scientist discovered 25 of these bacteria attached to each other to form a single line, what was the length of this bacteria string?

First we recognize that there is a repeated addition.
The bacteria (of the same length) are lining up one behind the other. This length is repeated 25 times.

Set up: (0.0037) (25)

Insert the decimal point.

```
  .0037
 x  25
  185
  74
  925
```

Answer: 0.0925 inches

You try it now:

e) A foot is about 0.00019 miles. If you hike to an elevation of 500 feet, how many miles above sea level are you?

f) A hardware store earns $0.27 on every box of nails that it sells. If it sold 900 boxes of nails last year, how much money did the store make on nails?

Sample #4: A mountain was slowly losing its mass as wind and winter rain tossed soil down the mountainside and deposited it into a small lake. If .4 tons of soil silted into the lake every week, how many tons of soil **would fall into the lake in a year?** If a local scientist predicted correctly that all life would die in the lake if more than 80 tons of soils ever silted into it, **would the lake be "dead" after 5 years?**

First we need to recognize the action. 0.4 tons of
soil fall into the lake every week. As there are
52 weeks in a year, this action is repeated 52 times
in a year.

$$\begin{array}{r} 5\,2 \\ \times\ \ .4 \\ \hline 2\,0\,8 \end{array}$$

Set up: 52 (0.4)

Insert decimal point.

1st Answer: 20.8 tons of soil/year

To find the second answer we must find out how much soil is deposited into the lake
in a 5-year period. The yearly amount of soil deposited is repeated 5 times.

Concept Set up: (amount of soil deposited yearly) • (number of years)

Math Set up: (20.8)   •   (5)

$$\begin{array}{r} 2\,0\,.8 \\ \times\ \ 5 \\ \hline 1\,0\,4\,0 \end{array}$$

Insert the decimal point. 104.0 tons of soil would be deposited in the lake in five years.
This is more than 80.

2nd Answer: Yes, the lake would be "dead.'
104 tons > 80 tons

You try it now:

g) On average Jacob moves 1.5 feet for every step he takes. If he took 80 steps, how far would he have
walked? If he takes 80 steps every minute would he have walked a mile in 15 minutes?

h) One morning a certain tree frog caught 12 bugs in an hour. If each bug weighed about 0.0825 ounces,
what was the total weight of the insects he caught? If this same frog needed to eat 3 ounces of insects a
day to survive, would it survive if it normally caught 40 bugs a day?

Answers to You try it now: a) $7.50; b) 122.2 acres; c) 42 months; d) 21,600 seconds; e) .095 miles; f) $243; g) 120 feet
in 80 steps, and No he would not have walked a mile in 15 minutes (he would have walked only 1800 feet; a
mile is 5280 feet); h) The 12 bugs would weigh 0.99 ounces, and Yes the frog would survive (it would eat 3.3
ounces if it ate 40 bugs)

Answer to Application: Subtract the 15 large shirts from the total 28 to find that we need to make 13 medium shirts.
To get the total amount of material needed, we recognize the following concepts: (number of large shirts
multiplied by the amount of the fabric needed per large shirt) + (number of medium shirts multiplied by the
amount of the fabric needed per medium shirt). We substitute numbers for these concepts and get the following
set up to solve the problem:

Set up: (15 • 2.2 yards) + (13 • 1.8 yards)

Solve each multiplication: (33 yards) + (23.4 yards)

Add: 56.4

Answer = 56.4 yards of fabric

1.3 Multiplication Problems

In exercises #1–12, multiply the following numbers.

1) 3789 • 62   2) 8046 • 46   3) 9007 • 20   4) 16 • 3.8

5) 2.71 • 62   6) 4 • 0.009   7) 0.29 of 0.07   8) 2.58 of 400

9) 0.028 of 0.173   10) 0.65 of 0.0004   11) 300 • 800   12) 6 • 5000

Solve #13 – 25.

13) Find the product of 8 and 12

14) Find the product of 2.7 and 2.8

15) 8.6 yards equals how many feet?

16) 25 feet equals how many inches?

17) 7 days equals how many hours?

18) 12.5 days equals how many hours?

19) 4.75 hours is how many minutes?

20) 144 hours is how many minutes?

21) 8 weeks is how many hours?

22) 4.8 feet is how many inches?

23) 3 miles is how many feet?

24) 1.25 years is how many weeks?

25) 6.5 yards is how many inches?

In exercises #26-40, translate the following words into math statements. Use the dot (•) for multiplication. (Remember: the x here is a variable, representing an unknown value, not a multiplication symbol). Do not solve.

26) Multiply 8 by 4, then subtract 7

27) 3 times 12, plus 11

28) Four times 7, then decrease by 4

29) 150 subtracted from the product of 20 and 10

30) Double 5, then add this to the product of 4 and 5

31) 47 less than triple 20

32) The difference of 6 times 4 and double 3

33) The difference of 8 times 8 and the product of 6 and 5

34) The product of 12 and x

35) The product of 10 and x

36) The product of 5 and x, minus 4

37) x multiplied by y, then subtract 6

38) Twice x, plus 3 more

39) Subtract 5 from twice x

40) Subtract y from the product of 3 and x

In exercise #41–57: (a) write a mathematical expression that will solve the problem, and (b) give the solution.

41-42) In a nearby rural county, 800 people use the bus service daily to go to work or school. It is   estimated 5.6 times as many people drive their own cars and .75 times as many people walk or ride a bike.

    41) How many people drive their own cars on a typical day?

    42) How many people walk or ride their bikes daily?

43-44) Mary, who works at the La Salle Auto factory, earns $11.50 an hour. She works 35 hours a week.

    43) How much money does Mary earn in a week?

    44) How much money does she earn in a year (52 weeks = 1 year) ?

45) Preparing for his first marathon race, Derrick ran 12 miles in the hills every Monday, Wednesday, and Friday and 6.5 miles on the track on Tuesdays and Thursdays. Every Saturday he jogged 20 miles. If Derrick maintained this workout for twelve weeks, how many miles did he run?

46) If a hospital emergency room uses an average of 3 quarts of blood every hour, how much blood does the hospital use in a typical week?

47-48) The *First Aid Fast* company mails out 100 sample first-aid kits every month. Postage costs eight dollars on every kit sent.

    47) During a four month period, how much money does First Aid Fast spend mailing out sample first-aid kits?

    48) If the company could mail their kits with a delivery service for only $6.50 per kit, how much money would it save each month?

49) Rohan delivered pizzas for 6 hours every Monday, Friday, and Saturday. He earned a wage of $6 per hour, and he averaged another $5 an hour in tips. His sister Serena worked in a clothing store 25 hours a work, earning $6 an hour. She also earned an averaged of $125 every two weeks in commissions. Who earned more money in four weeks? How much more?

50-51) While Joaquin was studying an ant colony for a school project, he painstakingly counted 16,200 ants marching out in single file from an ant hill. An average ant was .02 foot long, and the ants stayed head to end, touching each other as they marched toward a pile of garbage.

    50) How many feet long would this army of ants be?

    51) A football field is 100 (3600 inches) yards long. Would this line of ants be longer than a football field?

52-53) If a six-foot tall man ran 23,072.5 times his own height, he would have run a marathon (26 miles 385 yards) as they do in the Olympics. An ant is .02 of a foot in length.

52) How many feet would an ant need to travel in an ant marathon to match a human's feat?

53) How many inches is this?

54-57) An inch is approximately 0.028 yards in length. A grasshopper, which was .9 inches in length, leaped 25 inches in a single effort.

54) How many yards did it jump?

55) Did the grasshopper leap more than 30 times its length?

56) If the grasshopper had leaped three more inches, would it have jumped over 30 times its length?

57) Would the grasshopper have jumped a greater distance if it had leaped 40 times its length or 1 yard?

Skills Check

1. Which decimal is larger, 3.01 or 3.001?

2. Find the sum of 2.65 and 8.05

3. What is the difference in amount of rainfall between February's total of 9.5 inches and July's total of 0.7 inches?

4. Write the following value in words: 101.6

Answers to Skills Check: 1) 3.01 is larger; 2) 10.7; 3) 8.8 inches; 4) one hundred one and six tenths.

Section 1.4   Divide Whole Numbers & Decimals

Objectives:

- To divide whole numbers and decimals
- To convert common length and time English measurements
- To translate words to division math statements
- To set up/solve division application problems
- To manipulate equations with multiplication and division

Application:

George needs 120 ounces of mozzarella cheese for a banquet dinner. When he goes to the store he discovers that mozzarella only comes in packages of 11.5 **ounces. How many packages should he buy?**

Vocabulary:

quotient	The **quotient** is the answer to a division problem. Find the quotient of 15 and 3 means to write: $15 \div 3$
remainder	The **remainder** is the amount or the **part** left over after you have divided one number into another.
divisor	The **divisor** is the number you are dividing by. In the traditional long division box, it is the number outside the box. When spoken or written, it is the number which follows the words "**divided by**" or the $\div$ symbol. It is also the number below a fractional line.

15 is the divisor in each of the division problems below:

$15 \overline{)855}$ 3.3 divided by 15 $82.5 \div 15$ $\dfrac{3}{15}$ 15 goes into 855

Parts of a long division problem:

$$\text{divisor} \overline{)\begin{array}{c} \text{quotient} \\ \hline \\ \hline \text{remainder} \end{array}}$$

undefined	The word **undefined** is used in math for any division problem where **the divisor is** zero. In essence, undefined means we "**can't divide by zero.**" It is not possible to divide something up into some number of zero parts.

**Remember: Any number divided by 1 equals that same number.
      Any number divided by 0 is **undefined.**
      Zero divided by any non-zero number equals zero.

Key Concept: Multiplication and division are opposites. **Every multiplication equation can be rewritten as a division equation; every division equation can be rewritten as a multiplication equation.**

(Before looking at the examples below, it should be stated that when we multiply or divide both sides of an equation by some value, more complex processes are involved than with addition and subtraction. However, for a first-step, basic understanding of the truths stated above, these serve as good examples).

Examples:

The multiplication equation of $35 = 5 \cdot 7$
can be rewritten as the division equation
of $35 \div 7 = 5$ after both sides of the
equation have been "divided by 7."

$$35 = 5 \cdot 7$$
$$35 \div \mathbf{7} = (5 \cdot 7) \div \mathbf{7}$$
$$35 \div 7 = 5$$

The multiplication equation of $35 = 5 \cdot 7$
can also be rewritten as the division
equation of $35 \div 5 = 7$ after both sides of
the equation have been "divided by 5."

$$35 = 5 \cdot 7$$
$$35 \div \mathbf{5} = (5 \cdot 7) \div \mathbf{5}$$
$$35 \div 5 = 7$$

The division equation of $20 \div x = 4$ can be
rewritten as the multiplication equation
of $20 = 4 \cdot x$ after both sides of the equation
have been "multiplied by x."

$$20 \div x = 4$$
$$(20 \div x) \cdot \mathbf{x} = 4 \cdot \mathbf{x}$$
$$20 = 4 \cdot x$$

Why:

Is it hard to see that $(20 \div x) \cdot x$ is the same as 20? It is a mathematical truth that we can take a number, both divide it and multiply it by the same value, and it will equal the original number. For instance, say that $x = 10$. Substitute the value of 10 for x. We can see that $(20 \div 10) \cdot 10$ equals 20 by solving the expression. Say $x = 5$. Substitute the value of 5 for the x. We can see that $(20 \div 5) \cdot 5$ equals 20 by solving the expression. Thus from these specific examples (try $x = 2$ or $x = 4$ if you'd like), we can make the general statement that $(20 \div x) \cdot x = 20$, as long as the value of "x" is any number except zero.

Also: If we agree that $20 \div x = 4$ and $20 = 4 \cdot x$
are the same, we can take this one step
further to discover the value of x by
changing the multiplication statement of
$20 = 4 \cdot x$ to the division statement of
$20 \div 4 = x$

$$20 = 4 \cdot x$$
$$20 \div \mathbf{4} = (4 \cdot x) \div \mathbf{4}$$
$$20 \div 4 = x$$

By following the basic equation truth that we can always do the same thing to both sides of an equation, we see that $20 \div x = 4$ is the same as $20 = 4 \cdot x$ which is the same as $20 \div 4 = x$.

In fact, we can see that $x = 5$ in this equation.

If we agree that we have the ability to change division and multiplication statements, we now want to take this knowledge and apply it to concepts. In particular we want to look at a basic multiplication statement that we will all agree is true (if it helps, see the concrete example below first):

(Total) = (number of items) • (amount per item)

Examples: *(Total) = (number of items) • (amount per item)* can be rewritten as *(Total) ÷ (amount per item) = (number of items)* after both sides of the equation have been "divided by *(amount per item)*."

Also: *(Total) = (number of items) • (amount per item)* can be rewritten as *(Total) ÷ (number of items) = (amount per item)* after both sides of the equation have been "divided by *(number of items)*."

(Total) ÷ (amount per item) = (number of items) can be rewritten as *(Total) = (number of items) • (amount per item)* after both sides of the equation have been "multiplied by *(amount per item)*."

By following the basic equation truth that we can always do the same thing to both sides of an equation, we can see that the (Total) ÷ (amount per item) = (number of items) is the same as (Total) = (number of items) • (amount per item), which is the same as (Total) ÷ (number of items) = (amount per item).

The following three statements are all true:

(Total) ÷ (amount per item) = (number of items)

(Total) ÷ (number of items) = (amount per item)

(Total) = (number of items) • (amount per item)

A concrete example for the above equation(s) can be seen in a trip to a grocery store in which we buy 4 cartons of milk, each carton costing $2.00. We must pay the cashier a total of $8.00.

(Total)	=	$8.00
(number of items)	=	4 cartons
(amount per item)	=	$2.00

Substitute the numbers that we are given to fit the concepts above. Our math statements now look like:

(Total)	÷	(amount per item)	=	(number of items)
($8)	÷	($2)	=	(4 cartons)

(Total)	÷	(number of items)	=	(amount per item)
($8)	÷	4 cartons)	=	($2 per carton)

(Total)	=	(number of items)	•	(amount per item)
($8)	=	(4)	•	($2)

These statements are all true. Whenever we know 2 out of the 3 concepts above, we can solve for the other.

Examples: If we didn't know the *total*, we would write:

(Total)   =   (4)   •   ($2)

If we didn't know the *amount per item*, we would write:

($8)   ÷   (4 cartons)   =   (amount per item)

If we didn't know the *number of items*, we would write:

($8)   ÷   ($2)   =   (number of items)

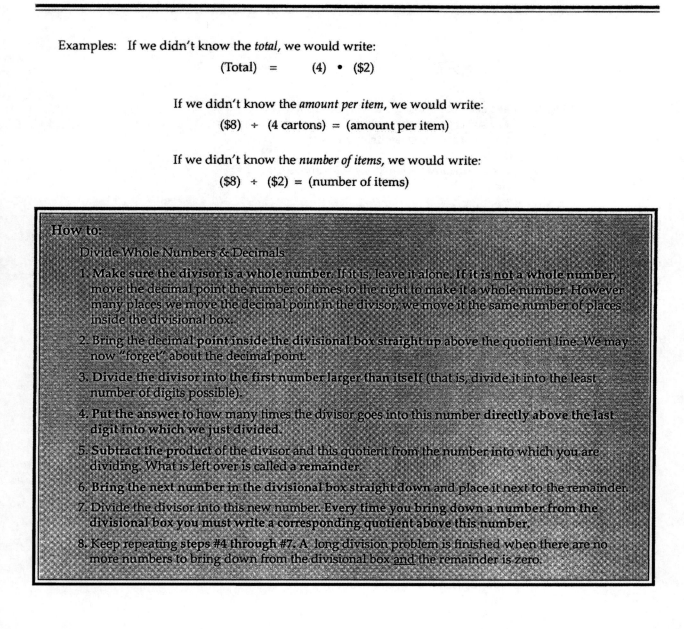

How to:

Divide Whole Numbers & Decimals

1. Make sure the divisor is a whole number. If it is, leave it alone. If it is <u>not</u> a whole number, move the decimal point the number of times to the right to make it a whole number. However many places we move the decimal point in the divisor, we move it the same number of places inside the divisional box.

2. Bring the decimal point inside the divisional box straight up above the quotient line. We may now "forget" about the decimal point.

3. Divide the divisor into the first number larger than itself (that is, divide it into the least number of digits possible).

4. Put the answer to how many times the divisor goes into this number directly above the last digit into which we just divided.

5. Subtract the product of the divisor and this quotient from the number into which you are dividing. What is left over is called a remainder.

6. Bring the next number in the divisional box straight down and place it next to the remainder.

7. Divide the divisor into this new number. Every time you bring down a number from the divisional box you must write a corresponding quotient above this number.

8. Keep repeating steps #4 through #7. A long division problem is finished when there are no more numbers to bring down from the divisional box <u>and</u> the remainder is zero.

Example #1: $6\overline{)258}$

Step #1: Make sure the divisor is a whole number. The
divisor is 6, already a whole number. We don't
need to move any decimal points.

Step #2: Bring the decimal point straight up above the
quotient line.

$6\overline{)258.}$

Steps #3 and #4: Divide the divisor into the first number
larger than itself. Put the answer directly above
the last digit into which we just divided.

6 does not divide into 2, but divides into 25.
6 goes into 25 four (4) times. Put the 4 in
the quotient directly above the 5, the last
digit into which we just divided.

$$\begin{array}{r} 4 \\ 6\overline{)258.} \end{array}$$

Step #5: Subtract the product of the divisor and
the quotient (6 x 4 = 24) from the number
into which we just divided (25).

$$\begin{array}{r} 4 \\ 6\overline{)258.} \\ -24 \\ \hline 1 \text{ (remainder)} \end{array}$$

Step #6: Bring down the next number (the 8) in
the divisional box.

$$\begin{array}{r} 4 \\ 6\overline{)258.} \\ -24 \\ \hline 18 \end{array}$$

Steps #7 and #8: Divide the divisor into this new
number (18). Then repeat steps #4-7 until
the problem is completed.

6 divides into 18 exactly 3 times.
Put the 3 in the quotient directly above
the 8, the last digit into which we just
divided.

$$\begin{array}{r} 4\;3 \\ 6\overline{)258.} \\ -24 \\ \hline 18 \\ -18 \\ \hline 0 \end{array}$$

Subtract the product (6 x 3 = 18) from the
number (18) into which we just divided.

Check: We know we are finished with this division problem because the two requirements
have been met: (1) there are no other numbers to bring down from the divisional
box, **and** (2) the remainder is zero.

Answer: 43

Example #2: $5.6\overline{)574}$

Step #1: Make sure the divisor is a whole number. $5.6\overline{)574}$

The divisor is 5.6 To make this a whole number   becomes
we must move the decimal point one place to
the right. We then must also move the decimal $56\overline{)5740.}$
point inside the divisional box the same number
of places, once in this case. **We fill in the one
blank space at the end with a zero.**

Step #2: Bring the decimal point straight up above the $56\overline{)5740.}$
quotient line.

Steps #3 and #4: Divide the divisor into the first number
larger than itself. Put the answer directly above
the last digit into which we divided.

56 divides into 57 one (1) time. Put the 1 in the $56\overline{)5740.}$ ... 1
quotient directly above the 7, the last digit into
which we just divided.

Step #5: Subtract the product of the divisor and the quotient   1
(56 x 1 = 56) from the number into which we just $56\overline{)5740.}$
divided (57). $\underline{-56}$
                                                                    1

Step #6: Bring down the next number (the 4) in the divisional   1
box. $56\overline{)5740.}$
          $\underline{-56}$
          14

Steps #7 and #8: Divide the divisor into this new number (14).
Then repeat steps #4-7 until the problem is completed.

56 divides into 14 zero (0) times. Put the 0 in the   10
quotient directly above the 4, the last digit into which $56\overline{)5740.}$
we just divided. $\underline{-56}$
          14
Subtract the product (56 x 0 = 0) from the number into $\underline{-0}$
which we just divided (14). 14 - 0 = 14. Now bring   140
down the next number (the 0) in the divisional box.

Divide the divisor into this new number. 56 divides into 140 two (2) times. Put the 2 in the quotient directly above the 0, the last digit into which we just divided.

```
        1 0 2 .
  56 ) 5 7 4 0 .
       -5 6
          1 4
        -   0
        1 4 0
       -  1 1 2
            2 8
```

Subtract the product (56 x 2 = 112) from the number into which we just divided (140). 140 - 112 = 28.

** **It is important to see that we are not yet finished with this problem.** We are not finished until there is no remainder left.

We need to bring down the next number. It may seem as if there is "nothing" to bring down, but there are always an infinite number of zeros to the right of any decimal number. Place a zero in the divisional box and bring this down.

Divide the divisor into this new number. 56 divides into 280 five (5) times. Put the 5 in the quotient directly above the 0, the last digit into which we just divided.

```
        1 0 2 . 5
  56 ) 5 7 4 0 . 0
       -5 6
          1 4
        -   0
        1 4 0
       -  1 1 2
          2 8 0
        -  2 8 0
              0
```

Subtract the product (56 x 5 = 280) from the number into which we just divided (280).   280 - 280 = 0

Check: Now we know we are finished with this division problem because the two requirements have been met: (1) there are no other numbers to bring down from the divisional box, **and** (2) the remainder is zero.

Answer: 102.5

Example #3:   68.1) 0 . 2 0 7 0 2 4

Step #1: Make sure the divisor is a whole number.

681) 0 . 2 0 7 0 2 4

The divisor is 68.1 To make this a whole number we must move the decimal point one place to the right. We then must also move the decimal point inside the divisional box the same number of places, once in this case.

becomes

681) 2 . 0 7 0 2 4

Step #2: Bring the decimal point straight up above the quotient line.

681) 2 . 0 7 0 2 4

Steps #3 and #4: Divide the divisor into the first number larger than itself. Put the answer directly above the last digit into which we divided.

681 does not divide into 207, but divides into 2070. 681 divides into 2070 three (3) times. Put the 3 in the quotient directly above the second 0, the last digit into which we just divided.

$$\begin{array}{r} 3 \\ 681) \overline{2 . 0 7 0 2 4} \end{array}$$

*** Notice that in the quotient there are two blank spaces (above the first 0 and the 7) to the right of the decimal point. We can't leave "gaps," so be sure to fill in these blank spaces with zeros.

$$\begin{array}{r} . 0 0 3 \\ 681) \overline{2 . 0 7 0 2 4} \end{array}$$

Step #5: Subtract the product of the divisor and the quotient (681 x 3 =2043) from the number into which we just divided (2070).

$$\begin{array}{r} . 0 0 3 \\ 681) \overline{2 . 0 7 0 2 4} \\ \underline{-2\ 0 4 3} \\ 2 7 \end{array}$$

Step #6: Bring down the next number (the 2) in the divisional box.

$$\begin{array}{r} . 0 0 3 \\ 681) \overline{2 . 0 7 0 2 4} \\ \underline{-2\ 0 4 3} \\ 2 7 2 \end{array}$$

Steps #7 and #8: Divide the divisor into this new number
(272). Then repeat steps #4-7 until the problem is
completed.

681 divides in 272 zero (0) times. Put the 0 in the
quotient directly above the 2, the last digit into
which we just divided.

```
          . 0 0 3 0
  681 ) 2 . 0 7 0 2 4
       - 2  0 4 3
             2 7 2
           -     0
             2 7 2 4
```

Subtract the product (681 x 0 = 0) from the number
(272) into which we just divided.   272 - 0 = 272.
Now bring down the next number (the 4).

Divide the divisor into this new number.
681 divides into 2724 exactly four (4) times.
Put the 4 in the quotient directly above the
4, the last digit into which we just divided.

```
          . 0 0 3 0 4
  681 ) 2 . 0 7 0 2 4
       - 2  0 4 3
             2 7 2
           -     0
             2 7 2 4
             2 7 2 4
                   0
```

Subtract the product (681 x 4 =2724) from the
number (2724) into which we just divided.
2724 - 2724 = 0

Check: We know we are finished with this division problem because the two
requirements have been met: (1) there are no other numbers to bring down
from the divisional box, **and** (2) the remainder is zero.

Answer: 0.00304

Example #4:   If we have a 110 foot long piece of lumber and need to cut it into pieces of 5 feet in
length, how many pieces will we get?

First identify what we start with—a single 110 foot long piece of lumber.

Second, identify the action—cutting this piece of lumber into pieces that are each 5 feet
in length. This is a division process, taking a whole or total and breaking it up into
smaller equal parts. To find the number of items, pieces of wood in this case, we
recognize the following:

Concept Set up: (Total) ÷ (amount (size) per item)

Set up: (110 feet) ÷ (5)

Answer: 22 pieces of lumber

Sample #1: A bowling team from Ukiah got lucky! Together the 8 members bought the winning lottery ticket. If the winning amount was $2,700,000, how much money would **each** person get?

First we need to recognize that there is a total amount of money which is being split up, or divided up by 8 people. We must divide the total amount by the number of winners to find the amount each person will win. In a division problem, **whatever comes after the word each or per is the divisor.**

```
          337500
    8 ) 2700000
       -24
         30
        -24
         60
        -56
         40
        -40
         00
        - 0
          00
```

Concept Set up: (Total) ÷ (number of items)

Set up: (2,700,000) ÷ (8)

Answer: **$337,500 per person**

You try it now:

a) In an average year the Green Lumber Company plants tree seeds on 124.8 acres of land. How many acres of land do they seed **each** month on average?

b) Ticket receipts for the concert totaled $135,000. If 6,000 people attended the concert, what was the cost **per** ticket?

Sample #2: In a chocolate factory, a single batch of chocolate weighs 912 pounds. If each *Sweet Treat* they make weighs 0.15 pounds, how many *Sweet Treats* are made from one batch of chocolate?

First we need to recognize that there is a total amount of chocolate which is being divided up into pieces that each weigh 0.15 pounds. We must divide the total amount of chocolate by the weight of **each** treat to find the number of treats that will be made.

Concept Set up: (Total) ÷ (amount per item)

Set up: (912 pounds) ÷ (0.15)

** **First step:** Remember to make the divisor a whole number (move the decimal point!). The problem 912 divided by 0.15 will become 91200 divided by 15

Answer: **6080 Sweet Treats**

```
           6080.
   15 ) 91200.
       -90
         12
        - 0
         120
        -120
          00
```

You try it now:

c) At a party a caterer served cups of fruit punch that each held 8 fluid ounces (0.0625 gallons). If she had 50 gallons of fruit punch, how many drinks was she able to serve?

d) Samantha needed 20 pieces of wood which would each be 0.75 inches in length. If she had a board which was 12 inches long, could she cut the needed number of pieces of wood?

Sample #3: Looking into a microscope, a scientist found a new bacterium which was 0.00016 inches in length. How many of these bacteria would have to be placed end to end to create a string 0.5 inches long?

First we need to recognize that there will be a total length of bacteria which is going to be divided up into parts that are 0.00016 inches in length, the length of each bacterium. We must divide the total length (0.5 inch) by the length of <u>each</u> bacterium to solve for the number of bacteria in this string.

Concept Set up: (Total) ÷ (amount per item)

Set up: (0.5 inches) ÷ (.00016 inches)

** **First step:** Remember to make the divisor a whole number (move the decimal point!). The problem 0.5 divided by 0.00016 will become 50000 divided by 16

Answer: 3125 bacteria

$$
\begin{array}{r}
3125. \\
16 \overline{)50000.} \\
-48 \\
\hline
20 \\
-16 \\
\hline
40 \\
-32 \\
\hline
80 \\
-80 \\
\hline
0
\end{array}
$$

You try it now:

e) City workers had to paint a double line in the center of a road for a distance of 2.8 miles. If each tank of paint which their truck has can paint a single line about .32 miles in length, how many tanks of paint will they use for this job?

f) There were 18336.5 gallons of oil left to be put in barrels. If each barrel holds 45.5 gallons, how many barrels could still be filled?

Sample #4: 171 inches is equal to how many feet? How many yards?

To change inches into feet we must first know that it takes 12 inches to equal 1 foot. To find how many feet (or how many 12-inch segments) are in 171 inches, we must divide the total inches (171) by each 12-inch segment.

Set up: 171 ÷ 12

1st Answer: 14.25 feet

To change feet into yards we must know that it takes
3 feet to equal 1 yard. To find how many yards (or how
many 3-foot segments) are in 14.25 feet, we must divide
the total feet (14.25) by each 3-foot segment.

$14.25 \div 3$

Set up: $(171 \div 12) \div 3$

2nd Answer: 4.75 yards

- **You try it now:**

g) 19,008 feet is equal to how many miles?

h) 900 seconds is how many minutes?

> Answers to You try it now: a) 10.4 acres; b) $22.50; c) 800 drinks; d) No, she could only cut 16 pieces; e) 17.5 tanks of paint; f) 403 barrels; g) 3.6 miles; h) 15 minutes
>
> Answer to Application: If each package is 11.5 ounces and the total amount needed is 120 ounces, we can divide 120 by 11.5 to find out the quantity (how many) of packages he bought. Our answer is 10.4347... Since he needs more than 10 packages, he would have to buy 11 packages.

1.4 Division Problems

In exercises #1-7, identify the divisor. Do not solve.

1) $31 \overline{)8153}$ 2) $90.2 / .41$ 3) $0.75 \div 7$

4) 16 goes into 8   5) $\dfrac{0.15}{24}$ 6) Find the quotient of 0.2 and 0.05

7) Find the quotient of 0.42 and 6

In exercises #8-25 divide the following numbers.

8) $9 \overline{)675}$ 9) $31 \overline{)8153}$ 10) $8.9 \overline{)267}$

11) 875 divided by .25   12) 1.0545 divided by 0.37   13) 15.81 divided by 6.2

14) 16 goes into 8   15) 0.4 goes into 30   16) $17 \div 0$

17) $90.2 / 0.41$ 18) $333.2 / 0.98$ 19) $30.25 / 0.05$

20) $7.252 \div 35$ 21) $0.175 \div 7$ 22) $0.272 \div 8$

23) $\dfrac{0.15}{0}$ 24) $\dfrac{0.234}{52}$ 25) $\dfrac{0.00549}{0.18}$

In exercises #26-33, (a) translate the following words into math expressions (use the ÷ symbol for division and the dot (•) for multiplication) and , (b) give the solution .

26) The quotient of 10 and 2, then add 5

27) Six more than the quotient of 15 and 3.

28) 20 increased by the quotient of 10 and 6.

29) 11 subtracted from the quotient of 26 and 2.

30) The product of 7 and 4, then divide by 2.

31) The product of 11 and 20, then decreased by 1.2

32) The difference of the sum of 4 and 2 and the quotient of 16 and 8.

33) The quotient of 5 and 25, then subtract .15

In exercises #34-41, translate the following words into math expressions.

34) The quotient of 15 and x

35) The quotient of 3 and x

36) The quotient of 8 and x, then minus 4

37) The quotient of x and y

38) x divided by y, then subtract 6

39) x divided by itself, then 3 more

40) The quotient of x and 5

41) Subtract y from the quotient of y and x.

In exercises #42-49, state whether the following statements are True or False.

42) Multiplication and division are opposite operations.

43) $8 • 3 = 24$ is the same as $8 = 24 ÷ 3$

44) $10 • 5 = 50$ is the same as $5 = 50 ÷ 10$

45) $40 ÷ 8 = 5$ is the same as $40 = 5 • 8$

46) $30 ÷ 6 = x$ is the same as $30 = x • 30$

47) $4 • x = 24$ is the same as $x = 24 • 4$

48) $100 ÷ x = 20$ is the same as $100 = 20 • x$

49) $40 • 80 = x$ is the same as $40 = x ÷ 80$

In exercises #50-57, write an equivalent equation which changes any given multiplication statement to a division statement or changes any given division statement to a multiplication statement. There is nothing to solve here.

50) $6 • 3 = 18$

51) $20 ÷ 5 = 4$

52) $x ÷ 25 = 8$

53) $x • 10 = 70$

54) $16 ÷ x = 4$

55) $x ÷ 18 = 3.5$

56) $5 • x = 85$

57) $11 • 7 = x$

In exercises #58-68, solve for the value of x, the unknown number.

58) $7 • x = 28$

59) $x • 4 = 40$

60) $16 • x = 32$

61) $5 • 4 • x = 80$

62) $x ÷ 8 = 7$

63) $x ÷ 15 = 8$

64) $\frac{x}{10} = 4$

65) $\frac{x}{4} = 2.5$

66) $30 ÷ x = 4$

67) $46 ÷ x = 8$

68) The quotient of x and 60 equals 12

In exercise #69–82: (a) write a mathematical expression that will solve the problem, and (b) give the solution.

69) When a company's profits soared, the owner distributed end-of-the-year bonuses in equal amounts to her 80 employees. If $200,000 was given in bonuses, how much extra money did each employee earn?

70) If 4 pounds of oranges cost $2.76, how much does 1 pound cost?

71-72) It takes Phyllis 2.5 hours to fill her four-foot deep, backyard pond with a hose; the pond holds 9000 gallons of water.

71) How many gallons of water flow through the hose per hour?

72) How many gallons of water flow through the hose per minute?

73) At a party attended by 300 people, a caterer used 50 gallons of fruit punch to serve 800 drinks. How much of a gallon was used for each drink?

74) When a traffic accident occurred, cars were stopped on the two northbound lanes of the freeway, bumper to bumper for 4 miles. If the average distance from the front of one car to the front of the next was 12 feet, how many car were stopped on the freeway (Reminder: 5280 feet equal 1 mile)?

75-76) In a class-action lawsuit against an HMO, a judge ruled that the company must pay a total of $25,219,200 to 240 patients.

75) How much would each patient receive?

76) If each patient received his money in 20 monthly payments, how much would each patient get each month?

77-80) During a drought year Joaquin found that ants were sometimes forced to travel great distances from their nest to find food and water. He found one line of ants that measured 2400 feet from the nest to an animal carcass. These particular ants he was studying were 0.24 of an inch in length.

77) How many feet long is an ant?

78) Approximately how many ants did it take to make this 2400 foot line?

79) If this ant nest was the home to a colony of fifty times as many ants as were in this line, how many ants lived there?

80) If all the ants in this colony formed a straight line, how many feet long would this line be?

81-82) A construction supplier ordered a thousand boxes of nails. Each box contained 100 nails; he was supposed to pay $.008 per nail.

81) If he was billed $8000 for his order, how much was he charged per nail?

82) Was he overcharged or undercharged? By how many cents per nail?

Skills Check

1. Find the product of .025 and 25.

2. 4 yards is equal to how many inches?

3. What does 5 more than twice 11 equal?

4. If it takes Martha 32 minutes to run around a lake, how long will it take her at the same pace to run around the lake 3.5 times?

Answers to Skills Check: 1) 0.625; 2) 144 inches; 3) 27; 4) 112 minutes or 1 hour and 52 minutes.

Section 1.5 Rounding and Estimation

Objectives:

• To round numbers

• To estimate (approximate) answers/outcomes

• To write repeating decimals

Application:

As you approach the checkout line at the supermarket, you reach into your pocket and discover you only have 20 dollars. Quickly scan your purchases and estimate your costs to the nearest dollar to see whether you have enough money to purchase all your selected items.

Soda $2.98	Bread $1.59	Chicken $3.29
Cereal $4.49	Milk $2.39	Cookies $3.60

Vocabulary:

rounding—Rounding off means to give the approximate value of a final answer to a *specific place value*. Sometimes an exact answer is not needed. Remember, rounding is done <u>after</u> the computation of a problem.

estimation—Estimation is the process of calculating an approximate answer <u>before</u> we start the computation of a problem. A good way to think of estimation is to think of it as a *general reality check*.

If we have a problem like 4.8 • 7.16, it is a good idea to get an estimated answer before we work this problem or punch numbers into a calculator. We can estimate to ourselves that 4.8 is about 5 and 7.16 is close to a value of 7. Therefore, our answer must be about 5 • 7 or about 35. If we were to make a decimal error and end up with an answer of 343.68 instead of the correct answer of 34.368, we would catch this mistake because we had estimated the answer already.

repeating decimal—A repeating decimal is a number in which a decimal digit (a number to the right of the decimal point) or digits repeat forever.

An example of a repeating decimal is the number $2.\overline{3}$ The bar above the 3 is called a **repeater bar** and tells us that the 3 repeats forever ($2.\overline{3}$ is the same as $2.33\overline{3}$). A second example would be $0.\overline{26}$. The repeater bar above the 26 tells us that the digits 26 repeat forever ($0.\overline{26}$ is the same as $0.262626\overline{26}$).

Another way to represent a decimal digit(s) that repeats forever is to put three dots after the repeating numbers. We could represent 2.$\overline{3}$ as 2.3... (the 3 dots telling us that the 3 repeats forever) or 0.$\overline{26}$ as 0.26... (the 3 dots telling us that the 26 repeat forever). In this book we will use the repeater bar to represent digits that repeat forever.

$\approx$ is the mathematical symbol which means "approximately."

**Remember: When you have an amount of money expressed with a dollar symbol:

Rounding to the nearest cent (penny) is the same as rounding to the hundredths place.

Rounding to the nearest tenth of a cent is the same as rounding to the thousandths place.

Convert a dollar symbol to a cent symbol by moving the decimal point two places to the right. \$0.76 = 76¢

Convert a cent symbol to a dollar symbol by moving the decimal point two places to the left. 84¢ = \$0.84

How to:

Round a number:

1. Locate the digit of the place value to which you are rounding.

2. Look to the number <u>immediately to the right</u> of this place value. If the number to the right of the digit to be rounded is 5 or higher, the rounded digit goes up 1. If the number to the right of the digit to be rounded is 4 or lower, the rounded digit stays the same.

3. All whole number digits to the right of the rounded number become zeros; all decimal digits to the right of the rounded number are dropped.

Example #1: Round 6372.45 to the tens place.

Step #1: Locate the digit of the place value to which you are rounding.

The $\underline{7}$ is in the tens place.

Step #2: Look to the number immediately to the right of this place value.

The digit to the right of the $\underline{7}$ (the tens place) is a $\underline{2}$. A $\underline{2}$ is "4 or lower," so the rounded digit will stay the same (stay a $\underline{7}$).

6 3 $\underline{7}$ 2 . 4 5

Step #3: All whole number digits to the right of the rounded number become zeros; all decimal digits to the right of the rounded number are dropped.

The only whole number digit to the right of the 7 is the 2 in the ones place. The 2 must change to a 0 (zero). Because you are rounding off to a whole number, all the decimal digits (.45 here) are dropped.

$$6\ 3\ \underline{7}\ \cancel{2}\ .\ \cancel{4}\cancel{5}$$
$$0$$

Answer: 6370

Example #2: Round 256.086 to the hundredths place.

Step #1: Locate the digit of the place value to which you are rounding.

The 8 is in the hundredths place.

Step #2: Look to the number immediately to the right of this place value.

The digit to the right of the 8 (the hundredths place) is a 6. A 6 is "5 or higher," so the rounded digit will go up one (to a 9).

$$2\ 5\ 6\ .\ 0\ \cancel{8}\ 6$$
$$9$$

Step #3: All decimal digits to the right of the rounded number are dropped.

$$2\ 5\ 6\ .\ 0\ \cancel{8}\ \cancel{6}$$
$$9$$

The 6 here is dropped.

Answer: 256.09

Example #3: Round 86.952 to the tenths place.

Step #1: Locate the digit of the place value to which you are rounding.

The 9 is in the tenths place.

Step #2: Look to the number immediately to the right of this place value.

The digit to the right of the 9 (the tenths place) is a 5. A 5 is "5 or higher," so the rounded digit will go up one (to a 10).

We cannot put 2 digits, the 10, in a single place value. Therefore, we must do exactly what we would do if adding. We put the zero in the tenths place and carry a 1 to the left (in this case to the ones place).

$$\overset{1}{8\ 6}\ .\ \cancel{9}\ 5\ 2$$
$$0$$

Step #3: All decimal digits to the right of the rounded number are dropped.

$$\overset{1}{8\,6}\,.\,\cancel{5}\,\cancel{5}\,\cancel{2}$$
$$0$$

The 5 and 2 are dropped.

Answer: 87.0

**It is important to notice here that we <u>must</u> keep the zero in the answer because this is the tenths place, the place to which we were asked to round.

Example #4: Round $42.\overline{59}$ to the thousandths place.

Step #1: Locate the digit of the place value to which you are rounding.

Here we must recognize that the repeater bar means that the five-nine combination will keep repeating forever.

Thus: $42.\overline{59}$ is equal to 42.595959

Now we can see that a <u>5</u> is in the thousandths place.

Step #2: Look to the number immediately to the right of this place value.

The digit to the right of the <u>5</u> (in the thousandths place) is a <u>9</u>. A <u>9</u> is "5 or higher," so the rounded digit will go up one (to an <u>6</u>).

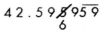

$$4\,2\,.\,5\,9\,\cancel{5}\,9\,5\,9$$
$$6$$

Step #3: All decimal digits to the right of the rounded number are dropped.

$$4\,2\,.\,5\,9\,\cancel{5}\,\cancel{9}\,\cancel{5}\,\cancel{9}$$
$$6$$

The $9\overline{59}$ are dropped.

Answer: 42.596

How to:

Estimate:

1. Round off each number in a particular problem to a chosen place value.

2. Perform the given problem with these estimated numbers.

Example #5: Estimate (to the tens place) the answer of 138 + 87 + 43.

Step #1: Round off each number in a particular problem to a chosen place value, in this case to the tens place.

138 is close to 140 (rounded to the nearest tens)

87 is close to 90

43 is close to 40

Step #2: Perform the given problem with these estimated numbers.

Add 140 + 90 + 40 = 270.

Answer: ≈ 270

Example #6: Estimate (to the thousands place) the answer of 3430 + 845 + 400 + 14,678.

Step #1: Round off each number in a particular problem to a chosen place value, in this case to the thousands place.

3430 is close to 3000 (rounded to the nearest thousands)

845 is close to 1000 (put a zero in the thousands place before rounding)

400 is close to 0 (put a zero is in the thousands place before rounding)

14,678 is close to 15000

Step #2: Perform the given problem with these estimated numbers.

Add 3000 + 1000 + 0 + 15000 = 19,000

Answer: ≈ 19,000

Sample #1: A company sold $86,574, 808 worth of merchandise last year. To the nearest million, how much merchandise was sold?

The digit in the millions place is the <u>6</u>.

The digit to the right of the <u>6</u> is a <u>5</u> (5 or higher) so the <u>6</u> must go up one to a <u>7</u>.

All whole number digits to the right of the rounded number become zeros.

86,574,808 rounded to the millions place is 87,000,000.

Answer: $87,000,000

You try it now:

a) Round 44,528.6 to the thousands place.

b) Laser technology recorded a distance between two objects at 12.1539 feet. What is the distance when rounded to the hundredths place?

Sample #2: A store sold 1490 boxes of cereal last year. If the average box sold for $2.80, how much did customers pay for cereal (round answer to the nearest hundred dollars)?

Do the problem: Customers spent $2.80 • 1490 boxes = $4172

The digit in the hundreds place is the 1.

The digit to the right of the 1 is a 7 (5 or higher) so the 1 goes up one to a 2.

Finally, all whole number digits to the right of the rounded number become zeros.

4172 rounded to the hundreds place is 4200.

Answer: $4200

You try it now:

c) Motor Oil was on sale for $1.39 per quart. If Clive bought 40 quarts, how much of the company's money did he spend (round answer to the nearest dollar)?

d) Dr. Sharp recorded the length of the new bacterium to be 0.00016 inches in length. If he found a single strand of 5205 of these bacteria, how long was the strand (round answer to the nearest hundredth of an inch)?

Sample #3: If grapes cost $0.95 a pound and there are about 35 grapes to a pound, how much does a customer pay per grape to the nearest cent? How much to the nearest tenth of a cent?

Do the problem: The total cost $0.95 is split by (divided by) the 35 grapes. This division problem keeps going. We could get to $0.027142...and still not finish. But we don't need to keep going.

To round to the nearest cent when we have a dollar symbol is the same as rounding to the hundredths place (there are 100 cents in a dollar).

The digit in the hundredths place is the 2.

The digit to the right of this 2 is a 7 (5 or higher) so the 2 goes up one to a 3.

We round this number to $0.03 We could leave the answer as it is with the dollar symbol or convert the dollar symbol to a cent symbol by moving the decimal point 2 places to the right.

Answer (to the nearest cent): 3¢ or $0.03

To round to the nearest tenth of a cent when we have a dollar symbol is the same as rounding to the thousandths place (the whole cents are taken up by the tenths and the hundredths place).

Here's our value again: $0.027142...

The digit in the thousandths place is the 7.

The digit to the right of this <u>7</u> is a <u>1</u> (4 or lower) so the <u>7</u> stays the same.

We round this number to $.027. We could leave this as the answer or convert the dollar symbol to a cent symbol by moving the decimal point 2 places to the right.

Answer (to the nearest tenth of a cent): 2.7¢ or $0.027

■ **You try it now:**

e) *Egg Farm Inc.* sells a dozen eggs for $1.19 at its ranch. If the McKenzie family bought 4 dozen eggs, how much did they pay per egg, rounded to the nearest tenth of a cent?

f) An international store sells its trademark candy bar for $.65 at a store in Sonoma. All costs considered, it takes $.436 to make and market the candy bar. How much does the store make per candy bar rounded to the nearest cent? Rounded to the nearest tenth of a cent?

Sample #4: While studying the eating potential of 3 different types of termites, Michelle measured a piece of wood that was exactly 89.94 centimeters (cm) in length. After she cut it into 3 equal lengths, how long was each cut piece of wood to the nearest tenth of a centimeter?

Do the problem. The total length, 89.94 is divided by 3.

This equals **29.98 cm.**

The digit in the tenths place is the <u>9</u> .

The digit to the right of this <u>9</u> is an <u>8</u> (5 or higher) so the <u>9</u> goes up one to a <u>10</u>.

We can't have a <u>10</u> (two digits in one place value) so the <u>9</u> becomes a <u>0</u> (zero) and we carry the <u>1</u> to the left, to the ones place in this case.

$$
\begin{array}{c}
^{1} \\
2\,9\,.\,\cancel{9}8 \\
0
\end{array}
$$

Now this carried <u>1</u> is added to the <u>9</u> in the ones place. We get <u>10</u>. We have to put down a <u>0</u> for the ones place and carry to the left another <u>1</u>, to the tens place this time.

$$
\begin{array}{c}
^{1}\;\;^{1} \\
2\cancel{9}\,.\,\cancel{9}8 \\
0\;\;0
\end{array}
$$

The <u>2</u> in the tens place becomes a <u>3</u>.

Answer: 30.0 centimeters

■ **You try it now:**

g) Round $19.985 to the nearest dollar.

h) Round $5.996 to the nearest cent.

Sample #5: The head of security at the art festival wanted an estimation to the nearest hundred the number of people at the event. A gate watcher had counted 887 people entering the festival and 314 leaving between 10 and 11 a.m. About how many more patrons were there at the festival at 11 than at 10?

Estimate the answer of: 887 - 314 to the hundreds place.

887 has a value of about 900 (rounded to the hundreds).

314 has a value of about 300 (rounded to the hundreds).

$900 - 300 = 600$. Therefore, $887 - 314 \approx 600$.

Answer: 600 patrons

You try it now:

i) A shrewd buyer went to Petaluma one Saturday and bought $684 worth of merchandise at a flea market. The next weekend he sold the same goods at the flea market in San Jose for $2038. By estimating each amount to the nearest hundred dollars, about how much money did he make?

j) Bill bought eleven screw drivers on sale for $6.78 each. About how much did he pay for the screw drivers (estimate by rounding the price of the screwdrivers to the nearest dollar)?

Answers to You try it now: a) 45,000; b) 12.15 feet; c) $56; d) .83 inches; e) 9.9¢ or $0.099; f) 21¢ and 21.4¢; g) $20; h) $6.00 or 600¢; i) $1300; j) $77

Answer to Application:

	Actual Cost		Estimated Cost (to the nearest dollar)
Soda	$2.98		$3.00
Bread	$1.59		$2.00
Chicken	$3.29		$3.00
Cereal	$4.49		$4.00
Milk	$2.39		$2.00
Cookies	$3.60		$4.00
		Total:	$18.00 You can estimate that you have enough money.

1.5 Rounding and Estimation Problems

In exercises #1-5, round each number to the nearest ones place.

1) 708.37   2) 42.81   3) 29.74   4) 599.097   5) 0.39

In exercises #6-10, round each number to the tens place.

6) 708   7) 62.9   8) 1040   9) 46,795   10) 4.99

In exercises #11-15, round each number to the hundreds place.

11) 16,284   12) 5,827   13) 57.04   14) 11,972   15) 408,007

In exercises #16-20, round each number to the thousands place.

16) 18,573   17) 72 08   18) 345,278   19) 643   20) 189,676

In exercises #21-25, round each number to the nearest tenths place.

21) 48.269   22) 13.82   23) 406.94   24) 35.952   25) 64.5

In exercises #26-29, round each number to the nearest hundredths place.

26) 566.282   27) 99.949   28) 137.626   29) 99.994

In exercises #30-37, round each number to the nearest whole value, and the nearest tenths, hundredths, and thousandths places.

30) 8.6593   31) 20.73   32) 49.3896   33) $2.79\overline{8}$

34) $999.9\overline{6}$ 35) $7.\overline{3}$ 36) $299.\overline{96}$ 37) $629.\overline{89}$

In exercises #38-41, round each dollar amount to (a) the nearest cent <u>and</u> (b) nearest tenth of a cent. Your answer may be written using either the dollar symbol or the cent symbol.

38) $ 0.0855   39) $ 0.9096   40) $1.075   41) $ 0.6\overline{6}

In exercises #42-46, round each cent amount to the nearest dollar.

42) 123¢   43) 958¢   44) 64¢   45) 37.9¢   46) 50.1¢

In exercises #47-50, identify the one letter of the expression that does not equal the others.

47) a) $.04   b) 4/100 of a dollar   c) 4 cents   d) 0.4 cents

48)   a) $17.62   b) 17 dollars and 62/100 cents   c) 1762 cents   d) 17 and 62/100 dollars

49) a) 256/100 of a dollar   b) 2 dollars and .56 cents   c) $2.56   d) 2 and 56/100 dollars

50) a) 25 and 12 thousandths   b) 25.012   c) 25 and $\dfrac{0.012}{1000}$ d) $25\dfrac{12}{1000}$

In exercises #51-60, (a) translate the following words into math expressions, and (b) give the solution to the created math expression.

51) The sum of 8.6 rounded to the ones place and 4.37 rounded to the tenths.

52) The sum of 126 rounded to the hundreds place and 86.256 rounded to the hundredths.

53) The difference of 1,086 rounded to the hundreds and 854.73 rounded to the tens.

54) The difference of 141.62 rounded to the nearest whole and 62.73 rounded to the hundreds.

55) Subtract 2548 rounded to the hundreds from 5406 rounded to the hundreds.

56) Subtract 12.762 rounded to the hundredths from 19.52 rounded to the nearest whole.

57) The product of 807 rounded to the tens and 56.728 rounded to the tenths.

58) The product of 336.25 rounded to the hundreds and 12.137 rounded to the tenths.

59) The quotient of 11.23 rounded to the tenths and 3.62 rounded to the nearest whole.

60) The quotient of 651.38 rounded to the ones and 9.32 rounded to the tenths.

For problems #61-71: (a) write a mathematical expression that will solve the problem, and (b) give the solution. If you only need to round to find the answer, just write *no set up*.

61) Last year Marcus earned $34,257.88. This year he earned $38,686.34. To the nearest hundred how much more money did he earn this year than last?

62) When flowers went on sale at a local nursery for only $1.68 each, Jacquiline bought twenty of them. How much did she spend (round answer to the nearest dollar).

63) Connie kept several exotic fish in her acquarium at home. She fed them with guppies that she bought at a wholesale store for the price of $3.10 per dozen. How much did she pay per guppy (round answer to the nearest cent)?

64) A box of cereal held 15 ounces and sold for $2.93. How much did the cereal cost per ounce, rounded to the nearest cent?

65-70) Below a box of cereal on the shelf at a grocery store, it was printed that the price was $.195 per ounce.

65) To the nearest cent, how much is this per ounce?

66) To the nearest tenth of a cent, how much is this per ounce?

67) If the box of cereal held 25 ounces, how much did the store sell it for after it rounded the final price to the nearest cent?

68) If a jumbo box (50 ounces) of the same cereal cost $0.1575 per ounce how much money did it sell for after the final price was rounded to the nearest cent?

69) How much money was saved buying the jumbo box of cereal instead of two smaller boxes?

70) If a family ate 50 ounces of cereal per week for an entire year, how much money would the family save buying cereal in the jumbo-sized boxes?

71) A square foot [12 inches in width by 12 inches in length or 144 times the size of a square inch (1 inch in width by 1 inch in length)] of carpet on display at a carpet store holds approximately 14,135 different types of viruses. If a customer holds a one square inch swatch of carpet in her hand, how many different types of viruses would she be holding in her hand? Round answer to the nearest whole virus.

In exercises #72-81, give an estimated answer to the <u>hundreds place</u> for the following problems. Remember: estimating means to round the numbers <u>before</u> we do our computation.

72) 866 + 281   73) 438 + 917   74) 1258 - 870

75) 1512 - 1158   76) 444 + 333 - 295   77) 829 - 472 + 253

78) 85 + 178 + 227 + 340   79) 354 + 206 + 28 + 161   80) $827.45 - $278.43

81) $36 + $227.12 + $248

In exercises #82-89, give an estimated answer to the nearest <u>whole number</u> for the following problems. Remember: estimating means to round the numbers <u>before</u> we do our computation.

82) 6.8 x 7.2   83) 3.715 x 4.79   84) 19.8 x 5.678

85) 15.23 (7. 5)   86) 40.2 /7.9   87) 17.59/2.78

88) 250.34/49.8   89) 34.5/6.93

In exercises #90-98, (a) translate the following words into math statements, and (b) give the solution to the created math statement.

90) The exact difference of the value of 8.6 and 4.8.

91) The difference of the value of 8.6 and 4.8 when estimated to the ones place.

92) The exact product of 7.8 and 12.4.

93) The product of 7.8 and 12.4 estimated to the ones place.

94) The product of 7.8 and 12.4 estimated to the tens place.

95) The product of 7.8 and 12.4 estimated to the hundreds place.

96) The exact quotient of 3.6 and 4.5.

97) The quotient of 3.6 and 4.5 estimated to the ones place.

98) The quotient of 42 and 8.5 estimated to the tens place.

For problems #99-106: (a) write a mathematical expression that will solve the problem, and (b) give the solution.

99-100) Anita's cash register kept track of her hourly sales. In her first three hours at work she sold $456.17, $395.20, and $510.87.

99) Estimated to the nearest hundred dollars, how much merchandise did she sell in the first three hours?

100) Estimated to the nearest ten dollars, how much did she sell?

101-103) After receiving his paycheck for $865.38, Ned paid two bills. His rent was $565, and his utility bill was $46.

101) Estimated to the nearest hundred dollars, how much money did he have left?

102) Estimated to the nearest ten dollars, how much did he still have?

103) Exactly how money did he have left?

104-105) When buying sodas for the company picnic, Margarita spent $1.82 for a six-pack.

104) If she bought 30 six-packs, how much money did she spend, estimated to the nearest dollar?

105) How much did she pay per soda, estimated to the nearest cent?

106) Jerry bought all the chickens for the picnic. If he paid $118.86 for 29 chickens, how much did he pay per chicken, estimated to the nearest dollar (hint: to get a quick estimate, Jerry estimated both the number of chickens and dollars to the tens place)?

Skills Check

1. Find the quotient of 837.8 and .59

2. 30 hours is equal to how many days?

3. What is 3 less than the quantity 40 divided by 8

4. If six friends split equally the dinner bill of $84, how much did each friend pay?

Answers to Skills Check: 1) 1420: 2) 1.25 days; 3) 2; 4) $14.

Section 1.6 A Certain Order of Operations

Objective:

- To solve order of operations problems
- To find an average
- To learn the Commutative and Associative Properties for addition & multiplication
- To utilize the Commutative and Associative Properties in mental math
- To set up/solve order of operations application problems

Application:

While camping in Canada, a mother measures the temperature of her son who is feeling ill. The thermometer reads 36° Celsius. Is this good or bad? Unfamiliar with the Celsius system, she uses a pocket dictionary she has to find the formula for converting a Celsius temperature to the Fahrenheit scale with which she is familiar. Is her son's temperature normal?

Formula: Fahrenheit temperature = (Celsius temperature) • 1.8 + 32

or

$$F = C \bullet 1.8 + 32$$

Vocabulary:

Order of Operations—The **Order of Operations** is a process established to ensure that we get a problem correct when we are given a sequence of **multiple (more than one) operations**. The acronym (a word formed by the first letters of other words—like SCUBA—which stands for Self-Contained Underwater Breathing Apparatus) to remember the order of operations is **PEMDAS**—each letter represents a particular operation.

P = Parenthesis.	We do what is <u>inside</u> a parenthesis **first**.
E = Exponent.	We do exponents **second**.
M & **D** = Multiply & Divide	We do multiplication & division **third**, working left to right.
A & **S** = Add & Subtract	We combine, or add & subtract **last**.

We will revisit the order of operations later in the book. Do not worry about exponents right now. For this chapter you need to remember two elements: (1) We do all work inside a parenthesis first, and (2) we do multiplication and division before we work addition and subtraction.

average—An **average** is a term used in statistics to represent a central value for a group of numbers. Mathematically, an average is a special type of problem that follows this process:

First: Add the values from the group together to get a total.

Second: Divide this total by the number of values.

Example: Find the average score for a student who received 68%, 82%, and 93% on three quizzes.

** Notice that in the set up below the sum of the three scores are placed inside a parenthesis. This is to ensure that we follow order of operations—first working inside a parenthesis.

Set up: (68 + 82 + 93) ÷ 3   or $\dfrac{(68 + 82 + 93)}{3}$

243 ÷ 3   or $\dfrac{(243)}{3}$

Answer: an 81% average

Commutative Property (for Addition & Multiplication)—The **Commutative Property** recognizes the fact that the answer will be the same when we change the order of the given numbers when the problem is either all addition or all multiplication.

The word commutative has the same root vocabulary as commute, to go back and forth, changing the order.

Addition: 6 + 4 is the same as 4 + 6. Both equal 10.

7 + 6 + 5 is the same as 6 + 7 + 5. Both equal 18.

Multiplication: (6) (4) is the same as (4) (6). Both equal 24.

(2) (5) (7) is the same as (7) (5) (2). Both equal 70.

** Remember that this works only if there is either all addition or all multiplication!!

Associative Property (for Addition & Multiplication)—The **Associative Property** recognizes the fact that the answer will be the same when we change the association or grouping (which numbers are inside a parenthesis) of numbers when the problem is either all addition or all multiplication.

Associating or grouping numbers together to represent a single amount or quantity is accomplished by putting these numbers inside a parenthesis.

Addition: (6 + 5) + 15 is the same as 6 + (5 + 15). Both equal 26.

Multiplication: 4 • (5 • 6) is the same as (4 • 5) • 6. Both equal 120.

** Remember that this works only if there is either all addition or all multiplication!!

> **How to:**
>
> Solve an Order of Operations problem (no exponents)
> 1. Do any work inside a parenthesis first.
> 2. Do any multiplication and division (working left to right)
> 3. Do any addition and subtraction.

Example #1: $8 + 3 \cdot 5$ <u>Step-by-step solution</u>

      Step #1: Do any work inside a parenthesis first. $8 + 3 \cdot 5$

           There is no parenthesis. There is nothing to do. $8 + 3 \cdot 5$

      Step #2: Do any multiplication and division.

           There is multiplication. Solve $3 \cdot 5$: $8 + \underline{3 \cdot 5}$

                    and rewrite as: $8 + 15$

      Step #3: Do any addition and subtraction.

           There is addition. Solve $8 + 15$: $\underline{8 + 15}$

                    and rewrite as: 23

                  Answer: 23

Example #2: $7 - 4 \div (7 - 5)$

      Step #1: Do any work inside a parenthesis first. $7 - 4 \div (7 - 5)$

           There is a parenthesis. Solve $(7 - 5)$: $7 - \underline{4 \div (7 - 5)}$

                    and rewrite as: $7 - 4 \div \quad (2)$

      Step #2: Do any multiplication and division.

           There is division. Solve $4 \div (2)$: $7 - \underline{4 \div (2)}$

                    and rewrite as: $7 - 2$

      Step #3: Do any addition and subtraction.

           There is subtraction. Solve $7 - 2$: $7 - 2$

                    and rewrite as: 5

                  Answer: 5

Example #3: $5 + 10 \div 2 \bullet (5)$

Step #1: Do any work inside a parenthesis first.

$5 + 10 \div 2 \bullet (5)$

There is a parenthesis, but no work to do <u>inside</u> that parenthesis. There is nothing to do.

$5 + 10 \div 2 \bullet (5)$

Step #2: Do any multiplication and division.

There is <u>both</u> multiplication and division. **Work left to right.** In this case, do the division first.

Solve $10 \div 2$:

$5 + \underline{10 \div 2} \bullet (5)$

and rewrite as:

$5 + 5 \bullet (5)$

Now do the multiplication. Solve $5 + \underline{5 \bullet (5)}$

and rewrite as:

$5 + 25$

Step #3: Do any addition and subtraction.

There is addition. Solve $5 + 25$:

$\underline{5 + 25}$

and rewrite as:

30

Answer: 30

How to:

Find an Average

1. Add the values to get a total.

2. Divide this total by the number of values.

Example #4: Monique is known as the "handy lady" in her condominium complex. Working at a variety of jobs in a recent four-week period, she earned $85, $325, $211, and $95 dollars. What were her average earnings per week?

Set up the expression to solve this problem so that by following the order of operations you will add up the values first. You ensure this by putting the sum of the values <u>inside</u> a parenthesis.

$(85 + 325 + 211 + 95) \div 4$

Step #1: Add the values to get a total. $(85 + 325 + 211 + 95) \div 4$

and rewrite as: $(716) \div 4$

Step #2: Divide this total by the number of values. $(716) \div 4$

and rewrite as: 179

Answer: $179 per week

How to:

Add/Multiply mentally using the Commutative & Associative Properties

1. Recognize that a problem is either all multiplication or all addition.

2. If all addition, add in any order that is easiest. If all multiplication, multiply in any order that is easiest.

Example #5: Oliva ran in a charity event at her elementary school for which she received 6 pledges from friends. What was the total amount of money she made for the charity if the pledges were for the following dollar amounts: 8 + 7 + 13 + 32 + 15 + 5.

Step #1: Recognize that this problem is all addition.

Step #2: Add in any order that is easiest.

It is typically easiest to add numbers in our heads by pairing up numbers that give a sum which ends in zero. If we look at the list above, instead of adding left to right, find numbers that when combined equal some amount of tens.

Rewrite the above problem, pairing up the following numbers:

$(7 + 13) + (8 + 32) + (5 + 15) =$
$(20) \quad + \quad (40) \quad + \quad (20) \quad = 80$ **Answer: $80**

Not all numbers will pair up as conveniently as these six numbers have done, but with practice you will see that the ability to change the order of numbers in either all addition or all multiplication will save you time.

Example #6:   Solve: $5 \cdot (8 \cdot 7)$

Step #1: Recognize that this problem is all multiplication.

Step #2: Multiply in any order that is easiest.

Again, take advantage of any pair of numbers that when multiplied will give us an answer that ends in a zero. We could rewrite this problem, changing its grouping. It could be written as:

$$(5 \cdot 8) \cdot 7 =$$
$$(40) \cdot 7 = 280 \qquad \text{Answer: 280}$$

Sample #1:   At two recent fund-raisers, $1200 and $1650 were respectively donated. A local philanthropist said he would double this sum of money. If $370 had to be subtracted from this total the next day because of various expenses, how much money was raised for charity?

Our first task here is to change words into math. To find the total money raised we would first have to add $1200 and $1650. What happened next? This total amount (now acting as one amount or one quantity and therefore needs to be put <u>inside</u> a parenthesis) was doubled (multiply by 2). Last, this amount was decreased by the $370 which was used for expenses. Therefore, the math expression would look like:

$(1200 + 1650)(2) - 370$ We now have a **multiple operation problem** which needs to be solved by following the order of operations (PEMDAS).

Do inside a parenthesis first:	$(1200 + 1650)(2) - 370 =$
Multiply before subtraction	$(2850)(2) - 370 =$
Subtract	$5700 - 370 = 5330$

Answer: $5330

■ **You try it now:**

a) In 1960 the population of the town of Dey was 850. By 1980, the population had tripled. Between 1980 and the present the population grew by another 2000 people. Set up a single math expression to find the population of Dey today. Then solve.

b) An electric car company decided to expand its operations. New investors were welcome if they were willing to make an initial investment of $6000. Unable to afford that much individually, three friends got together and each invested $2000. Together the 3 friends got $15,000 from their original investment. Set up a single math expression to find out how much money each friend made. Then solve.

Sample #2: As a freelance photographer, Lakeisha found that the time that she spent working varied tremendously. In the 4 weeks of February she worked 16, 45, 25, and 62 hours respectively. If she earned $14 per hour, what was the average amount of money she earned each week?

To find the average amount she earned each week, first we need to find the total amount of money she made: (total hours) • (wage per hour). Second, we find the average by dividing by the number of weeks.

Conceptually, the set up to solve this problem is:

$$\left[(\text{total hours}) \bullet (\text{wage per hour})\right] \div (\text{number of weeks})$$

Now substitute numbers for these concepts to get a set up that is

a math expression: $\quad \left[(16 + 45 + 25 + 62) \bullet (14)\right] \div (4)$

Answer = $518 per week

■ **You try it now:**

c) At a local poultry farm, a farmer sold 3500 dozen eggs in August, 4500 dozen in September, and 7000 dozen in October. If he earns 50¢ per dozen eggs sold, what is his average monthly income for these three months?

d) In the last 5 years, the county of Chillemuch received 55 inches of snow twice, 65 inches of snow a third year, and 40 inches of snow in each of two other years. What was the average annual snowfall for the last 5 years in Chillemuch?

Sample #3: A bookstore needs 8,000 cubic feet of space to hold all its books. The total space or volume of a room is found by multiplying its length by its width by its height (formula: V = L • W • H). If a room has a length of 60 feet, a width of 20 feet, and a height of 10 feet, we could find the volume of the room with the formula V = 60 • 20 • 10. Is it true or false that we could we also find the volume of the room with the following substitutions: (a) V = 20 • 60 • 10 and (b) (60 • 20) • 10? If yes, does the commutative or associative property support this conclusion?

The original formula is V = 60 • 20 • 10. We need to recognize here that the 60, the 20, and the 10 are **all connected by the same operation—multiplication.** Therefore we can recognize that the commutative and associative properties are both activated.

The commutative property supports the fact that *(a)* is true. All that has been switched is the order of the 60 • 20 to 20 • 60. The associative property supports the fact that *(b)* is true. The only difference in *(b)* is that the 60 • 20 have been associated or grouped together as (60 • 20).

- **You try it now:**

  e) Is $(200 \div 40) \div 5$ equal to $200 \div (40 \div 5)$? If true, does the commutative or associative property support this?

  f) Is $(8.247 + 2.02) + 1.67$ equal to $8.247 + (2.02 + 1.67)$?

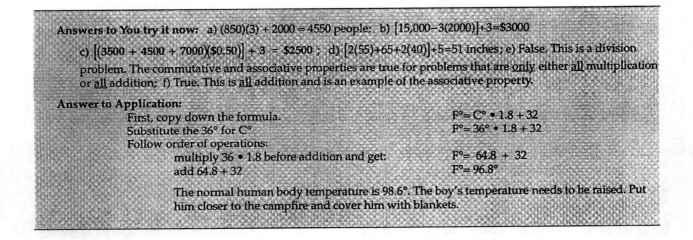

Answers to You try it now: a) $(850)(3) + 2000 = 4550$ people; b) $[15,000 - 3(2000)] \div 3 = \$3000$

c) $[(3500 + 4500 + 7000)(\$0.50)] \div 3 = \$2500$; d) $[2(55) + 65 + 2(40)] \div 5 = 51$ inches; e) False. This is a division problem. The commutative and associative properties are true for problems that are <u>only</u> either <u>all</u> multiplication or <u>all</u> addition; f) True. This is <u>all</u> addition and is an example of the associative property.

Answer to Application:

First, copy down the formula.	$F° = C° \cdot 1.8 + 32$
Substitute the 36° for C°	$F° = 36° \cdot 1.8 + 32$
Follow order of operations:	
multiply $36 \cdot 1.8$ before addition and get:	$F° = 64.8 + 32$
add $64.8 + 32$	$F° = 96.8°$

The normal human body temperature is 98.6°. The boy's temperature needs to be raised. Put him closer to the campfire and cover him with blankets.

1.6 Operations in a Certain Order

In exercises #1-17, solve the following problems (Remember: your guide is the order of operations):

1) $20 - 6 \cdot 2$

2) $15 \cdot (2 + 3)$

3) $4 + 4 \div 4 - 4$

4) $10 + 8(3)$

5) $30 - 6 \div 3$

6) $8 - 8 \div 8 + 8$

7) $3 \cdot 7 - 6 \div 3$

8) $2 + 4 (7 - 3)$

9) $8 \cdot 2 - (3 + 1)$

10) $10 \div 10 + 10 \cdot 10$

11) $6 + (25 - 7) \div 3$

12) $12 - 7 + 3(4 - 1)$

13) $(16) - (6)(2) \div 4$

14) $27 \div 3 - 4(2) + 2$

15) $7 \cdot 8 + 4 - 10 \div 5$

16) $3 \cdot 4 + 18 + 20 \div 4$

17) $(1 \cdot 1 \div 1 + 1) - (0)(1 + 1 \cdot 1 \div 1)$

In exercises 18-25 identify the letter of the one math expression that would solve the question asked in each word problem.

18) In a busy week at the maternity ward in a Chicago hospital, 45 mothers gave birth to a single child, 4 mothers had twins, and 2 mothers had triplets. How many children were born during this week?

a) $45 + 4 + 3$

b) $45 + 4(2 + 2 \cdot 3)$

c) $45(1) + 4(2) + 2(3)$

d) $45(1) + (4 + 3)(2 + 3)$

19) 500 tickets were sold for a Harvest celebration party. 200 of the tickets sold for $20 each and the rest sold for $15 each How much money was collected?

a) 500 – 200 (20) – 300 (15)   b) 200 (20) + (500-200)(15)

c) (200 + 300) (20 + 15)   d) 300 (20) + 200 (15)

20) 300 people were invited to spend three hours at a special opening of a new museum. 30 people couldn't make the opening. The people who attended were split into 5 groups and given a tour through different parts of the museum. How many people were in each group?

a) $(300-30) \div 5$ b) $300-30 \div 5$ c) $(300)-30 \div 5$ d) $300 \div 5-30$

21) Two companies were to evenly split a government research grant of $90,000. If one of the companies split its part of the grant evenly within three of its departments, how much money would each department receive?

a) $\left(\dfrac{90,000}{2}\right) \div 3$ b) $\left(\dfrac{90,000}{2}\right)$ c) $90,000 \div 3$ d) $90,000 (2) \div 3$

22) Odysseus was playing an adventure video game. He started with 300 points. He received 100 points for his bravery in fighting the Trojans, then lost 50 points for eating a lotus that made him forget where he lived. His total points were then doubled when he blinded a one-eyed giant! Finally, he lost 10 points for each of his 8 followers who were turned into pigs by Circe, an enchantress. How many points did Odysseus have now?

a) 300 + (100 – 50)(2) –10   b) 350 (2) – 10 ÷ 8

c) (300 + 100 – 50) (2) – 10(8)   d) 300 + (100 – 50)(2) – 10(8)

23) A day trader on the stock exchange anxiously watched the value of his stock rise and fall one week. He invested $800 on Monday morning. By Tuesday he had lost $350. On Wednesday his remaining money left over from Tuesday tripled in value. On Thursday he lost $100. How much is his investment worth now?

a) 800 – 350 (3) – 100   b) (800 – 350 –100) (3)

c) 3 (800 – 350) – 100   d) $\dfrac{(800-350)(3)}{100}$

24) A department store was keeping track of the number of customers in its store throughout the day. For each two-hour period, it recorded its highest number of customers as follows: 9-11am—110 customers; 11-1pm—380 customers, 1-3pm—310 shoppers; 3-5 pm—450 shoppers; and 5-7pm—250 customers. Based upon the highest number in each time period, what was the average number of customers in each time slot?

a) 110 + 380 + 310 + 450 + 250   b) 110 + 380 + 310 + 450 + 250 ÷ 5

c) 5 (110 + 380 + 310 + 450 + 250)   d) (110 + 380 + 310 + 450 + 250) ÷ 5

25) An accountant for *The Bard's Players*, a traveling theater group, looked over their financial books after a month's run of Shakespeare's *Romeo and Juliet*. For a hall they had paid $500 per evening for 20 nights. Lodging and food for each of the 20 members of the troupe had also cost $40 per day for 30 days. The play's run took in a total of $84,000. If the amount of money left over after expenses was divided evenly among the 20 players, how much money did each member earn?

a) $\dfrac{84,000 - [(500 \bullet 20) - (20 \bullet 40 \bullet 30)]}{20}$ b) $\dfrac{84,000 - [(500 \bullet 20) + (20 \bullet 40 \bullet 30)]}{20}$

c) $84,000 - (500 \bullet 20 - 20 \bullet 40 \bullet 30\ ) \div 20$ d) $\dfrac{84,000}{20} - [(500 \bullet 20) + (20 \bullet 40 \bullet 30)]$

In exercise #26–35: (a) write a math expression that will solve the problem, and (b) give the solution.

26) Find the average high temperature for Forestville if on three consecutive days it reached 80, 84, and 94 degrees respectively.

27) On four different fishing expeditions off the Aleutian Islands of Alaska, Sven's crew caught 300 pounds of salmon, 400 pounds, 820 pounds, and 480 pounds respectively. If he was able to sell the fresh salmon for $1.50 per pound, what was the crew's average earnings per trip?

28-29) At a track meet, the times for four runners in the mile were 4 minutes 32 seconds, 4 minutes 46 seconds, 5 minutes, and 5 minutes and 14 seconds.

28) What was the total number of seconds it took all 4 runners to finish the race (remember: 1 minute = 60 seconds)?

29) What was the average time it took the runners to finish the race?

30) At a factory there are three levels of employees. *A* level employees currently earn $8 per hour, *B* level workers earn $9 an hour, and *C* level employees earn $12 per hour. If there are currently 20 level *A* workers, 50 level *B* workers, and 20 level *C* employees, what is the average hourly wage per employee to the nearest cent?

31) When studying a bacteria population, Greg measured the length of 100 specimens to the nearest thousandths of an inch. He measured 20 at .019 inches, 30 at .018 inches and 50 at .017 inches. What was the average length of these bacteria?

32-33) Darlene measured a new tree in her yard when she was ten years old. It was 18 inches tall. In the next year it grew 12 inches. The following year it doubled its height. She didn't measure it again for another 3 years. To her surprise the tree was triple its size since the last time she had measured it.

32) What was the height of the tree in inches?

33) Its height in feet?

34) Yoshi worked 40 hours a week for an entire year at one job where he earned $12 an hour. At a second job he had for only 10 weeks, he earned $3500. How much money did he earn last year?

35) Five clerks each earn the same annual salary. An office manager with a salary of $45,000 makes more money than the clerks. If the average annual salary for these 6 workers is $35,000, how much money does each clerk earn in a year?

In exercises 36-39, answer the following to solidify some math manipulations.

36) What process is used to solve mathematical expressions that have different and multiple-operations?

37) If a mathematical expression consists of either all addition or all multiplication, what two properties can we use to our advantage?

38) Which property allows us to change the order of the given numbers?

39) Which property allows us to change the grouping of the given numbers?

In exercises 40-48, try to work these problems in your head, taking advantage of the commutative and associative properties for addition and multiplication which allow one to change the order or grouping of the given numbers (Remember it is easiest to add numbers together that have a sum that ends in zero).

40) $8 + 14 + 12 + 6$

41) $17 + (13 + 6)$

42) $32 + 14 + 28$

43) $(29 + 28) + 12$

44) $56 + 58 + 44$

45) $(7 + 29) + (41 + 23)$

46) $5 \bullet 7 \bullet 4$

47) $5 \bullet 3 \bullet 8$

48) $(6 \bullet 9) \bullet 5$

In exercises #49-60 use your knowledge of the commutative and associative properties and state whether the following equations are true or false. If true, state which property explains why the equation is true.

49) $(13 \bullet 7) \bullet 6 = 13 \bullet (7 \bullet 6)$

50) $(8 + 6) \div 3 = 8 + (6 \div 3)$

51) $(20 \div 8) \div 10 = 20 \div (8 \div 10)$

52) $18 \bullet 27 + 16 = 18 \bullet 16 + 27$

53) $(92 + 269) + 289 = 92 + (269 + 289)$

54) $8 \bullet 1.75 \bullet 2.8 = 2.8 \bullet 8 \bullet 1.75$

55) $(a + b) + c = a + (b + c)$

56) $x \bullet y \bullet z = z \bullet x \bullet y$

57) $(x + 5) + y = x + (5 + y)$

58) $(x + 5) \bullet y = x \bullet (5 + y)$

59) $(a \bullet b) \bullet c = a \bullet (b \bullet c)$

60) $x + y + z = z + x + y$

Skills Check

1. Round 8.473 to the nearest whole number, the tenths, and the hundredths.

2. Round 12.39 to the nearest tenths, hundredths, and thousandths.

3. Estimate to the nearest tens, the sum of the following three bills: $47, $104, and $39.

4. What is the product of 41.62 rounded to the nearest whole and 48 rounded to the nearest hundreds?

Answers to Skills Check: 1) to the nearest whole number: 8; to the nearest tenths place: 8.5; to the nearest hundredths place: 8.47; 2) to the nearest tenths: 12.4; to the nearest hundredths place: 12.39; to the nearest thousandths place: 12.394; 3) $190; 4) 0

Section 1.7 Mental Math: Utilizing Expanded Notation and the Powers of 10

As we move forward into this particular subsection of the book, it is important to realize that the skills which are discussed here are tools that can increase our working speed, decrease errors, and lessen some of our usage of paper and pencil and/or a calculator. These mental skills empower us. Many of us believe that we can't do mental math, that this is for geniuses. Most often, however, we haven't been taught a process to work mental math, or, once taught we haven't practiced it. We're about to change that.

Objectives:

To represent a number in expanded notation

To multiply mentally using expanded notation

To multiply mentally by powers of ten

To divide mentally by powers of ten

Application:

Lucia was asked by her company to order 200 reams of a particular grade of paper (500 sheets = 1 ream) for the cheapest price she could find. One paper wholesaler charged $.0055 per sheet of paper. A second wholesaler sold its paper for $4 per ream. Which wholesaler offered the better buy? By how much?

Vocabulary:

> **expanded notation** Expanded notation is a format in which we represent the value of a number by writing it as the sum of the values of each individual digit (Example: 152 = 100 + 50 + 2).

> **Powers of 10** To understand powers of 10, we start with the number <u>1</u> and recognize that the number 1 = 1.0
>
> In fact, the number 1 has infinite zeros on both sides of it. However many of these zeros we would write, the value of the number 1 would not change. 1 whole = 01 = 001 = 0001 = 1.00 = 1.000 = 1.000000 = 001.00
>
> **Powers of 10** are numbers which are created by moving the decimal point (to either the left or right) from this number 1 with its surrounding zeros. The only difference between any two powers of 10 is where you place the decimal point.

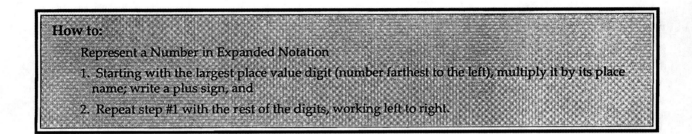

How to:

Represent a Number in Expanded Notation

1. Starting with the largest place value digit (number farthest to the left), multiply it by its place name; write a plus sign, and

2. Repeat step #1 with the rest of the digits, working left to right.

Example #1: Represent 4, 275.18 in expanded notation.

 Step #1: Multiply the largest place value digit by its place name.

  The **4** is in the thousands place, so the value of the 4 = 4 (1000) = **4000**

  So we have **4000 +**

 Step #2: Repeat step #1 with the rest of the digits, working left to right.

  The **2** is in the hundreds place, so the value of the 2 = 2 (100) = **200**

  So we have **4000 + 200 +**

  The **7** is in the tens place, so the value of the 7 = 7 (10) = **70**

  So we have **4000 + 200 + 70 +**

  The **5** is in the ones place, so the value of the 5 = 5 (1) = **5**

  So we have **4000 + 200 + 70 + 5 +**

  The **1** is in the tenths place, so the value of the $1 = 1\left(\dfrac{1}{10}\right) = \dfrac{1}{10}$

  So we have $4000 + 200 + 70 + 5 + \dfrac{1}{10} +$

  The **8** is in the hundredths place, so the value of the $8 = 8\left(\dfrac{1}{100}\right) = \dfrac{8}{100}$

  Expanded Notation $= \ 4000 + 200 + 70 + 5 + \dfrac{1}{10} + \dfrac{8}{100}$

How to:

Multiply a single-digit number with another number all in your Mind (no paper! no calculator!) using Expanded Notation

1. Start with the real value (the expanded notation) of the largest place value digit (number farthest to the left) first, and times it by the single digit you are multiplying; keep this number in your head, and

2. Repeat step #1 with the rest of the digits, working left to right.

3. Add the above results, working from largest to smallest.

Example #2:   Multiply 27 • 6

*** Remember: We know that 27 equals 20 + 7 in expanded notation.

Step #1: Take the actual value (the expanded notation) of the largest place value digit and times it by the number you are multiplying.

The 2 in the tens place has a real value of 20, so 20 • 6 = **120**

Step #2: Repeat step #1 with the rest of the digits, working left to right.

The 7 in the ones place has a real value of 7, so 7 • 6 = **42**

Step #3: Add the results.

120 + 42 = **162**

*** **Let's take a quick look at the difference between multiplying on paper and using mental math.**

$$\begin{array}{r} 2\,7 \\ \times\ 6 \\ \hline \end{array}$$

On paper we would multiply 6 • 7 and get 42, so we would write down the 2 and carry 4.

The problem would look like this:

$$\begin{array}{r} \overset{4}{2}\,7 \\ \times\ 6 \\ \hline 2 \end{array}$$

Now we would multiply the 6 • 2 and get 12, to which we would add the carried 4 and get 16. We would write this down and get a final answer of 162

*** <u>**In mental math we work in the opposite direction**</u>, multiplying the largest value first.

We worked: (20 • 6) + (7 • 6)
And got: (120) + (42) = **162**

How to:

Multiply numbers by powers of 10 in your Mind (no paper! no calculator!)

1. Decide what the answer would be if we were multiplying the given number by 1 (it equals the number itself!).

2. IF we are multiplying by a power of 10 which is larger than 1, move the decimal point in the answer to the right (larger) the same number of decimal places as our power of 10 number is larger than 1 whole (1.0).

   OR

   IF we are multiplying by a power of 10 which is smaller than 1, move the decimal point in the answer to the left (smaller) the same number of decimal places as our power of 10 number is smaller than 1 whole (1.0).

*** **Remember: the larger the number we multiply by the larger the answer.**

Example #3: In this case let's look at multiple examples to become comfortable with this process of multiplying by a power of 10.

Any number multiplied by 1 is itself.

$1 \cdot 5 = 5$ $1 \cdot 2.8 = 2.8$ $1 \cdot 172 = 172$

Any number multiplied by 10 is itself (times 1) plus moving the decimal point 1 place to the right.

$10 \cdot 5 = 50$ $10 \cdot 2.8 = 28$ $10 \cdot 172 = 1720$

Any number multiplied by 100 is itself (times 1) plus moving the decimal point 2 places to the right.

$100 \cdot 5 = 500$ $100 \cdot 2.8 = 280$ $100 \cdot 172 = 17{,}200$

Any number multiplied by 1000 is itself (times 1) plus moving the decimal point 3 places to the right.

$1000 \cdot 5 = 5000$ $1000 \cdot 2.8 = 2800$ $1000 \cdot 172 = 172{,}000$

Any number multiplied by .1 is itself (times 1) plus moving the decimal point 1 place to the left.

$0.1 \cdot 5 = 0.5$ $0.1 \cdot 2.8 = 0.28$ $0.1 \cdot 172 = 17.2$

Any number multiplied by 0.01 is itself (times 1) plus moving the decimal point 2 places to the left.

$0.01 \cdot 5 = 0.05$ $0.01 \cdot 2.8 = 0.028$ $0.01 \cdot 172 = 1.72$

Any number multiplied by 0.001 is itself (times 1) plus moving the decimal point 3 places to the left.

$0.001 \cdot 5 = 0.005$ $0.001 \cdot 2.8 = 0.0028$ $0.001 \cdot 172 = 0.172$

How to:

Divide numbers by powers of 10 in your Mind (no paper! no calculator!)

1. Decide what the answer would be if we were dividing the given number by 1 (it equals the number itself!).

2. IF we are dividing by a power of 10 which is larger than 1, move the decimal point in the answer to the left (smaller) the same number of decimal places as our power of 10 number is larger than 1 whole (1.0).

   OR

   IF we are dividing by a power of 10 which is smaller than 1, move the decimal point in the answer to the right (larger) the same number of decimal places as our power of 10 number is smaller than 1 whole (1.0).

***Remember: Division is the opposite of multiplication. The larger the number we divide by the smaller the answer.**

Example #4: In this case let's look at multiple examples to become comfortable with this process of dividing by a power of 10.

Any number divided by 1 is itself.

$$\frac{5}{1} = 5 \qquad \frac{2.8}{1} = 2.8 \qquad \frac{172}{1} = 172$$

Any number divided by 10 is itself (divided by 1) plus moving the decimal point 1 place to the left.

$$\frac{5}{10} = 0.5 \qquad \frac{2.8}{10} = 0.28 \qquad \frac{172}{10} = 17.2$$

Any number divided by 100 is itself (divided by 1) plus moving the decimal point 2 places to the left.

$$\frac{5}{100} = 0.05 \qquad \frac{2.8}{100} = 0.028 \qquad \frac{172}{100} = 1.72$$

Any number divided by 1000 is itself (divided by 1) plus moving the decimal point 3 places to the left.

$$\frac{5}{1000} = 0.005 \qquad \frac{2.8}{1000} = 0.0028 \qquad \frac{172}{1000} = 0.172$$

Any number divided by .1 is itself (divided by 1) plus moving the decimal point 1 place to the right.

$$\frac{5}{0.1} = 50 \qquad \frac{2.8}{0.1} = 28 \qquad \frac{172}{0.1} = 1720$$

Any number divided by .01 is itself (divided by 1) plus moving the decimal point 2 places to the right.

$$\frac{5}{0.01} = 500 \qquad \frac{2.8}{0.01} = 280 \qquad \frac{172}{0.01} = 17,200$$

Any number divided by .001 is itself (divided by 1) plus moving the decimal point 3 places to the right.

$$\frac{5}{0.001} = 5000 \qquad \frac{2.8}{0.001} = 2,800 \qquad \frac{172}{0.001} = 172,000$$

Sample #1: When packaging plums for the Southland Fruit Company, workers were asked to use the following procedure: first, fill as many crates as possible that hold 1000 plums; second, with the leftover plums fill as many crates as possible that hold 100 plums, and last, fill as many crates as possible that hold 10 plums. If 8653 plums were picked one day, how many total crates were filled?

If we know expanded notation, we recognize that 8653 is equal to 8,000 + 600 + 50 + 3. The 8,000 plums would fill 8 crates that each hold 1,000 plums. The 600 plums would fill 6 crates that each hold 100 plums; the 50 plums would fill 5 crates that each hold 10 plums. Therefore, the total number of crates filled would be 8 + 6 + 5 or **19 crates.**

You try it now:

a) A pet store owner bred brine shrimp. He first packaged the brine shrimp in bags that held about 1,000 shrimp, and then packaged any leftover shrimp in bags that each held about 100 shrimp. If he bred about 9,700 shrimp one week, how many bags of shrimp would he have?

b) An egg farm sold its eggs wholesale to the Best Cakes Company in crates of 100 eggs each. If one week the egg farm produced 2350 eggs, how many full crates could it sell to Best Cakes?

Sample #2: After volunteering to help paint a local recreation center, Maribel bought 24 cans of paint. If the paint cost $8 for each can, how much money did she spend?

Mental math: multiply using expanded notation:

8 • 24 is the same as 8 • (20 + 4) which is the same as
(8 • 20) + (8 • 4) = 160 + 32 = $192

You try it now:

c) In one afternoon, Barry wrote 7 parking tickets for $35 each. Barry wrote tickets for how much money?

d) 84 people were allowed on the roller coaster at one time. After 3 trips, how many people had ridden the roller coaster?

Sample #3: The manager of a supermarket agreed to let local farmers sell their fruit outside her store as long as the supermarket received $0.10 of every dollar that the farmers received. If the farmers sold $2850 worth of fruit, how much money did the store receive?

We recognize that the supermarket gets $.10 <u>of</u> every dollar or $.10 <u>of</u> the total earnings of $2850. From this wording (the form of a number of another number) we know that we have a multiplication problem.

In fact, we are multiplying by a power of 10.   Set up: $2,850 • 0.1

Any number multiplied by 0.1 is itself plus moving the decimal point 1 place to the left (to a smaller #). Therefore, the answer is **$285**.

■ **You try it now:**

e) As a salesperson for extremely powerful mainframe computers, Belinda sold very few machines. However, her commission was $10,000 on any computer she succeeded in selling to a new company. One year, her efforts paid off for her. She sold 16 computers to new companies. How much money did she make?

f) A pencil company earned about 1¢ ($0.01) on every pencil it sold. In August it sold 800,000 pencils. How much money did the company make?

Sample #4: A line of 1000 bacteria was measured to be 1.2 centimeters in length. What is the average length of each bacterium?

We are dividing by a power of 10.   Set up : $\dfrac{1.2 \text{ centimeters}}{1000}$

Any number divided by 1000 is itself plus moving the decimal point 3 places to the left (to a smaller #). Therefore, the answer is **0.0012 centimeters**.

■ **You try it now:**

g) At the county's annual fair to raise money for nonprofit organizations, a record $375,000 was collected last year. If that money was divided evenly among 100 organizations, how much money did each organization receive?

h) In an effort to eliminate various crop-eating insects on an organic farm, a company bred and released 200 pounds of lady bugs into their fields. If each lady bug weighed .01 of a pound, about how many lady bugs were released?

Answers to You try it now: a) 16 bags; b) 23 crates; c) $245; d) 252 people; e) $160,000; f) $8,000; g) $3,750; h) 20,000 lady bugs

Answer to Application: The first wholesaler sells its paper for $.0055 per sheet. To find the total number of sheets, we multiply 200 reams by 500 sheets to get 100,000 sheets (mental math tells us that 2 • 500 = 1000, then keep the two zeros in 200—1000 and 00 = 100,000). Now multiply $.0055 by 100,000. This is the same as multiplying by 1, then moving the decimal point 5 places to the right. The first company would charge $550.

The second wholesaler charges $4 per ream. (4 • 200) gives us a price of $800. The first wholesaler offers the better price by the difference of $800 and $550. The first wholesaler offered the better buy by $250.

1.7 Mental Math: Utilizing Expanded Notation and Powers of 10

It is important to try to solve all the following problems using mental math. With a little practice, you might be surprised how much you can solve in your head. If you aren't sure of your mental calculation, feel free to use paper and pencil to check your work—but try it in your mind first!.

In exercises #1-17, express the following numbers in expanded notation.

1) 452	2) 377	3) 4623	4) 8167	5) 7042	6) 12,865
7) 15,640	8) 156,022	9) 210,050	10) 2,803,006	11) 3,075,200	12) 8.47
13) 9.35	14) 12.026	15) 71.204	16) 4.2034	17) 0.6003	

In exercises #18-27, fill in the blanks as follows: (a) rewrite the multiplication problem again by expressing the number inside the parenthesis in expanded notation, (b) rewrite this new expression as the sum of the results after individually multiplying each expanded notation value by the single digit number, and (c) write the final answer to the problem. Look at the example below and follow this process for the following problems.

Example: $(24) \cdot 5 = $ (a) $(20 + 4) \cdot 5;\ = $ (b) $100 + 20;\ = $ (c) 120

18) $(36) \cdot 5 = $ (a) _____ = (b) _____ = (c) _____   19) $(52) \cdot 7 = $ (a) _____ = (b) _____ = (c) _____

20) $(48) \cdot 6 = $ (a) _____ = (b) _____ = (c) _____   21) $(79) \cdot 4 = $ (a) _____ = (b) _____ = (c) _____

22) $(66) \cdot 9 = $ (a) _____ = (b) _____ = (c) _____   23) $(85) \cdot 6 = $ (a) _____ = (b) _____ = (c) _____

24) $(72) \cdot 3 = $ (a) _____ = (b) _____ = (c) _____   25) $(96) \cdot 2 = $ (a) _____ = (b) _____ = (c) _____

26) $(94) \cdot 5 = $ (a) _____ = (b) _____ = (c) _____   27) $(34) \cdot 7 = $ (a) _____ = (b) _____ = (c) _____

In exercises #28-45, solve the following multiplication problems in your mind by utilizing expanded notation (remember: multiply by the largest digit first).

28) $53 \cdot 5$	29) $28 \cdot 3$	30) $34 \cdot 4$	31) $92 \cdot 4$
32) $45 \cdot 8$	33) $76 \cdot 9$	34) $140 \cdot 5$	35) $230 \cdot 4$
36) $860 \cdot 3$	37) $510 \cdot 6$	38) $170 \cdot 4$	39) $330 \cdot 7$
40) $216 \cdot 5$	41) $144 \cdot 6$	42) $300 \cdot 8$	43) $800 \cdot 7$
44) $900 \cdot 6$	45) $1200 \cdot 4$		

In exercises #46-59, write down the missing number or numbers.

46) The power-of-10 number that is larger than 10 and less than 1000.

47) The power-of-10 number that is smaller than 1 and larger than 0.01 .

48) The two power-of-10 numbers that are smaller than 1000, but larger than 1 .

49) The two power-of-10 numbers that are larger than 100, but smaller than 100,000 .

50) The two power-of-10 numbers that are smaller than 0.01 but larger than 0.00001 .

51) The two power-of-10 numbers that are larger than 0.0001, but smaller than 0.1 .

52) Multiply 0.06 by what to get 6?   53) Multiply 5.12 by what to get 51.2?

54) Multiply 833 by what to get 8.3?   55) Multiply 20 by what to get 2?

56) Multiply 8 by what to get 8000?   57) Multiply 14 by what to get 140?

58) Multiply 40 by what to get 0.04?   59) Multiply 36 by what to get 0.36?

In exercises #60-61, answer True or False to the following statements, then fill in the blanks.

60) The larger the number we multiply by, the larger the answer.   T or F

   Prove the answer by multiplying 8 by two different numbers: 8 • ___ = ___.

                                                                    8 • ___ = ___.

61) The smaller the number we multiply by, the smaller the answer.   T or F

   Prove the answer by multiplying 6 by two different powers of 10, one with a value of greater than 1 and one with a value of less than 1:   6 • ___ = ___.

                                                                    6 • ___ = ___.

In exercises #62-77, solve the following multiplication problems.

62) 450 • 10	63) 0.765 • 100	64) 8 • 100	65) 0.12 (10)
66) 200 (0.01)	67) 3.43 (0.01)	68) 0.22 (0.1)	69) 0.6 (100)
70) 400 (0.01)	71) 0.086 (1000)	72) 3.7 • 0.0001	73) 70 • 100,000
74) 3.5 • 10,000	75) 6.4 • 1000	76) 44 • 0.01	77) 5 • 0.1

In exercises #78-79, answer True or False to the following statements, then fill in the blanks.

78) The larger the number we divide by, the smaller the answer.   T or F

   Prove the answer by dividing 8 by two different numbers: 8 ÷ ___ = ___.

                                                                8 ÷ ___ = ___.

79) The smaller the number we divide by, the smaller the answer.   T or F

   Prove the answer by dividing 6 by two different powers of 10, one with a value of greater than 1 and one with a value of less than 1:   6 ÷ ___ = ___.

                                                                6 ÷ ___ = ___.

In exercises #80-87, write down the missing number.

80) Divide 8 by what to get .8?   81) Divide 2.6 by what to get .026?

82) Divide 83 by what to get 8300?   83) Divide 50 by what to get 500?

84) Divide 120 by what to get 1.2?   85) Divide 40 by what to get .04?

86) Divide 7 by what to get 700?   87) Divide 100 by what to get 1?

In exercises #88-99, solve the following division problems.

88) $\dfrac{8}{100}$ 89) $\dfrac{0.4}{1000}$ 90) $\dfrac{2.5}{10}$ 91) $\dfrac{75}{0.1}$

92) $\dfrac{20000}{100}$ 93) $\dfrac{0.86}{0.01}$ 94) $\dfrac{855000}{10}$ 95) $\dfrac{6.125}{0.001}$

96) $\dfrac{700}{1}$ 97) $\dfrac{105}{0.01}$ 98) $\dfrac{8}{0.1}$ 99) $\dfrac{0.4}{0.0001}$

In exercises #100-115. (a) write a math expression that will solve the problem, and (b) give the solution.

100) While shopping for a barbecue, Andy bought 8 packages of chicken that each sold for $15. How much did he spend on chicken?

101) Tires were on sale: 4 for $110 dollars. If Leona bought 20 tires for her car rental fleet, how much money did she spend?

102-103) 49,754 people attended a college football game. On average, each individual spent $10 on parking, souvenirs, food and drinks:

102) How much money did the stadium collect at this event?

103) Is this more than half a million dollars?

104) The United States Treasury made 500,000 dimes last year. How many dollars is this?

105) A wasp species gathers in nesting sites that on average consist of about 1000 wasps each. If there were about 250,000 wasps, how many nesting sites were there?

106-107) At a bank, an employee was given $14,684 and asked to put the money in rolls of $1,000 dollars each, then put the remaining money in rolls of $100 dollars each. The leftover money was to be put in a cash drawer.

106) How many total rolls of money did the employee make?

107) How much money was put in the cash drawer?

108-109) When packaging fish eggs, it was estimated that 10,000 eggs went into the largest can, 1000 eggs went into the medium-sized can, and 100 eggs went into a sample-sized can. A small family-owned company packaged about 835,600 fish eggs one day. The company first filled as many of the largest cans as they could. Second they filled as many of the medium-sized cans as possible; finally they filled as many sample cans as they could.

108) How many total cans would be filled?

109) If the company decided to package only 80 of the largest cans, how many medium-sized cans could still be filled?

110) A company produced 50,000 nails. If they earned a penny for every nail, how much money did they make?

111) A canning facility in Alaska canned 827,000 pounds of salmon one month. If each can held 1 pound of salmon, how many cans of salmon were produced?

112) Checking his money at the end of the day, Michael counted 8 $100 bills, 10 $20 bills, 3 $5 bills and 22 $1 bills. How much money did he have?

113) A string of 10,000 molecules was stretched out to 3 inches in length. What was the average length of each molecule?

114) A new, larger grape that weighed about .1 pound was farmed at a Northern California ranch. If about 5400 pounds of the grapes were harvested, how many total grapes were there?

115) On every car she sold, Mai received a $100 commission beyond her hourly wage. If she sold 18 cars one month, how much did she receive in commissions?

Skills Check

1. Solve: $18 - 3 \cdot 5 + 4 \div 2$

2. During a four-day period, a cougar traveled 8 miles the first day, 3 miles the second, 5 miles the third, and 11 the fourth. What was the average distance the cougar traveled daily?

3. Is the following true or false? If true, is this an example of the commutative or associative property?
   $7 + 8.4 + 3.02 = 7 + 3.02 + 8.4$

4. On their five-day vacation, a family of four (mom, dad, and Bonnie and Bert) spent an average of $30 per day on meals and snacks. It cost $15 per night for four nights of camping. Gas cost $2 per gallon, their car averaged 25 miles per gallon, and they drove exactly 500 miles on their trip. What was the daily cost of the family trip? Set up a math expression that will solve the problem, and then solve.

Answer to Skills Check: 1) 5; 2) 6.75 miles per day; 3) True. An example of the commutative property;

4) Set up: $[30(5) + 15(4) + 2 \cdot (500 \div 25)] \div 5$; solution = $50 per day

Chapter 2   Fractions

Section 2.1 The Meaning of Fractions

Objectives:

- To write a part out of a whole relationship as a fraction
- To write a ratio as a fraction
- To write a proportion
- To solve for an unknown value in an equivalent fractions or proportion problem
- To prove whether two fractions are equivalent and whether a proportion is true or false.

Application:

Miguel takes his first midterm and he answers 19 of the 25 questions correctly. Write a fraction that reflects the portion he got incorrect in relation to the total number of problems.

Vocabulary:

fraction—A **fraction** is a part out of a whole (or total). It is also a division problem (the numerator divided by the **denominator**).

numerator—The **numerator** of a fraction is the top number of a fraction. It represents the number of parts.

denominator—The **denominator** of a fraction is the bottom number of a fraction. It represents the whole or the total.

A fraction is written as: $\dfrac{\text{part}}{\text{whole}}$

out of—Whenever we see the words "**out of**," we know that we are dealing with the concept of "**part out of a whole**" or "**the numerator ÷ the denominator.**"

Example: 1 out of 10 people believe that Elvis is still alive is the same as saying $\dfrac{1}{10}$ of the people believe that Elvis lives. Sometime you might hear the words "1 of 10 people." The word "out" is omitted here, but the meaning is the same as "1 out of 10 people."

*** When the numerator and the denominator are the same, the value of that fraction is one (1) whole.

Example: 5 out of $5 = \dfrac{5}{5}$. If we eat all five pieces of a cake, we have eaten 1 whole cake.

Likewise, $\dfrac{7}{7}$ and $\dfrac{173}{173}$ are each equal to 1 whole.

probability—A **probability** is the number of chances (parts) that something specific will happen out of the total number of chances (whole). This can be written as a fraction.

Example: If there are 4 blue marbles and 1 red marble in a hat, and you pick one blindly, your chances of picking a blue marble are 4 (the part that are blue) out of 5 (the total number of marbles). We express this probability in the mathematical form as: $\dfrac{4}{5}$

equivalent fractions—**Equivalent fractions** are fractions that are equal to each other though different numbers are used (Example: 1/2 = 2/4). Here we can see that the same amount is shaded in both pictures.

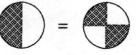

ratio—A **ratio** is the relationship of one number to another or one item to another. It can be written in a fractional form.

Example: If someone eats 2 eggs every 7 days, we express this in the mathematical form

as: $\dfrac{2 \text{ eggs}}{7 \text{ days}}$

proportion—A **proportion** is two ratios equal to each other. A proportion can be written as two equivalent fractions.

Example: If someone eats at the ratio of 2 eggs every 7 days, we can recognize that at this given ratio, that person would eat 4 eggs in 14 days. We express this in the mathematical

form as: $\dfrac{2 \text{ eggs}}{7 \text{ days}} = \dfrac{4 \text{ eggs}}{14 \text{ days}}$

** Before we begin working with fractions, let's make sure we can recognize the many different ways that a fraction or a division problem can be written and still have the exact same meaning. Remember, just as we read left to write in English, we usually read top to bottom with fractions. The fractional line means "divided by."

The following symbols and/or words all express the same mathematical statement:

$\dfrac{8}{9}$ $^8\!/_9$ 8 over 9   eight-ninths $8 \div 9$ 9 into 8 $9\overline{)8}$

Make sure you can comfortably move from one of these statements to another. Make up any fraction and write it the seven different ways as shown above.

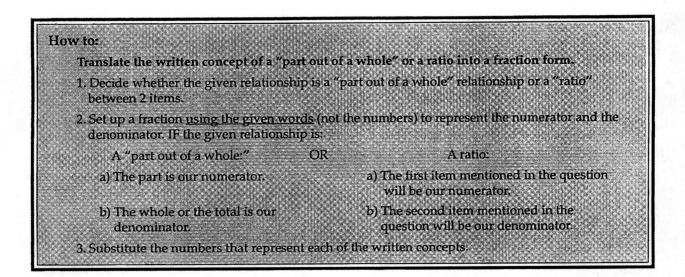

Example #1: You have a deck of normal playing cards which includes a single joker card that is printed in red. What is the probability of picking a red card?

    Step #1: Decide the relationship: "a part out of a whole" or a "ratio."

            This is a "part out of a whole" problem because it is a probability (part chances out of whole or total possibilities).

    Step #2: Set up a fraction <u>using the given words</u>.

            a) the *part* is the *red cards*

            b) the *whole* (total) is the *total cards*

$$\text{The concept set up:} \quad \frac{\text{number of red cards}}{\text{total number of cards}}$$

    Step #3: Substitute the numbers for each written concept.

            A deck of cards has 52 playing cards + 1 joker in this case. Thus, the whole deck of cards consists of 53 cards. The denominator will be 53.

            Half the 52 cards are red (the suits of hearts & diamonds). Therefore, 26 + the 1 joker card are red. 27 of the cards are red. The numerator is 27.

            Answer: $\dfrac{27}{53}$ of the cards are red.

Example #2: In a beginning internet course at a community college, there were 30 students enrolled, 17 men and 13 women. What was the relationship of women to men?

Step #1: Decide the relationship: "a part out of a whole" or a "ratio."

This is a "ratio" problem because it asks for the relationship between 2 items, not however many out of a total.

Step #2: Set up a fraction <u>using the given words</u>.

a) The question asks for the relationship of women to men. "Women" is mentioned first, so the numerator will be the *number of women*.

b) The second mentioned item is men, so the denominator will be the *number of men*.

$$\text{The concept set up:} \quad \frac{\text{number of women}}{\text{number of men}}$$

Step #3: Substitute the numbers for each written concept.

The numbers are given. There are 13 women and 17 men.

$$\text{Answer:} \quad \frac{13 \text{ women}}{17 \text{ men}}$$

*** **Note: When we give a ratio answer, we must include the words in the answer because there are two different items.**

How to:

Solve for a missing number in an equivalent fractions or a proportion problem.

1. Identify if we have an "equivalent fractions" problem or a "proportion" problem. The fractions that we set up must have the same items on top and the same items on the bottom. The problem set up is as follows for:

An Equivalent Fractions problem   OR   A Proportion problem

$$\frac{\text{part}}{\text{whole}} = \frac{\text{part}}{\text{whole}} \qquad\qquad \frac{\text{item\#1}}{\text{item\#2}} = \frac{\text{item\#1}}{\text{item\#2}}$$

2. Multiply the <u>known</u> diagonal pair of numbers (often called a cross product).

3. Divide this product by the third known number.

Example #3: If two out of every three consumers drink orange juice, how many consumers out of 21 will drink orange juice?

Step #1: Identify as an "equivalent fractions" or "proportion" problem.

This problem deals with the concept "part out of a whole" so it must be an "equivalent fractions" problem. The part is those who drink orange juice; the whole is the total number of consumers.

$$\text{The concept set up is:} \quad \frac{\text{part}}{\text{whole}} = \frac{\text{part}}{\text{whole}}$$

We are given "2 out of 3," our first fraction. The 21 represents the whole or total, so it will be the denominator of our second fraction. We are missing the part that belongs above the whole of 21. We represent this unknown part with an "x."

$$\text{Our final math set up is:} \quad \frac{2}{3} = \frac{x}{21}$$

Step #2: Multiply the <u>known</u> diagonal pair of numbers.

The <u>known</u> diagonal pair of numbers is the 2 and the 21.

$$2 \cdot 21 = 42$$

Step #3: Divide by the third known number.

The <u>3</u> is the 3rd known number.

$$\text{So:} \quad 42 \div 3 = 14$$

Answer: 14 of the consumers drink orange juice.

Example #4: Job hirings at a computer company show a ratio of 11 college graduates hired to every 2 high school graduates hired. At this given ratio, how many high school graduates would have been hired if there were 132 college graduates at this firm?

Step #1: Identify as an "equivalent fractions" or "proportion" problem.

This problem deals with the relationship between 2 items so it must be a "proportion" problem. The 2 items are the college graduates and the high school graduates.

$$\text{The concept set up is:} \quad \frac{\text{item \# 1}}{\text{item \# 2}} = \frac{\text{item \# 1}}{\text{item \# 2}}$$

We are given the relationship or ratio of 11 college graduates (item #1) to every 2 high school graduates (item #2); this is our first relation-

ship, to be written as: $\dfrac{11 \text{ college grads}}{2 \text{ high school grads}}$

This given ratio must be equal to the second ratio that must also be written as $\dfrac{\text{item \#1}}{\text{item \#2}}$. For this second ratio we are given the number 132 as the number of college graduates (item #1), so this must be written on the top. We are missing the number of high school graduates (item #2), so this unknown number of high school graduates, represented by "x," must go on the bottom.

Our final math set up is: $\dfrac{11 \text{ college grads}}{2 \text{ high school grads}} = \dfrac{132 \text{ college grads}}{x \text{ high school grads}}$

Step #2: Multiply the <u>known</u> diagonal pair of numbers.

The <u>known</u> diagonal pair of numbers is the 2 and the 132.

$$2 \cdot 132 = 264$$

Step #3: Divide by the third known number.

The <u>11</u> is the 3rd known number.

So: $264 \div 11 = 24$

Answer: 24 high school graduates would be hired.

How to:

Prove whether two given fractions are equivalent or not and whether a given proportion is true or false.

1. Multiply one diagonal pair of numbers (often called a cross product).

2. Multiply the second diagonal pair of numbers (the second cross product).

3. If the cross products equal each other, the given fractions are equivalent or the given proportion is true. If not, the statement is false.

Example #5: Is the following true: $\dfrac{12}{32} = \dfrac{3}{8}$

Step #1:   Multiply one diagonal pair of numbers.

Take one pair of numbers: $12 \cdot 8 = 96$

Step #2:   Multiply the second diagonal pair of numbers.

Take the second pair of numbers: $3 \cdot 32 = 96$

Step #3:   See if the cross products equal each other.

Both cross products equal 96.

Answer: The given statement is true.

Sample #1: At a local neighborhood street fair, six people each bought five tickets, three people each bought three tickets, and four people each bought two tickets. Zoey bought seven tickets. What is the probability that Zoey will win the raffle?

This is a $\dfrac{\text{part}}{\text{whole}}$ problem.

The concept set up is: $\dfrac{\text{tickets Zoey bought (her chances)}}{\text{total tickets bought (total chances)}}$

Substitute numbers. Read the problem above carefully and write the "whole" step by step. The set up is: $\dfrac{7}{[(6 \bullet 5) + (3 \bullet 3) + (4 \bullet 2) + 7]}$

Solve the denominator by following order of operations.

Answer: Zoey's chances of winning are $\dfrac{7}{54}$

You try it now:

a) On an algebra test five students received A's, eleven received B's, seven C's, 3 D's, and 4 got F's. If only a C or higher is considered a passing grade, what fraction of students *did not* earn a passing grade?

b) Robin worked eight hours each day, Monday through Friday, then each worked another six hours on both Saturday and Sunday. If he also slept seven hours each night for this week, what fraction of his week was spent working and sleeping?

Sample #2: In a recent survey, one question asked the participants to check a box which matched their age group. The box below shows the results:

Age Group	Number of Participants
12 – 18 years old	6
19 – 25 years old	10
26 – 32 years old	14
33 – 39 years old	19

What is the ratio of survey participants 25 years of age and younger to that of those 26-39 years old?

The is a ratio or $\dfrac{\text{item \# 1}}{\text{item \# 2}}$ problem.

The concept set up is: $\dfrac{\text{(participants 25 years and younger)}}{\text{(participants 26 years to 39 years)}}$

Substitute numbers. The set up is: $\dfrac{(6+10)}{(14+19)}$

Answer: The ratio is: $\dfrac{16 \text{ participants of age 25 or less}}{33 \text{ participants of ages } 26-39}$

You try it now:

c) When mixing a batch of dough to make bread for his restaurant, Jim used 9 teaspoons of baking powder, 4 teaspoons of salt, and 2 teaspoons of baking soda. What was the relationship of the amount of salt to the amount of baking powder and baking soda which he used in his recipe?

d) Asking for donations to help a family in need, a church received 20 donations of $10 each, 15 donations of $20 each, 8 donations of $40 each, 5 donations of $50 each, and 4 $100 donations. What is the ratio of donations for $20 or less to that of donations for $50 or more?

Sample #3: A salesperson for a book club sold 220 books in 5 weeks. If she kept up that sales rate, how many books would she sell in the spring quarter of 13 weeks? (Hint: first write the given ratio and then set up a proportion)

This is a proportion problem (2 ratios equal each other):

$$\frac{\text{item \#1}}{\text{item \#2}} = \frac{\text{item \#1}}{\text{item \#2}}$$

The given ratio is: $\dfrac{220 \text{ books}}{5 \text{ weeks}}$ where item #1 is books: item #2 is weeks.

Set up a proportion: $\dfrac{220 \text{ books}}{5 \text{ weeks}} = \dfrac{x \text{ books}}{13 \text{ weeks}}$

Solve for the missing number: $220 \cdot 13 = 2860$

$2860 \div 5 = 572$

Answer: **572 books**

You try it now:

e) Seven out of every one hundred people responded to a national survey on politics. If 1200 surveys were mailed, how many people responded?

f) Out of eight flights that left the airport in a half-hour period, five departed on time. If this same rate of on-time departures was maintained throughout the day, how many of the airport's two hundred twenty-four flights left late?

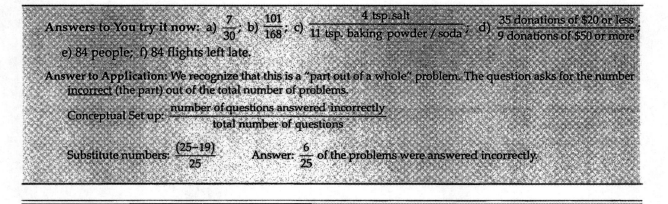

Answers to You try it now: a) $\dfrac{7}{30}$; b) $\dfrac{101}{168}$; c) $\dfrac{4 \text{ tsp. salt}}{11 \text{ tsp. baking powder / soda}}$; d) $\dfrac{35 \text{ donations of \$20 or less}}{9 \text{ donations of \$50 or more}}$;

e) 84 people; f) 84 flights left late.

Answer to Application: We recognize that this is a "part out of a whole" problem. The question asks for the number incorrect (the part) out of the total number of problems.

Conceptual Set up: $\dfrac{\text{number of questions answered incorrectly}}{\text{total number of questions}}$

Substitute numbers: $\dfrac{(25-19)}{25}$ Answer: $\dfrac{6}{25}$ of the problems were answered incorrectly.

2.1 Parts of A Whole Problems

In exercises #1-6, what fractional part of each figure is shaded?

1)
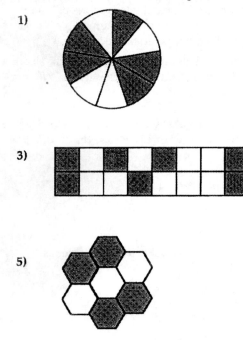

2)
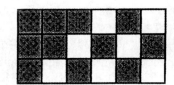

3)

4)

5)

6)
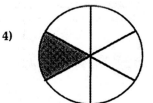

In exercises #7-21, answer the following questions.

7) Every fraction is which type of arithmetic problem?

8) In a fraction is the numerator or the denominator the divisor?

9) Does the 6 in the phrase "5 out of every 6" represent the part or the whole?

10) Is the 2 in $\frac{2}{3}$ the part or the whole?

11) What is the value of any fraction in which the numerator and the denominator are the same?

12) What is the numerator in the fraction 15/19?

13) What is the denominator in the fraction 2/3?

14) Name the numerator and denominator in the fraction 9/10.

15) What number in the fraction 5/8 tells us how many equal parts make up one whole?

16) Is it true that $\frac{9}{9} > 1$?

17) Is 4 over 9 and 9 into 4 the same fraction?

18) What is the numerator of $\frac{3}{y}$?

19) What is the denominator of $\frac{x}{y}$?

20) What is the denominator of $7 \div x$?   21) Is the x in $\frac{x}{4}$ the part or the whole?

In exercises #22-33, translate the following words or rewrite the given symbols into a fraction.

22) 7 divided by 8.   23) 14 divided by 11   24) Four-sevenths.

25) Five-sixths.   26) 7 into 17   27) 4 into 3

28) $7\overline{)8}$ 29) $9\overline{)5}$ 30) $a \div b$

31) $x\overline{)y}$ 32) $3\overline{)x}$ 33) x into y

In exercises #34-51, write the fractional answer.

34-35) Jessie got 9 out of 10 points on a test.

34) What fractional part of the points did he get?

35) What fractional part did he miss?

36-37) In a school election, Cynthia received 371 of the 700 votes cast.

36) What fraction of the votes did she get?

37) What fraction of the votes did other people get?

38-40) Hillary received $500.00 from financial aide. She spent $187.00 on books, $43.00 for a parking permit, and $37.00 for two compact disk study guides.

38) What fractional part of the $500.00 went for her books?

39) What fractional part of the money went for her parking permit?

40) What fractional part of her financial aide money has she spent?

41-43) Eric nets $757.00 a month from his job at Sonic Burger. His rent is $333.00 per month. He spends $127.00 on food, $50.00 on utilities, and $150.00 on his car payment.

41) What fractional part of his take-home pay goes for his rent?

42) What fractional part is spent on food?

43) What fractional part of his take-home pay does he still have after making the four payments mentioned above?

44) A deck of cards contains 52 playing cards plus 2 jokers. There are 13 spades in the deck. What is the probability of drawing a card with a spade on it?

45) Stephen received a shipment of T-shirts to sell in his store. He ordered 15 red shirts and 7 blue shirts. What is the probability that the first shirt he unwraps will be blue?

46-47) There are 25 checkers in a leather bag. 12 of them are black and 6 of them are red.

    46) What is the probability of picking a red checker?

    47) What is the probability of picking a checker that is neither red nor black?

48) Out of every 300 cassette disks manufactured at a St. Louis, Missouri factory, 31 are defective. What is the probability that a cassette disk produced at this factory will not be defective?

49) Richard planted 8 red lettuce seeds, 6 endive seeds, and 9 curly lettuce seeds in a clay planter box. What is the probability that a curly lettuce plant would be the first plant to push through the soil?

50) At a reception there were four cakes, each cut into 40 pieces. Two cakes were completely eaten. Twenty-four pieces of the third cake and thirty-three pieces of the fourth cake were eaten. What fraction of all the pieces of cake remains?

51) While Maxine went to school, she usually worked 15 hours a week at a job that paid $8 per hour. One week between semesters she picked up some other work, working for 7 hours at $11 per hour at a second job, and working two ten-hour shifts at a third job for $10 an hour. During that week what fraction of her earnings came from her usual job?

In exercises #52-57, write a fraction that represents the ratio of the shaded parts to the unshaded parts in each figure. You must use labels in your answers.

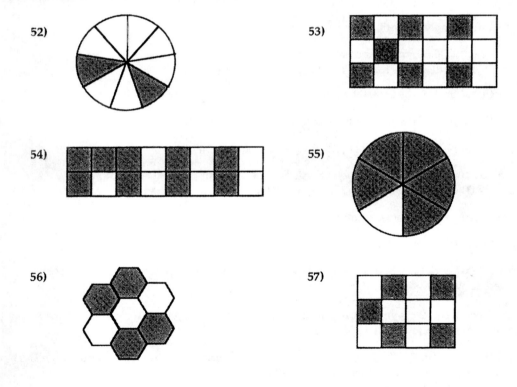

52)

53)

54)

55)

56)

57)

In exercises #58-71, translate the following words or rewrite the given ratio as a fraction. Remember that the words are a part of the answers!

58) 3 eggs every 10 days

59) 8 classes every 5 days

60) 3 teachers for every 65 students

61) 200 plums for every tree

62) $50 out of every 3 paychecks

63) 7 men for every 10 women

64) 5 countries at peace for every 2 countries at war

65) 4 people under the age of 21 for every 7 people over 21

66) x number of teachers for every 30 students

67) x classes every y days

68) 3 chickens for every x people

69) a dogs for every b cats

70-71) On a test of 15 questions, Jessie got 11 correct and 4 incorrect.

70) Write a ratio of correct answers to incorrect answers.

71) Write a ratio of incorrect answers to correct answers.

In exercises #72-81: (a) write a mathematical expression in a fractional form that will solve for the ratio, and (b) give the solution. Remember that the words are a part of the answers.

72-74) In a school election, Cynthia received 371 votes, Sergio received 265, and two other candidates received the rest of the 700 votes cast.

72) Write a ratio of the votes which Cynthia received to the votes which Sergio and the others received.

73) Write a ratio of the votes which Sergio received to the votes the two unnamed candidates received.

74) Write a ratio of the votes which Cynthia and Sergio received to the total number of votes cast.

75-76) Stephen received a shipment of 50 T-shirts which included 15 red shirts, 10 white shirts, and 8 blue shirts.

75) What is the ratio of blue shirts to red and white shirts?

76) What is the ratio of red, white, and blue shirts to shirts of all other colors?

77-78) For every $20 that Le Ly earns, she spends $8 on rent, $4 on food, and $5 on various bills.

77) What is the ratio of money which Le Ly spends for food to that which she spends on rent and various bills?

78) What is the ratio of money she still has left to that which she spends on rent, food, and various bills?

79-81) When Fish World received a shipment of fish, the manager checked the order. It was correct. There were 3 bags that each held 10 red swordfish, 5 bags that each held 15 guppies, 2 bags that each held 7 angel fish, and 1 bag that held 3 catfish and 6 other fish.

79) What is the ratio of sword fish and angel fish to guppies?

80) What is the ratio of the number of bags to the number of fish?

81) What is the ratio of angel fish and catfish to all the other fish?

In exercises #82-89, state whether it is true or false that the given fractions are equivalent.

82) $\dfrac{2}{5} = \dfrac{6}{15}$ 83) $\dfrac{4}{3} = \dfrac{20}{15}$ 84) $\dfrac{8}{3} = \dfrac{19}{7}$ 85) $\dfrac{3}{11} = \dfrac{14}{45}$

86) $\dfrac{2.5}{3} = \dfrac{0.5}{0.6}$ 87) $\dfrac{4}{0.75} = \dfrac{6}{1.125}$ 88) $\dfrac{0.3}{5} = \dfrac{0.15}{2}$ 89) $\dfrac{(4+2)}{0.4} = \dfrac{0.4}{6}$

In exercises #90-95, state whether the given proportion is true or false.

90) $\dfrac{15 \text{ cows}}{2 \text{ acres}} = \dfrac{45 \text{ cows}}{8 \text{ acres}}$ 91) $\dfrac{\$50}{3 \text{ units}} = \dfrac{\$250}{15 \text{ units}}$ 92) $\dfrac{\$6}{2.5 \text{ gallons}} = \dfrac{\$15}{6.25 \text{ gallons}}$

93) $\dfrac{\$3.50}{8 \text{ pens}} = \dfrac{\$8.75}{20 \text{ pens}}$ 94) $\dfrac{70 \text{ tickets}}{\$945} = \dfrac{5 \text{ tickets}}{\$70}$ 95) $\dfrac{0.7 \text{ wiggledigs}}{4.2 \text{ squirmugs}} = \dfrac{0.42 \text{ wiggledigs}}{2.52 \text{ squirmugs}}$

In exercises #96-104, solve for the value of "x."

96) $\dfrac{25}{x} = \dfrac{5}{2}$ 97) $\dfrac{2}{9} = \dfrac{x}{63}$ 98) $\dfrac{x}{10} = \dfrac{7}{4}$ 99) $\dfrac{4.8}{6} = \dfrac{72}{x}$

100) $\dfrac{0.25}{0.4} = \dfrac{x}{0.6}$ 101) $\dfrac{9 \text{ cows}}{2 \text{ acres}} = \dfrac{45 \text{ cows}}{x \text{ acres}}$ 102) $\dfrac{\$40}{1.5 \text{ units}} = \dfrac{\$ x}{9 \text{ units}}$

103) $\dfrac{x \text{ people}}{3 \text{ hospitals}} = \dfrac{45,000 \text{ people}}{1 \text{ hospital}}$ 104) $\dfrac{1,000,000 \text{ people}}{x \text{ car accidents}} = \dfrac{1000 \text{ people}}{45.5 \text{ car accidents}}$

In exercises #105-116: (a) write a mathematical equation (an equivalent fractions or proportion set up) that will solve the problem, and (b) give the solution.

105-108) Rinconfeld is a city of 18,000 people, recently developed by several immigrant populations. Originally a small farming town, it now also includes many growing high-tech businesses.

105) If three out of every eight people in the city of Rinconfeld read the daily newspaper, how many residents read the paper?

106) If one out of every twelve residents is now employed directly by a high-tech firm, how many residents are employed by high-tech companies?

107) Two out of every five residents of Rinconfeld were either first or second generation immigrants from Latin America. How many residents were either first or second generation Latin American immigrants?

108) The second biggest immigrant population in Rinconfeld had come from Canada when a Canadian corporation moved a part of its operations into the United States. If there were nine hundred Canadian-immigrant residents, what number out of every hundred residents was from Canada?

109) Studying a rare population of 200 earthworms in the Amazonian jungle, Joaquin discovered that one out of every four could secrete a liquid which might be beneficial in fighting several human diseases. How many of these worms could secrete this precious liquid?

110) At a chicken ranch with 5,000 chickens, there was an outbreak of a dangerous desease in one section of the ranch. Health inspectors ordered the ranch to kill the diseased chickens. If three out of every twenty chickens carried the disease, how many chicken would have to be killed?

111) A raffle that sold 800 tickets had 15 total winners. At this same rate, how many winners would there have been if only 160 tickets had been sold?

112) If four students could answer 30 mindbender questions in one hour, how many students would it take at this same rate to answer 105 questions?

113) When Ammad priced the lumber that he wanted, he found he could buy five boards for eighteen dollars. If he needed thirty boards, how much would he have to spend?

114) Delia's Nursery was selling 3 tomato seedlings for $5. If Delia sold 30 seedlings to one customer, how much money did she get?

115) A bookstore was offering a sale of 3 books for $10. If Rory had $25, how many books could he buy (reminder: he can't buy a part of a book)?

116) Organic whole wheat flour cost $1.75 for a 4 pound bag. How many bags could Susan buy if she had $8 (reminder: she can't buy a part of a bag)?

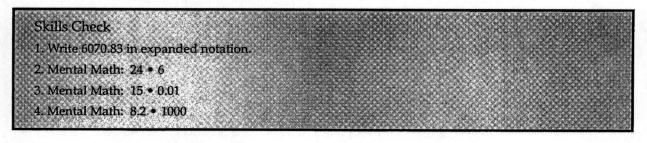

Skills Check
1. Write 6070.83 in expanded notation.
2. Mental Math: 24 • 6
3. Mental Math: 15 • 0.01
4. Mental Math: 8.2 • 1000

Answers to Skills Check: 1) $6000 + 70 + \frac{8}{10} + \frac{3}{100}$;   2) $(20 + 4) • 6 = 144$;   3) 0.15;   4) 8200

Section 2.2 Divisibility & Prime Factorization

Objectives:

- To know the divisibility rules for the numbers 2, 3, and 5
- To prime factor
- To evaluate an expression with exponents

Application:

After harvesting some trees on his property, Ivan had 200 slabs of lumber that were each 60 feet in length. However he decided to cut these slabs, he knew they would be easier to sell in a single business transaction if they were all the same whole number of feet in length. Refusing to waste any of the lumber, he wanted to be sure that however he cut the timber there would be no leftover scraps. How many different ways could he cut the slabs?

Vocabulary:

factor—A **factor** is a whole number multiplied by another whole number to get a **product**. (Example: 5 • 7 = 35, where 5 and 7 are factors of 35). It can also be said that a factor is a number that divides evenly into another number; it is the same as a **divisor** (5 and 7 are factors/divisors of 35 because they both divide into 35 evenly). The example number of 35 has 4 factors: 1 and 35; 5 and 7.

Factoring is a tool to math students like a tape measure is a tool for a carpenter. It allows us to break numbers apart and put them back together in a different configuration [Example: 36 = 3 • 12, but the number 36 can also be factored (broken apart) differently so that we can say that 36 = 4 • 9]. The example number of 36 has 9 factors: 1 and 36; 2 and 18; 3 and 12; 4 and 9; and 6 (as in 6 • 6)

prime number—A prime number is a whole number greater than one that can be divided evenly by **only** 1 and the number itself. Another way of saying this—a prime number's only factors or divisors are 1 and itself. A prime number can't be factored because it can't be broken down into different products.

composite number—A composite number is a whole number greater than one that has more than two factors.

prime factor—A prime factor is a factor that is also a prime number.

prime factorization—The **prime factorization** of a number is the **product** of that number's prime factors. The prime factorization of 30 is expressed as 2 • 3 • 5 (Notice that 6 • 5 = 30 is true, but 6 can be broken down into the smaller numbers of 2 • 3. 2, 3, and 5 are not only factors of 30, but also prime numbers and can't be broken apart anymore).

exponent—An **exponent** or **power** tells how many times that base number is multiplied by itself. It is placed above and to the right of a base number. (Example: 5^2 is an expression with an exponent of 2 that means 5 • 5).

*** Before we begin prime factoring, we want to learn a few skills which will help us excel at that process.

(A) **Learn/memorize the divisibility rules (or tests) for the prime numbers 2, 3, and 5.** Knowledge of these "tests" are a powerful tool when mastered because they allow us to see immediately if a number can be broken down into smaller parts.

> (1) The number 2 divides evenly into (is a prime factor of) any even number (an even number is a whole number in which the digit in the ones place is a 2, 4, 6, 8, or 0).
>
> > Example: 2 is a factor/divisor of 136 because the 6 in the ones place tells us that 136 is an even number.
>
> (2) The number 3 divides evenly into (is a prime factor of) any whole number whose digits add up to a number divisible by 3.
>
> > Example: 3 is a factor/divisor of 114 because the digits of the number 114 add up (1 + 1 + 4 = 6) to a number divisible by 3.
>
> (3) The number 5 divides evenly into (is a prime factor of) any whole number which ends in a 5 or 0.
>
> > Example: 5 is a factor/divisor of 235 because the last digit of 235 is a 5.

(B) **Become familiar with the prime numbers under 20.** If we read the definition of a prime number written above, we should be able to write a list of the prime numbers under 20, those numbers whose only factors are 1 and the number itself. A composite number has more than 2 factors. Let's check.

First, the number 1 is considered neither prime nor composite.

2 is prime because its only factors are 1 • 2

3 is prime because its only factors are 1 • 3

4 is not prime because it has more than two factors; 1 • 4 and 2 • 2 both equal 4.

Now look at the chart below to look at the numbers 2 through 20.

Number	Factors	Prime or Composite	Number	Factors	Prime or Composite
2	1•2 only	prime	8	1•8 and 2•4	composite
3	1•3 only	prime	9	1•9, and 3•3	composite
4	1•4 and 2•2	composite	10	1•10 and 2•5	composite
5	1•5 only	prime	11	1•11 only	prime
6	1•6 and 2•3	composite	12	1•12, 2•6 and 3•4	composite
7	1•7 only	prime	13	1•13 only	prime

Number	Factors	Prime or Composite	Number	Factors	Prime or Composite
14	1•14 and 2•7	composite	17	1•17 only	prime
15	1•15 and 3•5	composite	18	1•18 , 2•9 , and 3•6	composite
16	1•16 and 2•8 and 4•4	composite	19	1•19 only	prime

We learn that the prime numbers under 20 are 2, 3, 5, 7, 11, 13, 17, and 19.

Remember: We can see that the <u>only</u> **even number which is prime is the number 2. We can see why this is if we look at the divisibility rules above. The number 2 divides evenly into every even number.

> **How to:**
>
> **Determine Whether any/all the Numbers 2, 3, and 5 are factors of a given number.**
>
> 1. Individually apply the divisibility test for each number.
>
> 2. If the test is proven to work, we know that number is a factor of the given number.

Example #1: Determine if any of the numbers 2, 3, or 5, are factors of 435.

Step #1: Apply the divisibility tests.

For 2: 435 <u>is not</u> an even number (the digit in the ones place is a 5—an odd number); therefore, 2 is <u>not</u> a factor of 435.

For 3: The digits of 435 individually add up to 12 (4 + 3 + 5). 12 is divisible by 3; therefore, 3 <u>is</u> a factor of 435.

For 5: 435 ends in a 5 or 0; therefore, 5 <u>is</u> a factor of 435.

Answer: 3 and 5 are both factors of the number 435

> **How to:**
>
> **Determine Whether a Number is Prime or Composite**
>
> 1. Find the factors of the given number.
>
> 2. Determine the number of factors. If there are only two factors (1 and the number itself) the number is prime. If there are more than two factors the number is composite.

Example #2: Is 39 prime or composite?

Step #1: Find the factors: 1 • 39 and 3 • 13.

Step #2: Determine the number of factors: There are 4 factors (more than 2 factors).

Answer: 39 is composite

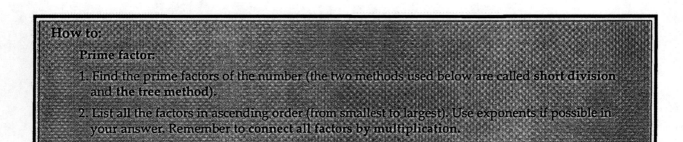

Example #3: (Solve by using the **Short Division Method**):

Prime factor the number 30.

Step #1: Find the prime factors.

A good method to use is to start our testing with the smallest prime number, 2, and work upward to 3, 5, etc.

Test for 2. Yes! 30 is an even number. 2 goes into thirty 15 times.

$$\frac{15}{2\overline{)30}}$$
$$\overline{)15}$$ answer of 15 goes down to the next division box

Continue. 2 won't divide evenly into 15.

Test for 3. Yes!

$$2\overline{)30}$$
$$3\overline{)15}$$
$$\overline{)5}$$ answer of 5 goes down to the next division box

Continue. We know that 3 won't divide evenly into 5.

We know 5 goes into 5.

$$2\overline{)30}$$
$$3\overline{)15}$$
$$5\overline{)5}$$
$$\overline{)1}$$ answer of 1 goes down to the next division box

**The 1 tells us we are done.

Step #2: List all the prime factors (in ascending order) that are written to the left of the division boxes.

Answer: 2 • 3 • 5

The same **Example #3:** (Solve by using the **Tree Method**):

Prime factor the number 30.

Step #1: Find the prime factors.

Test for 2. Yes! 30 is an even number. 30 = 2 • 15

30
⇓

(2) • 15   ...The 2 is prime. Leave it and prime factor 15.
⇓   Test for 3. Yes! 15 = 3 • 5

(3) • (5) ...The 3 and 5 are both prime.

The ends of all 3 tree "limbs" are prime, so we are done prime factoring.

Step #2: List all the prime factors (in ascending order), the numbers that are at the ends of the "limbs" of the tree (shown in parentheses).

Answer: 2 • 3 • 5

Example #4: (Solve by using the **Short Division Method**):

Prime factor the number 428.

Step #1: Find the prime factors.

Again, a good habit to get into is to start our testing with the smallest prime number, 2, and work upward to 3, 5, etc.

Test for 2. Yes. 428 is an even number. 428 ÷ 2 is 214

$$\begin{array}{r} 214 \\ 2\ )\overline{428} \\ 3\ )\overline{214} \end{array}$$] answer of 214 goes down to the next division box

Continue. 2 will divide evenly into 214 again. 214 ÷ 2 is 107

$$\begin{array}{r} 2\ )\overline{428} \\ 2\ )\overline{214} \\ )\overline{107} \end{array}$$] answer of 107 goes down to the next division box

Continue. We test quickly for 2, 3, and 5 using our divisibility tests, but see that they are not factors of 107. We then must try the next prime number—7—through good old-fashion long division. But it doesn't divide evenly into 107. So we try the next prime numbers, 11 and 13, but they don't work. Now...the question is, **for how long must we keep guessing?**

Large numbers can be prime numbers. In this case 107 is prime because 107 is the only number which divides evenly into 107. But, **how can we know if a larger number is prime or not?**

<u>Testing for Primality</u>

• There is a special way to **test if a number is prime**. Take the highest prime number for which we have just tested as a divisor. Square that number (multiply it by itself). If we get a product larger than the number we are trying to prime factor, we know that number is prime.

• Applying this **test for primality**, we can see that 107 is a prime number after we have tested and learned that 2, 3, 5, 7, and 11 are not factors of 107. We square 11 and get 121, a product higher than 107, the number we are still trying to factor. Because of this, 107 <u>must be prime</u>. Its only factor other than one is itself.

• Remember that this test for primality only works if first we have tried all the lower prime numbers as factors of the given number.

$$2\,\overline{)\,428}$$
$$2\,\overline{)\,214}$$
$$107\,\overline{)\,107}\text{ —} \rule{0pt}{0pt}$$
$$1 \longleftarrow \quad \text{answer of 1 goes down to the next division box}$$

**The 1 tells us we are done.

Step #2: List all the prime factors (in ascending order) that are written to the left of the division box.

2 • 2 • 107   Don't forget to use exponents in our answers when we can.

Answer: $2^2 • 107$

The same Example #4: (Solve by using the **Tree Method**):

Prime factor the number 428.

Step #1: Find the prime factors.

Test for <u>2</u>. Yes. 428 is an even number. 428 = <u>2</u> • <u>214</u>

428
⇓

(2) • 214 …The 2 is prime. Leave it and prime factor 214.
⇓   Test for 2 again. Yes! 214 = 2 • 107

(2) • (107) …The 2 and 107 are both prime.

The ends of all 3 tree "limbs" are prime, so we are done prime factoring.

Step #2: List all the prime factors (in ascending order), that are at the ends of the "limbs" of the tree (shown in parentheses).

2 • 2 • 107   Don't forget to use exponents in our answers when we can.

Answer: $2^2 • 107$

Sample #1: Prime factor 315.

Short Division Method	**Tree Method**

$$\overline{)\,315}$$
$$3\,\overline{)\,315} \longrightarrow 315 \div 3 = 105$$
$$3\,\overline{)\,105} \longrightarrow 105 \div 3 = 35$$
$$5\,\overline{)\,35} \longrightarrow 35 \div 5 = 7$$
$$7\,\overline{)\,7} \longrightarrow 7 \div 7 = 1$$
$$1$$

315
$$\Downarrow$$
$(3) \bullet 105$
$$\Downarrow$$
$(3) \bullet 35$
$$\Downarrow$$
$(5) \bullet (7)$

Answer: $3^2 \bullet 5 \bullet 7$

You try it now:

a) Prime factor 84

b) Prime factor 625

Sample #2: Prime factor 163.

The divisibility tests tell us quickly that 2, 3, and 5 do not divide evenly into 163.

Long division testing tells us that 7, 11, and 13 do not divide evenly into 163.

Primality test: $13 \bullet 13 = 169$. The square of the last prime factor we tested is greater than 163, so 163 must be prime.

Short Division Method	**Tree Method**

$$\overline{)\,163}$$
$$163\,\overline{)\,163}$$
$$1$$

163
$$\Downarrow$$
$(1) \bullet (163)$

Answer: prime

You try it now:

c) Prime factor 89

d) Prime factor 329

Sample #3: When making its national flag, a newly-formed country decided to recognize each of its 30 provinces with a yellow star. How many different ways could it create a perfect rectangular pattern of these stars (not counting 1 row of 30 stars)?

We need to recognize here that we are given a number—in this case, 30, and being asked to reorganize that number, break it apart, and put it back into different configurations.

To break down the number we prime factor it. We see that 30 = 2 • 3 • 5.

Envision a single row of 30 stars. Let's manipulate the prime factors (the 2, 3, and the 5) that make up the number 30 to create different rectangular configurations. The flag could have:

2 rows of 15 stars	This is <u>2</u> rows • 15, where the 15 is the <u>3</u> • <u>5</u>
3 rows of 10 stars	This is <u>3</u> rows • 10, where the 10 is the <u>2</u> • <u>5</u>
5 rows of 6 stars	This is <u>5</u> rows • 6, where the 6 is the <u>2</u> • <u>3</u>.

By switching the order of the three created rectangles above, we could also get:

15 rows of 2 stars; 10 rows of 3 stars; and 6 rows of 5 stars

Answer: 6 different rectangular configurations

They are: 2 • 15; 3 • 10; 5 • 6; 15 • 2; 10 • 3; 6 • 5

■ **You try it now:**

e) How many different rectangular shapes can be created from 24 books (not counting 1 row of 24 books)? List 4 of these.

f) If Ernest had 20 quarters, how many different ways could he create multiple stacks that had the same number of coins? List 3 of these.

Answers to You try it now: a) 2^2 • 3 • 7; b) 5^4; c) prime; d) 7 • 47; e) There are 6 possible rectangular shapes: 2 • 12, 4 • 6, 8 • 3, 12 • 2, 6 • 4, and 3 • 8; f) There are 4 possible combinations: 2 stacks of 10 quarters each, 4 stacks of 5 quarters each, 5 stacks with 4 quarters each, and 10 stacks with 2 quarters each.

Answer to Application: We take a piece of lumber, 60 feet in length, and are asked to cut it into smaller pieces that will all be the same size. In fact we are taking the number 60 and reconfiguring it. We need to prime factor 60. We find out that 60 = 2 • 2 • 3 • 5. We could cut:

2 pieces of 30 feet in length	This is 2 pieces by 30 feet (<u>2</u> • <u>3</u> • <u>5</u>)
4 pieces of 15 feet in length	This is 4 pieces (<u>2</u> • 2) by 15 feet (<u>3</u> • <u>5</u>)
3 pieces of 20 feet in length	This is 3 pieces by 20 feet (<u>2</u> • 2 • <u>5</u>)
5 pieces of 12 feet in length	This is 5 pieces by 12 feet (<u>2</u> • 2 • <u>3</u>)
6 pieces of 10 feet in length	This is 6 pieces (<u>2</u> • <u>3</u>) by 10 feet (<u>2</u> • <u>5</u>)

By switching the order of the numbers in the five examples above, we get 5 more possibilities.

These would be: 30 pieces of 2 feet in length; 15 pieces of 4 feet in length; 20 pieces of 3 feet in length; 12 pieces of 5 feet in length; and 10 pieces of 6 feet in length.

Answer: There are 10 different ways to cut his lumber in preparation for sale.

2.2 Divisibility and Prime Factorization Problems

In exercises #1- 10, write any of the listed divisors/factors (2, 3, or 5) of each of the following numbers. If more than one, separate by commas.

1) 46   2   3   5   2) 99   2   3   5

3) 120   2   3   5   4) 135   2   3   5

5) 245   2   3   5   6) 620   2   3   5

7) 1355   2   3   5   8) 1230   2   3   5

9) 1188   2   3   5   10) 950,250   2   3   5

In exercises #11-18, state whether the following statements are true or false?

11) $3^2 \cdot 5 = 9 \cdot 5$ 12) $5^3 = 125$ 13) $2^3 \cdot 3^2 = 72$

14) $3^3 \cdot 7 = 63$ 15) $2^5 = 10$ 16) $3^2 \cdot 5 \cdot 7 = 9 \cdot 35$

17) $2^3 \cdot 3^2 = 3^2 \cdot 2^3$ 18) $5^3 \cdot 3^2 = 5^2 \cdot 3^3$

In exercises #19-28, write whether the given number is prime or composite.

19) 37   20) 57   21) 8115   22) 73   23) 119

24) 4072   25) 143   26) 91   27) 251   28) 219

In exercises #29-46, answer the following questions.

29) How many factors does a prime number have?

30) What is the lowest prime number?

31) What prime number is closest to 10?

32) What prime number is closest to 25?

33) 11 has how many factors?   34) 19 has how many factors?

35) 35 has how many factors?   36) How many prime factors does 35 have?

37) 57 has how many factors?   38) How many prime factors does 57 have?

39) 70 has how many factors?   40) How many prime factors does 70 have?

41) If x is a prime number, what are its factors?

42) If y is a prime number, what are its factors?

43) If x is the highest prime number between 12 and 40, what is the value of x?

44) If y is the lowest prime number between 12 and 40, what is the value of y?

45) If x has 4 factors, is it a prime or composite number?

46) If x has only 2 factors, is it a prime or composite number?

In exercises #47-62, prime factor each number. Write your factorization answer in ascending order and remember to use exponents when you can. If the number is prime, simply write the word "prime" for your answer.

47) 24	48) 36	49) 45	50) 135
51) 99	52) 132	53) 147	54) 210
55) 126	56) 504	57) 83	58) 67
59) 209	60) 665	61) 1331	62) 363

In exercises #63-70, answer the following questions.

63-64) When storing 100 chairs at a local community center, an attendant was asked to stack the chairs in columns of equal height against the back wall. The back wall space was wide enough for 20 columns of chairs. None of the stacks were to be more than 15 chairs in height.

63) What is one way the attendant could stack the chairs (give answer as the number of columns of how many chairs each)?

64) What is the second way the attendant could stack the chairs (give answer as the number of columns of how many chairs each)?

65-66) In setting up a window display for a casino, Madelaine was given 200 blue chips and asked to place these in piles of equal amounts on the table before a mannequin. She wanted to use at least 3 piles and the display area allowed enough room for up to 8 piles.

65) What is one option she had to display the chips in the window (give answer as the number of piles of how many chips each)?

66) What are the other two options she had (give answers as the number of piles of how many chips each)?

67-68) Morris wanted to place 20 candles in the cake in the shape of a rectangle. He wanted to have at least 2 rows.

67) What is one of the ways he could create rows with the same number of candles in each row?

68) How many different ways could he create rows with same number of candles in each row?

69-70) At a doll show, Lisa was given 7 shelves upon which she could display her 42 dolls. The shelves were long enough to hold as many as 15 dolls. To make her display look good, she knew she had to use at least 3 of the shelves.

69) If she wanted each shelf she used to display the same number of dolls, what is one option she had (give answer as the number of shelves of how many dolls each)?

70) How many options did she have (how many shelves of how many dolls each)?

Skills Check

1-3) In a small bag, there are 15 pieces of candy. 6 are peppermint-flavored, 5 are caramel-flavored, and 4 are lemon-flavored. A big bag with 90 pieces of candy has the same ratio of candy types.

1. In the small bag, what fraction of the candy is lemon-flavored?

2. In the small bag, what is the ratio of lemon-flavored candies to caramel-flavored candies?

3. How many pieces of peppermint-flavored candy are there in the big bag?

4. True or false: $\dfrac{7}{5} = \dfrac{5.25}{3.75}$

Answers to Skills Check: 1) $\dfrac{4}{15}$; 2) $\dfrac{4 \text{ lemon-flavored}}{5 \text{ caramel-flavored}}$; 3) 36 pieces; 4) true.

Section 2.3   Greatest Common Factor (GCF), Reducing Fractions, and Improper Fractions & Mixed Numbers

Objective:

- To find the Greatest Common Factor (GCF)
- To reduce fractions
- Convert Equivalencies between Improper Fractions & Mixed Numbers

Application:

Taking a quick inventory of candles at a neighborhood store, Ned counted 105 red candles and 60 green candles. The manager wanted all these candles to be put into bundles to be sold quickly. If the manager wanted each bundle to have the same number of red candles and the same number of green candles, what is the greatest number of bundles that Ned could make? If the manager wanted to sell each candle for $.30, how much would each bundle be sold for?

Vocabulary:

greatest common factor—The greatest common factor (GCF) is the greatest or highest whole number that can divide evenly into two or more numbers. It is the same as the greatest common divisor (GCD). (Example: the GCF for the numbers 10 and 15 is 5 because $10 = 2 \bullet 5$ and $15 = 3 \bullet 5$. The 5 is the common factor).

We should notice now that a GCF must be equal to or lower than the smallest given number because by definition it must divide evenly into the given numbers.

reducing—Reducing a fraction is a process where the numerator and the denominator in a fraction are divided by the same divisor (a common factor) to create an equivalent fraction using smaller numbers (Example: $\frac{2}{4} = \frac{1}{2}$).

Reducing is mathematically possible because it is the same as dividing a number by the value of 1 (any fraction with the same numerator and denominator equals 1). We can agree that $\frac{6}{8} \div 1 = \frac{6}{8}$ as any value divided by 1 is equal to the number itself. We could restate this exact problem as $\frac{6}{8} \div \frac{2}{2} = \frac{6}{8}$ because $\frac{2}{2}$ is the same as 1. Reducing takes the same problem of $\frac{6}{8} \div \frac{2}{2}$ and works out the math. The numerators: $6 \div 2 = 3$; the denominators $8 \div 2 = 4$. Thus, the reduced answer is $\frac{3}{4}$. We know that $\frac{6}{8} = \frac{3}{4}$ because both answers were obtained by dividing $\frac{6}{8}$ by a value of 1.

*** A question often arises. When do we reduce a fractional answer? The answer is ALWAYS...and now we never need to ask this question again. Remember: ALWAYS!

proper fraction—A **proper fraction** is a fraction in which the numerator is less than the denominator. This means that a proper fraction has a value of less than 1 whole (Examples: $\frac{3}{4}$, $\frac{5}{11}$, $\frac{2}{7}$).

improper fraction—An **improper fraction** is a fraction in which the numerator is equal to or greater than the denominator. In essence this means that an improper fraction has a value of at least one whole (Examples: $\frac{7}{5}$, $\frac{8}{3}$, $\frac{6}{6}$).

mixed number—A **mixed number** is a number value that consists of a whole number and a fraction. By definition it has a value of more than one whole (Examples: $2\frac{3}{5}$, $3\frac{1}{7}$).

How to:

Find the Greatest Common Factor of 2 or more given numbers.

1. Prime factor each of the given numbers individually.

2. Locate the prime factors that the numbers have in common. If they have only one factor that is in common, this is the GCF. If they have more than 1 factor in common, multiply the common factors (of **only** one of the numbers) together to get the GCF.

Example #1: Find the GCF of 20 and 55

　　　Step #1: Prime factor each number separately.

$$2\,)\overline{20} \qquad\qquad 5\,)\overline{55}$$
$$2\,)\overline{10} \qquad\qquad 11\,)\overline{11}$$
$$5\,)\overline{5} \qquad\qquad\quad 1$$
$$\quad 1$$

$$20 = 2 \bullet 2 \bullet 5 \qquad\qquad 55 = 5 \bullet 11$$

　　　Step #2: Locate the prime factors they have in common.

　　　　The only factor they have in common is a 5.

　　　　Answer: GCF = $\underline{5}$

Example #2: Find the GCF of 60 and 84

　　　Step #1: Prime factor each number separately.

$$2\,)\overline{60} \qquad\qquad 2\,)\overline{84}$$
$$2\,)\overline{30} \qquad\qquad 2\,)\overline{42}$$
$$3\,)\overline{15} \qquad\qquad 3\,)\overline{21}$$
$$5\,)\overline{5} \qquad\qquad 7\,)\overline{7}$$
$$\quad 1 \qquad\qquad\qquad 1$$

$$60 = 2 \bullet 2 \bullet 3 \bullet 5 \qquad\qquad 84 = 2 \bullet 2 \bullet 3 \bullet 7$$

Step #2: Locate the prime factors they have in common.

The factors they have in common are 2 • 2 • 3.

Multiply these together.

Answer: GCF = <u>12</u>

Example #3: Find the GCF of 13 and 51

Step #1: Prime factor each number separately.

$13\overline{)13}$ $3\overline{)51}$
$\quad\;1$ $17\overline{)17}$
                          $\qquad 1$

13 = prime   51 = 3 • 17

Step #2: Locate the prime factors they have in common.

At first glance it may seem as if there is no common factor, but every whole number has a factor of one. Therefore:

Answer: GCF = <u>1</u>

How to:

Reduce Fractions:

1. Find a common factor for (a number that divides evenly into) the numerator and denominator.

2. Divide this factor into both the numerator and the denominator to find the reduced equivalent fraction.

Example #4: Reduce $\dfrac{6}{30}$ to lowest terms.

One method:	OR	**A second method:**

Step #1: Find any common factor. (Use our knowledge of the divisibility rules for 2, 3, and 5 and testing other prime numbers as possible factors)

Both 6 and 30 are even numbers, so the divisibility rules tell us that 2 will divide evenly into both 6 and 30.

Step #1: Find the GCF

$2\overline{)6}$ $2\overline{)30}$
$3\overline{)3}$ $3\overline{)15}$
$\;\;1$ $5\overline{)5}$
                $\quad 1$

GCF = 6

Step #2: Divide the common factor into both the numerator and the denominator.

$$\frac{6}{30} \div \frac{2}{2} = \frac{3}{15}$$ OR $$\frac{6}{30} \div \frac{6}{6} = \frac{1}{5}$$

You now need to see if you can reduce the new equivalent fraction of $\frac{3}{15}$

3 goes evenly into both 3 and 15, so divide both the numerator and the denominator by the 3.

After you reduce by the GCF, you are finished. The fraction will be in its lowest terms.

$$\frac{3}{15} \div \frac{3}{3} = \frac{1}{5}$$

Either way you solve the problem, you will get the same **answer:** $\frac{1}{5}$

How to:

Change an Improper Fraction into a Mixed Number

1. Divide the numerator by the denominator

2. Write the mixed number. The quotient will be the whole number; the remainder [part(s) left over] will be the numerator above the same denominator.

Example #5: Change $\frac{14}{5}$ to a mixed number.

Step #1: Divide the numerator by the denominator.

$$5 \overline{)\begin{array}{l} 2 \\ 14 \\ \underline{10} \\ 4 \end{array}}$$

2 (whole number quotient)

4 (remainder)

Step #2: Write the mixed number.

Answer: $2\frac{4}{5}$

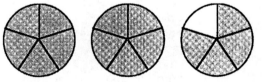

How to:

Change a Mixed Number to an Improper Fraction:

1. Multiply the whole number by the denominator.

2. Add this product to the numerator.

3. Place this new number over the denominator.

Example #6: Change $3\frac{3}{5}$ to an improper fraction.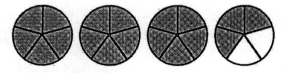

Step #1: Multiply the whole number by the denominator.

$3 \bullet 5 = 15$

Step #2: Add this to the numerator.

15 + the numerator of 3 = 18

Step #3: Place this new number over the denominator.

Answer: $\frac{18}{5}$

Sample #1: Find the GCF of 54, 90, and 150.

Prime factor each number separately.

$2\overline{)54}$	$2\overline{)90}$	$2\overline{)150}$
$3\overline{)27}$	$3\overline{)45}$	$3\overline{)75}$
$3\overline{)9}$	$3\overline{)15}$	$5\overline{)25}$
$3\overline{)3}$	$5\overline{)5}$	$5\overline{)5}$
1	1	1

The common prime factors for the 3 numbers are 2 • 3.

Answer: the GCF equals 6

- **You try it now:**
- a) Find the GCF of 210 and 285
- b) Find the GCF of 36, 81, and 117

Sample #2: In an effort to protect certain species of birds, two naturalists looked for specific types of birds on two sides of a mountain ridge. The first naturalist found 3 Northern Pygmy Owls, 2 Marbled Murrelets, 5 Western Bluebirds, and 1 Bald Eagle. The second naturalist found 2 Chestnut-backed Chickadees, a single Marbled Murrelet, 2 Western Bluebirds, and 2 Yellow-bellied Sapsuckers. What types of birds and what is the greatest number of each type of bird which both naturalists spotted?

When looking for the greatest area of commonality, first look at the individual sightings for each naturalist.

Naturalist #1	Naturalist #2
3 Northern Pygmy-Owls	2 Chestnut-backed Chickadees
2 Marbled Murrelets	1 Marbled Murrelet
5 Western Bluebirds	2 Western Bluebirds
1 Bald Eagle	2 Yellow-bellied Sapsuckers

The types of birds and the greatest number of each type of bird which both naturalists spotted were:

Answer: 1 Marbled Murrelet and 2 Western Bluebirds

You try it now:

c) Two friends grew vegetables in their home gardens. Marcie had 2 tomato plants, 2 zucchini plants, 3 lettuce plants, and a cucumber plant. Jim had 3 tomato plants, an acorn squash plant, a zucchini plant, and a broccoli plant. What vegetables and what number of each vegetable did both friends grow?

d) At a Halloween party, two brothers each received a bag of candy. Anthony got 6 candy bars, 5 jaw breakers, 5 packs of gum, and 10 lollipops. Andrew got 10 candy bars, 3 packs of gum, 6 lollipops, and 7 fruit rolls. What types of candy and what number of each type of candy did both boys receive?

Sample #3: Jackie had said that she would make and donate floral arrangements to decorate various areas at a local fair. She counted the flowers she had picked from her garden—20 carnations, 35 roses, and 60 daisies. If Jackie was determined to use all her flowers and to have all the floral arrangements be identical, how many floral arrangements could she make? How many of each type of flower would be in each arrangement?

First we need to recognize that if the flowers are to be divided up identically, the number of floral arrangements must divide evenly into 20, 35, and 60. In fact, we need to find a common factor for 20, 35, and 60.

Prime factor each number.

20 carnations	35 roses	60 daisies
$2\,\overline{)20}$	$5\,\overline{)35}$	$2\,\overline{)60}$
$2\,\overline{)10}$	$7\,\overline{)7}$	$2\,\overline{)30}$
$5\,\overline{)5}$	1	$3\,\overline{)15}$
1		$5\,\overline{)5}$
		1

The only common factor for all three types of flowers is <u>5</u>. Therefore, if she is to use all the flowers, she has only one choice. She would make:

Answer: <u>5</u> **floral arrangements**. Each arrangement would consist of: **4 carnations** (the number of carnations—the factors 2 • 2—left after factoring out the 5 from 20), **7 roses** (the number of roses—a 7—left after factoring out the 5 from 35), **and 12 daisies** (the number of daisies—the factors of 2 • 2 • 3—left after factoring out the 5 from 60].

■ **You try it now:**

e) The pet store *Fish World* received a shipment of 100 guppies, 40 swordfish, and 30 angel fish. A clerk was asked to split up the fish identically in fish tanks so that each tank would have the exact same number of each type of fish. The tanks were to have at least 15 fish and no more than 30 fish. How many tanks did the clerk set up? How many of each type of fish were in each tank?

f) When a marble company donated marbles to the *Toys for Kids* program, Maribel counted 88 green marbles, 40 red marbles, and 24 black marbles which had fallen out of their packaging. She decided to make up new identical packages, each package having the same number of each colored marble. What was the greatest number of packages she could make? How many of each type of marble would be in each package?

Sample #4: Reduce $\dfrac{60}{165}$ to lowest terms.

One method:	OR	**A second method:**

One method:

Use the rules of divisibility.
5 divides into both 60 and 165 because they both end in either a zero or a five.
Divide 5 into both the numerator and the denominator.

$$\frac{60}{165} \div \frac{5}{5} = \frac{12}{33}$$

Reduce $\dfrac{12}{33}$ by the common factor of 3.

$$\frac{12}{33} \div \frac{3}{3} = \frac{4}{11}$$

By either method the **answer** is $\dfrac{4}{11}$

OR

A second method:

Find the GCF of 60 and 165.

$2\overline{)60}$ $3\overline{)165}$
$2\overline{)30}$ $5\overline{)55}$
$3\overline{)15}$ $11\overline{)11}$
$5\overline{)5}$ 1
1

The GCF is <u>15</u>.

Divide the numerator and denominator by 15.

$$\frac{60}{165} \div \frac{15}{15} = \frac{4}{11}$$

■ **You try it now:**

g) Reduce $\dfrac{45}{150}$ to lowest terms.

h) The *Better Banana Company* wanted to establish what fraction of their bananas were bruised. If a thousand bananas were counted and fifty were bruised, what fraction of the bananas (in lowest terms) were bruised?

Sample #5: The *Better Banana Company* picked and boxed 8,000 pounds of bananas one day. If each box held 60 pounds of bananas, what mixed number represents how many boxes were filled?

First, we recognize that 60 pounds represents 1 whole box. Second, we have 8,000 parts (each pound being 1 part of the 60 that makes a whole box).

Now remember the basic meaning of a fraction: $\dfrac{part}{whole}$

In this case we have 8,000 parts. 60 parts make one whole. The number of boxes filled can be represented by the improper fraction of $\dfrac{8000}{60}$.

Change the improper fraction to a mixed number.

$$
\begin{array}{r}
133 \text{ (whole number)} \\
60 \overline{)\,8000} \\
-\;60 \\
\hline
200 \\
-\;180 \\
\hline
200 \\
-\;180 \\
\hline
20 \text{ (remainder)}
\end{array}
$$

Therefore: $\dfrac{8000}{60} \;=\; 133\dfrac{20}{60}$ Reduce the fractional part to lowest terms.

Answer: $133\dfrac{1}{3}$ **boxes**

*** We also could have done this problem by first reducing the fraction to lowest terms. 20 is the GCF. So:

$$\frac{8000}{60} \;\div\; \frac{20}{20} \;=\; \frac{400}{3}$$

Then, when dividing the numerator (400) by the denominator (3), we get the same answer of $133\dfrac{1}{3}$ **boxes.**

You try it now:

i) Each school bus could hold 35 people. If 310 children were going to the Science Fair, how many buses would be filled by the children (give answer as a mixed number)?

j) The local phone book listed 420 people with the last name of Smith. If 120 names were listed on each page, how many pages were filled with people who had the last name of Smith (give answer as a mixed number)?

Sample #6: An office supply store was taking inventory of its stock. A carton of staples held 8 smaller boxes of staples. If $20\frac{3}{8}$ cartons were still filled, how many boxes of staples did the store still have?

Change the mixed number to an improper fraction: $20\frac{3}{8} = \frac{163}{8}$

The numerator of 163 represents the number of parts, or in this case the number of boxes of staples inside the cartons.

Answer: 163 boxes

▪ **You try it now:**

k) 12 eggs are in a carton of eggs. If $15\frac{3}{12}$ cartons of eggs were used by a restaurant one morning, how many eggs were used?

l) After a play rehearsal, a group of actors went to a pizza parlor. Each pizza was cut into 10 slices; the group ate $6\frac{7}{10}$ pizzas. How many pieces of pizza did they eat?

Answers to You try it now: a) 15; b) 9; c) 2 tomato plants and 1 zucchini plant; d) 6 candy bars, 3 packs of gum, and 6 lollipops; e) 10 fish tanks; each tank has 10 guppies, 4 swordfish, and 3 angel fish; f) 8 packages; each package would have 11 green marbles, 5 red marbles, and 3 black marbles; g) $\frac{3}{10}$; h) $\frac{1}{20}$; i) $8\frac{6}{7}$ buses; j) $3\frac{1}{2}$ pages; k) 183 eggs; l) 67 pieces of pizza

Answer to Application: To use all the candles and to create the greatest number of bundles of candles that have the same number of each type of candle, we must find the GCF of the 105 red candles and the 60 green candles.

Red Candles

$3\,)\overline{105}$
$5\,)\overline{35}$
$7\,)\overline{7}$
$\qquad 1$

Green Candles

$2\,)\overline{60}$
$2\,)\overline{30}$
$3\,)\overline{15}$
$5\,)\overline{5}$
$\qquad 1$

They both have 3 • 5 in common, so the GCF is 15. 15 is the greatest number of bundles that Ned could create. Each bundle would have 7 red candles (the number left after factoring out 3 • 5 from 105) and 4 green candles (the number left after factoring out 3 • 5 from 60).

If each bundle has 11 candles (7 red and 4 green) and each candle was to be sold for $.30, each bundle would be sold for $3.30.

2.3 GCF, Reducing, Improper Fractions & Mixed Numbers Problems

1) Two fruit baskets lie on a kitchen table. The first basket has 3 plums, 2 figs, and 2 bananas. The second basket has 2 plums, 4 oranges, and a banana. What types of fruit and what number of each type of fruit do they have in common?

2) A handyman had two tool boxes. One tool box had 3 screwdrivers, 10 screws, 50 nails, and a hammer. The second tool box had a screwdriver, 2 wrenches, and a tape measure. What tools and what number of each tool do they have in common?

3) Three children each had a pile of coins. Jenny had a quarter, 2 dimes, and 5 pennies. Veejay had 2 quarters, a dime, 2 nickels, and 4 pennies. Sandra had 3 quarters, a nickel, and 3 pennies? What coins and what number of each coin do they have in common?

4) A Human Rights group looked at and compared the civil rights available in 3 different countries. Country A guaranteed the rights of free speech, religion, travel, and assembly. Country B guaranteed the rights of religion, travel, and a job. Country C guaranteed free speech, religion, travel, and a job. What civil rights do these 3 countries have in common?

In exercises #5-16 find the GCF.

5) 12 and 52	6) 42 and 35	7) 25 and 84	8) 42 and 84
9) 45 and 150	10) 27 and 48	11) 174 and 204	12) 360 and 820
13) 143 and 198	14) 50, 65 and 90	15) 196, 140, and 56	16) 17, 21, and 38

In exercises #17-28, reduce the fractions to lowest terms.

17) $\dfrac{3}{21}$ 18) $\dfrac{6}{20}$ 19) $\dfrac{30}{45}$ 20) $\dfrac{42}{18}$ 21) $\dfrac{55}{22}$

22) $\dfrac{13}{40}$ 23) $\dfrac{56}{105}$ 24) $\dfrac{16}{64}$ 25) $\dfrac{91}{63}$ 26) $\dfrac{121}{154}$

27) $\dfrac{174}{204}$ 28) $\dfrac{360}{820}$

In exercises #29-46, change any improper fraction into a mixed number and any mixed number into an improper fraction.

29) $\dfrac{16}{3}$ 30) $\dfrac{29}{8}$ 31) $2\dfrac{5}{8}$ 32) $4\dfrac{2}{5}$ 33) $\dfrac{30}{4}$

34) $\dfrac{56}{6}$ 35) $2\dfrac{6}{16}$ 36) $5\dfrac{3}{12}$ 37) $\dfrac{155}{3}$ 38) $\dfrac{208}{7}$

39) $6\dfrac{9}{11}$ 40) $4\dfrac{5}{13}$ 41) $\dfrac{88}{4}$ 42) $\dfrac{133}{11}$ 43) $20\dfrac{4}{30}$

44) $25\dfrac{6}{40}$ 45) $\dfrac{820}{360}$ 46) $\dfrac{204}{174}$

Solve the following problems. Whenever possible, give your answer in a mixed number form.

47-48) Ten out of a dozen donuts have nuts. Randomly choose one of the donuts.

47) Will the probability that you choose a donut with nuts be written as a proper or an improper fraction? Why?

48) What is the probability that you will choose a donut with nuts?

49) At a fair's fishing booth, children under 5 can catch a plastic fish for two dollars. If there are 8 fish and 6 of them award a prize, what is the probability that a child will get a prize?

50-53) A theater complex had 12 different rooms which could each hold 300 people. At 6 pm there were 1600 people watching movies at the complex.

50) What mixed number represents the equivalent number of rooms which were filled?

51) What fraction of the total seats in the theater complex were filled?

52) What fraction of the total seats in the theater complex were empty?

53) By 8 pm on a typical Friday night, the average number of seats filled in each theater is 200. What fraction of the theater's seats are usually filled on Friday nights?

54) A small, family-owned furniture company currently makes 30 desks per year. Every few months the company sells 8 desks to a local retailer. How many orders to this retailer can be met each year with its current output?

55-56) There are twenty pencils in every Eraser *Leadhead* pencil package. A teacher had $7\dfrac{3}{20}$ packages of the pencils.

55) Did she have enough pencils to give to the 120 students taking the school's exam?

56) How many more or less pencils did she have than she needed?

57-66) Ten reams (a ream = 500 sheets) of paper fit into each standard packaging box. 24 standard packaging boxes fit into a crate.

Which of the following are true or false?

57) 10 reams = 5000 sheets of paper

58) 240 reams = 1 crate

59) 1 box = 2400 sheets

60) 24 boxes = 1 crate

61) 24 boxes = 100 reams

62) 24 reams = 24(500 sheets)

63) If you have 2200 sheets of paper, what fraction of a packaging box do you have?

64) If you have 2200 sheets of paper, how many reams do you have?

65) If you have enough paper to fill 10 boxes, what fraction of a crate would you have?

66) If you had 8000 sheets of paper, what fraction of a box could be filled?

67-68) Andrew was given 3 boxes of fruit. The first held 60 peaches, the second 80 plums, and the third 90 bananas. His boss told him to divide up all the fruit so that each fruit basket he created would have the exact same number of each type of fruit.

67) What is the greatest number of fruit baskets he could make?

68) How many of each type of fruit would be in each basket?

69-70) A jeweler had 18 topaz stones, 30 rubies, and 45 emeralds. Using all the jewels, she created identical dazzling window displays, each display possessing the exact same number of each type of jewel.

69) What is the largest number of displays she could create?

70) How many of each type of jewel was in each display?

71-72) For a July 4th window display at a casino, Madelaine was given 65 red chips, 65 blue chips, and 130 white chips. She was asked to display all the chips on a blackjack table in identical piles, each pile having the exact same number of each color of chip. The display would have four mannequins so she wanted to have at least 8 piles of chips, but no more than 16 piles.

71) How many piles of chips did she have in her final display?

72) How many of each colored chip were in each display?

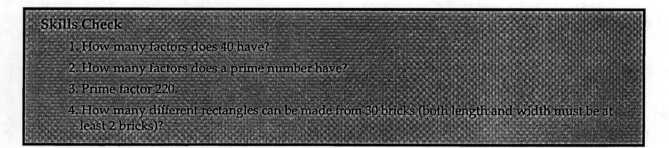

Skills Check

1. How many factors does 40 have?

2. How many factors does a prime number have?

3. Prime factor 220.

4. How many different rectangles can be made from 30 bricks (both length and width must be at least 2 bricks)?

Answers to Skills Check: 1) 8 factors (1, 2, 4, 5, 8, 10, 20, 40);   2) 2 factors (1 and the number itself);
3) 2•2•5•11; 4) 6 rectangles (2 • 15; 3 • 10; 5 • 6; 15 • 2; 10 • 3; 6 • 5).

Section 2.4   Multiply and Divide Fractions

Objectives:

- To multiply fractions
- To divide fractions
- To set up/solve multiplication & division of fractions application problems

Application:

A contractor bought a piece of land that was $\frac{7}{8}$ of an acre in size. He had a planning permit to divide the land into three parcels. What would be the size of each new parcel of land?

Vocabulary:

> **canceling**—Canceling is a process used <u>only</u> when multiplying fractions. **We cancel by dividing a single numerator and a single denomina**tor by a common divisor or factor. The cancellation process can involve numbers above and below each other (the same as reducing as we learned in the previous section) or two numbers which are diagonal to each other.

> **of**—When there is a statement "a number **of** another number," the **of** means multiply (Example: $\frac{2}{5}$ of 15 means $\frac{2}{5} \bullet 15$).

> **integer**—An **integer** is any positive or negative **whole number or zero.**

> **reciprocal**—The **reciprocal** of a number is the inversion (flipping over) of a number written as a fraction (Example: the reciprocal of $\frac{5}{8}$ is $\frac{8}{5}$).

> **divisor**—The **divisor** is the number you are dividing by. It follows the "divided by" symbol (÷). (Example: In $\frac{2}{3} \div \frac{5}{6}$, the divisor is $\frac{5}{6}$).

> ***Remember these **3 powerful rules** of mathematics:

> (1) **Any number multiplied or divided by 1 whole equals that same number.**

> (2) **Any fraction with the same numerator & denominator has a value of 1 whole.**

> Thus:

> If 10 • 1 = 10, we also know that 10 • $\frac{5}{5}$ = 10 because $\frac{5}{5}$ is equal to 1 whole.

If $\dfrac{3}{7} \div 1 = \dfrac{3}{7}$, we also know that $\dfrac{3}{7} \div \dfrac{3}{3} = \dfrac{3}{7}$ because $\dfrac{3}{3}$ is equal to 1 whole.

(3) Any number multiplied by its reciprocal equals one whole.

Thus:

$$\dfrac{5}{8} \bullet \dfrac{8}{5} = 1 \text{ because } \dfrac{8}{5} \text{ is the reciprocal of } \dfrac{5}{8}.$$

How to:

Multiply Fractions

1. Cancel any single numerator with any single denominator until no more canceling is possible.

2. Multiply straight across, the numerators together, and then the denominators together.

Example #1: $\dfrac{18}{11} \bullet \dfrac{33}{9}$

Step #1: Cancel.

The numerator of 18 and the denominator of 9 both have a common factor of 9. Nine divides into 18 two times while 9 divides into 9 one time. Thus, after our first cancellation, the problem would look like the following:

$$\dfrac{\overset{2}{\cancel{18}}}{11} \bullet \dfrac{33}{\underset{1}{\cancel{9}}}$$

A second cancellation is also possible. The numerator of 33 and the denominator of 11 both have a common factor of 11. Eleven divides into 33 three times and 11 divides into eleven one time. Thus, after our second cancellation, the problem would look like the following:

$$\dfrac{\overset{2}{\cancel{18}}}{\underset{1}{\cancel{11}}} \bullet \dfrac{\overset{3}{\cancel{33}}}{\underset{1}{\cancel{9}}}$$

Step #2: Multiply straight across.

$$\dfrac{\overset{2}{\cancel{18}}}{\underset{1}{\cancel{11}}} \bullet \dfrac{\overset{3}{\cancel{33}}}{\underset{1}{\cancel{9}}} = \dfrac{6}{1} = 6$$

Answer: 6

How to:

Divide Fractions.

1. Determine which fraction is the divisor and take the reciprocal of <u>only</u> the divisor.

2. The problem now becomes a multiplication of fractions problem. Cancel any single numerator with any single denominator until no more canceling is possible.

3. Multiply straight across, the numerators together, and then the denominators together.

Example #2: $\dfrac{4}{13} \div \dfrac{2}{7}$

Step #1: Determine the divisor and take its reciprocal.

$\dfrac{2}{7}$ is the divisor; its reciprocal is $\dfrac{7}{2}$.

Step #2: Change the problem to multiplication. Cancel.

The problem becomes: $\dfrac{4}{13} \cdot \dfrac{7}{2}$

The numerator of 4 and the denominator of 2 both have a common factor of 2. Two divides into 4 two times and 2 divides into 2 one time. Thus, after the cancellation, the problem would look like the following:

$$\dfrac{\overset{2}{\cancel{4}}}{13} \cdot \dfrac{7}{\underset{1}{\cancel{2}}}$$

Step #3: Multiply straight across.

$$\dfrac{\overset{2}{\cancel{4}}}{13} \cdot \dfrac{7}{\underset{1}{\cancel{2}}} = \dfrac{14}{13}$$

Answer: $\dfrac{14}{13}$ or $1\dfrac{1}{13}$

Sample #1: Find $\dfrac{3}{8}$ of $\dfrac{5}{27}$ • $\dfrac{42}{5}$

We first recognize that of in this case means multiply because it is written in the form of a number of another number. This problem is the same as:

$$\dfrac{3}{8} \quad \bullet \quad \dfrac{5}{27} \quad \bullet \quad \dfrac{42}{5}$$

Whether there are 2 or 3 or many fractions being multiplied makes no difference. We can still cancel any single numerator with any single denominator.

The 3 and the 27 can be canceled. They both have a common factor of 3.
The 8 and the 42 can be canceled. They both have a common factor of 2.
The 5 and the 5 can be canceled. They both have a common factor of 5.

This gives us:
$$\dfrac{\overset{1}{\cancel{3}}}{\underset{4}{\cancel{8}}} \quad \bullet \quad \dfrac{\overset{1}{\cancel{5}}}{27} \quad \bullet \quad \dfrac{\overset{21}{\cancel{42}}}{\underset{1}{\cancel{5}}}$$

Always after you have done some canceling, check again to see if another numerator and denominator can be canceled. In this case the numerator of 21 and the denominator of 9 have a common factor of 3.

Cancel the 9 and the 21 and we get:

$$\dfrac{\overset{1}{\cancel{3}}}{\underset{4}{\cancel{8}}} \quad \bullet \quad \dfrac{\overset{1}{\cancel{5}}}{\underset{3}{\cancel{27}}} \quad \bullet \quad \dfrac{\overset{7}{\cancel{\overset{21}{\cancel{42}}}}}{\underset{1}{\cancel{5}}} \quad = \quad \dfrac{7}{12}$$

Answer: $\dfrac{7}{12}$

■ **You try it now:**

a) $\dfrac{14}{5}$ • $\dfrac{4}{3}$ • $\dfrac{5}{2}$

b) $\dfrac{7}{15}$ of $\dfrac{6}{21}$ of $\dfrac{3}{2}$

Sample #2:   A recent study of 4 elementary schools showed that only four-sevenths of third graders were learning the math skills necessary for them to succeed in fourth grade. If this study involved 112 students, how many students were learning the skills they needed? How many students were not learning the appropriate skills?

We must first look at the given words (the language!). Where is the math in the English?

The math exists in the phrase four-sevenths of third graders. This is a phrase looking at a fraction __of__ a number (a total), in this case:

$\frac{4}{7}$ of 112, where the 112 is the total number of third-graders

We know that __of__ means multiply and that every whole number has a denominator of 1. Therefore, we write a set up that is a math expression:

$$\frac{4}{7} \cdot \frac{112}{1}$$

We cancel the 7 and 112 (7 is the common factor).

$$\frac{4}{\frac{\boxed{7}}{1}} \cdot \frac{\overset{16}{\boxed{112}}}{1} = \frac{64}{1}$$

1st Answer: 64 students are currently successful.

Concepts to solve the second question:

(Total students) - (successful students) = (unsuccessful students)

$\Downarrow$ $\Downarrow$

Math Set up: $(112) - \left(\frac{4}{7} \cdot \frac{112}{1} \right)$

$(112) - (64) = 48$

2nd Answer: 48 students are not currently successful

You try it now:

c) When the city did a study of its 800 elm trees which lined many of its streets, it discovered that five out of every eight (five-eighths!) suffered from the Dutch elm disease. How many trees were infected with the disease? If it would cost $800 dollars to remove each diseased tree and replace it with another tree, how much would the city (the taxpayers!) need to spend?

d) The city of Chesterton has known for a long time that $\frac{1}{3}$ of all its teenage crimes occur in the afternoon hours between 3:00 and 6:00 when many parents are not at home. What many parents do not know is the fact that $\frac{2}{7}$ of these crimes in the afternoon are solved. If there were a total of 660 crimes committed by teenagers in Chesterton last year, how many were committed between 3 and 6 pm? How many of these crimes were solved (round your answer to the nearest whole)?

Sample #3: $\frac{30}{6} \div \frac{10}{16} \div 2$

> The first thing we recognize is that we have 2 divisors in this problem (2 numbers that come after a "divided by" symbol).
>
> We change division to multiplication by taking the reciprocals of the divisors. The problem now looks like this:
>
> $$\frac{30}{6} \cdot \frac{16}{10} \cdot \frac{1}{2}$$
>
> The 30 and the 10 can be canceled. They both have a common factor of 10. The 6 and the 16 can be canceled; both have a common factor of 2.
>
> $$\frac{\overset{3}{\cancel{30}}}{\underset{3}{\cancel{6}}} \cdot \frac{\overset{8}{\cancel{16}}}{\underset{1}{\cancel{10}}} \cdot \frac{1}{2}$$
>
> We notice that we can still do more canceling. The numerator of 3 and the denominator of 3 have 3 as a common factor. The numerator of 8 and the denominator of 2 have 2 as a common factor.
>
> $$\frac{\overset{1}{\cancel{\overset{3}{\cancel{30}}}}}{\underset{1}{\cancel{\underset{3}{\cancel{6}}}}} \cdot \frac{\overset{4}{\cancel{\overset{8}{\cancel{16}}}}}{\underset{1}{\cancel{10}}} \cdot \frac{1}{\underset{1}{\cancel{\underset{1}{\cancel{2}}}}} = \frac{4}{1}$$

Answer: 4

- **You try it now:**

e) $\dfrac{4}{15} \div \dfrac{12}{25} \div \dfrac{4}{3}$

f) $\dfrac{21}{5}$ of $\dfrac{2}{9} \div 5$

Sample #4: A catering company had 140 quarts of punch. It had agreed to provide 200 servings of punch at the wedding reception. If each serving of punch was $\dfrac{5}{8}$ of a pint, how many servings of punch could the caterer provide (Need to know: 2 pints = 1 quart)?

Again: Where is the math in the English?

First we need to recognize that there is a total amount of punch which is going to be split up or divided up into servings of $\dfrac{5}{8}$ of a pint each. We must divide the total amount (140 quarts = 280 pints) by the size of each serving to get the number of servings.

<u>In English</u>	then:	<u>Set up in a math expression</u>
(total amount of punch) ÷ (size of each serving)	=	$280 \div \dfrac{5}{8}$

We take the reciprocal of the divisor and then multiply.

Answer: 448 servings

- **You try it now:**

g) The swimming part of a local triathlon was $\dfrac{3}{5}$ of a mile. If each race participant had to swim this distance using 4 different swimming strokes (the crawl, breast, back, and butterfly) equally, how far did each racer swim the back stroke?

h) [Try to solve the following problem without changing feet into inches] As a part of a Fourth of July celebration, a group of firemen cooked 13 "long dogs" that were each thirty feet in length, then cut them into 5 inch long (five-twelfths of a foot), ready-to-eat hot dogs. How many hot dogs were made from each 30 foot long dog? How many hot dogs were made from all the "long dogs"?

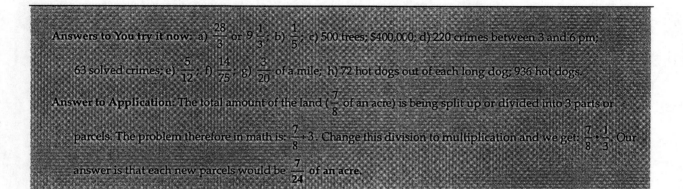

Answers to You try it now: a) $\frac{28}{3}$ or $9\frac{1}{3}$; b) $\frac{1}{5}$; c) 500 trees; $400,000; d) 220 crimes between 3 and 6 pm;

63 solved crimes; e) $\frac{5}{12}$; f) $\frac{14}{75}$; g) $\frac{3}{20}$ of a mile; h) 72 hot dogs out of each long dog; 936 hot dogs.

Answer to Application: The total amount of the land ($\frac{7}{8}$ of an acre) is being split up or divided into 3 parts or

parcels. The problem therefore in math is: $\frac{7}{8} \div 3$. Change this division to multiplication and we get: $\frac{7}{8} \cdot \frac{1}{3}$. Our

answer is that each new parcels would be $\frac{7}{24}$ of an acre.

2.4 Multiplication and Division of Fractions Problems

In exercises #1-12, round each number to the nearest whole number. If you end up with a half, round up (i.e. $3\frac{1}{2}$ would round up to 4 wholes).

1) $\frac{2}{3}$ 2) $\frac{3}{6}$ 3) $\frac{8}{3}$ 4) $\frac{12}{5}$ 5) $\frac{87}{7}$

6) $\frac{92}{8}$ 7) $4\overline{)11}$ 8) $16\overline{)7}$ 9) $46\overline{)16}$ 10) $16\overline{)46}$

11) 19 over 3   12) $4 \div 9$

In exercises #13-30, solve for the product or the quotient. If you get a non-integer answer of a value of greater than 1, be sure to give both an improper fraction and a mixed number answer.

13) $\frac{3}{4} \cdot \frac{1}{5}$ 14) $\frac{5}{14} \cdot \frac{7}{10}$ 15) $\frac{8}{5}$ of $\frac{3}{2}$ 16) $\frac{16}{17}$ of $\frac{3}{8}$ 17) $\frac{4}{3} \cdot \frac{7}{20}$

18) $\frac{4}{3} \div \frac{3}{5}$ 19) $\frac{5}{12} \div \frac{10}{3}$ 20) $\frac{11}{7} \div \frac{44}{9}$ 21) $\frac{16}{31} \div \frac{16}{31}$ 22) $\frac{8}{45} \div \frac{14}{15}$

23) $\frac{2}{9} \cdot \frac{14}{17} \cdot \frac{18}{7}$ 24) $\frac{3}{11} \cdot \frac{1}{6} \cdot \frac{22}{27}$ 25) $8 \cdot \frac{3}{5} \div \frac{2}{7}$ 26) $\frac{6}{5} \div \frac{5}{6} \div \frac{1}{5}$

27) $3 \div 8 \cdot \frac{2}{3}$ 28) $12 \div 7 \cdot \frac{5}{36}$ 29) $\frac{49}{7} \cdot 7 \div 42$ 30) $\frac{11}{13} \div \frac{17}{12} \div \frac{22}{39}$

In exercises #31-40, (a) translate the following words into math statements. Use the dot (•) for multiplication and the ÷ symbol for division [the problems with an asterisk (*) need one or more parentheses to ensure that order of operations are followed] and, (b) give the solution.

31) The product of $\frac{3}{7}$ and $\frac{4}{5}$.   32) The product of $\frac{2}{3}$ and 15.

33) The quotient of 11 and $\frac{1}{9}$.   34) The quotient of $\frac{3}{4}$ and $\frac{7}{8}$.

35) $\frac{5}{8}$ of 320.   36) $\frac{3}{4}$ of 480.

37) Find the quotient of $\frac{1}{5}$ and $\frac{2}{3}$, then divide by 4.

*38) Find the sum of 5 and 4, then multiply by the product of $\frac{7}{5}$ and $\frac{1}{6}$.

o *39) Find the difference of 11 and 3, then divide by the product of $\frac{3}{8}$ and 2.

*40) Subtract 6 from the second prime number larger than 6, then multiply by the product of $\frac{2}{5}$ and $\frac{5}{1}$.

In exercises #41-50, translate the following words into math statements. Use the dot (•) for multiplication and the ÷ symbol for division. (Remember: the x here is a variable, representing an unknown value, not a multiplication symbol). Do not solve.

41) The product of $\frac{3}{13}$ and x   42) The quotient of $\frac{7}{6}$ and x

43) The quotient of x and $\frac{5}{6}$ 44) The product of x and $\frac{5}{8}$

45) 14 less than the quotient of $\frac{8}{3}$ and 4   46) 8 more than the product of $\frac{8}{3}$ and y

47) $\frac{3}{4}$ of x, then divide by $\frac{4}{7}$ 48) $\frac{4}{7}$ of y, then 4 less

49) Add 11 to twice $\frac{5}{8}$ 50) Subtract x from twice $\frac{5}{6}$

In exercises #51-60 identify whether each statement is true or false. To solve these problems, remember the 3 powerful rules on the first page of this section (2.4). You shouldn't have to do any calculations on paper to answer these problems.

51) $\dfrac{3}{4} = \dfrac{3}{1} \div \dfrac{4}{1}$

52) $\dfrac{3}{7} \cdot \dfrac{869}{869} = \dfrac{3}{7}$

53) $\dfrac{6}{5} \div \dfrac{57}{57} = \dfrac{5}{6}$

54) $\dfrac{7}{8} \cdot \dfrac{8}{7} = \dfrac{8}{7}$

55) $\left(\dfrac{97}{3} \div \dfrac{97}{3} \right) + \left(\dfrac{67}{6} \cdot \dfrac{6}{67} \right) = 1$

56) $\left(\dfrac{97}{3} \div \dfrac{97}{3} \right) \div \left(\dfrac{52}{41} \cdot \dfrac{41}{52} \right) = 1$

57) $\dfrac{x}{7} = \dfrac{x}{1} \div \dfrac{7}{1}$

58) $x \div \dfrac{89}{89} = x$

59) $\left(\dfrac{x}{3} \div \dfrac{x}{3} \right) \div x = \dfrac{1}{x}$

60) $\left(\dfrac{a}{b} \div \dfrac{a}{a} \right) \cdot \left(\dfrac{b}{b} \cdot \dfrac{b}{b} \right) = \dfrac{b}{a}$

In exercises #61-69, decide whether each group of expressions all have the same value. Answer yes if they all have the same value or if not, identify the one letter that gives the math expression that does not equal the others.

61) a) $\dfrac{3}{5} \cdot 104$ b) $\dfrac{3}{5} \cdot \dfrac{104}{1}$ c) $\dfrac{312}{5}$ d) $5 \div 312$

62) a) $6 \div 3 \div 5$ b) $3\overline{)6} \div 5$ c) $6 \cdot \dfrac{1}{3} \div \dfrac{5}{1}$ d) $6\overline{)3} \div 5$

63) a) $\dfrac{5}{3} \div 7 \div \dfrac{1}{5}$ b) $\dfrac{5}{3} \div \dfrac{1}{7} \cdot \dfrac{5}{1}$ c) $\dfrac{5}{3} \cdot \dfrac{1}{7} \cdot \dfrac{5}{1}$ d) $\left(\dfrac{5}{3} \cdot \dfrac{1}{7} \right) \div \dfrac{1}{5}$

64) a) $90 \div \dfrac{3}{8}$ b) $90 \cdot \dfrac{8}{3}$ c) $720 \div 3$ d) $\dfrac{30}{1} \div 8$

65) a) $\dfrac{2}{5} of \left(100 \div \dfrac{1}{2} \right)$ b) $\dfrac{2}{5} \left(\dfrac{100}{\frac{1}{2}} \right)$ c) $\dfrac{2}{5} \div (100 \cdot 2)$ d) $\dfrac{2}{5} \cdot \left(\dfrac{100}{1} \div \dfrac{1}{2} \right)$

66) a) $20 \div x$ b) $20 \cdot \dfrac{x}{1}$ c) $20 \cdot \dfrac{1}{x}$ d) $20 \div \dfrac{x}{1}$

67) a) $\dfrac{3}{5} \cdot \dfrac{1}{x}$ b) $\dfrac{3}{5} of x$ c) $\dfrac{3}{5} \cdot x$ d) $\dfrac{3}{5} \cdot \dfrac{x}{1}$

68) a) $x \div \dfrac{2}{5}$ b) $x \cdot \dfrac{5}{2}$ c) $\dfrac{1}{x} \cdot \dfrac{5}{2}$ d) $\dfrac{x}{1} \div \dfrac{2}{5}$

69) a) $\dfrac{1}{3} \div \dfrac{x}{5}$ b) $\dfrac{1}{3} \cdot \dfrac{5}{x}$ c) $\dfrac{1}{3} \div (x \div 5)$ d) $\dfrac{1}{3} \cdot (x \div 5)$

In exercise #70 – 84: (a) write a mathematical expression that will solve the problem, and (b) give the solution.

70) Barbara estimated that she needed to earn $3600 during the 3 summer months so she would have enough money for the next school year. If she had already earned two-thirds of this money, how much more did she still need to earn to reach her goal?

71-74) After 2 hours a hose had filled $\frac{3}{5}$ of a restaurant's pond. The pond held 200,000 gallons of water when filled.

71) How much water was in the pond after 2 hours?

72) How many gallons of water were traveling through the hose per hour?

73) How many gallons of water were still needed to fill the pond?

74) If we know that 3 parts out of 5 (the whole) of the pool are filled, write the proportion that would also solve question #71 (remember that $\frac{part}{whole} = \frac{part}{whole}$). Be sure to use the variable x in your set up.

75) When a farmer sold his 240 acre farm, it was decided that the property would be developed and sold in $\frac{3}{16}$ acre parcels. How many parcels of land were eventually put up for sale?

76) Jack had mowed $\frac{1}{6}$ of the soccer field by himself in 20 minutes. Then, if he and a friend mowed equal amounts of the remaining field, what fraction of the field did Jack mow after his friend arrived?

77) A cake was cut into 8 pieces. After seven pieces of the cake were eaten, the lone remaining piece was cut again into 5 pieces? What size of the original cake was each one of these five pieces?

78) When 3 friends won a lottery of 900,000, state and federal taxes took $\frac{3}{10}$ of the money. After getting her equal share of the remains, Monica spent $\frac{3}{5}$ of her winnings to buy her house. How much money did Monica still have left from her lottery winnings?

79) Out of a city's 40 million dollar budget, one-fiftieth of it was set aside for road building and repairs. How much money was spent on roads this year?

80) Three hundred people were to attend a wedding reception. The bride and groom predicted that about $\frac{1}{2}$ of these guests would drink champagne. If the caterer estimated that each champagne drinker would consume $\frac{3}{8}$ of a bottle, how many bottles of champagne did the caterer need (round to the nearest whole bottle) to order?

81-83) A research scientist studying shrews in a state park discovered that the tiny animals had an average weight of 140 grams. If a typical shrew didn't eat for 6 hours it would lose $\frac{1}{10}$ of its body weight. If it didn't eat for another 6 hours, it would lose another $\frac{2}{7}$ of its original weight. After a period of about 15 hours without food, the shrews began to die.

81) After 6 hours without food, how much would a typical shrew weigh?

82) After 12 hours without food, how much would a typical shrew weigh?

83) What fraction of its original weight would a shrew weigh after 12 hours without food?

84) One shrew slowly journeyed from one part of the park to another. If it traveled $\frac{1}{20}$ of a mile every day, how long did it take this shrew to travel $\frac{3}{5}$ of a mile?

Skills Check

1) Find the GCF of 12, 84, and 114.

2) Find the GCF of 6, 7, and 21

3) True or false: $\frac{29}{7} > 3\frac{6}{7}$

4) Eighty cookies were on sale. Twenty-five of the cookies were oatmeal, thirty were chocolate chip, and another twenty-five were raisin-nut. What fraction of the cookies were either oatmeal or chocolate chip?

Answers to Skills Check: 1) GCF is 6; 2) GCF is 1; 3) True. $\frac{29}{7} = 4\frac{1}{7}$ which is larger than $3\frac{6}{7}$; 4) $\frac{11}{16}$ of the cookies are either oatmeal or chocolate chip.

Section 2.5   Multiply & Divide Mixed Numbers & Fractions

Objectives:

- To multiply/divide mixed numbers
- To set up/solve mixed number and fraction application problems
- To manipulate equations with fractions and mixed numbers

Application:

The Hungry Mouse corporation sells organically produced cheddar cheese. The cheese is cut and then sold in packages that weigh $1\frac{1}{3}$ pounds. If George needs 10 pounds of cheese to make enough chili for his company's picnic, how many packages of cheese will he need to buy?

Vocabulary:

**Remember: In any problem we can change any mixed number into an improper fraction.

Examples: We know that $1\frac{3}{5}$ is the same as $\frac{8}{5}$. Therefore, the equation

$8 = 5 \bullet 1\frac{3}{5}$ is the same as $8 = 5 \bullet \frac{8}{5}$.

We know that $2\frac{1}{3}$ is the same as $\frac{7}{3}$. Therefore, the equation

$15 = 35 \div 2\frac{1}{3}$ is the same as $15 = 35 \div \frac{7}{3}$

Key Concept Review: Multiplication and division are opposites. Every multiplication statement can be rewritten as a division statement; every division statement can be rewritten as a multiplication statement. This is true whether we are talking about whole numbers, decimals, or fractions.

If we lack the experience and confidence in the equation manipulations below, go ahead and work out the examples and see that they are all true. The values on the left and right sides of the equation <u>are</u> equal.

Examples:

The multiplication statement of $2 = \frac{3}{5} \bullet \frac{20}{6}$

can be rewritten as the division statement of

$2 \div \frac{20}{6} = \frac{3}{5}$ after both sides of the equation

have been "divided by $\frac{20}{6}$."

$2 = \frac{3}{5} \bullet \frac{20}{6}$

$2 \div \frac{20}{6} = \left(\frac{3}{5} \bullet \frac{20}{6}\right) \div \frac{20}{6}$

$2 \div \frac{20}{6} = \frac{3}{5}$

The multiplication statement of $\dfrac{7}{15} = \dfrac{1}{3} \cdot \dfrac{7}{5}$

can be rewritten as the division statement of

$\dfrac{7}{15} \div \dfrac{7}{5} = \dfrac{1}{3}$ after both sides of the equation

have been "divided by $\dfrac{7}{5}$."

$$\dfrac{7}{15} = \dfrac{1}{3} \cdot \dfrac{7}{5}$$

$$\dfrac{7}{15} \div \dfrac{7}{5} = \left(\dfrac{1}{3} \cdot \dfrac{7}{5}\right) \div \dfrac{7}{5}$$

$$\dfrac{7}{15} \div \dfrac{7}{5} = \dfrac{1}{3}$$

The division statement of $6\dfrac{2}{3} \div x = 10$ can be

rewritten as the multiplication statement of

$6\dfrac{2}{3} = 10 \cdot x$ after both sides of the equation

have been "multiplied by x."

$$6\dfrac{2}{3} \div x = 10$$

$$\left(6\dfrac{2}{3} \div x\right) \cdot x = 10 \cdot x$$

$$6\dfrac{2}{3} = 10 \cdot x$$

Students sometimes forget that all the arithmetic processes that one has learned are still <u>all</u> <u>absolutely</u> <u>true</u> in algebra and still <u>must</u> <u>be</u> <u>followed</u>. Let's take another look at the above problem:

$$\left(6\dfrac{2}{3} \div x\right) \cdot x = 10 \cdot x$$

Change the mixed number to an improper fraction.

Take the reciprocal of the divisor "x." (The reciprocal of x or $\dfrac{x}{1}$ is $\dfrac{1}{x}$).

Rewrite the equation to get: $\left(\dfrac{20}{3} \cdot \dfrac{1}{x}\right) \cdot \dfrac{x}{1} = 10 \cdot x$

Looking at just the left side of the equation, we have <u>all</u> multiplication. The commutative property tells us that we can multiply (in this case cancel) in any order we want. Cancel out the x's. We are left with (as shown above):

$$\dfrac{20}{3} = 10 \cdot x \qquad \text{or} \qquad 6\dfrac{2}{3} = 10 \cdot x$$

Also: If we agree that $6\dfrac{2}{3} \div x = 10$ and $6\dfrac{2}{3} = 10 \cdot x$

are the same, we can take this one step further

to discover the value of x by changing the

multiplication statement of $6\dfrac{2}{3} = 10 \cdot x$ to the

division statement of $6\dfrac{2}{3} \div 10 = x$.

$$6\dfrac{2}{3} = 10 \cdot x$$

$$6\dfrac{2}{3} \div 10 = \left(10 \cdot x\right) \div 10$$

$$6\dfrac{2}{3} \div 10 = x$$

If we solved the left side of the equation, we would find that

$6\frac{2}{3} \div 10$ **is equal to** $\frac{2}{3}$. $x = \frac{2}{3}$

By following the basic equation truth that we must always do the same thing to both sides of an equation, we see that $6\frac{2}{3} \div x = 10$ is the same as $6\frac{2}{3} = 10 \bullet x$ which is the same as $6\frac{2}{3} \div 10 = x$.

How to:

Multiply & Divide Mixed Numbers.

1. Change all mixed numbers into improper fractions.

2. Follow the rules for divide and multiply fractions.

Example #1: $3\frac{3}{5} \bullet 2\frac{1}{6}$

Step #1: Change all mixed numbers into improper fractions.

Rewrite as: $\frac{18}{5} \bullet \frac{13}{6}$

Step #2: Follow rules for multiplication of fractions.

Cancel: $\frac{\overset{3}{\cancel{18}}}{5} \bullet \frac{13}{\underset{1}{\cancel{6}}} = \frac{39}{5}$ **Answer:** $\frac{39}{5}$ or $7\frac{4}{5}$

Example #2: $4\frac{3}{8} \div 5$

Step #1: Change all mixed numbers into improper fractions.

Rewrite as: $\frac{35}{8} \div \frac{5}{1}$

Step #2: Follow rules for division of fractions. Take the reciprocal of the divisor.

Rewrite as: $\frac{35}{8} \bullet \frac{1}{5}$

Follow rules for multiplication of fractions.

Cancel: $\frac{\overset{7}{\cancel{35}}}{8} \bullet \frac{1}{\underset{1}{\cancel{5}}} = \frac{7}{8}$ **Answer:** $\frac{7}{8}$

Sample #1: $2\frac{3}{4} \cdot 2 \cdot 8\frac{1}{3}$

Change mixed numbers to improper fractions: $\frac{11}{4} \cdot \frac{2}{1} \cdot \frac{25}{3}$

Look to cancel. The numerator of 2 and the denominator of 4 have a common factor of 2. Cancel these numbers.

$$\frac{11}{\overset{4}{\underset{2}{}}} \cdot \frac{\overset{1}{2}}{1} \cdot \frac{25}{3}$$

Answer: $\frac{275}{6}$ or $45\frac{5}{6}$

- **You try it now:**
-
- a) $5\frac{1}{3} \cdot 2\frac{2}{5} \cdot 5$
-
- b) $3\frac{1}{7} \cdot 3\frac{3}{4} \cdot \frac{1}{8}$
-

Sample #2: $3\frac{1}{5} \div 2\frac{2}{3} \cdot \frac{5}{6}$

Change mixed numbers to improper fractions: $\frac{16}{5} \div \frac{8}{3} \cdot \frac{5}{6}$

Take the reciprocal of the divisor and change the problem to multiplication.

It now looks like: $\frac{16}{5} \cdot \frac{3}{8} \cdot \frac{5}{6}$

Cancel: The common factor for 8 & 16 is 8.
                The common factor for 3 & 6 is 3.
                The common factor for 5 & 5 is 5.

$$\frac{\overset{2}{16}}{\underset{1}{5}} \cdot \frac{\overset{1}{3}}{\underset{1}{8}} \cdot \frac{\overset{1}{5}}{\underset{2}{6}}$$ Now we can still see the common factor for 2 and 2 is 2.

Answer: 1

■ **You try it now:**

c) $10\frac{1}{2} \div 2\frac{2}{3} \div 7$

d) $3\frac{2}{3} \div 7\frac{2}{5} \cdot \frac{3}{8}$

Sample #3: In building a new road to connect two rural towns, part of a mountain had to be torn
down. In total 200 truck loads of dirt were removed and transported to another site. If
each truck carried off $4\frac{1}{3}$ tons of dirt, how much dirt was moved?

We can recognize that the **action** in this problem is $4\frac{1}{3}$ tons of dirt being
removed 200 times. There is a repeated addition, and **a repeated addition**
is represented by multiplication in mathematics. In this case:

Solve: $4\frac{1}{3} \cdot 200$

$= \dfrac{13}{3} \cdot \dfrac{200}{1}$

$= \dfrac{2600}{3}$

Answer: $866\frac{2}{3}$ tons of dirt

■ **You try it now:**

e) In a walk-a-thon to raise money for a local junior high school 300 participants averaged walking $16\frac{2}{3}$
laps. If two dollars were raised for every lap walked, how much money was raised at the walk-a-thon?

f) In another charity event 20 people each ran $\frac{3}{8}$ of a marathon (a marathon is 26 miles). If this group of
runners earned $5 for each mile they ran, how much money did they raise?

Sample #4: A softball team (14 players) volunteered to pick up trash along a $3\frac{1}{2}$ mile stretch of freeway. If each player cleaned up the same distance of freeway, what distance would each player walk?

We first recognize that there is a total distance of roadway ($3\frac{1}{2}$ miles) which is going to be split up or divided up into 14 equal parts.

In English	**In Math**
(total miles) ÷ (number of parts)	$3\frac{1}{2} \div 14$

Solve this division of mixed number problem.

Answer: $\frac{1}{4}$ mile

You try it now:

g) In a laboratory, 420 fluid ounces of a solution needed to be put into packets that each held $5\frac{1}{4}$ ounces of the solution. How many packets could be filled?

h) A business of seven professional weavers hand-wove an average of $12\frac{3}{5}$ large floor rugs per week. If each weaver worked 40 hours a week, how many hours of labor did it take to make one rug?

Answers to You try it now: a) 64; b) $^{165}/_{112}$ or $1\frac{53}{112}$; c) $^{9}/_{16}$; d) $^{55}/_{296}$; e) \$10,000 (5000 laps • \$2); f) \$975 (195 miles • \$5); g) 80 packets; h) $22\frac{2}{9}$ hours (total of 280 hours of labor divided by $12\frac{3}{5}$ completed rugs).

Answer to Application: If each package weighs $1\frac{1}{3}$ pounds and the total amount needed is 10 pounds of cheese, we can divide the total amount of 10 pounds by $1\frac{1}{3}$ to find out the quantity of packages he bought.

Set up: $10 \div 1\frac{1}{3}$

Change the mixed number to an improper fraction: $\frac{10}{1} \div \frac{4}{3}$

$\frac{10}{1} \cdot \frac{3}{4}$

$\frac{\overset{5}{10}}{1} \cdot \frac{3}{\underset{2}{4}} = \frac{15}{2}$ or $7\frac{1}{2}$

Since George needs more than 7 packages, he must buy 8 packages to have enough cheese.

2.5 Multiplication and Division of Mixed Numbers Problems

In exercises #1-18 solve for the product or the quotient. If you get a non-integer answer of a value of greater than 1, be sure to give both an improper fraction and a mixed number answer.

1) $2\frac{2}{5} \cdot 3\frac{2}{3}$

2) $6\frac{1}{3} \cdot \frac{1}{8}$

3) $1\frac{5}{7} \cdot 21$

4) $2\frac{11}{12} \cdot 2\frac{1}{7}$

5) $5\frac{5}{8} \cdot 12 \cdot 3\frac{3}{5}$

6) $5\frac{5}{6} \cdot 8$

7) $\frac{2}{3} \cdot 1\frac{1}{2} \cdot \frac{54}{105}$

8) $2\frac{7}{8} \cdot 20$

9) $3\frac{2}{7} \div 4\frac{3}{7}$

10) $5\frac{1}{16} \div 3\frac{3}{4}$

11) $30 \div 8\frac{2}{5}$

12) $8\frac{3}{5} \div 2\frac{1}{2}$

13) $4\frac{1}{4} \div 13\frac{3}{5} \div 2$

14) $3\frac{1}{7} \div 4\frac{2}{3} \cdot 1\frac{2}{5}$

15) $600 \div 2\frac{5}{8}$

16) $8\frac{1}{2} \div 4\frac{1}{2} \cdot 1\frac{1}{2}$

17) $500 \cdot 2\frac{3}{4} \div 50$

18) $\frac{3}{8} \div 10 \cdot 5\frac{1}{2}$

In exercises #19-30, state whether the following math statements are true or false. These problems are meant as "mental math" problems. You don't need to do lots of math computation, but want to recognize certain truths and basic processes.

19) $8\frac{1}{2} \div \frac{29}{29} = 8\frac{1}{2}$

20) $\frac{6\frac{2}{5}}{3\frac{1}{9}} = 6\frac{2}{5} \div 3\frac{1}{9}$

21) $\frac{7\frac{3}{4}}{2} = 7\frac{3}{4} \cdot \frac{2}{1}$

22) $\frac{4\frac{2}{3}}{4\frac{2}{3}} \div 8 = \frac{1}{8}$

23) $\left(3\frac{3}{4} \div 3\frac{3}{4}\right) \div \frac{7}{7} = 3\frac{3}{4}$

24) $\left(7\frac{1}{6} \cdot 7\frac{1}{6}\right) \cdot \frac{5}{5} = 1$

25) $\frac{3}{x} \cdot \frac{x}{3} = 3$

26) $\frac{3\frac{2}{5}}{a} = 3\frac{2}{5} \div a$

27) $\frac{4\frac{x}{y}}{4\frac{x}{y}} \div \frac{x}{y} = \frac{y}{x}$

28) $\frac{\left(\frac{a}{6} \div \frac{a}{6}\right)}{c} = \frac{a}{c}$

29) $\frac{11}{11} \div \frac{2}{x} = 1 \cdot \frac{x}{2}$

30) $\frac{\left(\frac{3\frac{2}{3}}{3\frac{2}{3}}\right)}{a} = \frac{1}{a}$

In exercises #31-35, decide whether each group of expressions all have the same value. Answer yes or no. If your answer is no, identify the <u>one</u> letter or math phrase that does not equal the others. Like the exercise above, these are meant to be "mental math" problems.

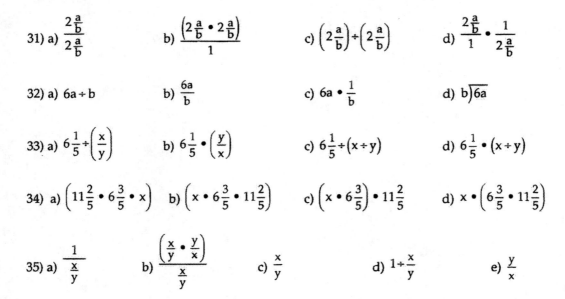

31) a) $\dfrac{2\frac{a}{b}}{2\frac{a}{b}}$ b) $\dfrac{\left(2\frac{a}{b} \bullet 2\frac{a}{b}\right)}{1}$ c) $\left(2\frac{a}{b}\right) \div \left(2\frac{a}{b}\right)$ d) $\dfrac{2\frac{a}{b}}{1} \bullet \dfrac{1}{2\frac{a}{b}}$

32) a) $6a \div b$ b) $\dfrac{6a}{b}$ c) $6a \bullet \dfrac{1}{b}$ d) $b \overline{)6a}$

33) a) $6\frac{1}{5} \div \left(\dfrac{x}{y}\right)$ b) $6\frac{1}{5} \bullet \left(\dfrac{y}{x}\right)$ c) $6\frac{1}{5} \div (x \div y)$ d) $6\frac{1}{5} \bullet (x \div y)$

34) a) $\left(11\frac{2}{5} \bullet 6\frac{3}{5} \bullet x\right)$ b) $\left(x \bullet 6\frac{3}{5} \bullet 11\frac{2}{5}\right)$ c) $\left(x \bullet 6\frac{3}{5}\right) \bullet 11\frac{2}{5}$ d) $x \bullet \left(6\frac{3}{5} \bullet 11\frac{2}{5}\right)$

35) a) $\dfrac{1}{\frac{x}{y}}$ b) $\dfrac{\left(\frac{x}{y} \bullet \frac{y}{x}\right)}{\frac{x}{y}}$ c) $\dfrac{x}{y}$ d) $1 \div \dfrac{x}{y}$ e) $\dfrac{y}{x}$

In exercises #36-40, decide whether each group of equations are all the same. Answer yes or no. If your answer is no, identify the <u>one</u> equation that does not match the others. Look for what is the same or different for each equation. Remember equations stay equal to each other when you do exactly the same thing to both sides of the equation.

36) a) $x \div 1\frac{3}{4} = \frac{4}{5}$ b) $\left(x \div 1\frac{3}{4}\right) \bullet 1\frac{3}{4} = \frac{4}{5} \bullet 1\frac{3}{4}$ c) $x \bullet \frac{4}{7} \bullet \frac{7}{4} = \frac{4}{5} \bullet \frac{7}{4}$ d) $x = \frac{7}{5}$

37) a) $x \bullet \frac{2}{7} = 2\frac{1}{4}$ b) $\left(x \bullet \frac{2}{7}\right) \bullet \frac{2}{7} = \frac{9}{4} \div \frac{2}{7}$ c) $\left(x \bullet \frac{2}{7}\right) \div \frac{2}{7} = \frac{9}{4} \div \frac{2}{7}$ d) $x = \frac{9}{4} \bullet \frac{7}{2}$

38) a) $\frac{10}{3} \div y = \frac{3}{8}$ b) $\left(\frac{10}{3} \div y\right) \bullet y = \frac{3}{8} \bullet y$ c) $\frac{10}{3} \bullet \frac{1}{y} \bullet \frac{y}{1} = \frac{3}{8} \bullet y$ d) $\frac{10}{3} = \frac{3}{8} \bullet y$

39) a) $5\frac{1}{4} \bullet y = 2\frac{5}{8}$ b) $\frac{21}{4} \bullet \frac{y}{1} = \frac{21}{8}$ c) $\left(\frac{21}{4} \bullet \frac{y}{1}\right) \div \frac{21}{4} = \frac{21}{8} \div \frac{21}{4}$ d) $y = 2$

40) a) $2\frac{3}{5} \bullet x = 3\frac{9}{10}$ b) $\left(\frac{13}{5} \bullet x\right) \div \frac{13}{5} = \frac{39}{10} \div \frac{13}{5}$ c) $\left(\frac{13}{5} \bullet x\right) \bullet \frac{13}{5} = \frac{39}{10} \bullet \frac{5}{13}$ d) $x = 1\frac{1}{2}$

In exercises #41-48, state whether the following statements are True or False. Check to see if you would get the second equation if you did the "same thing" to both sides of the original equation.

41) $\frac{3}{5} \bullet 8 = \frac{24}{5}$ is the same as $\frac{3}{5} = \frac{24}{5} \div 8$

42) $2\frac{3}{5} \bullet 1\frac{1}{2} = 3\frac{9}{10}$ is the same as $1\frac{1}{2} = 3\frac{9}{10} \div 2\frac{3}{5}$

43) $\frac{2}{3} \div 1\frac{1}{4} = \frac{8}{15}$ is the same as $\frac{2}{3} = \frac{8}{15} \bullet 1\frac{1}{4}$

44) $1\frac{1}{7} \div \frac{4}{7} = 2$ is the same as $\frac{4}{7} = 2 \div 1\frac{1}{7}$

45) $\frac{3}{4} \div \frac{1}{2} = x$ is the same as $\frac{3}{4} = x \div \frac{1}{2}$

46) $x \bullet \frac{3}{7} = \frac{4}{5}$ is the same as $x = \frac{4}{5} \div \frac{3}{7}$

47) $\frac{5}{3} \div x = \frac{3}{8}$ is the same as $\frac{5}{3} = \frac{3}{8} \bullet x$

48) $4\frac{1}{3} \bullet \frac{5}{8} = x$ is the same as $4\frac{1}{3} = x \div \frac{5}{8}$

In exercises #49-56, write an equivalent equation which changes any given multiplication statement to a division statement or changes any given division statement to a multiplication statement. There is nothing to solve here.

49) $\frac{3}{5} \bullet \frac{15}{2} = 4\frac{1}{2}$

50) $7\frac{1}{2} \div \frac{5}{6} = 9$

51) $4 \div \frac{2}{3} = 6$

52) $\frac{1}{6} \bullet 2\frac{2}{5} = \frac{2}{5}$

53) $\frac{3}{8} \bullet x = \frac{1}{2}$

54) $x \div 1\frac{3}{4} = \frac{4}{5}$

55) $y \div \frac{3}{8} = 1\frac{2}{3}$

56) $3\frac{3}{4} \bullet y = \frac{4}{3}$

In exercises #57-67, solve for the value of x, the unknown number.

57) $\frac{3}{5} \bullet x = \frac{2}{7}$

58) $x \bullet \frac{2}{3} = \frac{1}{5}$

59) $x \bullet 1\frac{1}{6} = 4\frac{2}{3}$

60) $2\frac{1}{2} \bullet x = 1\frac{3}{8}$

61) $x \div \frac{4}{5} = \frac{7}{4}$

62) $x \div 1\frac{1}{8} = 2$

63) $1\dfrac{2}{5} \div 1 = x$

64) $\dfrac{2}{3}$ of $2\dfrac{1}{4} = x$

65) $\dfrac{x}{\frac{3}{4}} = 1\dfrac{1}{2}$

66) $\dfrac{3}{4} \div x = \dfrac{3}{5}$

67) $1\dfrac{2}{3} \div x = \dfrac{1}{4}$

For the following problems: (a) write a mathematical expression that will solve the problem, and (b) give the solution.

68) A new internet company had an excellent first year. Over twelve months it averaged 4 ⅓ million dollars a month in profits. How much money did the company make its first year?

69) A movie complex has 10 theaters which each hold 250 people. At 8 o'clock one night 7 ½ theaters were filled. How many people were at the movie complex?

70) After building a 3-foot high rock wall around a property, a mason was asked to line the top of this 320 foot-long wall with a different color rock. If the mason used rocks which were cut to a length of 1 ⅓ feet, how many rocks did he use to line the fence?

71) The Green Lumber Company seeded 55 ½ acres of land last year. What was the average amount of land they seeded each month?

72) Mark now runs 3 ¾ miles three times a week. If he figures that he burns 200 calories for every mile he runs, how many calories does Mark burn off in a week?

73) A single-file line of red ants reached 400 feet from their nest to an unclean kitchen. If the ants averaged $\dfrac{5}{8}$ of an inch in length and were touching head to end, how many ants did this line consist of (remember: 12 inches = 1 foot)?

74-78) Jorge moves an average 2 ⁹⁄₁₀ feet with each step he takes. Alexa moves an average of 2 ⅖ feet per step she takes. Answer the following questions (remember: 3 feet in 1 yard).

74) If Jorge walked a hundred yards, how many steps would he take (round answer to the nearest whole)?

75) If Alexa walked a hundred yards, how many steps would she take?

76) What fraction of a yard does Jorge cover with each step?

77) What fraction of a yard does Alexa walk with each step?

78) How many steps would Alexa need to take to walk once around the school's track (440 yards)?

79) A foot is approximately ¹⁹⁄₁₀₀₀₀₀ of a mile. If a backpacker hikes to an elevation of 10,000 feet, how many miles above sea level is he ?

80-81) A local contractor ordered 500 boards cut to the length of 5 $\frac{1}{2}$ feet. The lumber company had to cut these boards from 30-foot long boards which they had in stock.

80) How many 5 $\frac{1}{2}$ foot boards could be cut from each 30-foot board?

81) How many 30-foot boards would be used to fill this order?

82) A particular bacterium had a width of $\frac{3}{100}$ of an inch. Amassed in a science lab, a population of this bacteria, body to body, had a width of 2 inches. At least how many bacteria were needed to create this 2 inch width?

Skills Check

1. $\frac{7}{8} \div 0$

2. If $\frac{3}{5}$ of 105 third graders stated that they preferred chocolate ice cream to vanilla, how many of these third graders said they preferred chocolate?

3. If $b = 6$ and $a = 0$, what is the value of $\frac{b}{a}$?

4. What is the value of x for the following equation: $\frac{5}{11} \bullet x = 1$?

Answers to Skills Check: 1) undefined; 2) 63 3rd graders; 3) undefined; 4) $\frac{11}{5}$ because any value multiplied by its reciprocal is equal to 1 whole.

Section 2.6   Find Lowest Common Multiples (LCM), Build Fractions, and Add Fractions & Mixed Numbers

Objectives:

• To find an LCM of given numbers
• To find a common denominator and build fractions
• To add fractions/mixed numbers using the vertical method
• To add fractions/mixed numbers using the horizontal method

Application:

At the Emergency Evacuation Center scientists monitored rainfall. If the hurricane produced over 15 inches of rain in the next 24 hours, they knew that Sugar Dam could overflow and that it might even breach. Eight hours later is had rained $6\frac{3}{4}$ inches. After a second eight hours another $4\frac{2}{3}$ inches had fallen as the storm started to lose some of its strength. In the third eight hour period $3\frac{5}{8}$ inches fell. Should the Emergency Evacuation Center have residents in the valley below the dam evacuate their homes?

Vocabulary:

natural numbers—The **natural numbers** are also known as the counting numbers. They are the set of **positive whole numbers**, starting at one and going upward forever (1, 2, 3, 4, 5...)

multiple—A **multiple** is the answer to a **specific number** multiplied by a natural number. For instance, the first 3 multiples of 2 (the 2 here is the specific number) are 2, 4, and 6 because $2 \cdot 1 = 2$, $2 \cdot 2 = 4$, and $2 \cdot 3 = 6$. The first 3 multiples of 3 are 3, 6, and 9 because $3 \cdot 1 = 3$, $3 \cdot 2 = 6$, and $3 \cdot 3 = 9$. We can see that a number is only a multiple of another number if that specific number divides into it evenly.

lowest common multiple—The **lowest common multiple (LCM)** is the lowest number that 2 or more specific numbers can divide into evenly. What is important to remember here is that, by definition, **a multiple always means going to a higher number**. The LCM is always equal to or larger than the greatest specific number.

building a fraction—**Building a fraction** is the process of finding an equivalent fraction which has a larger denominator than the current fraction. We build fractions by multiplying the current numerator and denominator by the same number ($\frac{2}{3} = \frac{10}{15}$ because we get $\frac{10}{15}$ when we multiply both the numerator of 2 and the denominator of 3 by the number 5)

**Building a fraction is a process that is a mathematical truth because it is based upon the concept that any number multiplied by 1 is itself. We know that $\frac{2}{3} \cdot 1 = \frac{2}{3}$. We know that $1 = \frac{5}{5}$. Thus, $\frac{2}{3} \cdot \frac{5}{5} = \frac{2}{3}$. Another way of writing $\frac{2}{3}$ is $\frac{10}{15}$.

**Building a fraction is the opposite of reducing a fraction (finding an equivalent fraction with a smaller denominator) which is based upon the mathematical truth that any number divided by 1 equals itself.

common denominator—A **common denominator** is the same denominator. We need to find a common denominator when **adding or subtracting fractions**, ensuring that the parts we are adding or subtracting are of the same value or amount. The **lowest common denominator (LCD)** is the lowest common multiple of the given denominators.

How to:

Find the Lowest Common Multiple (LCM) of 2 or more given numbers:

1. Put the given numbers inside the same short division box.

2. Prime factor the numbers at the same time. If a prime factor divides into 1 number, but doesn't divide into another given number, simply drop that other given number down to the next box.

3. After all the given numbers are factored down to 1, multiply all the prime factors together. This product is our LCM.

Example #1: Find the LCM of 15 and 20.

Step #1: Put the given numbers inside the same short division box.

$$\overline{)15 \quad 20}$$

Step #2: Prime factor the numbers at the same time.

5 divides evenly into both 15 (3 times) and 20 (4 times), so:

$$5\overline{)15 \quad 20} \quad \text{answers of 3 and 4 go down to the next division box}$$
$$\overline{)3 \quad 4}$$

We can see now that 3 divides evenly into 3 (1 time), but not into 4, so bring down the 4.

$$3\overline{)3 \quad 4} \quad \text{answers of 1 and 4 go down to the next division box}$$
$$\overline{)1 \quad 4}$$

2 divides evenly into 4 (2 times)

$2\overline{)1\quad4}$ The 1 is done. The answer of 2 goes down to the next division box

2 divides evenly into 2 again (1 time)

$2\overline{)1\quad2}$ The answer of 1 goes down to the next division box
    1   1

Our prime factoring is now completed as both numbers are factored down to 1.

Without the explanations above, the problem would look like the following after you worked it out:

$5\overline{)15\quad20}$

$3\overline{)3\quad4}$

$2\overline{)1\quad4}$

$2\overline{)1\quad2}$
    1   1

Step #3: Multiply all the prime factors together. $2 \bullet 2 \bullet 3 \bullet 5 = 60$

The LCM = 60   60 is the lowest number that is both a multiple
of 15 and 20 (the lowest number that both 15
and 20 can divide into evenly).

The Listing Method: By "listing" the multiples of each number, we see the answer.

The multiples of 15 are: 15, 30, 45, 60, 75...

The multiples of 20 are 20, 40, 60, 80...

We can see that **60** is the lowest multiple they have **in common**.

Example #2: Find the LCM of 9, 14, and 21.

Step #1: Put the given numbers inside the same short division box.

$\overline{)9\quad14\quad21}$

Step #2: Prime factor the numbers at the same time.

$$\overline{)\ 9\quad 14\quad 21}$$

3 divides evenly into 9 and 21. Bring down the 14.

$$3\overline{)\ 9\quad 14\quad 21}$$

3 divides evenly into 3.   Bring down the 14 and 7.

$$3\overline{)\ 3\quad 14\quad 7}$$

2 divides evenly into 14. Bring down the 7.

$$2\overline{)\ 1\quad 14\quad 7}$$

7 divides evenly into both 7's.

$$7\overline{)\ 1\quad 7\quad 7}$$

Prime factoring is completed as all numbers
are factored down to 1.

$$1\quad 1\quad 1$$

Step #3: Multiply all the prime factors together. $3 \cdot 3 \cdot 2 \cdot 7 = 126$

The **LCM = 126**   126 is the lowest number that is a multiple of
9, 14, and 21 (the lowest number that 9, 14, and
21 can divide into evenly).

The Listing Method: By "listing" the multiples for each number, we see the answer.

The multiples of 9 are 9, 18, 27, 36, 45, 54, 63, 72, 81, 90, 99, 108, 117, **126**...

The multiples of 14 are 14, 28, 42, 56, 70, 84, 98, 112, **126**, 140...

The multiples of 21 are 21, 42, 63, 84, 105, **126**, 147...

We can see that **126** is the lowest multiple that 9, 14, and 21 have in common. We
can also see how long this problem took to solve by the "listing method"—a
good process, but best used for smaller numbers.

How to:

Add fractions:

1. We must have or find a common denominator for the given fractions (if we can't tell what the
   lowest common denominator will be by looking at the numbers, we can get it by finding the
   LCM of the given denominators).

2. Make equivalent fractions using the common denominator.

3. Add the numerators of these new equivalent fractions. The common denominator stays the
   same!!

Fractions can be added either **vertically** (one number lined up beneath another) or **horizontally** (left to right across the page). We should be able to work in both formats. Both are "correct." However, as we move forward into algebra the standard format is horizontal, so it is important that we use and get used to this style. Remember, the math itself is exactly the same!

Example #3: $\dfrac{2}{5} + \dfrac{3}{7}$

Step #1: Find a common denominator for the given fractions.
Here we look at the given denominators of 5 and 7. Knowing our multiplication tables, we can see that both 5 and 7 divide evenly into 35. The lowest common denominator(LCD) is 35.

Step #2: Make equivalent fractions using the common denominator.

Vertical Method: OR   **Horizontal Method:**

$$\dfrac{2}{5} = \dfrac{}{35}$$
$$+\dfrac{3}{7} = \dfrac{}{35}$$

$$\dfrac{2}{5} + \dfrac{3}{7}$$
$$\dfrac{}{35} + \dfrac{}{35}$$

Look at the first fraction. To change the denominator of 5 to 35 we would have to multiply it by 7. Therefore, according to the process of **building fractions**, we also must multiply the numerator of 2 by 7. Thus, $\dfrac{2}{5}$ (multiplied by $\dfrac{7}{7}$) is equal to $\dfrac{14}{35}$.

Now look at the second fraction. To change the denominator of 7 to 35 we would have to multiply it by 5. Therefore, according to the process of **building fractions**, we also must multiply the numerator of 3 by 5. Thus, $\dfrac{3}{7}$ (multiplied by $\dfrac{5}{5}$) is equal to $\dfrac{15}{35}$.

The problem now looks like the following:

$$\dfrac{14}{35}$$
$$+\dfrac{15}{35}$$

OR

$$\dfrac{14}{35} + \dfrac{15}{35}$$

Step #3: Add the numerators of these new equivalent fractions. The denominator stays the same!!

$$14 + 15 = 29$$

Answer: $\dfrac{29}{35}$

Example #4: $\dfrac{7}{8} + \dfrac{1}{6} + \dfrac{5}{16}$

Step #1: Find a common denominator for the given fractions.

Here we look at the given denominators of 8, 6, and 16. Probably most of us can't calculate the lowest common denominator in our heads, so we'll get the common denominator by finding the LCM of the denominators.

$$
\begin{array}{r|lll}
2 & 6 & 8 & 16 \\ \hline
3 & 3 & 4 & 8 \\ \hline
2 & 1 & 4 & 8 \\ \hline
2 & 1 & 2 & 4 \\ \hline
2 & 1 & 1 & 2 \\ \hline
 & 1 & 1 & 1
\end{array}
$$

The LCM is 48. This is also the lowest common denominator (LCD).

Step #2: Make equivalent fractions using the common denominator.

Vertical Method: OR   **Horizontal Method:**

$$\dfrac{7}{8} = \dfrac{}{48}$$

$$\dfrac{1}{6} = \dfrac{}{48}$$

$$+\ \dfrac{5}{16} = \dfrac{}{48}$$

$$\dfrac{7}{8} + \dfrac{1}{6} + \dfrac{5}{16}$$

$$\dfrac{}{48} + \dfrac{}{48} + \dfrac{}{48}$$

We now work out the **building fractions** process:

$$\dfrac{7}{8} \bullet \dfrac{6}{6} = \dfrac{42}{48} \qquad \dfrac{1}{6} \bullet \dfrac{8}{8} = \dfrac{8}{48} \qquad \dfrac{5}{16} \bullet \dfrac{3}{3} = \dfrac{15}{48}$$

The problem now looks like the following:

$$\dfrac{42}{48}$$

$$+\ \dfrac{8}{48}$$

$$+\ \dfrac{15}{48}$$

OR

$$\dfrac{42}{48} + \dfrac{8}{48} + \dfrac{15}{48}$$

Step #3: Add the numerators of these new equivalent fractions. The denominator stays the same!!

$$42 + 8 + 15 = 65$$

We get $\dfrac{65}{48}$, which cannot be reduced.

Answer: $\dfrac{65}{48}$ or $1\dfrac{17}{48}$

How to:

Add Mixed Numbers:

1. Make equivalent fractions with a common denominator.

　　　Method #1 (vertical)　　　　　OR　　　　　Method #2 (horizontal)

2. Add the numerators of these　　　　　2. Change the mixed numbers into improper
　　new equivalent fractions. The　　　　　　fractions.
　　denominator stays the same!!　　　　　3. Add the numerators of these fractions.
3. Add the whole numbers last!　　　　　　　The denominator stays the same!!

Example #5:　　　$5\frac{2}{3} + 3\frac{1}{5}$

Step #1: Make equivalent fractions with a common denominator.

The lowest common denominator for 3 and 5 is 15. The problem now looks like the following:

Method #1 (vertical)　　　OR　　　**Method #2 (horizontal)**

$$5\frac{10}{15}$$

$$+\ 3\frac{3}{15}$$

$$5\frac{10}{15} + 3\frac{3}{15}$$

Step #2: Add the fractions.　　　OR　　　Change mixed numbers to improper fractions.

$$\frac{10}{15} + \frac{3}{15} = \frac{13}{15}$$

$$\frac{85}{15} + \frac{48}{15}$$

Step #3: Add the whole numbers last!　　　Add the fractions.

$$5\frac{10}{15}$$

$$+\ 3\frac{3}{15}$$

$$\frac{85}{15} + \frac{48}{15} = \frac{133}{15}$$

Answer:　$8\frac{13}{15}$　　　OR　　　$\frac{133}{15}$

Sample #1: Using the lowest common denominator, find equivalent fractions for $\frac{5}{21}$, $\frac{3}{10}$, and $\frac{11}{18}$.

The LCM of the denominators will give us the lowest common denominator (LCD).

$$
\begin{array}{r|ccc}
3 & 21 & 10 & 18 \\
\hline
7 & 7 & 10 & 6 \\
\hline
2 & 1 & 10 & 6 \\
\hline
5 & 1 & 5 & 3 \\
\hline
3 & 1 & 1 & 3 \\
\hline
 & 1 & 1 & 1
\end{array}
$$

$3 \bullet 7 \bullet 2 \bullet 5 \bullet 3$ yields a LCM of 630

Now we have three fractions with a common denominator. We now need to fill in the missing numerators.

$$\frac{5}{21} = \frac{\quad}{630} \qquad \frac{3}{10} = \frac{\quad}{630} \qquad \frac{11}{18} = \frac{\quad}{630}$$

To fill in the missing numerator of the first fraction we know we must see how many times 21 goes into 630 and then multiply this times the numerator of 5.

Once you have found the LCM there is an easy way to see how many times 21 goes into 630 without doing a division problem. Look at all the prime factors that made up 630—$3 \bullet 7 \bullet 2 \bullet 5 \bullet 3$. Eliminate the factors that when multiplied equal the denominator of 21. In this case we can eliminate $3 \bullet 7$. Our factorization now looks like $3 \bullet 7 \bullet 2 \bullet 5 \bullet 3$. We are left with $2 \bullet 5 \bullet 3$ or 30. In fact, we now know that 21 will divide into 630 thirty (30) times. We multiply $30 \bullet 5$ and get the numerator of 150.

$$\frac{5}{21} = \frac{150}{630}$$

For the second fraction we can eliminate the factors $2 \bullet 5$ that equal the denominator of 10. Our factorization now looks like $3 \bullet 7 \bullet 2 \bullet 5 \bullet 3$. The remaining factors of $3 \bullet 7 \bullet 3$ equal 63. We know that 10 divides into 630 sixty-three (63) times. Multiply $63 \bullet 3$ and get the numerator of 189.

$$\frac{3}{10} = \frac{189}{630}$$

For the third fraction we can eliminate the factors 2 • 3 • 3 that equal the denominator of 18. Our factorization now looks like 3 • 7 • 2 • 5 • 3. The remaining factors of 7 • 5 equal 35. We know that 18 divides into 630 thirty-five (35) times. Multiply 35 times 11 and get the numerator of 385.

$$\frac{11}{18} = \frac{385}{630}$$

■ **You try it now:**

a) After finding the LCD, write the equivalent fractions for $\frac{3}{42}$ and $\frac{7}{30}$.

b) After finding the LCD, write the equivalent fractions for $\frac{7}{11}$, $\frac{5}{66}$, and $\frac{7}{10}$.

Sample #2: A naturalist was following the travel patterns of a troop of baboons in Africa. The troop moved $\frac{3}{16}$ of a mile the first day, $\frac{1}{4}$ of a mile the second, and $\frac{1}{5}$ of a mile on the third day. What was the average distance they traveled each day?

To find the average, remember that we divide the total amount by the number of parts.

Concept set up: (total miles) ÷ (# of days)

Math set up: $\left(\frac{3}{16} + \frac{1}{4} + \frac{1}{5} \right) \div 3$

This gives us $\left(\frac{51}{80} \right) \div 3$ after adding the miles <u>inside</u> the parenthesis <u>first.</u>

$\frac{51}{80} \div \frac{3}{1}$ becomes $\frac{51}{80} \cdot \frac{1}{3}$. Then: cancel the 51 and the 3 to get: $\frac{\overset{17}{\cancel{51}}}{80} \cdot \frac{1}{\underset{1}{\cancel{3}}}$

Average is $\frac{17}{80}$ **mile per day**

■ **You try it now:**

c) The cake recipe called for $\frac{1}{3}$ cup of melted butter, $\frac{3}{4}$ cup of milk, and $\frac{1}{3}$ cup of water. What was the total amount of these three liquids needed for this cake?

d) The prospector weighed 3 pieces of gold which he had found in a creek. The first weighed $\frac{4}{15}$ of an ounce, the second $\frac{2}{5}$ of an ounce, and the third $\frac{2}{3}$ of an ounce. How much money did he earn if he could sell the gold for $300 an ounce? What was the average amount of money he made on each piece of gold (round to the nearest dollar)?

Sample #3: Change the value of $1\frac{2}{5}$ thousand dollars into its whole number value.

$1\frac{2}{5}$ thousand dollars means $1\frac{2}{5}$ "of" a thousand dollars. The form "a number of another number" means to multiply. Here it tells us to set up the following:

$$1\frac{2}{5} \cdot \$1000$$

$$\frac{7}{5} \cdot \frac{1000}{1}$$

Answer: $1400

Your try it now:

e) A company made $\frac{7}{8}$ thousand dollars. How much money is this in whole or actual dollars?

f) A painting sold for $1\frac{2}{3}$ million dollars. How much is this in actual dollars (round to the nearest whole dollar) ?

Sample #4: A proposal was brought to the city council to add bike lanes to connect both a mall and a subdivision of homes to the largest city park. It was $2\frac{1}{4}$ miles from the mall to the park and $3\frac{2}{3}$ miles from the subdivision to the park. If the estimated cost to build the bike lanes was $4\frac{1}{2}$ thousand dollars per mile, how much did the proposal say the project would cost?

Concept Set up: (total distance) • (the cost per mile of bike lane)

Math Set up: $(2\frac{1}{4} + 3\frac{2}{3}) \cdot (4\frac{1}{2}$ thousand$)$

First, find the total distance of the bike lanes. $2\frac{1}{4} + 3\frac{2}{3} = 5\frac{11}{12}$ miles. Now, multiply this distance times the cost per mile of bike lanes.

$$5\frac{11}{12} \cdot 4\frac{1}{2} = \frac{213}{8}$$

The cost of $\frac{213}{8}$ thousands doesn't make any sense, so we change this to a mixed number and get $26\frac{5}{8}$ **thousand dollars** .

How much is $26\frac{5}{8}$ thousands exactly?

We know it is $26,000 + \left(\frac{5}{8} \text{ of } \$1,000\right)$.

Now let's do the math inside the parenthesis: $26,000 + \left(\frac{5}{8} \cdot \frac{1000}{1}\right)$.
This gives us: $26,000 + \$625$

Answer: **$26,625**

You try it now:

g) Esmeralda wanted to find out how many gallons of gas she was using per month. In April she filled up her gas tank three times. She pumped in $8\frac{3}{10}$ gallons, $7\frac{4}{5}$ gallons, and $8\frac{1}{2}$ gallons respectively. How many gallons of gas did she use that April?

h) As the city grew in population, so grew its budget. In its first year it had a budget of $2\frac{1}{2}$ million dollars. In its second and third years it had budgets of 3 million and $3\frac{2}{5}$ million dollars respectively. What was the total amount of money budgeted by the city in its first three years?

Answers to You try it now: a) lowest common denominator is 210; $\frac{3}{42} = \frac{15}{210}$, $\frac{7}{30} = \frac{49}{210}$; b) lowest common denominator is 330: $\frac{7}{11} = \frac{210}{330}$, $\frac{5}{66} = \frac{25}{330}$, $\frac{7}{10} = \frac{231}{330}$; c) $1\frac{5}{12}$ cups; d) $400 in total, an average of $133 per piece of gold; e) $875 f) $1,666,667 g) $24\frac{3}{5}$ gallons; h) $8\frac{9}{10}$ million dollars or $8,900,000

Answer to Application: The Emergency Evacuation Center must find the total amount of rainfall that fell in the last 24 hours. Find what $6\frac{3}{4} + 4\frac{2}{3} + 3\frac{5}{8}$ equals.

Method #1 (vertical)   OR   **Method #2 (horizontal)**

$6\frac{3}{4} = 6\frac{18}{24}$

$+ 4\frac{2}{3} = 4\frac{16}{24}$

$+ 3\frac{5}{8} = 3\frac{15}{24}$

$13\frac{49}{24}$

$6\frac{3}{4} + 4\frac{2}{3} + 3\frac{5}{8}$

$\frac{27}{4} + \frac{14}{3} + \frac{29}{8}$

$\frac{162}{24} + \frac{112}{24} + \frac{87}{24}$

$\frac{361}{24}$

Method #1: Never leave an improper fraction as a part of a mixed number answer. The fraction $\frac{49}{24}$ equals $2\frac{1}{24}$. Thus, $13 + 2\frac{1}{24}$ gives the answer $15\frac{1}{24}$ inches of rain.

Method #2: The answer of $\frac{361}{24}$ inches of rain is correct, but in the real world we don't communicate in improper fractions. For application problems always change improper fractions into mixed number answers.

$\frac{361}{24}$ equals $15\frac{1}{24}$ inches of rain.

Yes, the Evacuation Center should have the residents in the valley below the dam evacuate their homes.

2.6 LCM and Addition of Fractions & Mixed Number Problems

In exercises #1-6, tell if the given statement is true or false. Explain why or why not.

1) 25 is a multiple of 5   2) 7 is a multiple of 35   3) 87 is a multiple of 3

4) 86 is a multiple of 11   5) 5 is a factor of 30   6) 2 is a factor of 58

In exercises #7-14, choose numbers which are multiples of each specific given number, separating the numbers in each answer with a comma.

7) Multiples of 2:	16	28	49	62
8) Multiples of 3:	9	27	109	321
9) Multiples of 5:	40	58	200	5024
10) Multiples of 7:	15	37	84	340
11) Multiples of 3:	3	14	57	381
12) Multiples of 2:	22	242	274	87,665
13) Multiples of 11:	11	111	121	471
14) Multiples of 17:	34	136	172	201

In exercises #15-22, write the number equal to the given expression.

15) The 3rd multiple of 7   16) The 2nd multiple of 5

17) The 1st multiple of 2   18) The 4th multiple of 10

19) The 7th multiple of 12   20) The 3rd multiple of 19

21) The 6th multiple of 6   22) The 11th multiple of 2

In exercises #23-30, find the LCM of the following numbers.

23) 4 and 16   24) 5, 6, and 12   25) 6, 7, and 8   26) 4, 6, and 11

27) 8, 12, and 15   28) 7, 13, and 91   29) 2, 9, and 45   30) 6, 9, and 10

In exercises #31-34 find the lowest common denominator (LCD) for the given fractions.

31) $\frac{3}{8}$, $\frac{1}{2}$, and $\frac{2}{5}$ 32) $\frac{4}{3}$, $\frac{5}{6}$, and $\frac{5}{12}$ 33) $\frac{3}{14}$ and $\frac{1}{6}$ 34) $\frac{3}{10}$, $\frac{7}{15}$, and $\frac{7}{66}$

In exercises #35-53 solve for the sum. If you get a non-integer answer of a value of greater than 1, be sure to give <u>both</u> an improper fraction and a mixed number answer.

35) $\frac{2}{3} + \frac{1}{6}$ 36) $\frac{1}{5} + \frac{3}{7}$ 37) $\frac{7}{6} + \frac{3}{3}$ 38) $\frac{5}{7} + \frac{3}{4}$

39) $\frac{7}{12} + \frac{1}{8} + \frac{5}{6}$ 40) $\frac{1}{3} + \frac{7}{10} + \frac{3}{6}$ 41) $\frac{3}{2} + \frac{1}{9} + \frac{5}{12}$ 42) $\frac{2}{11} + \frac{1}{12} + \frac{1}{4}$

43) $\frac{3}{7} + \frac{5}{6} + \frac{2}{9}$ 44) $\frac{5}{12} + \frac{4}{9} + \frac{2}{13}$ 45) $3\frac{2}{5} + 2\frac{3}{5}$ 46) $8\frac{1}{8} + 6\frac{3}{5}$

47) $2 + \frac{3}{16}$ 48) $15\frac{17}{100} + \frac{4}{50}$ 49) $5\frac{9}{11} + 4 + 2\frac{1}{2}$ 50) $2\frac{1}{3} + 2\frac{1}{4} + 2\frac{2}{6}$

51) $1\frac{29}{1000} + 2\frac{87}{100}$ 52) $30\frac{3}{4} + 25\frac{3}{8} + 10\frac{6}{16}$ 53) $6\frac{1}{2} + 5\frac{1}{2} + 3\frac{1}{2} + \frac{1}{2}$

In exercises #54-63, translate the following words into math expressions. Do not solve.

54) The sum of $\frac{8}{3}$ and 3.

55) The sum of $\frac{3}{4}$ and $1\frac{1}{5}$

56) The product of $\frac{2}{3}$ and 7, then add $\frac{3}{8}$

57) $\frac{4}{5}$ times $1\frac{1}{2}$, then subtract $\frac{1}{3}$

58) $\frac{9}{10}$ more than the quotient of $2\frac{3}{4}$ and $\frac{3}{4}$

59) $\frac{2}{7}$ more than $5 \cdot 2\frac{3}{5}$

60) $\frac{1}{3}$ less than x

61) x more than the product of $\frac{2}{7}$ and $2\frac{3}{5}$

62) The sum of $\frac{1}{x}$ and $\frac{3}{x}$

63) $\frac{1}{4}$ of x, plus the quotient of $\frac{x}{y}$ and 2

For the following problems, #64-76: (a) write a mathematical expression that will solve the problem, and (b) give the solution.

64) Martha walked around a lake three days a week. There were two different trails. Martha walked the first trail, $3\frac{3}{8}$ miles in length, twice a week, and the second trail, $4\frac{1}{4}$ miles long, once a week. How far did she walk every week?

65) Three days of spring showers brought a $\frac{1}{2}$ inch of rain to Santa Rosa the first day, $\frac{1}{12}$ of an inch the second day, and $\frac{2}{5}$ of an inch on the third day. How much rain did Santa Rosa receive in the three days?

66-68) Andy worked as a handyman while attending the local community college. Last week he worked $3\frac{1}{4}$ hours on Monday, 4 hours on Wednesday, $2\frac{5}{6}$ hours on Thursday, and $7\frac{1}{2}$ hours on Saturday.

66) How many hours did Andy work last week?

67) Knowing that Andy worked for four days, what was the average time he worked each of those days?

68) If Andy usually worked $5\frac{1}{2}$ hours more per week than he worked this last week, how many hours a week did he average working?

69-70) The latest Census Report declared that the population of County X, which had a population of $1\frac{1}{8}$ million people ten years earlier, had grown by another $\frac{1}{4}$ million people.

69) How many people live in County X now (give answer as a mixed number)?

70) Given as a whole number, how many people live in County X now?

71-72) A large parent corporation announced a breakdown of the year's earnings for three of the companies it owned. Company A earned 12 million, company B earned $3\frac{2}{5}$ million, and Company C earned $\frac{1}{2}$ million dollars.

71) How much money did the 3 companies earn (give answer as a mixed number)?

72) Given as a whole number, how much money did the 3 companies earn?

73) It was announced in the paper that the football star signed a two-year contract for $2\frac{1}{3}$ million dollars and also received a signing bonus of $\frac{3}{4}$ million. In dollars given as a whole number, how much money would the athlete get?

74) Two paintings by Vincent van Gogh were sold for $1\frac{7}{10}$ million dollars and $3\frac{1}{2}$ million dollars respectively. In dollars given as a whole number, how much money was this?

75-76) A winter storm lasted 3 days. Petaluma received $\frac{1}{8}$ of an inch the first day, $2\frac{1}{3}$ inches the second day, and $1\frac{3}{8}$ inches on the third day.

75) What was the total rainfall received in the three days?

76) What was the average rainfall each day?

Solve the following problems.

77) Two extra-large pizzas were delivered to Erica's house for her daughter's seventh birthday party. Unfortunately, one of the pizzas was cut into six slices and the other into only four. Erica knew that she had a problem. This group of seven-year olds would want their slices of pizza to be the same size. Into *at least* how many pieces would Erica have to cut each pizza to ensure that the pieces were the same size?

78) One evening Omar's two children brought home packets of raffle tickets to sell for a school district fund-raiser. The packets which his middle-school son brought home sold in packets of 6 tickets. The packets which his elementary-school daughter brought home sold in packets of 8 tickets. Omar didn't have a lot of spare money, so he wanted to spend as little money as possible, but still equally support both his children. What would be the least number of packets of tickets he could buy from each child to ensure that he bought the same number of tickets from each of his children?

In exercises #79-85, solve the following problems. This exercise provides you with a good review of vocabulary and concepts.

79) $\left(\text{the reciprocal of } \frac{3}{4} \right) + (\text{the LCM of 8 and 12})$

80) $\left(\dfrac{\text{the sum of } \frac{6}{6} \text{ and } \frac{5}{5}}{2} \right)$

81) $\left(\dfrac{\text{the GCF of 24 and 30}}{10} \right)$

82) $\left(\dfrac{\frac{3}{5} \text{ of } 5}{\text{the second multiple of 3}} \right)$

83) $\left(\dfrac{\text{the lowest common denominator of } \frac{2}{3} \text{ and } \frac{3}{7}}{2 \left(\text{the LCM of 4 and 12} \right)} \right)$

84) $\left(\dfrac{\text{the sum of } \frac{3}{11} \text{ and } \frac{1}{5}}{\frac{2}{11}} \right)$

85) $\left(\dfrac{\text{the second multiple of 5}}{(\text{the third multiple of 4})} \right) + \left(\dfrac{\text{difference of 6 and 4}}{\text{the reciprocal of } \frac{1}{3}} \right)$

In exercises #86-93, decide whether the given math expressions all have the same value. Answer yes or no. If your answer is no, identify the one number or math phrase that does not equal the others. (Help: Look at the commutative and associative properties for addition and multiplication [section 1.6])

86) a) $\left(\frac{3}{5} + \frac{2}{7} \right) + \frac{1}{4}$ b) $\left(\frac{3}{5} \right) + \left(\frac{2}{7} + \frac{1}{4} \right)$ c) $\frac{3}{5} + \frac{2}{7} + \frac{1}{4}$

87) a) $2\frac{3}{88} + \frac{5}{38}$ b) $\frac{5}{38} + 2\frac{3}{88}$ c) $\left(\frac{5}{38} \right)\left(2\frac{3}{88} \right)$

88) a) $8\frac{2}{3} \cdot \left(2\frac{41}{53} \cdot \frac{8}{19} \right)$ b) $\left(8\frac{2}{3} \cdot 2\frac{41}{53} \right) \cdot \left(\frac{8}{19} \right)$ c) $\left(\frac{8}{19} \right)\left(2\frac{41}{53} \right)\left(8\frac{2}{3} \right)$

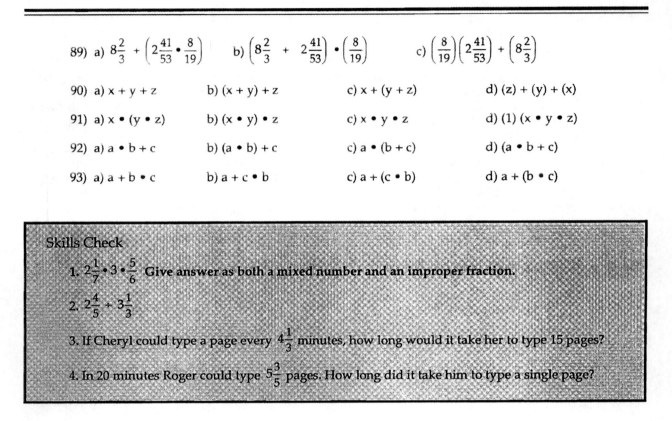

89) a) $8\frac{2}{3} + \left(2\frac{41}{53} \cdot \frac{8}{19}\right)$ b) $\left(8\frac{2}{3} + 2\frac{41}{53}\right) \cdot \left(\frac{8}{19}\right)$ c) $\left(\frac{8}{19}\right)\left(2\frac{41}{53}\right) + \left(8\frac{2}{3}\right)$

90) a) $x + y + z$ b) $(x + y) + z$ c) $x + (y + z)$ d) $(z) + (y) + (x)$

91) a) $x \cdot (y \cdot z)$ b) $(x \cdot y) \cdot z$ c) $x \cdot y \cdot z$ d) $(1)(x \cdot y \cdot z)$

92) a) $a \cdot b + c$ b) $(a \cdot b) + c$ c) $a \cdot (b + c)$ d) $(a \cdot b + c)$

93) a) $a + b \cdot c$ b) $a + c \cdot b$ c) $a + (c \cdot b)$ d) $a + (b \cdot c)$

Skills Check

1. $2\frac{1}{7} \cdot 3 \cdot \frac{5}{6}$ Give answer as both a mixed number and an improper fraction.

2. $2\frac{4}{5} \div 3\frac{1}{3}$

3. If Cheryl could type a page every $4\frac{1}{3}$ minutes, how long would it take her to type 15 pages?

4. In 20 minutes Roger could type $5\frac{3}{5}$ pages. How long did it take him to type a single page?

Answers to Skills Check: 1) $\frac{75}{14}$ and $5\frac{5}{14}$; 2) $\frac{21}{25}$; 3) 65 minutes or 1 hr. 5 minutes; 4) $3\frac{4}{7}$ minutes.

Section 2.7　Subtract Fractions and Mixed Numbers

Objectives:

• To subtract fractions/mixed numbers using the vertical method

• To subtract fractions/mixed numbers using the horizontal method

• To set up/solve mixed number and fraction application problems

• To manipulate equations with fractions and mixed numbers

Application:

According to measuring instruments, the county's water reservoir system was full at the end of May. By the end of June the reservoir had lost $\frac{1}{5}$ of its supply from human usage and another $\frac{3}{100}$ from evaporation. No measureable water was added to the reservoir. What fraction of the county's water supply still remained as of July first? Assume that the same amount of water continued to evaporate each month and that the county maintained this same water usage for the dry months of July, August, and September. What fraction of the water would be left in the reservoir system as of the first of October? Should we be nervous if we were responsible for supplying the county with enough water?

Vocabulary:

borrowing—**Borrowing** is a process used in subtraction of mixed number problems when the fractional part of the number we are subtracting is larger than the fractional part of the mixed number we started with. We must borrow one or more whole numbers to make the top fraction greater in value than the fraction we are subtracting.

Example:　　$6\frac{3}{7} - 2\frac{5}{7}$　　In this case the fractional part of the mixed number we are subtracting (the $\frac{5}{7}$) is larger than the fractional part we started with (the $\frac{3}{7}$).

We correct this situation by borrowing 1 whole from the 6. That 1 whole (remember that one whole as a fraction has the same number for both numerator and denominator) is the same as $\frac{7}{7}$. Add $\frac{7}{7}$ to the fractional part (the $\frac{3}{7}$) of the mixed number.

We can now recognize that $6\frac{3}{7} = 5\frac{3}{7} + \frac{7}{7} = 5\frac{10}{7}$

Therefore, borrowing now allows us to rewrite the original problem as:

$$5 \ \frac{10}{7}$$
$$-2 \ \frac{5}{7}$$

Key Concept Review: **Addition and subtraction are opposites.** Every addition statement can be rewritten as a subtraction statement; every subtraction statement can be rewritten as an addition statement. This is true whether we are talking about whole numbers, decimals, or fractions.

If we lack the experience and confidence in the equation manipulations below, go ahead and work out the examples and see that they are all true. The values on the left and right sides of the equation are equal.

Examples:

The addition statement of $4\frac{1}{2} = 3\frac{1}{3} + 1\frac{1}{6}$ can be rewritten as the subtraction statement of $4\frac{1}{2} - 1\frac{1}{6} = 3\frac{1}{3}$ after both sides of the equation have been "subtracted by $1\frac{1}{6}$."

$$4\frac{1}{2} = 3\frac{1}{3} + 1\frac{1}{6}$$
$$4\frac{1}{2} - 1\frac{1}{6} = \left(3\frac{1}{3} + 1\frac{1}{6}\right) - 1\frac{1}{6}$$
$$4\frac{1}{2} - 1\frac{1}{6} = 3\frac{1}{3}$$

The subtraction statement of $\frac{9}{10} - \frac{3}{5} = \frac{3}{10}$ can be rewritten as the addition statement of $\frac{9}{10} = \frac{3}{10} + \frac{3}{5}$ after both sides of the equation have "added $\frac{3}{5}$."

$$\frac{9}{10} - \frac{3}{5} = \frac{3}{10}$$
$$\frac{9}{10} - \frac{3}{5} + \frac{3}{5} = \frac{3}{10} + \frac{3}{5}$$
$$\frac{9}{10} = \frac{3}{10} + \frac{3}{5}$$

The subtraction statement of $2\frac{1}{5} - x = \frac{3}{4}$ can be rewritten as the addition statement of $2\frac{1}{5} = \frac{3}{4} + x$ after both sides of the equation have "added x."

$$2\frac{1}{5} - x = \frac{3}{4}$$
$$2\frac{1}{5} - x + x = \frac{3}{4} + x$$
$$2\frac{1}{5} = \frac{3}{4} + x$$

Also: If we agree that $2\frac{1}{5} - x = \frac{3}{4}$ and $2\frac{1}{5} = \frac{3}{4} + x$. are the same, we can take this one step further

to discover the value of x. We change the

addition statement of $2\frac{1}{5} = \frac{3}{4} + x$ to the

$$2\frac{1}{5} = \frac{3}{4} + x$$

subtraction statement of $2\frac{1}{5} - \frac{3}{4} = x$ by

$$2\frac{1}{5} - \frac{3}{4} = \left(\frac{3}{4} + x\right) - \frac{3}{4}$$

subtracting $\frac{3}{4}$ from both sides of the equation.

$$2\frac{1}{5} - \frac{3}{4} = x$$

If we solved the left side of the equation, we would find that

$2\frac{1}{5} - \frac{3}{4}$ is equal to $1\frac{9}{20}$.

$x = 1\frac{9}{20}$ or $\frac{29}{20}$

By following the basic equation truth that we can always do the same thing to both sides of an equation, we see that $2\frac{1}{5} - x = \frac{3}{4}$ is the same as $2\frac{1}{5} = \frac{3}{4} + x$ which is the same as $2\frac{1}{5} - \frac{3}{4} = x$.

How to:

Subtract fractions:

1. We must have or find a common denominator for the given fractions (if we can't tell what the lowest common denominator will be by looking at the numbers, we can find it by obtaining the LCM of the given denominators).
2. Make equivalent fractions using the common denominator.
3. Subtract the numerators of these new equivalent fractions. The denominator stays the same!

Fractions can be subtracted either **vertically** (one number lined up beneath another) or **horizontally** (left to right across the page). We should be able to work in both formats. Both are "correct." However, as we move forward into algebra the standard format is horizontal, so it is important that we use and get used to this style. Remember, the math itself is exactly the same!

Example #1: $\frac{2}{3} - \frac{4}{7}$

Step #1: Find a common denominator for the given fractions.

Here we look at the given denominators of 3 and 7. Knowing our multiplication tables, we can see that both 3 and 7 divide evenly into 21. 21 is the lowest common denominator (LCD).

Step #2: Make equivalent fractions using the common denominator.

| Vertical Method: | OR | Horizontal Method: |

$$\frac{2}{3} = \frac{}{21}$$

$$-\frac{4}{7} = \frac{}{21}$$

$$\frac{2}{3} - \frac{4}{7}$$

$$\frac{}{21} - \frac{}{21}$$

Look at the first fraction. To change the denominator of 3 to 21 we would have to multiply it by 7. Therefore, according to the process of **building fractions**, we also must multiply the numerator of 2 by 7. Thus, $\frac{2}{3}$ (multiplied by $\frac{7}{7}$) is equal to $\frac{14}{21}$.

Look at the second fraction. To change the denominator of 7 to 21 we would have to multiply it by 3. Therefore, according to the process of **building fractions**, we also must multiply the numerator of 4 by 3. Thus, $\frac{4}{7}$ (multiplied by $\frac{3}{3}$) is equal to $\frac{12}{21}$.

The problem now looks like the following:

$$\frac{14}{21}$$
$$-\frac{12}{21}$$

OR

$$\frac{14}{21} - \frac{12}{21}$$

Step #3: Subtract the numerators of these new equivalent fractions. The denominator stays the same!!

14 - 12 = 2   **Answer:** $\frac{2}{21}$

Example #2: $\left(\dfrac{7}{8} - \dfrac{1}{2}\right) - \dfrac{3}{16}$

Step #1: Find a common denominator for the given fractions.

We can either calculate in our heads or use the LCM process to find out that the lowest common denominator is **16**.

Step #2: Make equivalent fractions using the common denominator.

| **Vertical Method:** | OR | **Horizontal Method:** |

Vertical Method:

$$\dfrac{7}{8} = \dfrac{14}{16}$$

$$-\dfrac{1}{2} = \dfrac{8}{16}$$

$$-\dfrac{3}{16} = \dfrac{3}{16}$$

OR

Horizontal Method:

$\left(\dfrac{7}{8} - \dfrac{1}{2}\right) - \dfrac{3}{16}$ becomes

$\left(\dfrac{14}{16} - \dfrac{8}{16}\right) - \dfrac{3}{16}$

Step #3: Subtract the numerators of these new equivalent fractions. The denominator stays the same!!

**Maintain good math habits! Following the order of operations, we do the work inside the parenthesis first. $\left(\dfrac{14}{16} - \dfrac{8}{16}\right) = \dfrac{6}{16}$. The problem should now look like:

$$\dfrac{6}{16}$$
$$-\dfrac{3}{16}$$

OR

$\left(\dfrac{6}{16}\right) - \dfrac{3}{16}$

Answer: $\dfrac{3}{16}$

How to:

Subtract Mixed Numbers:

1. Make equivalent fractions with a common denominator.

| **Method #1 (vertical)** | OR | **Method #2 (horizontal)** |

Method #1 (vertical)

2. Make sure the top numerator is larger than the numerator of the fraction we are subtracting (If the top numerator is smaller, borrow 1 or more wholes from the whole number part of the top number).

3. Subtract the bottom numerator from the top numerator. The denominator stays the same!!

4. Subtract the whole numbers last!

Method #2 (horizontal)

2. Change the mixed numbers into improper fractions.

3. Subtract the second numerator from the first.
   The denominator stays the same!

Example #3: $5\frac{1}{5} - 3\frac{2}{3}$

Step #1: Make equivalent fractions with a common denominator.

The lowest common denominator for 3 and 5 is 15. The problem now looks like the following:

Method #1 (vertical)   OR   **Method #2 (horizontal)**

$$5\frac{3}{15}$$
$$-\ 3\frac{10}{15}$$

$$5\frac{3}{15} - 3\frac{10}{15}$$

Step #2: Make the top numerator larger than the bottom numerator.

OR

Change the mixed numbers to improper fractions.

$$\frac{78}{15} - \frac{55}{15}$$

In this case we need to borrow 1 whole $\left(\frac{15}{15}\right)$ and add it to the $\frac{3}{15}$.

$5\frac{3}{15}$ becomes $4 + \frac{15}{15} + \frac{3}{15}$ or $4\frac{18}{15}$

The problem looks like this now:

$$4\frac{18}{15}$$
$$-\ 3\frac{10}{15}$$

Steps #3 & #4: Subtract the bottom numerator from the top numerator. Subtract the whole numbers last!

OR

Subtract the numerators.

$$78 - 55 = 23$$

$$4\frac{18}{15}$$
$$-\ 3\frac{10}{15}$$

Answer: $1\frac{8}{15}$ OR $\frac{23}{15}$

Sample #1: In a chemistry experiment $\frac{3}{10}$ of a bottle was filled with an acid; $\frac{1}{6}$ of the bottle was filled with water. The rest of the bottle was filled with a gas. What fraction of the bottle was filled with gas?

First we recognize that we have 1 whole bottle (as a fraction this will be represented with the same numerator and denominator). To find the fractional part that is filled with gas, we must subtract the fractional part of the bottle filled with acid and water from the full bottle.

Concept Set Up: (one whole bottle) – (fractional part of bottle filled with acid and water)

Math Set Up: (1)   – $\left(\frac{3}{10} + \frac{1}{6}\right)$

Solve: (1)   – $\frac{7}{15}$

                      $\frac{15}{15}$ – $\frac{7}{15}$

Answer: $\frac{8}{15}$ of the bottle is filled with gas

You try it now:

a) After surgery, Julie's rehabilitation required that she walk one mile every day. If she had walked $\frac{1}{4}$ of a mile that morning and $\frac{5}{9}$ of a mile shortly after lunch, how much farther did she still need to walk that day?

b) A juice container at a restaurant that can hold a total of 64 fluid ounces had 50 fluid ounces in it when Alice served 3 juices (8 ounces each) to some customers. What fraction of the juice container is full now?

Sample #2: Two friends held a competition to see who could swim farther in two hours. Jessie swam $2\frac{3}{5}$ of a mile and Enrique swam $1\frac{7}{8}$ of a mile. How much farther did Jessie swim than Enrique?

First, to compare fractions, we must get a common denominator. In this case the common denominator is 40.

Jessie swam $2\frac{3}{5}$ of a mile = $2\frac{24}{40}$ of a mile

Enrique swam $1\frac{7}{8}$ of a mile = $1\frac{35}{40}$ of a mile

We can see that Jessie swam more. To find the exact difference, we always subtract the smaller amount from the larger. In this case:

$$2\frac{24}{40} - 1\frac{35}{40} = \frac{29}{40}$$

Answer: Jessie swam $\frac{29}{40}$ of a mile more than Enrique.

■
■   **You try it now:**
■
■   c) A city spent $12\frac{2}{5}$ million dollars one year, but collected revenues of only $10\frac{5}{6}$ million. How much had
■
■   the city overspent?
■
■   d) A wrestler had to maintain a weight of between 165 and 175 pounds to wrestle in his weight division.
■   ○
■   Two weeks before his match he weighed $176\frac{1}{2}$ pounds. A week later he had lost $2\frac{5}{8}$ pounds. What is
■
■   the most weight he could gain to stay at 175 pounds or lower and still participate in his match?

Answers to You try it now: a) $\frac{7}{36}$ of a mile; b) $\frac{13}{32}$ filled; c) $1\frac{17}{30}$ million dollars; d) $1\frac{1}{8}$ lb.

Answer to Application: To check what fraction of the reservoir is still filled, we first have to see how much of the water was either used or evaporated. In June $\frac{1}{5}$ of the water was used and $\frac{3}{100}$ of the water evaporated. Together $\left(\frac{1}{5} + \frac{3}{100}\right)$, the reservoir lost $\frac{23}{100}$ of its water in June, thus leaving $\left(\frac{100}{100} - \frac{23}{100}\right)$ it only $\frac{77}{100}$ filled as of July 1st.

If the same amount of $\frac{23}{100}$ of the reservoir was lost each of the three months of July, August, and September, we can say that the reservoir lost $\left(\frac{23}{100} \cdot \frac{3}{1}\right)$ another $\frac{69}{100}$ of its capacity. By October 1st the reservoir would be $\left(\frac{77}{100} - \frac{69}{100}\right)$ only $\frac{8}{100}$ or $\frac{2}{25}$ filled. Finally, yes, we should be very nervous about our very low water supply.

2.7 Subtraction of Fractions & Mixed Number Problems

In exercises #1-35 solve for the difference. If you get a non-integer answer of a value of greater than 1, be sure to give <u>both</u> an improper fraction and a mixed number answer.

1) $\frac{3}{4} - \frac{5}{8}$ 2) $\frac{4}{5} - \frac{2}{3}$ 3) $\frac{7}{18} - \frac{1}{3}$ 4) $\frac{8}{11} - \frac{4}{55}$ 5) $\frac{1}{3} - \frac{2}{10}$

6) $\frac{7}{6} - \frac{3}{4}$ 7) $\frac{7}{3} - \frac{1}{7}$ 8) $\frac{5}{2} - \frac{3}{16}$ 9) $\frac{15}{8} - \frac{2}{3}$ 10) $\frac{9}{7} - \frac{1}{5}$

11) $\frac{3}{4} - \frac{9}{12}$ 12) $\frac{1}{11} - \frac{7}{77}$ 13) $2\frac{2}{5} - 1\frac{1}{3}$ 14) $7\frac{5}{6} - 3\frac{5}{12}$ 15) $3\frac{1}{4} - 1\frac{3}{5}$

16) $5\frac{3}{10} - 2\frac{1}{2}$　　17) $8\frac{2}{3} - 4\frac{6}{7}$　　18) $3\frac{3}{8} - 2\frac{4}{7}$　　19) $16 - \frac{3}{16}$

20) $11 - \frac{3}{11}$　　21) $4\frac{2}{7} - 3$　　22) $10\frac{1}{8} - 6$　　23) $7 - 3\frac{4}{13}$

24) $9 - 2\frac{7}{9}$　　25) $8 - 7\frac{2}{3}$　　26) $25 - 3\frac{2}{8}$　　27) $100\frac{4}{5} - 7\frac{3}{8}$

28) $99\frac{99}{100} - 9\frac{999}{1000}$　　29) $\left(7\frac{2}{5} - 4\frac{1}{2}\right) - 2\frac{3}{4}$　　30) $\left(11\frac{2}{7} - 2\frac{3}{4}\right) - 7\frac{3}{14}$

31) $\frac{8}{5} - \frac{2}{3} + 1\frac{1}{6}$　　32) $\frac{2}{5} - \frac{1}{4} + \frac{1}{2}$　　33) $2\frac{1}{8} - 2\frac{1}{16} + \frac{3}{16}$

34) $\frac{11}{11} - \frac{1}{10} - \frac{3}{5}$　　35) $\frac{39}{39} - \frac{27}{27}$

In exercises #36-45, translate the following words into math expressions. Then solve.

36) The sum of $2\frac{4}{5}$ and 2

37) The sum of $5\frac{3}{10}$ and $3\frac{3}{100}$

38) $8\frac{1}{5}$ more than $4\frac{1}{5}$

39) $\frac{2}{3}$ more than 1

40) The difference of $3\frac{1}{10}$ and $\frac{1}{100}$

41) The difference of $\frac{1}{7}$ and $\frac{1}{14}$

42) Subtract $\frac{6}{8}$ from $\frac{6}{5}$

43) Subtract 7 from $7\frac{1}{4}$

44) 4 less than $6\frac{7}{8}$

45) $\frac{2}{3}$ less than 2

In exercises #46-58, translate the following words into math expressions. Do not solve.

46) The difference of x and $\frac{9}{10}$

47) The difference of $\frac{9}{10}$ and x

48) The difference of $\frac{4}{3}$ and x

49) The difference of x and $2\frac{3}{7}$

50) Subtract $\frac{3}{5}$ from x

51) Subtract x from $4\frac{1}{5}$

52) $2\frac{4}{15}$ less than x

53) x less than $4\frac{1}{3}$

54) x more than $\frac{2}{3}$

55) $1\frac{5}{6}$ more than x

56) $\frac{3}{5}$ of x, subtracted from $1\frac{5}{6}$

57) the difference of $\frac{1}{2}$ of x and $\frac{3}{x}$

58) $\frac{1}{2}$ more than the quotient of $\frac{3}{x}$ and $\frac{1}{x}$

In exercises #59-66, state whether the following statements are True or False.

59) Addition and subtraction are opposite operations.

60) $6 + \frac{2}{5} = 6\frac{2}{5}$ is the same as $6 = 6\frac{2}{5} - \frac{2}{5}$

61) $11 + 1\frac{3}{4} = 12\frac{3}{4}$ is the same as $11 = 12\frac{3}{4} - 1\frac{3}{4}$

62) $2\frac{2}{3} - \frac{4}{5} = 1\frac{13}{15}$ is the same as $2\frac{2}{3} = 1\frac{13}{15} + \frac{4}{5}$

63) $x - \frac{5}{8} = 1\frac{1}{10}$ is the same as $x = 1\frac{1}{10} - \frac{5}{8}$

64) $\frac{3}{4} + x = 2$ is the same as $\frac{3}{4} = 2 + x$

65) $\frac{2}{5} - x = \frac{3}{10}$ is the same as $\frac{2}{5} - \frac{3}{10} = x$

66) $1\frac{5}{8} - x = \frac{3}{4}$ is the same as $1\frac{5}{8} + \frac{3}{4} = x$

In exercises #67-74, write an equivalent equation which changes any given addition statement to a subtraction statement or change any given subtraction statement to an addition statement. There is nothing to solve here.

67) $8 - \frac{1}{8} = 7\frac{7}{8}$

68) $3\frac{2}{5} + \frac{1}{30} = 3\frac{13}{30}$

69) $\frac{7}{10} - x = \frac{2}{5}$

70) $x - \frac{5}{12} = \frac{7}{8}$

71) $x + 2\frac{1}{3} = 5\frac{3}{7}$

72) $1\frac{1}{5} + x = 2$

73) $\frac{9}{10} - x = \frac{1}{4}$

74) $x + \frac{1}{4} = 3\frac{7}{20}$

In exercises #75-80, solve for the value of x, the unknown number.

75) $\frac{1}{5} + x = \frac{3}{5}$

76) $x + \frac{1}{4} = \frac{3}{4}$

77) $\frac{3}{7} - \frac{1}{4} = x$

78) $x - \frac{4}{5} = \frac{3}{10}$

79) $x - \frac{1}{3} = \frac{1}{4}$

80) $\frac{4}{5} + x = \frac{8}{10}$

For exercises #81-91: (a) write a mathematical expression that will solve the problem, and (b) give the solution.

81) Santa Rosa averages 30 inches of rain a year. If by the end of February the city had received $22\frac{23}{100}$ inches of rain, how much more rain needed to fall to reach the annual average?

82) Marsha ran $6\frac{1}{2}$ miles every Wednesday. Alicia, her jogging partner, normally ran $4\frac{7}{8}$ miles. What was the difference between the distances which Marsha and Alicia typically ran?

83) At the midpoint in the 100-problem final exam, Manny had finished 76 problems. Xena had completed 61. What fraction represents how much more of the exam Manny had completed than Xena?

84) The state budget was $60\frac{7}{10}$ billion dollars last year. This year it was $64\frac{3}{4}$ billion. What was the increase in the budget?

85) If Elena worked $6\frac{1}{4}$ hours on Monday, $5\frac{1}{2}$ hours on Tuesday, and 7 hours on Thursday, how many hours did she still need to work to fulfill her contract that said she had to work 25 hours per week?

86-87) Harrison made potpourri from the dahlia flowers he grew. For each package of potpourri he made he used about 30 dahlia petals. One day he harvested 110 petals from one plant and 70 from a second plant.

86) How many packages of potpourri were filled from the day's harvest?

87) How many more packages of the potpourri were filled from the first dahlia than the second one?

88-89) A train ride from Elkington to Deerborn takes $1\frac{3}{5}$ hours during the night. During the day, because of numerous stops, it takes $2\frac{1}{4}$ hours.

88) What fraction of an hour longer does the ride take during the day than at night?

89) How many more minutes does the ride during the day take than at night (60 minutes = 1 hour)?

90) When studying two groups of hares, field biologists discovered that one group of adults on average weighed about $4\frac{3}{8}$ pounds while the second healthier group weighed an average of $6\frac{1}{5}$ pounds. What was the average difference in weight between rabbits in the two groups?

91) When state legislators met with environmentalists and lumber company executives, each group put forth a forest-management plan for the Evergreen Valley. The environmentalists requested that lumber companies be allowed to cut an average of only $\frac{1}{10}$ of an acre per day for the 200-day cutting season. The lumber companies asked that they be allowed to cut $\frac{1}{4}$ of an acre per day. How many more acres of forest per year (200 days of cutting trees) did the lumber company plan allow them to cut than the environmentalists' plan?

In exercises #92-103, add or subtract the following expressions.

92) $\frac{4}{x} + \frac{3}{x}$

93) $\frac{7}{y} + \frac{1}{y}$

94) $\frac{6}{xy} - \frac{3}{xy}$

95) $\frac{11}{a} - \frac{6}{a}$

96) $\left(\frac{14}{r} - \frac{3}{r}\right) + \frac{6}{r}$

97) $\left(\frac{7}{v} - \frac{7}{v}\right) + \frac{3}{v}$

98) $\left(\frac{2}{x} - \frac{1}{x}\right) + \frac{y}{y} - \frac{z}{z}$

99) $\frac{y}{y} + \left(\frac{11}{z} - \frac{11}{z}\right)$

100) $\left(5\frac{4}{5}x - 3\frac{1}{5}x\right)$

101) $\left(5\frac{7}{10}b - 2\frac{5}{10}b\right)$

102) $100\frac{9}{10}m - 3\frac{9}{100}m$

103) $\left(\frac{a}{a} + \frac{b}{b}\right) - \frac{cde}{cde}$

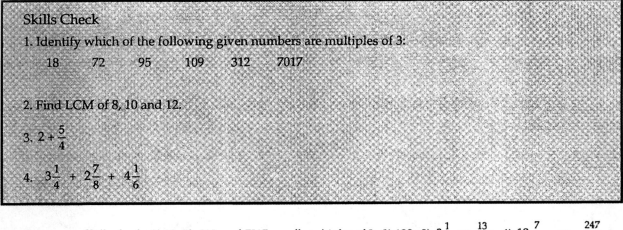

Skills Check

1. Identify which of the following given numbers are multiples of 3:

   18   72   95   109   312   7017

2. Find LCM of 8, 10 and 12.

3. $2 + \frac{5}{4}$

4. $3\frac{1}{4} + 2\frac{7}{8} + 4\frac{1}{6}$

Answers to Skills check: 1) 18, 72, 312, and 7017 are all multiples of 3; 2) 120; 3) $3\frac{1}{4}$ or $\frac{13}{4}$; 4) $10\frac{7}{24}$ or $\frac{247}{24}$

Section 2.8   Conversions and Comparisons between Fractions and Decimals

Objective:

- To convert number values between fractions and decimals
- To compare fraction and decimal values
- To solve problems with both fraction and decimal values
- To set up/solve application problems with both fraction and decimal values

Application:

As the inventory manager for a mid-sized retail company, Gabriella spent much of her time on a computer trying to find discounts and order items from various wholesalers. In January she ordered items from three regular suppliers that cost her company 1.6 million dollars, $\frac{3}{4}$ of a million dollars, and 0.3 million. She also received $\frac{1}{5}$ off a fourth order for 1.4 million before the discount. What was the final cost of Gabriella's orders in actual dollars?

Vocabulary:

*** Remember that **every fraction** **is** a division problem (the numerator ÷ the denominator).

We read $\frac{2}{3}$ as two-thirds, and as 2 over 3, but we can also read (top to bottom) the fraction as $2 \div 3$. The denominator is always the **divisor**.

Here are two common decimal and fraction equivalencies that we should have memorized:

$$\frac{1}{3} = 0.\overline{3} \text{ and } \frac{2}{3} = 0.\overline{6}$$

Here are other common equivalencies that occur regularly and that we should learn:

<u>fourths</u>   <u>fifths</u>

$\frac{1}{4} = 0.25$ $\frac{3}{4} = 0.75$ $\frac{1}{5} = 0.2$ $\frac{4}{5} = 0.8$

$\frac{2}{4} = \frac{1}{2} = 0.5$ $\frac{4}{4} = 1.0$ $\frac{2}{5} = 0.4$ $\frac{5}{5} = 1.0$

$\frac{3}{5} = 0.6$

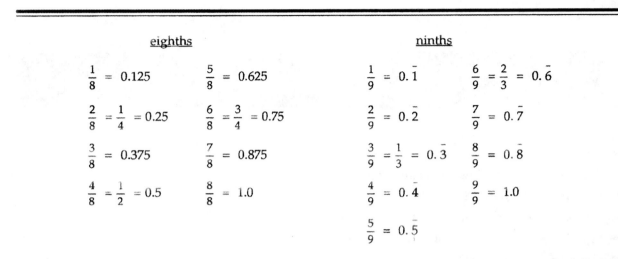

eighths

$$\frac{1}{8} = 0.125 \qquad \frac{5}{8} = 0.625$$

$$\frac{2}{8} = \frac{1}{4} = 0.25 \qquad \frac{6}{8} = \frac{3}{4} = 0.75$$

$$\frac{3}{8} = 0.375 \qquad \frac{7}{8} = 0.875$$

$$\frac{4}{8} = \frac{1}{2} = 0.5 \qquad \frac{8}{8} = 1.0$$

ninths

$$\frac{1}{9} = 0.\overline{1} \qquad \frac{6}{9} = \frac{2}{3} = 0.\overline{6}$$

$$\frac{2}{9} = 0.\overline{2} \qquad \frac{7}{9} = 0.\overline{7}$$

$$\frac{3}{9} = \frac{1}{3} = 0.\overline{3} \qquad \frac{8}{9} = 0.\overline{8}$$

$$\frac{4}{9} = 0.\overline{4} \qquad \frac{9}{9} = 1.0$$

$$\frac{5}{9} = 0.\overline{5}$$

How to:

Convert a Fraction or a Mixed Number to a Decimal:

1. If you have a mixed number, change it into an improper fraction.

2. Take the numerator and divide it by the denominator.

Example #1: Change $\frac{1}{4}$ to a decimal.

Step #1: You don't have a mixed number, so go to step #2.

Step #2: Take the numerator and divide it by the denominator.

This is a long division problem. Read the problem as 1 ÷ 4 where the divisor is 4. So the set up is:

$4\overline{)1}$ which is the same as $4\overline{)1.0}$

Solve: $4\overline{)1.00}$ (.25)   Answer: $\frac{1}{4}$ is the same as **0.25**

Example #2: Change $3\frac{2}{5}$ to a decimal.

Step #1: Change the mixed number to an improper fraction.

$$3\frac{2}{5} = \frac{17}{5}$$

Step #2: Take the numerator and divide it by the denominator.

This is a long division problem. Read the problem as 17 ÷ 5 where the divisor is 5. So the set up is:

$5\overline{)17}$ which is the same as $5\overline{)17.0}$

Solve: $5\overline{)17.0}$ (3.4)   Answer: $3\frac{2}{5}$ is the same as **3.4**

*** IMPORTANT SHORT CUT!! We really don't need to do step #1. The whole number value doesn't change when we convert between mixed numbers and decimals. In this case we can see that the 3 wholes is consistent in the mixed number of $3\frac{2}{5}$ and the decimal number of 3.4. In fact, mathematically we only have to convert the fraction of $\frac{2}{5}$ to the decimal of 0.4 When we keep the 3 wholes we get 3 + 0.4 which equals 3.4

How to:

Convert a Decimal to a Fraction or a Mixed Number:

1. Say the number and write it, the whole number (if there is one) and then the decimal number (the number of parts) over its place value. The place value is the denominator of the fraction.

2. ALWAYS reduce the fraction to its lowest term.

Example #3: Change 0.18 to a fraction.

Step #1: Say the number and write it.

There are zero wholes and 18 parts out of the place value of 100.

We read this as eighteen hundredths and write $\frac{18}{100}$.

Step #2: ALWAYS reduce the fraction.

$\frac{18}{100}$ reduces to $\frac{9}{50}$ **Answer:** 0.18 is the same as $\frac{9}{50}$

Example #4: Change 56.125 to a mixed number.

Step #1: Say the number and write it.

There are fifty-six wholes and 125 parts out of the place value of 1000.

We read this as fifty-six and one hundred twenty-five thousandths. We write $56\frac{125}{1000}$.

Step #2: ALWAYS reduce the fraction.

In $56\frac{125}{1000}$ the fraction reduces to $\frac{1}{8}$

Answer: 56.125 is the same as $56\frac{1}{8}$

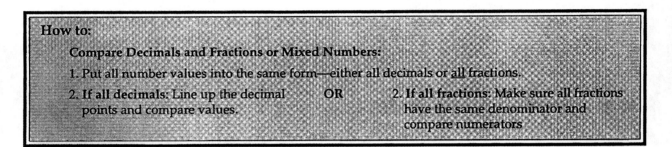

*** It is often easiest to compare decimals and fractions by changing our fractions into decimals.

Example #5: Which is larger, 3.21 or $3\frac{1}{4}$?

Step #1: Put all number values into the same form.

Make values all decimals	OR	Make values all fractions
Change $3\frac{1}{4}$ to its decimal		Change 3.21 to its fractional
form of 3.25		form of $3\frac{21}{100}$

Step #2: Line up decimal points.

the decimal: 3.21

$3\frac{1}{4}$ as the decimal: 3.25

Step #2: Get Same Denominators

3.21 as the mixed number: $3\frac{21}{100}$

$3\frac{1}{4}$ as the mixed number: $3\frac{25}{100}$

Answer: $3\frac{1}{4}$ is the larger than 3.21

*** When giving an answer to a comparison problem, we always use the original form of the given number. In the example above, we would <u>not</u> say that $3\frac{25}{100}$ is the larger number because this was not the original form of the given value of $3\frac{1}{4}$.

Sample #1: True or False: $14.3 > \frac{43}{3}$

First, we must decide whether to present both numbers in a decimal or a fractional form. Let's solve this both ways:

Solving by presenting both values as Mixed Numbers:

Change 14.3 to its mixed number form of $14\frac{3}{10}$

Change the improper fraction of $\frac{43}{3}$ to its mixed number form of $14\frac{1}{3}$

Our inequality now reads: $14\frac{3}{10} > 14\frac{1}{3}$

To compare $14\frac{3}{10}$ and $14\frac{1}{3}$ we need to represent both fractions with a common denominator. In this case the LCD of 10 and 3 is 30.

$$14\frac{3}{10} = 14\frac{9}{30} \text{ and } 14\frac{1}{3} = 14\frac{10}{30}$$

Our inequality would now read: $14\frac{9}{30} > 14\frac{10}{30}$

We can see that this statement is not true. **Answer: False**

Solving by presenting both values as Decimals:

Change $\frac{43}{3}$ to its decimal form. $\Rightarrow$ $3\overline{)43} = 14.\overline{3}$

Our inequality would now read: $14.3 > 14.\overline{3}$

We can see that this is a false statement because 14.3 is the same as 14.30 and $14.\overline{3}$ is the same as 14.3333....

Answer: False

You try it now:

a) True or False: $\frac{27}{7} < 3.86$

b) True or False: $2\frac{11}{36} > 2.3$

Sample #2: Put the following numbers in order from smallest to largest:

$$7\frac{3}{50}, \ 7.62, \ 7.062, \ 7\frac{1}{20}, \text{ and } \frac{23}{3}$$

Change all mixed numbers and fractions to decimals.

$7\frac{3}{50} = 7.06$ $7\frac{1}{20} = 7.05$ $\frac{23}{3} = 7.\overline{6}$

Line up the decimal points and compare the values.

$7\frac{3}{50}$ = 　　7.06　　$\Rightarrow$　second smallest

　　　　　　　7.62　　$\Rightarrow$　fourth smallest

　　　　　　　7.062　$\Rightarrow$　third smallest

$7\frac{1}{20}$ = 　　7.05　　$\Rightarrow$　smallest

$\frac{23}{3}$ = 　　　$7.\overline{6}$　　$\Rightarrow$　largest

Answer: $7\frac{1}{20}$, $7\frac{3}{50}$, 7.062, 7.62, and $\frac{23}{3}$

■
■
■
■
■
■

You try it now:

c) Put in order from smallest to largest: 12.165, $12\frac{1}{8}$, 12.1, $\frac{49}{4}$, and 12.025

d) Put in order from smallest to largest: 8.508, $8\frac{1}{2}$, 8.85, $8\frac{4}{5}$, and 8.58

Sample #3: Max and Imelda paddled their way down a river. They went 2.4 miles to get past a first series of rapids, then another 3.15 miles to reach the river's largest rapids, and finally another $2\frac{1}{8}$ miles before they reached their campsite. How far did Max and Imelda travel on the river? If the trip took $4\frac{1}{2}$ hours, how many miles per hour did they average (round answer to the nearest tenth of a mile per hour)?

First, find the total distance traveled.　　　　**Set up:**　$2.4 + 3.15 + 2\frac{1}{8}$

Change $2\frac{1}{8}$ to its decimal form of 2.125.　　$\Rightarrow$　　$2.4 + 3.15 + \textbf{2.125}$

First **answer:** They traveled **7.675 miles.**

Second, find the average:　　　　　　**Set up:** $(2.4 + 3.15 + 2\frac{1}{8}) \div 4\frac{1}{2}$

Change all mixed numbers to decimals.　　$\Rightarrow$　　$(2.4 + 3.15 + \textbf{2.125}) \div \textbf{4.5}$

　　　　　　　　　　　　　　$(7.675) \div 4.5$　$\Rightarrow$　$4.5\overline{)7.675}$

Make the divisor a whole number. The problem now is:　$45\overline{)76.75}$

　　　　　　　　　　　　　　　　$1.70\overline{5}$
　　　　　　　　Solve:　$45\overline{)76.750}$

Answer: **1.7 miles per hour**

- **You try it now:**

e) After the Christmas Holidays, regional managers of the *All Purposes* store chain had to report their earnings or loses for December to their corporate headquarters. Region A and Region B made 2.37 million dollars and $3\frac{3}{8}$ million dollars respectively. Region C lost $\frac{3}{5}$ of a million dollars while Region D lost 1.4 million. How much money did the four regions earn together? What was the average earnings of each region (round to the nearest tenth of a million dollars)?

f) To live rent-free at the West-end Apartments, Clyde had to work 15 hours a week for the owner of the apartment complex. If Clyde worked 3 hours and 20 minutes on Monday, 2.25 hours on Tuesday, and $4\frac{1}{3}$ hours on Thursday, how many how did he still have to work that week (give answer as a mixed number)?

Answers to You try it now: a) True; b) True; c) 12.025, 12.1, $12\frac{1}{8}$, 12.165; $\frac{49}{4}$;

d) $8\frac{1}{2}$, 8.508, 8.58, $8\frac{4}{5}$, and 8.85; e) Company earned 3.745 million dollars or $3,754,000; each region averaged $.9 million or $900,000 in earnings; f) $5\frac{1}{12}$ hours

Answer to Application: To find the dollar amount of Gabriella's order, we must find the sum of the 4 orders. The first three orders are given as 1.6 million, $\frac{3}{4}$ million and 0.3 million. The fourth order goes for 1.4 million, but Gabriella got a discount— $\frac{1}{5}$ off. If she got $\frac{1}{5}$ off, that means she paid $\frac{4}{5}$ of the 1.4 million. Remembering that "a number of another number" means multiply, we know she really only paid $\frac{4}{5}$ • (1.4 million) for the fourth order.

Set up (remembering that these values are in millions of dollars): $\left(1.6 + \frac{3}{4} + 0.3\right) + \frac{4}{5} \cdot (1.4)$

Change fractions to decimals: $(1.6 + 0.75 + 0.3) + 0.8 \cdot (1.4)$

Solve: 3.77 million dollars

3.77 • $1,000,000 give the answer in actual dollars: $3,770,000

2.8 Fraction and Decimal Conversion and Comparison Problems

In exercises #1-14, state which given number has the greatest value.

1) $\frac{3}{4}$ or $\frac{5}{8}$

2) $\frac{2}{7}$ or $\frac{1}{3}$

3) $\frac{1}{2}$, $\frac{3}{8}$, or $\frac{5}{16}$

4) $\frac{1}{3}$, $\frac{5}{12}$, or $\frac{7}{18}$

5) $\frac{3}{4}$, $\frac{3}{5}$, or $\frac{7}{9}$

6) $\frac{2}{3}$, $\frac{3}{5}$, or $\frac{5}{8}$

7) 2.8, 2.085, or 2.181

8) 8.7, 8.075, or 8.19

9) 124, 124.01, or 124.1

10) 6.14, 6.0014, or 6.004

11) $3.02\overline{7}$, $3.027\overline{1}$, or 3.00895

12) 11.022, 11.0082, 11.102

13) 5.76, $5.70\overline{6}$, or $5.7\overline{1}$

14) 4.16, 4.1527, or 4.1618

In exercises #15-26, convert the following decimals to either fractions or mixed numbers. If the value of the decimal is greater than 1, give your answer as both an improper fraction and a mixed number.

15) 0.27

16) 0.217

17) 0.126

18) 0.84

19) 2.7

20) 4.8

21) 4.16

22) 3.45

23) 2.004

24) 5.0015

25) $4.\overline{3}$

26) $2.\overline{6}$

In exercises #27-44, convert the following fractions or mixed numbers to decimals.

27) $\frac{3}{4}$

28) $\frac{5}{8}$

29) $\frac{11}{5}$

30) $\frac{37}{4}$

31) $\frac{2}{3}$

32) $\frac{28}{3}$

33) $\frac{7}{40}$

34) $\frac{14}{25}$

35) $\frac{6}{100}$

36) $\frac{11}{10000}$

37) $\frac{12}{800}$

38) $\frac{6}{3000}$

39) $3\frac{4}{9}$

40) $2\frac{1}{9}$

41) $20\frac{1}{8}$

42) $12\frac{3}{50}$

43) $5\frac{5}{12}$

44) $4\frac{11}{36}$

In exercises #45-60, state which given number has the greatest value.

45) $\frac{2}{5}$ or 0.43

46) $\frac{7}{8}$ or 0.79

47) $\frac{7}{20}$ or 0.7

48) $\frac{3}{10}$ or 0.45

49) $5\frac{1}{4}$ or 5.025

50) $10\frac{3}{40}$ or 10.3

51) $\frac{2}{3}$ or 0.06

52) $\frac{1}{3}$ or 0.3

53) $\frac{3}{10}$ or $0.\overline{3}$

54) $\frac{66}{100}$ or $0.\overline{6}$

55) $\frac{67}{100}$ or $0.\overline{6}$

56) $\frac{33}{100}$ or $0.\overline{3}$

57) $4\frac{1}{12}$ or 4.08

58) $3\frac{3}{16}$ or 3.18

59) $\frac{51}{20}$ or 2.5

60) $\frac{316}{5}$ or 60.315

In exercises #61-68 write the given numbers in order from smallest to largest.

61) $\frac{3}{8}$, 0.3, $\frac{3}{4}$, 0.38, and 0.7

62) $\frac{1}{3}$, 0.04, 0.35, $\frac{2}{5}$, and 0.039

63) $\frac{4}{5}$, 0.78, $\frac{7}{9}$, 0.81, and 0.0801

64) $\frac{3}{200}$, 0.002, 0.0142, $\frac{7}{500}$, and 0.01

65) $2\frac{1}{5}$, $2\frac{3}{10}$, 2.25, 2.03, and $2\frac{1}{40}$

66) $8\frac{2}{3}$, 8.6, 8.265, $\frac{33}{4}$, and $8.0\overline{6}$

67) $15\frac{5}{6}$, 15.8, 15.0084, $\frac{46}{3}$, and 15.084

68) $1\frac{69}{100}$, 1.0676, $1.00\overline{9}$, $1\frac{27}{40}$, and 1.67

In exercises #69-87, state whether the given statement is True or False.

69) $3\frac{1}{5} + 2.2 > 5.6$

70) $2\frac{1}{4} + 3 > 5.2$

71) $5\frac{1}{3} + 0.\overline{6} > 5.99$

72) $7.25 + 3\frac{3}{4} > 11$

73) $4\frac{1}{3} + 0.\overline{3} > 4.63$

74) $8\frac{1}{5} - 0.27 > 7.06$

75) $14.002 - 2\frac{3}{100} > 10\frac{97}{100}$

76) $8.06 - 4\frac{33}{100} > 4\frac{53}{100}$

77) $\frac{2}{6} + 2.5 < 2\frac{2}{3}$

78) $1\frac{1}{7} + 1.25 < 2\frac{3}{10}$

79) $7.2 - 2\frac{1}{4} < 4.9$

80) $2.2\left(4\frac{1}{50}\right) < 8\frac{24}{25}$

81) $\left(6.2 \cdot \frac{1}{3}\right) < 2.6$

82) $\frac{2}{5}$ of $3.5 < \frac{1}{2}$ of 4

83) $\frac{1}{3}$ of $7.6 > 2\frac{4}{5}$

84) $4\frac{3}{5} \div 0.02 > 23$

85) $7\frac{7}{8} \div 1.05 < 7.25$

86) $3.6 \div \frac{1}{5} < 17\frac{3}{5}$

87) $16.87 \div \frac{7}{20} < 48.4$

In exercise #88–104: (a) write a mathematical expression that will solve the problem, and (b) give the solution.

88-90) Two mountain climbers raced each other up the face of a steep mountain side. Climber A ascended about 500 feet the first hour and another $1\frac{1}{3}$ thousand feet the second hour. Climber B ascended about $\frac{5}{8}$ of a thousand feet the first hour and 1.1 thousand feet the second hour?

88) Climber B had climbed farther than climber A after the first hour. By how much?

89) Climber A had ascended farther than climber B after 2 hours. By how much?

90) What was the average distance climbed per hour by Climber B?

91-92) A board of lumber is $10\frac{1}{4}$ feet in length. Chuck needs pieces of wood that are 0.45 feet in length.

91) How many 0.45 foot-long pieces of wood can Chuck get from one board (Remember: you can't buy a part of a board)?

92) If Chuck needs 200 pieces of 0.45 foot-long piece of wood, how many boards will he have to buy?

93-95) Gwen originally bought 50 shares of stock for the independent book store *Books are We* at $5\frac{3}{16}$ dollars per share. After 2 months the shares had increased by 50¢ each. By the end of the year, the stocks gained another $\$1\frac{5}{8}$.

93) What was the worth of each share of *Books are We* by the end of the year?

94) How much were Gwen's shares of stock worth by the end of the year?

95) If Gwen sold her stock at the end of the year, how much money would she make (round answer to the nearest cent)?

96-100) After temporary paralysis, several back surgeries, and the general atrophy of his muscles, Rafael began his rehabilitation by swimming. A lap at the pool where he swam was 50 yards. The first three days he managed to swim 15 yards, 25 yards, and 40 yards respectively. On his fourth day he swam a whole lap and on the fifth day he swam $1\frac{1}{4}$ laps. A month later Rafael swam 4.5 laps without stopping.

96) What fraction of a lap did Rafael swim his first day?

97) How many laps had Rafael swum in his first three days (Give answer as both a mixed number and a decimal)?

98) Did Rafael swim a longer distance his first 3 days or his fifth day? By how many laps (Give answer as both a mixed number and a decimal)?

99) Did Rafael swim a longer distance his first 5 days or the 4.5 laps he swam a month later? By how many laps (Give answer as both a mixed number and a decimal)?

100) If another rehabilitation patient could swim only $\frac{3}{10}$ of a lap a day, how many days would it take the patient to swim the 4.5 laps?

101-104) George was a Paperback Writer who made $0.75 on every book he sold and earned another $2\frac{1}{4}$ thousand dollars a month as a sitar player in a semi-famous band. His roommate, Ringo worked at an amusement park, giving rides in a yellow submarine. He had a salary of $2500 a month. Last month George sold 800 paperbacks and Ringo earned another $\frac{1}{4}$ of his salary on tips. George, as he had pledged as a younger man, gave $\frac{1}{5}$ of his earnings to a charity while Ringo always gave $\frac{1}{10}$ of his earnings to charity.

101) Who earned more money during the last month—and by how much?

102) Who gave more money to charity—and by how much?

103) If Ringo had given another $\frac{3}{8}$ of a thousand dollars to charity, how much more money would he have given to charity than George?

104) If George had earned another $1\frac{1}{8}$ thousand on his book sales, how many more books would he have sold?

In exercises #105-116, state which given expression has the greatest value. (All variables are positive integers with a value of at least 2.)

105) $\frac{x+1}{x}$, $\frac{x+2}{x}$, or $\frac{x+3}{x}$

106) $\frac{x}{x}$, $\frac{x}{x+1}$, or $\frac{x}{x+2}$

107) $x + 0.23$, $x + 0.05$, or x

108) $x - 0.4$, $x - 0.04$, or $x - 0.004$

109) $\frac{3}{4} \bullet x$, $0.7 \bullet x$, or $0.\overline{7} \bullet x$

110) $2\frac{2}{5} \bullet x$, $2.3 \bullet x$, or $2.395 \bullet x$

111) $\frac{a}{5}$, $\frac{a}{0.5}$, or $\frac{a}{0.2}$

112) $\frac{x}{\frac{4}{5}}$, $\frac{x}{0.085}$, or $\frac{x}{0.58}$

113) $\frac{a}{a}$, $\frac{9}{10}$, or $\frac{b}{b-1}$

114) $\frac{x}{x}$, $\frac{x+1}{x}$, or $\frac{x}{x+1}$

115) $\frac{a}{a}$, $\frac{a+b}{a+b}$, or $\frac{3}{2}$

116) $\frac{x}{x}$, $\frac{x-5}{x-5}$, or $\frac{13}{12}$

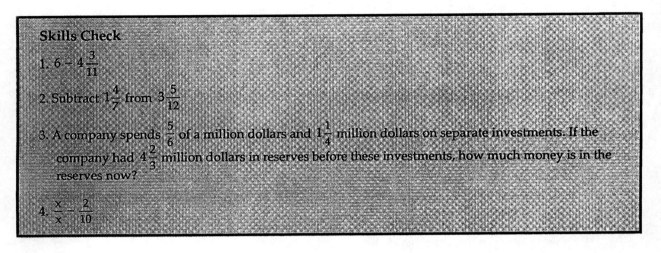

Skills Check

1. $6 - 4\frac{3}{11}$

2. Subtract $1\frac{4}{7}$ from $3\frac{5}{12}$

3. A company spends $\frac{5}{6}$ of a million dollars and $1\frac{1}{4}$ million dollars on separate investments. If the company had $4\frac{2}{3}$ million dollars in reserves before these investments, how much money is in the reserves now?

4. $\frac{x}{x} - \frac{2}{10}$

Answers to Skills Check: 1) $1\frac{8}{11}$ or $\frac{19}{11}$; 2) $1\frac{71}{84}$ or $\frac{155}{84}$; 3) $2\frac{7}{12}$ million dollars; 4) $\frac{4}{5}$

Chapter 3   Signed Numbers

Moving from the material learned in the first two units of this book to the material covered here in the third unit, is one of real transition in mathematics. It is movement from arithmetic into prealgebra. We get to explore a larger system of numbers—rational numbers—a system that moves us from a world of positive numbers into a system that includes both negative and positive number values.

We know that <u>negative numbers exist</u>. They are commonly used in three different areas—**money, temperature,** and <u>altitude</u>. Regarding money, we all know that owing money is negative; our balance is less than zero. If we owe someone $20 this can be expressed as -$20. For any of us who have lived in a place that experiences a harsh winter, we know that temperatures below zero (negative!) are indeed cold! When a thermometer dips below zero by 10 degrees, we express this as -10°. Finally, altitude is always measured in units above or below sea level. Sea level is at an altitude of zero. The tallest mountain in the world, Mt. Everest is 29,028 feet above sea level. The lowest point on the North American continent is Death Valley in California at 282 feet below sea level. It has an altitude or elevation of -282 feet.

Before we can take full advantage of the mathematics concerning negative numbers, in Section 3.1 we must first learn some new vocabulary, symbols, and concepts which are important to this new area of math.

Section 3.1   The Number Line and the Meaning of Signed Numbers

Objective:

- To read and recognize negative and positive values on a number line
- To learn new vocabulary associated with rational numbers
- To solve for the value of an expression which has a number inside a parenthesis with a negative sign in front of the parenthesis
- To solve for the absolute value of a number
- To compare number values that belong to the system of rational numbers

Application:

A day on the planet earth is 24 hours; the distance around the earth at its equator is almost 25,000 miles. Rounded to the nearest hundred, how many miles in distance along the equator correspond to one hour? Approximately how many miles west from one point on the equator would you have to be for the time to be three hours earlier? Approximately how many miles east from this same point on the equator would you have to be for the time to be two hours later?

Vocabulary:

signed numbers – Signed numbers is the term that refers to all negative and positive values

positive number – A **positive number** has a value greater than zero.

negative number – A **negative number** has a value less than zero.

zero – The value of **zero** is neither negative nor positive.

Two new inequality symbols:

$\geq$ is the symbol meaning "greater than <u>or</u> equal to."

$\leq$ is the symbol meaning "less than <u>or</u> equal to."

A Look at Different <u>Systems of Numbers</u>:

natural numbers – The system of natural numbers consists of all the positive whole numbers, starting at one and going upward forever {1, 2, 3, 4, 5...}. This is the simplest system of numbers, often called the system of counting numbers.

whole numbers – The system of whole numbers consists of zero <u>and</u> all the natural numbers {0, 1, 2, 3, 4, 5...}.

integers – The system of integers consists of zero and <u>all</u> negative and positive whole numbers {...-3, -2, -1, 0, 1, 2, 3...}.

rational numbers – The system of rational numbers consists of any number that can be written as either a terminating or repeating decimal. This includes all integers, and simple fractions (one integer over a second integer, excluding zero). The system of rational numbers is new to us in this chapter as we expand our knowledge of numbers to include both negative and positive values.

Examples of rational numbers: -3, $\frac{2}{5}$, $-6\frac{1}{3}$, **0.271**, **–0.7**, $\frac{11}{2}$, $0.\overline{3}$

The Number Line – A number line is a horizontal or vertical line which gives a pictorial representation of values. Whenever we look at a number line, we first need to identify the distance between any two dash marks on the line

As we move farther to the right on a horizontal number line (or up on a vertical number line) we move to a greater value; conversely, the farther we move to the left on a horizontal number line (or down on a vertical number line) we move to a lower value.

origin – The **origin** of a number line is point zero.

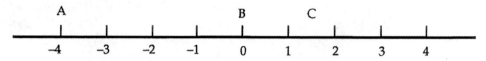

Looking at the number line above, we <u>first</u> identify the distance between any two dashes on the number line. We see that there is a value of 1 whole between each dash mark.

Pt. A is equal to –4.

Pt. B is 0 (the origin of the number line)

Pt. C is about halfway between positive 1 and positive 2, so we can estimate that its value is

$1\frac{1}{2}$ or its decimal equivalent of 1.5

additive inverse—The **additive inverse** is the opposite value (opposite sign) of any given value. The sum of any number and its additive inverse is zero.

Examples: The additive inverse (opposite sign) of positive 3 or +3 is negative 3 or –3. The additive inverse (opposite sign) of negative 5 or –5 is positive 5 or +5.

absolute value—The **absolute value** of a number is the **distance** between any value on a number line and the origin (zero). It is important to remember that <u>a distance is always positive</u> (we can't walk a negative mile), so **the absolute value of any number is <u>always</u> positive.**

The symbol for absolute value is two vertical lines — $|\ \ |$

We read $|4|$ as "the absolute value of four." In this case the absolute value of 4 is 4 because it is 4 units away from zero on the number line.

We read $\left|-2\frac{1}{4}\right|$ as "the absolute value of negative two and one-fourth. In this case the

absolute value of $-2\frac{1}{4}$ is $2\frac{1}{4}$ because it is $2\frac{1}{4}$ units from zero on the number line.

***To lessen any confusion we might experience later, let's clarify **these** five <u>important facts</u>:

• **A sign affects the value to its right.**

Example:　　　　　– 3　The minus sign affects the number to its right. In this case the 3 has a value of "negative three."

Example:　　　　　+ 7　The plus sign affects the number to its right. In this case the 7 has a value of "positive seven."

- A number is positive unless it has a negative sign or subtraction symbol in front of it. There does not need to be a plus sign before a number for it to be positive.

  Example: 3   There is no sign so the value is positive—just as we have viewed numbers our entire lives. 3 has the same value as ⁺3, but why insert a symbol we don't need? The plus sign shown here is usually used only for emphasis.

- The negative sign in front of a parenthesis means "take the opposite sign" of the value inside the parenthesis. The negative sign "distributes" into a parenthesis.

  Example: – (3)   In a very limited sense, we can say that the "3" inside the parenthesis is positive, but this indeed is a very limited way of looking at this example.

     If we were to state whether this **math expression** has a negative or positive value, the answer is that it has a negative value. The minus sign in front of the parenthesis tells us to "take the opposite sign" of the value inside the parenthesis.

     The opposite of positive 3 is negative three. Symbolically we say that – (3) is the same as –3

  Example: – (–6)   In a very limited sense, we can say that the "6" inside the parenthesis is negative, but this indeed is a very limited way of looking at this example.

     If we were to state whether this **math expression** has a negative or positive value, the answer is that it has a positive value. The minus sign in front of the parenthesis tells us to "take the opposite sign" of the value inside the parenthesis.

     The opposite of negative 6 is positive six. Symbolically we say that – (–6) is the same as ⁺6 or simply 6.

- The negative sign is "the strong sign." It <u>always</u> determines whether the number value is negative or positive.

- The plus sign is the "weak sign." It is not needed to identify a positive number, and it <u>never</u> changes the sign of any given number. We will see in the next section of the book that the only purpose for a plus sign is to tell us to combine number values. In this section it tells us nothing.

  Example: ⁺3   There is only a plus sign (which really tells us nothing!), so the number must be positive.

  Example: – (⁺3)   The 3 <u>inside</u> the parenthesis (very limited sense) is positive with or without the plus sign. (Get rid of it because it means nothing!) – (⁺3) is the same as – (3), which means take the opposite of positive three. This equals –3.

     So: – (+3) is the same as – (3), which is the same as –3.

Example: + (–3)   The plus sign is the weak sign. It is not needed to identify a positive number, and it <u>NEVER</u> changes the sign of a given number. The 3 inside the parenthesis (very limited sense) is negative. There is no negative sign in front of the parenthesis to change this value, so it stays negative.

+ (–3) is the same as –3

Two Strategies to Remember:

(1) Don't worry about labeling a minus sign (–) as a subtraction symbol or a negative sign. Both mean you are going to a lesser value. That is what is important.

(2) Write or rewrite mathematical expressions with the least number of plus or minus signs as possible.

How to:

Identify a Point on a Number Line:

1. Determine the distance between any two dashes on the number line.

2. Identify whether the point(s) is negative or positive.

3. Write the value of the point(s) based on steps #1 and #2.

Example #1: Find the values of Points A, B, and C.

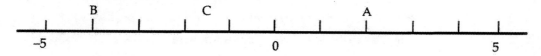

Step #1: Determine the distance between any two dashes on the number line.

We are only given three labels on this graph — 0, 5 and –5. Count the number of dashes to the right of zero to reach the dash labeled as the value of 5. There are five dashes to get to positive five. Therefore, the distance between each dash is equal to one whole.

Step #2: Identify whether the point(s) is negative or positive.

Point A is to the right of zero, so it is positive.

Points B and C are to the left of zero, so they are negative.

Step #3: Write the value of the point(s) based on steps #1 and #2.

Pt. A is two dashes to the right of zero $(1 + 1)$, so its value is **2**.

Pt. B is four dashes to the left of zero $[(-1) + (-1) + (-1) + (-1)]$, so its value is **-4**.

Pt. C is more than 1 dash, but less than 2 dashes to the left of zero. We can estimate

that it is about $1\frac{1}{2}$ dashes to the left of zero $\left[(-1) + \left(-\frac{1}{2}\right)\right]$, so its value is $-1\frac{1}{2}$ or

its decimal value of **-1.5**

Example #2: Find the values of Points X, Y, and Z.

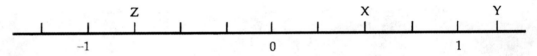

Step #1: Determine the distance between any two dashes on the number line.

We are only given three labels on this graph—0, 1, and -1. Count the number of dashes to the right of zero to reach the dash labeled as the value of 1. There are four dashes to get to positive 1. Therefore, each dash is "one part out of four," the four being one whole. The distance between each dash is one whole divided by 4, other

wise known as $\frac{1}{4}$ or 0.25 in its decimal form.

Step #2: Identify whether the point(s) is negative or positive.

Points X and Y are to the right of zero, so they are positive.

Point Z is to the left of zero, so it is negative.

Step #3: Write the value of the point(s) based on steps #1 and #2.

Pt. X is two dashes to the right of zero $\left(\frac{1}{4} + \frac{1}{4}\right)$, so its value is $\frac{1}{2}$ or its decimal

equivalent of **0.5**

Pt. Y is one dash to the right of positive one $\left(1 + \frac{1}{4}\right)$, so its value

is $1\frac{1}{4}$ or **1.25**

Pt. Z is three dashes to the left of zero $\left[\left(-\frac{1}{4}\right) + \left(-\frac{1}{4}\right) + \left(-\frac{1}{4}\right)\right]$, so its value is $-\frac{3}{4}$

or **-0.75**

> **How to:**
>
> **Solve for the value of an expression where there is a minus sign in front of a parenthesis:**
>
> 1. Always follow order of operations. Work inside a parenthesis first. If you have multiple parentheses, work inside the innermost parenthesis first.
>
> 2. Solve step by step, remembering that a minus sign in front of a parenthesis means to take the "opposite sign" of the value inside the parenthesis.

Example #3: Solve for the value of the following expression: $-(3 + 2 \bullet 5)$

Step #1: Always follow order of operations.

We must work inside the parenthesis first. Inside the parenthesis are two operations—addition and multiplication. We must multiply first. Solve $2 \bullet 5$: $-(3 + \underbrace{2 \bullet 5})$

and rewrite as: $-(3 + 10)$

Finish work inside the parenthesis. Solve $3 + 10$: $-(\underbrace{3 + 10})$

and rewrite as: $-(13)$

Step #2: A minus sign in front of a parenthesis means to take the "opposite sign" of the value inside the parenthesis.

$\underbrace{-(13)}$

The opposite sign of positive 13 is negative 13, so write the solution as: -13

Example #4: Solve for the value of the following expression: $-\left(-\left(4 + 6\right)\right)$

Step #1: Always follow order of operations.

There are two parentheses, so we must work inside the innermost parenthesis first. Solve $(4 + 6)$: $-(-\underbrace{(4 + 6)})$

and rewrite as: $-\left(-\left(10\right)\right)$

Step #2: A minus sign in front of a parenthesis means to

take the "opposite sign" of the value inside the

parenthesis.

Having solved for the value inside the innermost

parenthesis and getting 10, we now solve for the

value inside the outer parenthesis. Solve –(10) $-(\underbrace{-(10)})$

The opposite sign of the positive 10 (inside the

parenthesis) is negative 10, so

rewrite the expression as: –(–10)

Notice how the innermost parenthesis disappeared

when we distributed the minus sign to the (10).

Finally, we must distribute the negative sign outside

the remaining parenthesis into that parenthesis. $-(\underbrace{-10})$

The opposite sign of –10 is positive 10, so

write the solution as: **10**

How to:

Solve for the value of an expression where there is an absolute value symbol:

1. Solve any math inside an absolute value symbol.

2. Pull out the positive value of whatever number is inside the absolute value symbol. The absolute value symbol disappears.

3. If necessary, finish solving the expression by following order of operations.

Example #5: Solve the following expression: $\left| -7 \right|$

Step #1: Solve any math inside an absolute value symbol.

There is nothing to solve. There is simply a negative value inside the absolute value symbol.

Step #2: Pull out the positive value of whatever number is inside the absolute value symbol. The absolute value symbol disappears.

The positive value or distance of –7 to zero
(the origin) on the number line is 7.

So: $|-7|$ becomes 7.

Example #6: Solve the following expression: $-|8-3.5|$

Step #1: Solve any math inside an absolute value symbol.

Solve 8 – 3.5 which equals 4.5

Rewrite the expression as: $-|4.5|$

Step #2: <u>Pull out</u> the <u>positive value</u> of whatever number   ↓
is inside the absolute value symbol. The absolute
value symbol disappears.
          ↓

The positive value or distance of 4.5 to zero
(the origin) on the number line is 4.5.   ↓

Write the solution as: -4.5

Notice that the solution to this expression is negative because the minus sign was
"waiting" <u>outside</u> the absolute value symbol to pounce upon the positive value that
we pulled out of the absolute value symbol.

***Remember: <u>Never</u> distribute a negative sign into an absolute value symbol (we only distribute a
negative sign into a parenthesis!). The absolute value symbol is like a wall where the number
value can only exit; nothing can enter this walled area.

Sample #1: Find the values for the points A, B, C, and D. Give your answers in both fractional and
decimal form.

```
        D               C           A       B
  ──┬──┬──┬──┬──┬──┬──┬──┬──┬──┬──┬──┬──
     -1                 0                   1
```

First we find the distance between any two dashes. It takes 5 dashes to make one whole, so

the distance between any two dashes is "one part out of five" $\Rightarrow \frac{1}{5}$ in fractional form and 0.2
in decimal form.

Points A and B are positive because they are to the right of zero.

Pt A is one dash to the right of zero so it equals $\frac{1}{5}$ or 0.2

Point B is approximately halfway between $\frac{3}{5}$ and $\frac{4}{5}$.

In fact , Pt. B is $\frac{3}{5} + \left(\frac{1}{2}\ of\ \frac{1}{5}\right)$

Solve: $\frac{3}{5} + \left(\frac{1}{2} \cdot \frac{1}{5}\right)$ and find out that **Pt. B** is about $\frac{7}{10}$ or 0.7

Points C and D are negative because they are to the left of zero.

Pt. C is two dashes to the left of zero , so it equals $-\frac{2}{5}$ or - **0.4**

Pt. D is approximately halfway between –1 and $-1\frac{1}{5}$.

In fact, Pt D is $-1 + \left(\frac{1}{2}\ of\ -\frac{1}{5}\right)$

Solve: $-1 + \left(\frac{1}{2} \cdot -\frac{1}{5}\right) \Rightarrow -1 + \left(-\frac{1}{10}\right) \Rightarrow$ Pt. D is about $-1\frac{1}{10}$ or –1.1

You try it now:

a) Find the values for the points A, B, C, and D. Give your answers in both fractional and decimal form.

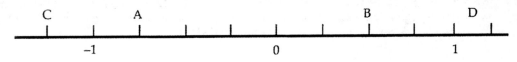

b) Find the values for points W, X, Y, and Z. Give your answers in both fractional and decimal form.

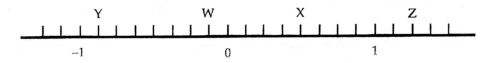

Sample #2: Read the chart below and answer the following questions.

    1) How many companies made a profit?

    2) How much money did company C make?

    3) How much more money did company E make than company B?

    4) How much more money did company A make than company D?

The Zip Corporation consists of five companies. For this chart the companies are known as A, B, C, D, and E. Their placement on the number line to the left is based upon their earnings or losses for the corporation during the last fiscal year. All numbers represent dollar amounts in millions of dollars.

To answer any questions regarding a number line, we first discover the distance between any two dashes. On this vertical number line we see that it takes two dashes to reach 20 (million), so the distance between any two dashes is equal to 10 (million)

1) **4** companies made a profit (companies B, E, A, and C are above zero).

2) Company C makes halfway between 40 and 50 million dollars. Mathematically we can

    write this as: $40 \text{ million} + \left(\frac{1}{2} \text{ of } 10 \text{ million} \right)$.

    Company C made \$45 million.

3) Company E made 20 million dollars. Company B made 10 million. We find the difference
    between the profits of the two companies:

    Concept: (Profit of Company E) - (Profit of Company B)

    Set up: (20 million) - (10 million)

    Company E made \$10 million more than Company B

4) Company A made 30 million dollars. Company D lost 10 million dollars.

One way to look at this problem is to view <u>the distance</u> between Company A and Company D on the number line. This is the <u>absolute value</u> between the two points.

Start at Pt. A. To get to zero, the distance is 30 (million). From zero to Pt. D, the distance is 10 (million).

Mathematically we can see this as: $\left|30\right| + \left|-10\right| \Rightarrow 30 + 10 \Rightarrow 40$

Company A made $40 million more than Company D.

You try it now:

c) Read the chart below and answer the following questions.

(1) What is the difference in the temperature of the soil at sites M2 and M4?

(2) If the soil temperature at site M3 has averaged –4° for the past ten years and never reached a temperature higher than –1°, would this year's temperature reading tend to support or deny the possibility of global warming? Why?

(3) As a general rule, the farther one travels northward in Canada, the colder it gets. Which site do you think is farthest north? Which site is farthest south?

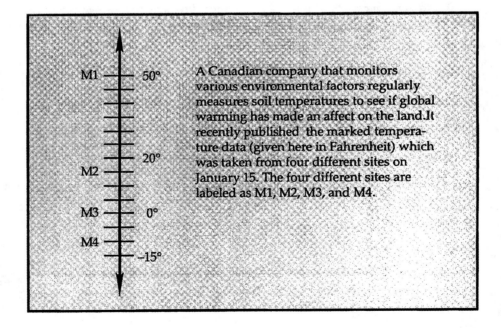

A Canadian company that monitors various environmental factors regularly measures soil temperatures to see if global warming has made an affect on the land. It recently published the marked temperature data (given here in Fahrenheit) which was taken from four different sites on January 15. The four different sites are labeled as M1, M2, M3, and M4.

d) Figure out the altitudes of the three climbers on Mt. Everest (29,028 foot elevation) from the information provided below. Then draw a vertical number line that reaches from an elevation of zero to 30,000 feet. Each dash should represent 5,000 feet. Plot the altitudes of three climbers, labeling them as Persons R, S, and T.

> Climber R is 560 feet short of 2 miles above sea level.
> Climber S is 2000 yards from the peak of Mt. Everest.
> Climber T is 1 mile below the sum of the heights of climbers R and S.

Sample #3: At a small investment company seven employers each earned $30,000 dollars for the company in July. In August those same employers each lost $30,000 dollars for the company.

First, write an expression inside a parenthesis that represents the amount of money the employees made in July. Second, write an expression that represents how much money the employees made in August. Use only the given numbers in the set up. Don't solve for a final answer.

1) Draw a set of parenthesis. Figure out the expression that represents how much money the employees made in July.

> If 7 people each earned $30,000 dollars in July, the total amount earned would be found through multiplication. Put this inside a parenthesis and we get the following set up:
> $$(7 \cdot 30,000)$$

2) Now write an expression that represents how much money the employees made in August. The set up must include the identical answer to question #1 with no alterations inside the parenthesis. Don't solve for a final answer.

The set up for August is exactly the opposite of July's set up. Since we mathematically represent the "opposite of" by putting a negative sign in front of a parenthesis the set up for August would be:
$$-(7 \cdot 30,000)$$

You try it now:

Use only the given numbers for the following:

e) Betty earned $50 on 4 consecutive days last week. This week she spent $50 on 4 consecutive days.

First, write an expression inside a parenthesis that represents Betty's financial standing for last week. Second, write an expression that represents her financial standing for the second week (the content inside the parenthesis must be the same for both answers).

f) Imelda's stock lost $3 per share 5 times last month. This month her stock gained $3 per share 5 times.

First, write an expression inside a parenthesis that represents the change in value of Imelda's stock per share last month. Second, write an expression that represents the change in the value of her stock per share for the second month (the content inside the parenthesis must be the same for both answers).

Sample #4: Solve for the value of this expression: $-\left|-4\right|$

Once we see the absolute value symbol, we recognize (or solve if necessary) the value inside the symbol and pull out its "positive value," that is its distance from zero on the number line.

The absolute value of -4 is 4.

$$-\left|-4\right|$$

Bring down the sign <u>outside</u> the $\downarrow$
absolute value symbol; then pull $\downarrow$
out the 4 and we get the solution of -4

You try it now:

g) Solve for the value of this expression: $-\left|-\dfrac{2}{5}\right|$

h) Solve for the value of this expression: $-\left(-\left|5\right|\right)$

Answers to You try it now: a) Pt. A = $-\dfrac{3}{4}$ and -0.75; Pt. B = $\dfrac{1}{2}$ and 0.5; Pt. C = $-1\dfrac{1}{4}$ and -1.25; Pt. D = $1\dfrac{1}{8}$ and 1.125; **b)** Pt. W = $-\dfrac{1}{8}$ and -0.125; Pt. X = $\dfrac{1}{2}$ and 0.5; Pt. Y = $-\dfrac{7}{8}$ and -0.875; Pt. Z = $1\dfrac{1}{4}$ and 1.25; **c)** (1) 25°; (2) This year's temperature reading at site M3 would tend to support global warming because the temperature measurement this year is at 0° for the first time in 10 years and well above the average soil temperature of -4°; (3) The site farthest north would be M4 because that soil has the lowest recorded temperature. The site farthest south would be M1 because that soil has the highest recorded temperature; **d)** Climber R (solved from the expression of $\left|5280(2)-560\right|$) is at 10,000 feet; Climber S (solved from the expression of $\left(29,028-2000(3)\right)$) is at 23,028 feet; Climber T (solved from the expression of $\left[\left(23,028+10,000\right)-5280\right]$) is at 27,748 feet; See graph below; **e)** expression for last week: $\left(\$50 \bullet 4\right)$; expression for this week: $-\left(\$50 \bullet 4\right)$; **f)** expression for last month: $\left(-\$3 \bullet 5\right)$; expression for this month: $-\left(-\$3 \bullet 5\right)$; **g)** $-\dfrac{2}{5}$; **h)** 5;

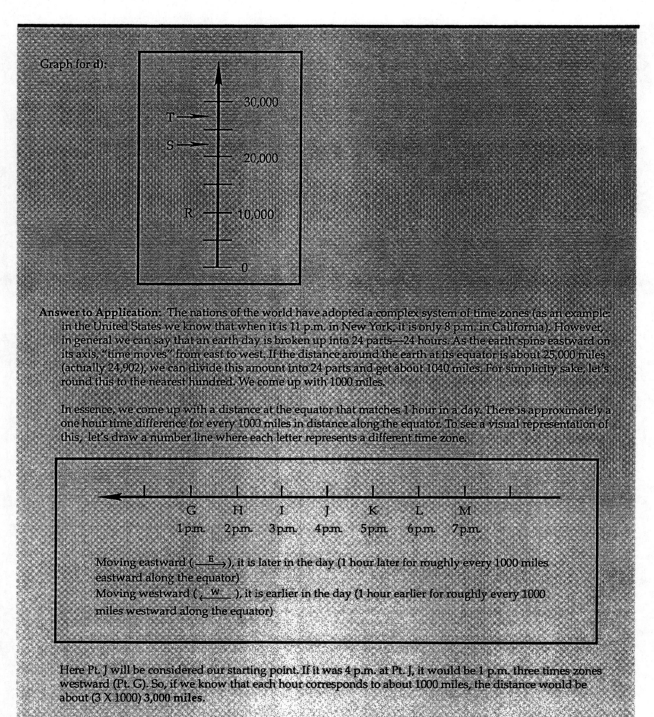

Graph for d):

Answer to Application: The nations of the world have adopted a complex system of time zones (as an example: in the United States we know that when it is 11 p.m. in New York, it is only 8 p.m. in California). However, in general we can say that an earth day is broken up into 24 parts—24 hours. As the earth spins eastward on its axis, "time moves" from east to west. If the distance around the earth at its equator is about 25,000 miles (actually 24,902), we can divide this amount into 24 parts and get about 1040 miles. For simplicity sake, let's round this to the nearest hundred. We come up with 1000 miles.

In essence, we come up with a distance at the equator that matches 1 hour in a day. There is approximately a one hour time difference for every 1000 miles in distance along the equator. To see a visual representation of this, let's draw a number line where each letter represents a different time zone.

Moving eastward (──E──→), it is later in the day (1 hour later for roughly every 1000 miles eastward along the equator)

Moving westward (←──W──), it is earlier in the day (1 hour earlier for roughly every 1000 miles westward along the equator)

Here Pt. J will be considered our starting point. If it was 4 p.m. at Pt. J, it would be 1 p.m. three times zones westward (Pt. G). So, if we know that each hour corresponds to about 1000 miles, the distance would be about (3 X 1000) **3,000 miles.**

Likewise, two hours eastward (Pt. L) would be about (2 X 1000) **2,000 miles.**

In fact, if we took out an atlas of the Western Hemisphere, (North and South America), we would see that an example that would fit this model would be the cities of New York (Pt. J), San Francisco (Pt. G), and Rio de Janeiro in Brazil (Pt. L).

3.1 The Number Line and the Meaning of Signed Number Problems

Use the number line below to answer the questions #1-8.

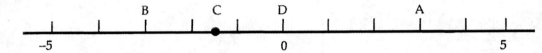

1) What letter lies on the origin of the number line?

2) How many of the letters represent negative values?

3) Is Pt. B a natural number?

4) Is Pt. C an integer?

5) How many letters represent integers?

6) What is the value of Pt. B?

7) What is the approximate value of Pt. C? Give the answer in both a fractional and decimal form.

8) What is the distance (the absolute value) between Pt. B and Pt. A?

Use the number line below to answer the questions #9-16.

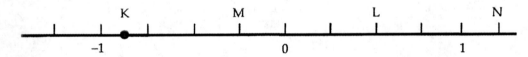

9) How many letters represent positive values?

10) What letter lies closest to the origin of the number line?

11) How many letters represent integers?

12) Is Pt. L a rational number?

13) Is Pt. M a rational number?

14) Is Pt. K a rational number? Explain your chosen answer.

15) What is the distance (the absolute value) between Pt. N and Pt. M? Give the answer in both a fractional and decimal form.

16) What is the approximate value of Pt. K?

Use the number line below to answer the questions #17-24.

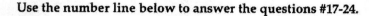

17) What is the value of Pt. C?

18) What is the distance from Pt. D to Pt. C?

19) Does Pt. C have a greater value than Pt. B?

20) Does Pt. C have a greater value than Pt. D?

21) What is the approximate value of Pt. A? Give the answer in both a fractional and decimal form.

22) Which has the greater value: Pt. A or the absolute value of Pt. D?

23) Which has the greater value: $|Pt.C|$ or $|Pt.D|$?

24) True or False: $|Pt.A|$ = Pt. A?

In exercises #25-55, solve for the value of the following expressions.

25) $-(5)$

26) $-(-3)$

27) $-(-2.3)$

28) $-(0.25)$

29) $+(-3)$

30) $+(12)$

31) $+(+4)$

32) $+(+38.4)$

33) $-(+7)$

34) $-(+0.4)$

35) $-\left(-\dfrac{1}{5}\right)$

36) $+\left(-\dfrac{3}{4}\right)$

37) $-(-(-2))$

38) $+(-(-2))$

39) $-(-(+4))$

40) $-[-(-(10))]$

41) $|28|$

42) $|-9|$

43) $|-3|$

44) $|+2|$

45) $-|-5|$

46) $-|6+3|$

47) $-\left|\dfrac{2}{3}\right|$

48) $-\left|-\dfrac{3}{11}\right|$

49) $-(6-2)$

50) $-(3 \bullet 4)$

51) $-(7+2 \bullet 4)$

52) $-(12 \div 2 - 1)$

53) $+(3-2)$

54) $+[-(15+4 \bullet 3)]$

55) $-[-(6+4 \div 2)]$

In exercises #56-63, find the additive inverse for each expression.

56) -7 57) $-(3)$ 58) $+(4)$ 59) $-(-10)$

60) $-\dfrac{3}{8}$ 61) $-[-(-1)]$ 62) $\dfrac{4}{7}$ 63) $\left(-\left(-\dfrac{1}{3}\right)\right)$

In exercises #64-71, state whether the given inequalities are true or false. If not sure, remember the number line. The farther to the right on the number line the greater its value.

64) $-6 \geq 2$ 65) $-4 \leq 3$ 66) $-9 \leq -2$ 67) $-7 \geq 0$

68) $-(-3) \geq -5$ 69) $-(6) \geq -(-6)$ 70) $|-10| \leq -10$ 71) $-|-8| \leq -|8|$

Use the number line below to answer questions #72-77.

Several non-governmental organizations (NGO's) provided money and technological assistance to three failing farming cooperatives in an African nation in an effort to expand their production of millet and corn. The harvests of the farming cooperatives, known here as cooperatives A, B, and C are recorded below on the number line. The letters with the subscript of a 0 mark the financial gain or loss for each cooperative in 1998, the year before receiving assistance. The letters with the subscript of a 2 mark the financial gain or loss for each cooperative in 2000, the second year after receiving NGO assistance.

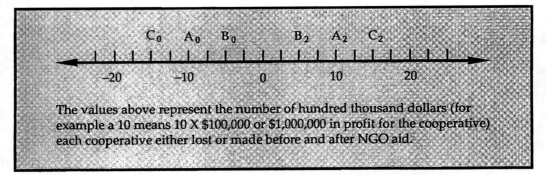

The values above represent the number of hundred thousand dollars (for example a 10 means 10 X $100,000 or $1,000,000 in profit for the cooperative) each cooperative either lost or made before and after NGO aid.

72) How much money did Cooperative A lose in the year before (A_0) NGO aid?

73) How much money did Cooperative A earn in profit two years after (A_2) it received NGO aid?

74) How much more money did Cooperative A earn in the year 2000 than it had made in 1998?

75) Which Cooperative showed the least gain in earnings between 1998 and 2000? How much was the gain?

76) Which Cooperative showed the greatest gain in earnings between 1998 and 2000? How much was the gain?

77) Similar-sized farming cooperatives in this nation had averaged an annual earnings of $400,000 in 1998 and $450,000 in annual earnings in 2000. If this is true, should the NGO project here be considered a success or not? Explain why or why not.

Use the information and the number line below to answer questions #78-83.

For its own use, a multi-national corporation has labeled time zones throughout the world with letters of the alphabet. The corporate headquarters are in Chicago (time zone F). Here is a list of the company's other six office sites along with their respective time zones: Los Angeles and Vancouver (zone D); Mexico City (zone F); New York City (zone G); Buenos Aires, Argentina (zone I); and Anchorage, Alaska (zone C).

Each letter represents a time zone in the Western Hemisphere. Remember that moving eastward (__E→), it is one hour later in each time zone. Moving westward (←__W), it is one hour earlier in each time zone.

78) At 12 noon in the Chicago office, an employee called the company office in Los Angeles. What time did the employee answer the phone in Los Angeles?

79) At 9 a.m. in Alaska, an employee called the company office in Chicago. What time did the employee answer the phone in Chicago?

80) Working in Vancouver, Glen had called a tele-conferencing meeting for 10 a.m. New York City time. What time would Glen have to call New York?

81) Working in the Buenos Aires, Argentina office, Jorge was told to e-mail a report to the Chicago headquarters before noon Chicago time. If Jorge returned to his office at 1 p.m. Argentinian time after a lunch meeting, how much time did he have to prepare the report?

82) Anita worked in the Mexico City office. She wanted to tele-conference simultaneously with Chicago and the other five world-wide corporate offices. Assuming that each office was open from 9 a.m. to 5 p.m. local times at each office, what window of Mexico City time could Anita offer as a time to start an hour long meeting?

83) When a salesperson in Rome (zone M) called the Los Angeles office, an employee answered the phone at 10 a.m. What time was it in Rome?

Use the number line below to answer questions #84-89.

Listed are times and heights of the Diablo River on May 25.

84) At what height does the Diablo River begin to flood?

85) The Diablo River reached its greatest height at about 5 p.m. What was the river's height then?

86) Write the number that tells the height of the Diablo River at 2 p.m. in relation to its flood level (think of the flood level as zero on a number line).

87) At 8 a.m. the river had reached a height of 20 feet. Write the number that tells the height of the river in relation to it flood level (think of the flood level as zero on a number line).

88) The river's normal height in May is about 15 feet. Write the number that tells the height of the river at its normal May height in relation to it flood level (think of the flood level as zero on a number line).

89) By 10 p.m. the river's waters had receded and returned to a height of 30 feet. Between 10 a.m. and 10 p.m. what was the total distance which the river had both risen and fallen?

90) Figure out the location of each of the four race car drivers in the *River Road race* from the information provided below. Then draw a horizontal number line that reaches from the starting point of the race to its finish 800 miles east. Label the number line so that the river (which runs north to south) is labeled as zero (the origin) and is exactly the halfway point of the race. Labels to the west (left) of the origin should be written as negative values; labels to the east (right) of the origin should be written as positive values. Each dash should represent 100 miles. Finally, plot the locations of the four drivers, labeling them as drivers A, B, C, and D.

- Driver A is 200 miles west of the origin.
- Driver B has driven 100 miles farther than Driver A.
- Driver C has driven 50 miles less than the combined distances which Drivers A and B have travelled together.
- Driver D is currently the same distance from both Drivers A and C.

91) We are given the following expression: $(7-2)$. Now write an expression (do not solve) that means the opposite of this (in your answer the content inside the parenthesis must be identical to that of the given expression).

92) We are given the following expression: $(-6 \bullet 2)$. Now write an expression (do not solve) that means the opposite of this (in your answer the content inside the parenthesis must be identical to that of the given expression).

93) We are given the following expression: $(-2 + 7 \bullet 3)$. Now write an expression (do not solve) that means the opposite of this (in your answer the content inside the parenthesis must be identical to that of the given expression).

94) We are given the following expression: $-(2 + 3)$. Now write an expression (do not solve) that means the opposite of this (use the given expression exactly as it is for a part of your answer).

95) Mike earned $70 on 3 consecutive days last week. This week he spent $70 on 3 consecutive days. First, write an expression inside a parenthesis that represents Mike's financial standing for last week. Second, write an expression that represents his financial standing for the second week (the content inside the parenthesis must be the same for both answers).

96) Sharon's stock lost $2 per share 5 times last month. This month her stock gained $2 per share 5 times. First, write an expression inside a parenthesis that represents the change in value of Sharon's stock per share last month. Second, write an expression that represents the change in the value of her stock per share for the second month (the content inside the parenthesis must be the same for both answers).

For exercises #97-102, answer the asked questions.

97) If x is a positive number, is the value of the expression $-(x)$ negative or positive?

98) If x is a positive number, is the value of the expression $-(-(x))$ negative or positive?

99) If x is a negative number, is the value of the expression $-(x)$ negative or positive?

100) If x is a negative number, is the value of the expression $-(-(x))$ negative or positive?

101) If x is a positive number, is the value of the expression $|x|$ negative or positive?

102) If x is a negative number, is the value of the expression $|x|$ negative or positive?

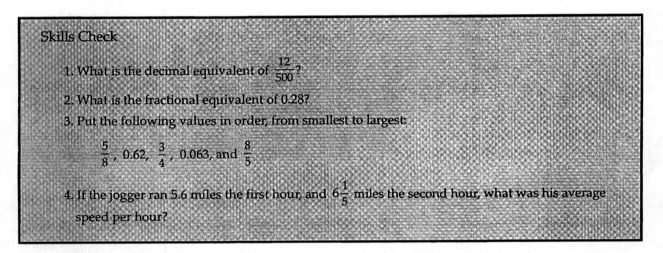

Skills Check

1. What is the decimal equivalent of $\frac{12}{500}$?

2. What is the fractional equivalent of 0.28?

3. Put the following values in order, from smallest to largest:

$$\frac{5}{8}, \ 0.62, \ \frac{3}{4}, \ 0.063, \text{ and } \frac{8}{5}$$

4. If the jogger ran 5.6 miles the first hour, and $6\frac{1}{5}$ miles the second hour, what was his average speed per hour?

Answers to Skills Check: 1) 0.024;   2) $\frac{7}{25}$;   3) 0.063, 0.62, $\frac{5}{8}$, $\frac{3}{4}$, and $\frac{8}{5}$;   4) $5\frac{9}{10}$ *miles per hour*

Section 3.2 Combining Integers & Decimals

Objectives:

- To recognize similar combining expressions, whether they are written in the "addition" or "subtraction" format
- To combine (add/subtract) whole numbers and decimals
- To set up/solve combining signed number application problems

Application:

The Math club on campus (cool!) had one hundred twenty dollars in its account after its last meeting. Since then, it had invested in some computer accessories which cost $87 and a new calculator that cost $105. The club also collected semester dues which added up to $60. Finally, the treasurer (a coveted position!) paid a $40 bill. What is the account balance for the Math club?

Vocabulary:

combine — To **combine** means to either add **or** subtract values. Don't get confused by language that will call some combining problems "addition" problems and refer to others as "subtraction" problems. **This labeling** of problems as either addition or subtraction can only confuse us right now as it **has** <u>nothing</u> **to do with how we will solve these signed number problems.**

Example: $-10 + 6$ It is true that we can call this an addition problem. There is an addition symbol.

Example: $5 - 7$ It is true that we can call this a subtraction problem. There is a subtraction symbol.

However, **instead of seeing these as different problems, we can think of both of these examples as** <u>combining</u> **problems.** We'll see why as we move through the examples in this section.

double negative — A **double negative** is two negative signs next to each other with no values between them. We have already seen double negatives, such as $-(-3)$, which means "take the opposite of -3." We know now that this equals just 3 or $+3$.

In fact, what is important is that **any double negative becomes a positive,** or thinking more actively, **it becomes a plus.**

Example: $10 - (-4)$

  $-(-4)$ is a double negative. It needs to be rewritten as: $+4$

  $10 - (-4)$ becomes $10 + 4$

Take note — The following examples are <u>not</u> double negatives. They are expressions that each have two negative values.

  Example: $-3 - 7$ **Example:** $-4 + -6$

The Plus Sign — One of the best ways to view the plus sign is to no longer view it as an actual sign (it is weak and meaningless in this regard!). The plus sign is simply the connector of two values (telling us the problem is a combining problem and not a multiplication or division problem); any plus sign can be read as "<u>and</u>."

Example: $-4 + -6$ can be read as "-4 and -6"

In fact, because the plus sign has no value as a sign, we can rewrite this expression as $-4 - 6$

These 3 expressions are all exactly the same:

  $-4 + -6$ -4 and -6 $-4 - 6$

****Remember:**   It won't matter right now, but as problems get more complex, remember that first and foremost we <u>always</u> follow the order of operations (PEMDAS).

How to:

Solve a combining problem:

1. Get rid of all double negatives. A double negative becomes a plus.

2. Identify the signs of the values in the expression.

3. If the signs of the values are the same: <u>ADD</u> (the absolute values of the two numbers) and **KEEP THE SAME SIGN**.

                    or

If the signs of the values are **different:** <u>Take the difference</u> (of the absolute values of the two numbers), always subtracting the smaller value from the larger, and **KEEP THE SIGN OF THE INITIAL LARGER NUMBER.**

Example #1: $-5 + -4$

Step #1: Get rid of all double negatives. A double negative becomes a plus.

There are no double negatives here. There is nothing to do.

Step #2: Identify the signs of the values in the expression.

When identifying the sign of a number value, always remember that a sign affects the value immediately to its right.

There is a minus sign before the number 5. Therefore the
5 is negative.

The 4 has "+ –" in front of it. We know the plus sign is only a connector of two values. It means "and.' So, + – 4 means "and – 4." The minus sign affects the 4. Thus, the **4 is negative**.

The signs are **the same**. The numbers are both negative.

Step #3: If the signs of the values are **the same**: <u>ADD</u> (the absolute values of the two numbers) and **KEEP THE SAME SIGN**.

Add the absolute values: $5 + 4 = 9$

Keep the same sign: The signs were negative so the answer is: -9

Why this works: To visually see why this process works, picture the number line. We start at -5 <u>and</u> (the + sign) we move -4. Count 4 spaces to the left and we arrive at -9

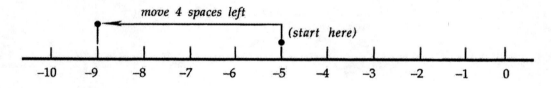

This visual process will always work. However, we will absolutely want to learn, in fact <u>memorize</u> the process in the *How to* box, but this is a handy helper for now.

Example #2: $-4-6$

Step #1: Get rid of all double negatives. A double negative becomes a plus.

There are no double negatives here. There is nothing to do.

Step #2: Identify the signs of the values in the expression.

There is a minus sign before the number <u>4</u>. Therefore the
4 is negative.

There is a minus sign before the number <u>6</u>. Therefore the
6 is negative.

The signs are **the same**. The numbers are both negative.

Step #3: If the signs of the values are **the same**: <u>**ADD**</u> (the absolute values of the two numbers) and **KEEP THE SAME SIGN**.

Add the absolute values: $4 + 6 = 10$

Keep the same sign: The signs were negative so the answer is: **–10**

Example #3: $3 - 7$

Step #1: Get rid of all double negatives. A double negative becomes a plus.

There are no double negatives here. There is nothing to do.

Step #2: Identify the signs of the values in the expression.

There is no sign before the number <u>3</u>. Therefore the
3 is positive.

There is a minus sign before the number <u>7</u>. Therefore the
7 is negative.

The signs are **different**. The 3 is positive and the 7 is negative.

Step #3: If the signs of the values are different: <u>**Take the difference**</u> (of the absolute values of the two numbers), always subtracting the smaller value from the larger, and **KEEP THE SIGN OF THE INITIAL LARGER NUMBER**.

Take the difference of the absolute values: $7 - 3 = 4$

Keep the sign of the larger number: The initial larger number
was negative so the answer is: **– 4**

Why this works: To visually see why this process works, picture the number line. We start at 3 and we move -7. Count 7 spaces to the left and we arrive at – 4

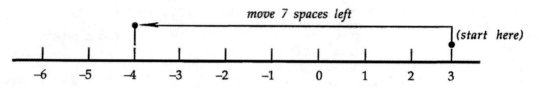

Example #4:   5 – (–9)

>   Step #1: Get rid of all double negatives. A double negative becomes a plus.
>
>   There is a double negative: – (–9). This becomes: + 9
>
>   Rewrite the expression as: 5 + 9
>
>   Step #2: Identify the signs of the values in the rewritten expression of 5 + 9.
>
>   Both signs are positive. They have to be positive because there are no minus signs.
>
>   The signs are the **same**.
>
>   Step #3: If the signs of the values are **the same**: <u>ADD</u> (the absolute values of the two numbers) and **KEEP THE SAME SIGN**.
>
>   Add the absolute values: 5 + 9 = 14
>
>   Keep the same sign: The signs were positive so the answer is: **14**

Example #5:   –6 – (–4)

>   Step #1: Get rid of all double negatives. A double negative becomes a plus.
>
>   There is a double negative: – (– 4). This becomes: + 4
>
>   Rewrite the expression as: – 6 + 4
>
>   Step #2: Identify the signs of the values in the rewritten expression of – 6 + 4.
>
>   There is a minus sign before the number <u>6</u>. Therefore the **6 is negative**.
>
>   There is a plus sign (no minus sign!) before the number <u>4</u>. Therefore the **4 is positive**.
>
>   The signs are **different**. The 6 is negative and the 4 is positive.

Step #3: If the signs of the values are different: <u>**Take the difference**</u> (of the absolute values of the two numbers), always subtracting the smaller value from the larger, and **KEEP THE SIGN OF THE INITIAL LARGER NUMBER.**

Take the difference of the absolute values: $6 - 4 = 2$

Keep the sign of the larger number: The initial larger number was negative so the answer is: **–2**

Why this works: To visually see why this process works, picture the number line. We start at –6 and we move 4. Count 4 spaces to the right and we arrive at –2

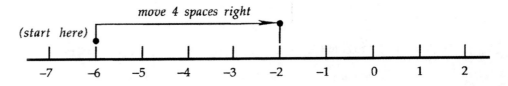

Sample #1: Without solving these problems, identify the one expression that is different from the others.

   a) $-8 + -3$ b) $-8 - 3$ c) $-8 + (-3)$ d) $-8 - (+3)$ e) $-8 - (-3)$

The way to tell if combining problems are the same is to identify the sign of each of the values.

For a, b, c, and d, we find that both the 8 and the 3 are negative. They are same signs.

The expression "e" is different. If we get rid of the double negative (which we always do first in a combining problem!!), we get: **– 8 + 3**.

In this case the 8 is negative and the 3 is positive. They are different signs – and thus "e" is the different problem.

You try it now:

a) Identify the one expression that is different from the others.

   a) $-4 - -3$ b) $-4 + 3$ c) $-4 + (-3)$ d) $-4 - (-3)$ e) $-4 + (+3)$

b) Identify the one expression that is different from the others.

   a) $5 - 7$ b) $5 + -7$ c) $5 - (+7)$ d) $5 - (-7)$ e) $+5 - +7$

Sample #2: $5 - 8 + (-7) - (-4) - (6)$

First, we identify this problem as a combining problem because it is all addition and subtraction (there is no multiplication and/or division).

Once identified as a combining problem, follow the *How to* process.

There is one double negative: $-(-4)$ Change this to $+4$. The expression of

$5 - 8 + (-7) \underbrace{-(-4)} - (6)$ becomes $5 - 8 + (-7) + 4 - (6)$

At this point we can solve this problem two different ways:

First we could just work left to right:

$$\underbrace{5 - 8} + (-7) + 4 - (6)$$

$$\Rightarrow \quad \underbrace{-3 + (-7)} + 4 - (6)$$

$$\Rightarrow \quad \underbrace{-10 + 4} - (6)$$

$$\Rightarrow \quad \underbrace{-6 - (6)}$$

Answer: -12

A second way to solve a long combining problem is to separately identify all negative-signed values and all positive-signed values.

Positive values are the 5 and the 4. Add the same signs to get 9.

Negative values are the 8, the 7, and the 6. Add the same signs to get -21.

The set up would have looked like this: $(5 + 4) + (-8 + -7 + -6)$

Now combine the results: $9 + -21$ Answer: -12

■ **You try it now:**
■
■
■   c) $-11 - (-6) + 2 - 9 + (+7)$
■
■   d) $-(-10) - (5) - (-8) + -4$
■

Sample #3: Rafique had $240 in his checking account on Monday. On Tuesday he paid his phone and utility bills—$87.25 for his phone bill and $80.17 for his utility bill. The next day he deposited his paycheck for $634.44 into his account and wrote checks for $500 and $220 to cover his rent and car insurance respectively. What number represents the change in Rafique's checking account after Monday? What was Rafique's checking account balance?

To answer the first question–what was the change in Rafique's account–we <u>don't</u> need to know the original amount of his balance, <u>only the changes</u>.

Concept: (amount of $ deposited into his account) + (amount of money spent)

Set up: $(634.44) + (-87.25 + -80.17 + -500 + -220)$

Solve: $(634.44) + (-887.42)$

<u>**Different signs**</u>–so take the difference (of the absolute values) and keep the sign of the larger number.

$$\begin{array}{r} 887.42 \\ -\ 634.44 \\ \hline 252.98 \end{array}$$ ⟹ the sign of the larger number is negative, giving us the **answer** of: **– $252.98**

Rafique spent more money than he deposited into his account!

***There were different ways to set up this problem. For example, one correct set up would have been:

$(634.44) - (87.25 + 80.17 + 500 + 220)$

In this second set up the amount in the second parenthesis will become negative because the minus sign before it means "the opposite of" the value inside the parenthesis.

$(634.44) - (887.42)$ ⟹ the numbers are still different signs.

We still get the same solution.

To solve the second question–what is Rafique's balance now–we <u>do</u> need to know the original amount of his balance.

Concept: (amount of $ in his account) + (amount of $ spent)

Set up: $(240 + 634.44) + (-87.25 + -80.17 + -500 + -220)$

Solve: $(874.44) + (-887.42)$

<u>**Different signs**</u>—so take the difference (of the absolute values) and keep the sign of the larger number.

$$\begin{array}{r} 887.42 \\ -\ 874.44 \\ \hline 12.98 \end{array}$$ ⟹ the sign of the larger number is negative, giving us the **answer** of: **– $12.98**

Rafique needs to deposit more money into his account!

***There were different ways to set up this problem. Two other correct set ups would have been:

$$(240 + 634.44) + (-87.25 - 80.17 - 500 - 220)$$

and $(240 + 634.44) - (87.25 + 80.17 + 500 + 220)$

- **You try it now:**

e) A group of hikers began their walk at an elevation of 4,000 feet. The first morning they gained 2,450 feet in elevation, but from that point they dropped 1,200 feet by nightfall. The second morning they climbed another 560 feet; in the afternoon they dropped 800 feet. The third and last day of their hike they dropped 1800 feet. What number represents the change in elevation from the start to the end of the hike? What was their elevation when the hike ended?

f) Lesya watched anxiously the value of her stock in *Future Tech* throughout the day. It started out at a value of $28.50 per share. By 10 in the morning it lost $2.15 in value. By noon it had lost another $4.05 in value. Between noon and 1 p.m. it gained $0.75 per share, but then lost another $0.40 by 2 p.m. By the time the stock market closed, the stock had regained $3.80 in value. What was the stock's change in value by the end of the day? What was the stock's value per share at the end of the day?

Sample #4: Looking at the graph below, answer the following questions.

1) What was the company's earnings for October?
2) What was the company's earnings for November?
3) What was the company's earning for the four-month period of September through December?

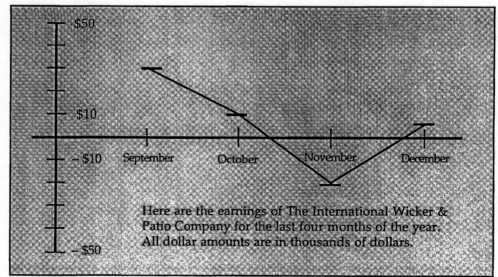

Here are the earnings of The International Wicker & Patio Company for the last four months of the year. All dollar amounts are in thousands of dollars.

Understand the graph first. <u>It consists of two number lines</u>. The **vertical number line** gives the amount of earnings. The **horizontal number line** shows the respective months of the year.

This graph is called a line graph because a line connects the monthly results, clearly showing us whether earnings rose or fell from month to month.

1) October's earnings are shown at $10. Because the graph shows that all dollar amounts are in thousands of dollars (Be sure to read the paragraph inside the box of the graph because it gives us vital information!), we actually have $10 • 1000 or an **answer** of: **$10,000**

2) November's earnings are at – $20 (times 1000) = – **$20,000**

3) Three of the months are earnings [September ($30,000), October ($10,000), and December ($5,000)] which must be combined with the loss in November (–$20,000).

Set up: (30,000 + 10,000 + $5,000) + (–$20,000)

Answer: $25,000 profit

You try it now:

g) The Department of Defense monitored a test flight over the Pacific Ocean of a new mechanical spying device (that utilized nanotechnology)–only the size of a baseball–which could fly over 800 miles, reach an altitude of 5000 feet and travel through water to a depth of about 300 feet. Use the graph below to answer the following questions.

1) What was the highest elevation which the spying device reached?
2) What was the lowest elevation which the spying device reached?
3) At about what time did the device enter the ocean?

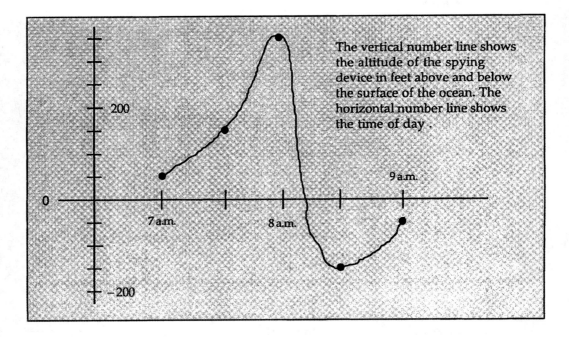

The vertical number line shows the altitude of the spying device in feet above and below the surface of the ocean. The horizontal number line shows the time of day.

h) Draw a graph where the vertical number line represents inches of rain above or below the annual average (make the amount between each dash be 1 inch). Zero would mean that the normal seasonal rainfall is occurring. The horizontal number line will be the first 6 months of the year. Plot (by drawing a darkened circle) the following data and then connect the plots with a single line.

January:	3 inches above normal	April:	normal amount
February:	1 inch below normal	May:	1 inch above normal
March:	3 inches below normal	June	1 inch above normal

Answers to You try it now: a) the letter "c" is different; b) the letter "d" is different; c) –5; d) 9; e) the change in the hikers' elevation was –790 feet; the elevation at the end of the hike was 3210 feet; f) the stock lost $2.05 per share so its change in value was –$2.05; it is now worth $26.45 per share; g) 1) about 350 feet; 2) about –150 feet; 3) about 8:10 a.m. (1/3 of the way between 8 and 8:30); h) see graph below:

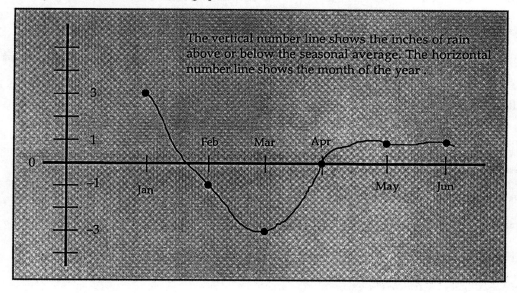

Answer to Application: To find the financial balance for the Math Club, we must combine all the values.

Concept: (amount of $ in the math account) + (amount of $ spent)

Set up: (120 + 60) + (– 87 + – 105 + – 40)

Solve: (180) + (– 232)

Take the difference of their absolute values: (232 – 180 = 52) and keep the sign of the larger number (the negative). The answer is – 52

The Math Club's financial balance is: – $52.

3.2 Combining Problems with Integers and Decimals

In exercises #1-10, answer the following questions.

1) When we use the word "combining" in this book, to which operation or operations are we referring?

2) If we identify a problem as a combining problem only, what is the first thing we need to do?

3) What is a double negative?

4) State whether the following expression is a double negative or not: $-(-5)$

5) State whether the following expression is a double negative or not: $-(-12)$

6) State whether the following expression is a double negative or not: $-6-5$

7) State whether the following expression is a double negative or not: $-4-10$

8) Is a double negative the same as a plus?

9) If we identify the signs of the numbers in a combining problem to be the same, will we add or subtract to solve the problem (if unsure, see the "How to" box on page 204)?

10) If we identify the signs of the numbers in a combining problem to be different, will we add or subtract to solve the problem (if unsure, see the "How to" box on page 204)?

In exercises #11-20, state whether the following expressions are True or False. When answering questions #15 – 20, refer to the "How to" box on page 204 if you are unsure.

11) A sign affects the value to its right.

12) A plus sign changes the value of the number to its right.

13) The value of the following expression is negative: $-(-6)$

14) The value of the following expression is positive: $-(5)$

15) We would add to solve the following problem: $-4-7$

16) We would add to solve the following problem: $-4+-7$

17) We would add to solve the following problem: $-4+7$

18) We would add to solve the following problem: $4-7$

19) We would add to solve the following problem: $4+(-7)$

20) We would add to solve the following problem: $-4-(-7)$

In exercises #21-26, identify the letter of the one expression that is different from the others. Do not solve.

21) a) $-2 + -3$ b) $-2 - 3$ c) $-2 + (-3)$ d) $-2 - (-3)$

22) a) $-8 + 5$ b) $-8 + (-5)$ c) $-8 + (5)$ d) $-8 - (-5)$

23) a) $7 - (2)$ b) $7 - (-2)$ c) $7 + (-2)$ d) $7 - (+2)$

24) a) $-10 + 3$ b) $-10 - 3$ c) $-10 - (3)$ d) $-10 - (+3)$

25) a) $-(-4) + -4$ b) $-(-4) - 4$ c) $-(-4) + (-4)$ d) $-(-4) - (-4)$

26) a) $-(-6) - -2$ b) $-(-6) + 2$ c) $-(-6) + (-2)$ d) $-(-6) + (+2)$

In exercises #27-34, look at the combining problems. (a) Identify (following the *How to* process) whether we should view the values in each problem as same signs or different signs and, (b) whether we should add or subtract to solve this particular problem.

27) $-4 + -7$ 28) $-5 + 7$ 29) $5 - 9$ 30) $-5 - 5$

31) $-12 + (+4)$ 32) $7 + (-8)$ 33) $6 - (-2)$ 34) $-8 - (-10)$

In exercises #35-76, solve the combining problems.

35) $-5 + -3$ 36) $-7 + (-2)$ 37) $8 + (-3)$ 38) $6 + -4$

39) $-4 - 6$ 40) $6 + (+8)$ 41) $-4 - (3)$ 42) $4 - 3$

43) $-7 - (-7)$ 44) $-11 - (-3)$ 45) $5 - (-6)$ 46) $10 - (-6)$

47) $-100 - 300$ 48) $200 - 300$ 49) $300 - (-100)$ 50) $-3 + (-3)$

51) $-10 - (-100)$ 52) $9 + (-3)$ 53) $-(9) + (-4)$ 54) $-(7) + 3$

55) $-8.6 + 3.4$ 56) $-12.43 - 7.2$ 57) $6.55 - (4.3)$

58) $7.02 + (-8.8)$ 59) $-9.3 - (-6.1)$ 60) $-3.25 - (-3.05)$

61) $4 - (-6.34)$ 62) $10.8 - (-6.9)$ 63) $-50 - 12.2$

64) $-(-6.8) - (6.8)$ 65) $-5.875 - (+4.3)$ 66) $-111.1 + (-11.1)$

67) $-8 - 4 + (-7) - (+4)$ 68) $-3 + -8 - (-6) + 7$ 69) $15 - (5) + (-2) - (-7)$

70) $-10 - (-7) - (-11) + (-2)$ 71) $-50 - (30) + (-10) - (-40)$

72) $-6 + -9 - 7 + 18 + -6 - 8 - 3 + 5$ 73) $-7.7 + (-4.1) - (6.6) + 5.25$

74) $8 - 5.2 - (-4.3) + 7.6 - (6.9)$ 75) $-12.125 - (+4.375) + (1.875) - 3.5$

76) $-(-18.5) - (+4.6) - (-9.9) + (-4.1)$

In exercises #77-81: (a) identify the letter of the one math expression that would solve the question asked in each word problem, and (b) give the solution.

77) Luther headed a local charity which gave small, interest-free loans to needy families. He started with a budget of $2,000 for the month of May. In the first week, he issued two loans, one for $350 and a second for $220. On the fifteenth of the month, he received two payments, for $40 and $25. He made one other loan for $200 that month; he also received another payment of $60. How much money did the charity have at the end of May?

a) $2000 - (-350 - 220 - 200) + (40 + 25 + 60)$ b) $-350 - 220 - 200 + 40 + 25 + 60$

c) $2000 + (40 + 25 + 60) - (350 + 220 + 200)$ d) $(40 + 25 + 60) + (-350 - 220 - 200)$

78) Etta worked out a budget for herself for the last month of school. She had $600 in the bank. She would need to pay her share of the rent ($450), her car payment ($150), and phone, utilities, and miscellaneous expenses ($300). She would get a paycheck for $700 from her job. Oh, and she would need to eat—another $250 expense. What would Etta's financial standing be at the end of the month if her predictions came true?

a) $600 + (-450 + 150 + 300 + 250) + 700$ b) $(600 + 700) - (-450 - 150 - 300 - 250)$

c) $600 - 450 - 150 - 300 + 700 + 250$ d) $600 - (450 + 150 + 300) + 700 - 250$

79-80) After a winter freeze in Florida, no one seemed to know if the orange crop had been ruined or not. On Monday the stock for *Uh-huh Orange Juice* sold for $18.65 a share. The chart below shows the changing value of the stock over the next four days.

Day of the Week	Change in value of the *Uh-huh Orange Juice* stock per share
Tuesday	- $1.45
Wednesday	- $2.60
Thursday	+ $0.55
Friday	- $0.20

79) What was the price per share of *Uh-huh Orange Juice* at the close of the stock market on Friday?

a) $18.65 - (1.45 + 2.60) + 0.55 - 0.20$ b) $-(1.45 + 2.60) + 0.55 - 0.20$

c) $18.65 - (1.45 - 2.60) + (0.55 - 0.20)$ d) $-(-1.45 - 2.60 - 0.20) + 0.55$

80) What was the change in the value of the stock after the four days?

a) $18.65 - (1.45 + 2.60) + 0.55 - 0.20$ b) $-(1.45 + 2.60) + 0.55 - 0.20$

c) $18.65 - (1.45 - 2.60) + (0.55 - 0.20)$ d) $-(-1.45 - 2.60 - 0.20) + 0.55$

81) The average starting salary for an employee at Troy's Market was $2500 per month. If three new employees started at monthly salaries of $2200, $2350, and $2600 respectively, how many dollars did they earn per month in relationship to the amount that three new employees would normally earn (hint: normal here would mean that $2500 is the equivalent of $0 above the norm)?

a) 2200 + 2350 + 2600

b) (2200 − 2500) + (2350 − 2500) + (2600 − 2500)

c) 2500 − (2200 + 2350 + 2600)

d) (2500 − 2200) + (2500 − 2350) + (2500 − 2600)

In exercises #82-92: (a) write a mathematical expression that will solve the problem, and (b) give the solution.

82) Maisie had $1000 in her checking account when she wrote checks for $560 and $127, respectively paying for her rent and school books. The next day Maisie used her ATM card and withdrew $60 from her checking account. What was her checking account balance now?

83) Testing a new airplane for its structural soundness, a pilot started at an elevation of 30,000 feet and dove nearly straight downward 18,000 feet before leveling off. She then veered upward and climbed 6,000 feet, before once again turning the nose of the plane back to the ground. At a high speed she spiraled downward for another 11,000 feet before leveling the plane off a second time. What was her altitude as she now headed back toward the airport.

84-85) When Andy turned thirty years old, he bought his first stock. He invested in a small import/export company whose stock was worth $34.50 per share. He carefully watched the stock's value for the first month he owned it. The first week it gained $1.25 in value, but then it lost $1.60 the second week and another $0.45 the third week. After the fourth week the stock lost yet another $1.05.

84) How much was the stock worth per share after the fourth week?

85) What was the change in the value of the stock after the four weeks?

86) Joel averaged a score of 182 as a bowler. In a recent tournament he scored 188, 194, and 168 in three games. After combining the number of points Joel scored above or below his average in each game, what number represents how many points he scored higher or lower than his average score for the three games?

87-88) The chart below shows the normal high temperatures for each date and then the actual high temperature readings for those three dates this summer in the city of Plains. If we look at July 1, we can see that this year's high temperature of 76° is 4 degrees lower than the normal high temperature of 80° for that date. In relationship to the average or normal high temperature (we consider the normal as being 0° above or below normal) for July 1, it is − 4.°

	Normal High Temperature	Current Year's High Temperature
July 1	80°	76°
July 2	81°	75°
July 3	81°	82°

87) What number represents how many degrees different is this year's high temperature for July 2 versus its normal high temperature for this date?

88) What is the sum of the differences in the high temperature reading for the three dates this year as compared to the normal temperature readings?

89-92) Look at the graph below.

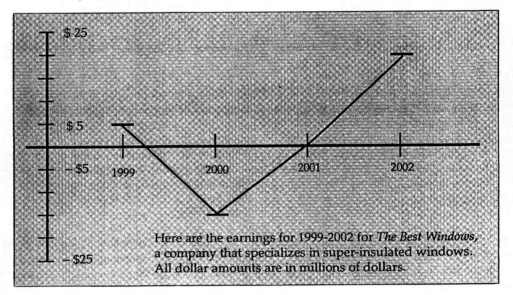

Here are the earnings for 1999-2002 for *The Best Windows*, a company that specializes in super-insulated windows. All dollar amounts are in millions of dollars.

89) What was the company's balance for 1999 and 2000?

90) What was the company's balance for the four-year period from 1999 through 2002?

91) How much more money did the company earn in 2002 than in 2001?

92) How much more money did the company earn in 2002 than in 2000?

93) Draw a graph where the vertical number line represents the value of a stock above or below its opening price (make the amount between each dash be $0.50). Zero would mean that the stock is selling for the same price as its initial opening. The horizontal number line will be the first 6 months of the year. Plot (by drawing a darkened circle) the following data in the chart below and then connect the plots with a single line.

Month Opening December	Change in value of the stock
January	+ $3
February	+ $1.25
March	- $0.75
April	- $2.50
May	- $2
June	+ $1.25

In exercises #94-96: (a) write a mathematical expression that will solve the problem, and (b) give the solution. See the information for problem #93 to answer these questions.

94) What was the change in the value of the stock from its opening value to its value at the end of March?

95) What was the overall change in the value of the stock from its opening value to its value at the end of June?

96) What was difference in the value of the stock from its highest value to its lowest?

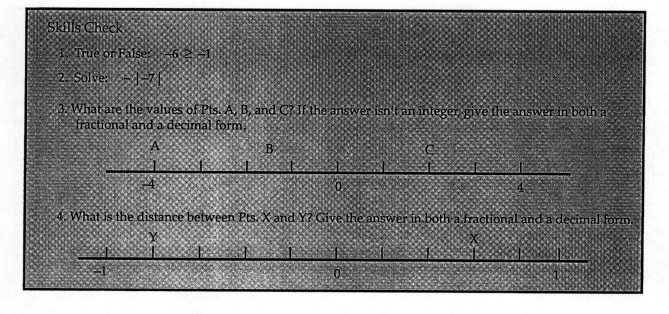

Skills Check

1. True or False: −6 ≥ −1

2. Solve: −|−7|

3. What are the values of Pts. A, B, and C? If the answer isn't an integer, give the answer in both a fractional and a decimal form.

4. What is the distance between Pts. X and Y? Give the answer in both a fractional and a decimal form.

Answers to Skills Check: 1) False;   2) −7;   3) Pt. A = −4; Pt. B = $-1\frac{1}{2}$ and −1.5; Pt. C = 2;   4) $\frac{7}{5}$ or $1\frac{2}{5}$ and 1.4

Section 3.3 Multiply and Divide Integers & Decimals

Objectives:

- To multiply and divide integers and decimals
- To translate words to multiplication/division statements
- To solve order of operations problems with both combining and multiplication/division of integers and decimals
- To set up/solve application problems

Application:

Three friends each invested $15,000 to start a small local restaurant. Two years later these equal business partners had lost not only all the money from their original investments, but were forced to close the restaurant because the business was another $27,000 in debt. If Marcellus paid off $5,000 of his debt in the next year, what number represents his financial balance in regards to his overall restaurant investment?

Vocabulary:

***Recognizing the operation of the problem: Although this is easy with a little practice, we must make sure that we know the operation of a given problem. When a value has two operations in front of it, remember that the first sign is <u>always the operation</u>. The second sign is the negative or positive value of a number.

Example: $7 \bullet -5$ The 5 has both a multiplication symbol and a minus sign in front of it, but this is definitely not a minus or subtraction problem. It is a multiplication problem. We are multiplying positive 7 by negative 5.

Example: $-8 \div -2$ The 2 has both a division symbol and a minus sign in front of it, but this is definitely not a minus or subtraction problem. It is a division problem. We are dividing negative 8 by negative 2.

Also: A parenthesis doesn't change the meaning of these expressions.

$7 \bullet -5$ is the same as $7 \bullet (-5)$ is the same as $(7) \bullet (-5)$

$-8 \div -2$ is the same as $-8 \div (-2)$ is the same as $\dfrac{(-8)}{(-2)}$

***Reviewing the meaning of the negative sign:** We have learned that the negative sign is the "go less" sign whether we call it "minus," "negative," or "subtract." However, we also learned that it can mean "**the opposite sign of.**" It is this last meaning that we utilize when multiplying and dividing signed numbers. Every negative sign means "take the opposite sign of."

Look at the following progression to understand negative signs in a multiplication and/or division problem.

5 • 6   There are no negative signs so the **answer** is positive 30.

–5 • 6   There is one negative sign so the answer is "the opposite sign of" five times six. Translating these words to math, we get the following expression:

$$- (5 \bullet 6) \qquad \text{We get an \textbf{answer} of } -30$$

–5 • –6   There are two negative signs so the answer is "the opposite sign of" the "opposite sign of" five times six. Translating these words to math, we get the following expression:

$$- (- (5 \bullet 6)) \qquad \text{We get an \textbf{answer} of } +30$$

Before moving to the next example make sure that we understand both the translations and the solutions to the problems above.

–5 • –6 • –2   There are three negative signs so the answer is "the opposite sign of" the "opposite sign of" the "opposite sign of" five times six times 2. Translating these words to math, we get the following expression:

$$- (-(- (5 \bullet 6 \bullet 2))) \qquad \text{We get an \textbf{answer} of } -60$$

At this point our translations are getting long and laborious.

All we really have to remember about negative signs in a multiplication and/or division problem is that every two negative signs cancel each other out and make a positive. This is not new to us. We know well that – (–4) means the opposite of –4 which is of course +4.

The sign of the answer in a multiplication and/or division problem is always dependent upon <u>only</u> the number of negative signs. If there are an odd number of **negative signs** the **answer** is negative. <u>If</u> there are an **even number of negative signs** the answer is positive.

How to:

Multiply and Divide Integers and Decimals:

1. Determine the sign of the answer first. If there are an odd number of negative signs the answer is negative. If there are an even number of negative signs the answer is positive.

2. Solve as we normally would (pretending that every number is positive).

3. Insert the correct sign of the answer.

Example #1: −2 • −7

Step #1: Determine the sign of the answer first.

There are two negative signs (an even number of negative signs) so they will cancel out each other. The sign of the answer will be positive.

Step #2: Solve as we normally would.

2 • 7 = 14

Step #3: Insert the correct sign of the answer.

The answer is positive, so the **answer is: +14**

Example #2: −20 ÷ 10

Step #1: Determine the sign of the answer first.

There is only one negative sign (an odd number of negative signs) so it will not be canceled out by another negative sign. The sign of the answer will be negative.

Step #2: Solve as we normally would.

20 ÷ 10 = 2

Step #3: Insert the correct sign of the answer.

We determined the answer is negative, so the **answer is: −2**

Example #3: $-3 \bullet 4 \bullet -2 \div -6$

Step #1: Determine the sign of the answer first.

There are three negative signs (<u>an odd number of negative signs</u>) so the sign of the answer will be negative. We know this even though this is a multiple–operation problem because <u>the operations are all multiplication and division</u>.

Step #2: Solve as we normally would.

In any problem that has multiple operations, we always follow the order of operations. In this case, because we have all multiplication and division, we work left to right.

Solve $-3 \bullet 4$. A negative times a positive (<u>an odd number of negative signs</u>) is a negative (-12 here).

$$-3 \bullet 4 \bullet -2 \div -6$$

Solve $-12 \bullet -2$. A negative times a negative (<u>an even number of negative signs</u>) is a positive ($+24$ here).

$$-12 \bullet -2 \div -6$$

Solve $24 \div -6$. A positive divided by a negative (<u>an odd number of negative signs</u>) is a negative (-4 here).

$$24 \div -6 = -4$$

Step #3: Insert the correct sign of the answer.

We determined earlier that the answer is negative. Our step–by–step solution has shown this to be true. The **answer is:** -4

Example #4: $-6.2 \bullet 0.02 \div -0.4$

Step #1: Determine the sign of the answer first.

There are two negative signs (<u>an even number of negative signs</u>) so the answer will be positive. We know this even though this is a multiple–operation problem because <u>the operations are all multiplication and division</u>.

Step #2: Solve as we normally would.

We follow the order of operations. Because we have all multiplication and division, we work left to right.

Solve $-6.2 \bullet 0.02$. A negative times a positive (<u>an odd number of negative signs</u>) is a negative (-0.124 here).

$$-6.2 \bullet 0.02 \div -0.4$$

Solve $-0.124 \div -0.4$. A negative divided by a
negative (<u>an even number of negative signs</u>)
is a positive (+0.31 here).

$-0.124 \div - 0.4 = 0.31$

Step #3: Insert the correct sign of the answer.

We determined earlier that the answer is positive. Our step–by–step solution has
shown this to be true. The **answer** is: **0.31**

How to:

Solve a Problem with both Combining and Multiplication/Division:

1. Follow the order of operations (PEMDAS). As we individually work each operation we still
follow the rules for combining signed numbers and the rules for multiplication/division of
signed numbers. However, we <u>cannot tell the sign of the answer immediately</u> because we
have mixed operations (not all multiplication and division!).

Example #5: Solve: $-2 + 4 \cdot -3$

Step #1: Follow the order of operations.

We must follow the order of operations here because we recognize that this problem
has a mixed set of operations (both combining and multiplication/division).

The problem has two operations (<u>A</u>dd and <u>M</u>ultiply). We know **we must multiply
before we add** (notice that we are not simply working left to right!)

<u>Multiplication</u>: A positive times a negative (an odd
number of negative signs) is a negative.

$-2 + 4 \cdot -3$

<u>Combining</u>: Same signs (both negatives), so ADD
and Keep the SAME SIGN.

$-2 + - 12$

Answer: -14

Example #6: Solve: $-16 - 10 \div -2$

Step #1: Follow the order of operations.

We must follow the order of operations here because we recognize that this problem
has a mixed set of operations (both combining and multiplication/division).

The problem has two operations (<u>S</u>ubtract and <u>D</u>ivide). We know **we must divide
before we subtract** (notice that we are not simply working left to right!)

Division: A negative divided by a negative (an even number of negative signs) is a positive. (Notice that the minus sign in front of the 10 belongs to the 10). $-10 \div -2 = +5$

So: $-16 \underbrace{\; -10 \div -2 \;}_{+5}$

Combining: Different signs (one negative and one positive), so TAKE THE DIFFERENCE and Keep the SIGN OF THE LARGER NUMBER.

$\underbrace{-16 + 5}$

Answer: -11

Sample #1: Give the sign of the answer to the following problem without solving it. Then tell how we know the sign of the answer.

$-3 \bullet 6 \bullet (-4) \div 2 \bullet -5$

We identify this as a multiple–operation problem which is <u>all</u> multiplication and division. There are three negative signs.

Answer: The answer will be negative because there is an odd number of negative signs.

■ **You try it now:**
■
■ a) Give the sign of the answer to the following problem without solving it. Then tell how we know
■   the sign of the answer. $-6 \div -1 \bullet 10 \bullet (5)$
■
■ b) Give the sign of the answer to the following problem without solving it. Then tell how we know
■   the sign of the answer. $(-200)\,(-450)\,(8.421) \div (-3.6)$

Sample #2: Solve: $8 - \left(-10 - 5 \bullet -2\right)$

We identify this as an order of operations problems because we have multiple operations—both combining and multiplication.

We must work inside the <u>parenthesis</u> first. Inside the parenthesis we have two operations—<u>addition</u> and <u>multiplication</u>.

We must work the multiplication first. $8 - (-10 \underbrace{\; - 5 \bullet - 2})$

Now we do the addition inside the parenthesis. $8 - (\underbrace{-10 + 10})$

Now, do the subtraction. $8 - \underbrace{(0)}$

Answer: 8

■ **You try it now:**
■
■   c) Solve: $-10 - 4 \div -2$
■
■   d) Solve: $(-3 \bullet 7 - 6) \div 9$
■

Sample #3: Set up a mathematical expression that will solve the word problem below; then give the solution.

Find the product of –50 and 5. Then, take that answer and divide it by –10.

Translate words to math. The "product of –50 and 5" means to multiply –50 and 5. To show that this represents one segment or one quantity in a longer problem, put this in parenthesis.

So: (–50 • 5)   Next, we are told to divide this by –10.

We can complete our set up two different ways (using either the " ÷ " or the " / " to mean "divided by."

Set up #1:   (–50 • 5) ÷ –10   or   Set up #2: $\dfrac{(-50 \bullet 5)}{-10}$

Either way we set up the problem we will get the same solution.

(–50 • 5) ÷ –10   or $\dfrac{(-50 \bullet 5)}{-10}$

(–250) ÷ –10 $\dfrac{(-250)}{-10}$

                25   ⇐ **Answer** ⇒   25

○

■ **You try it now:**
■
■   e) Set up a mathematical expression that will solve the word problem below; then give the solution.
■   Find the quotient of –18 and –2. Then, multiply that answer by –3.
■
■   f) Translate the following problem into a mathematical expression; then solve it.
■
■ $\dfrac{(\text{the product of } - 2 \text{ and } 8)}{(\text{the quotient of } - 4 \text{ and } 1)}$
■

Sample #4: Four investors for a small company each lost $8,000 last week, but a smart financial move by the company cut this loss by one half. What number represents the company's investment balance for last week?

First we see that there is a repeated action ($8,000 was lost 4 times). This would translate into following set up: (4 • –8,000).

Second, this loss was cut in half. To "cut in half" is the same as to "divide by 2."

Therefore, the set up to solve the problem would be: $\dfrac{\left(4 \bullet -8,000\right)}{2}$

Answer: – $16,000

- **You try it now:**

g) Six investors lost a total of $96,000 last month. What number represents the average investment balance of each investor for the month? Give both a set up and a solution to this problem.

h) The high temperature in Anchorage, Alaska on February 6th was –10 degrees. If the high temperature increased 4° each day for the next 6 days, what was the high temperature on February 12th? Give both a set up and a solution to this problem.

Answers to You try it now: a) the answer is positive because there is an even number (two) of negative signs in a problem which is all multiplication and division; b) the answer is negative because there is an odd number (three) of negative signs in a problem which is all multiplication and division; c) –8; d) –3; e) set up: $\left(\dfrac{-18}{-2}\right) \bullet -3$; solution: –27; f) set up: $\left(\dfrac{-2 \bullet 8}{-4 + 1}\right)$; solution: 4; g) set up: $\dfrac{-96,000}{6}$; solution: –$16,000 is the average investment balance; h) set up: $-10 + (4 \bullet 6)$; solution: +14°.

Answer to Application: Marcellus lost his original $15,000 investment. He then lost more—an equal share of another $27,000. Because he was one of three investors, his loss from this $27,000 would be found by dividing the amount by three.

The set up to find his financial investment balance when the restaurant closed would be the following:

$$-15,000 + \left(\dfrac{-27,000}{3}\right)$$

We are not done yet because Marcellus paid off $5,000 dollars on this debt. This was a positive thing to do.

The set up to solve the entire problem is: $-15,000 + \left(\dfrac{-27,000}{3}\right) + 5,000$

Solve by following the order of operations: $-15,000 + (-9,000) + 5,000$

$-24,000 + 5,000$

Answer: Marcellus' financial balance was –$19,000

3.3 Multiplication and Division of Integers and Decimals Problems

In exercises #1–6, answer the following questions.

1) If a problem has only multiplication and division, how can we tell whether the answer is negative or positive?

2) If there are an even number of negative signs in a multiplication problem, what will the sign of the answer be?

3) If there are an odd number of negative signs in a division problem, what will the sign of the answer be?

4) If we multiply a negative times a positive, what will the sign of the answer be? Why?

5) If we divide a negative by another negative, what will the sign of the answer be? Why?

6) If we have an order of operations problem that includes combining and multiplying and dividing, is there an easy automatic way to tell what the sign of the answer will be? Why or why not?

In exercises #7–15, tell whether the answer to the given expression will be negative or positive. Do not solve.

7) $-5 \bullet -4$

8) $-14 \div 7$

9) $-8.6 \, (-0.44) \bullet -5$

10) $4.5 \div -10 \bullet 2.7$

11) $-2 \div -3 \div -4$

12) $-(-6 \bullet -4)$

13) $-(20 \div -2)$

14) $|-5| \bullet -8$

15) $|-2| \div |1|$

In exercises #16–23, identify the letter of the one expression that would have a different solution from the others. Do not solve.

16) a) $-7 \bullet -4$

b) $-7 \bullet (-4)$

c) $-(7 \bullet 4)$

d) $(-7) \bullet (-4)$

17) a) $-10 \div 50$

b) $10 \div -50$

c) $\dfrac{10}{-50}$

d) $\dfrac{-10}{-50}$

18) a) $\dfrac{-12}{-3}$

b) $(-12) \div (-3)$

c) $12 \div 3$

d) $\dfrac{-12 \div -3}{(-1)}$

19) a) $8.6 \bullet (-3) \div (-1)$

b) $\dfrac{-8.6 \bullet (-3)}{(-1)}$

c) $-8.6 \bullet -3 \div -1$

d) $\dfrac{-8.6 \bullet 3}{1}$

20) a) $0.8 \div 4 \bullet -1$

b) $-0.8 \div 4 \bullet 1$

c) $\dfrac{-0.8}{4} \bullet 1$

d) $\dfrac{0.8}{-4} \bullet -1$

21) a) $\dfrac{-8}{-2}$

b) $-2 \div -8$

c) $(-2) \div -8$

d) $2 \div 8$

22) a) $\dfrac{(5 \bullet -3)}{(-15)}$ b) $(5 \bullet -3) \div (-15)$ c) $\dfrac{(-5 \bullet -3)}{15}$ d) $\dfrac{(5 \bullet 3)}{(-15)}$

23) a) $\dfrac{(24 \div -1)}{(-2 \bullet 3)}$ b) $(24 \div 1) \div (-2 \bullet 3)$ c) $\dfrac{(24 \div 1)}{(-2 \bullet -3)}$ d) $\dfrac{-(24 \div 1)}{(-2 \bullet 3)}$

In exercises #24–61, solve these multiplication and division problems.

24) $-3 \bullet 3$ 25) $(-7) \bullet (-5)$ 26) $8 \bullet -6$ 27) $(-5)(-2)$

28) $-40 \div -10$ 29) $-16 \div 4$ 30) $10 \div -5$ 31) $(-36) \div -9$

32) $\dfrac{-7}{-1}$ 33) $\dfrac{(-100)}{(-20)}$ 34) $\dfrac{-8.6}{(4)}$ 35) $\dfrac{-0.04}{-0.05}$

36) $-2 \bullet -2 \bullet -2$ 37) $(-3) \bullet (8) \bullet (-1)$ 38) $-8 \bullet (-10) \bullet (2) \div -5$

39) $(4)(-2)(0)(-1)$ 40) $-6 \bullet (-4)(-1) \bullet 1$ 41) $-(-5 \bullet 2 \bullet -3)$

42) $\dfrac{0}{-7}$ 43) $\dfrac{0}{7}$ 44) $\dfrac{-3}{0}$ 45) $\dfrac{3}{0}$

46) $\dfrac{(-3 \bullet -2)}{(-1)}$ 47) $\dfrac{80 \div -2}{(-5 \bullet 4)}$ 48) $(5 \bullet 8) \div (5 \bullet -1)$ 49) $\dfrac{(-6 \bullet 3)}{(-3 \bullet 6)}$

50) $(-2.1)(-0.3)$ 51) $(6.24) \bullet (-1)$ 52) $-4.3 \bullet 10$ 53) $-0.08 \bullet 1000$

54) $0.001 \bullet (-54)$ 55) $-0.1(-2)$ 56) $-1000 \bullet -4.231$ 57) $7.8 \bullet (-10)$

58) $\dfrac{(-5 \div 0.2)}{-4}$ 59) $\dfrac{-7 \div -0.35}{-0.1}$ 60) $-446.4 \div 36$ 61) $(18.2) \div (-100)$

In exercises #62–84, solve these order of operations problems.

62) $5 + -6 \bullet 2$ 63) $-8 + 5 \bullet 3$ 64) $4 - (7 \bullet -1)$ 65) $-3 - (-2 \bullet -5)$

66) $-5 - 2 \bullet 3$ 67) $4 - 3 \bullet -1$ 68) $(4) - 1 \bullet 5$ 69) $-2 - 2 \bullet -2$

70) $6 \div (-2) - 1$ 71) $-14 \div (-1) + (-3)$ 72) $-8 \div 4 + -3 \bullet -2$

73) $(-3 \bullet 7 - 6) \div 9$ 74) $(8 \bullet -4 - 4) \div -6$ 75) $\dfrac{(-30 + 10 \div 2)}{6}$

76) $\dfrac{(20 - 8 \div -2)}{-4}$ 77) $3.1 + -0.5 \bullet 1.3$ 78) $-2.4 - 0.3 \div -0.1$

79) $\dfrac{(3 - 5)(-4)}{-2}$ 80) $\dfrac{(2 - 6) \bullet (-3 - 1)}{-2}$ 81) $[7 - (-7)] \div 2$

82) $\left[-5 - (-15)\right] \div -3$

83) $\dfrac{\left|-7\right| - \left|-2-2\right|}{1-(-2)}$

84) $\dfrac{(-3)(-2+\left|-3\right|)}{-1}$

In exercises #85–92, translate the following words into a math expression. After this set up, give the solution.

85) The product of –8 and –4

86) The quotient of 6 and –6.

87) The product of 6 and –2, then add the quotient of 40 and –8.

88) The quotient of 10 and –5, then subtract the product of 4 and –7.

89) Find the sum of the product of –4 and –10 and the quotient of –44 and 4.

90) Find the difference of the quotient of –100 and –1 and the product of –1 and 7.

91) $\dfrac{\text{(the sum of } -4 \text{ and } -5)}{\text{(the difference of 1 and } -2)}$

92) $\dfrac{\text{(the product of } -4, -3 \text{ and } -6)}{\text{(the quotient of } -24 \text{ and 6)}}$

In exercises #93–100, (a) write a mathematical expression that will solve the problem, and (b) give the solution.

93) A plane lost 600 feet in altitude every minute for eight consecutive minutes. What number represents the change in the plane's altitude after those eight minutes?

94–95) The high temperature in Toronto, Canada was 4° Celsius on February 22nd. The next three days the high temperature decreased 5° Celsius each day.

94) What number represents the change in the high temperature over the three–day period?

95) What was the high temperature on February 25th?

96) Climbing down the face of Mt. Dolomite, hikers dropped 3200 feet in five hours? What number represents their average change in altitude per hour?

97–98) The stock for a coffee company originally valued at $28.50 a share plunged over a four–week period after a newspaper reported that the company was ruining the environment and underpaying its employees. The stock dropped $2.10 the first week, $5.20 the second week, $0.60 the third week, and $1.10 the fourth week.

97) What number represents the change in value of a share of the coffee company's stock for the four week period?

98) What was the average change in the value of a share per week over the four–week period?

99–100) An international monetary trader watched the value of the U.S. dollar lose strength against the Italian lira. Originally one U.S. dollar equaled 1300 liras, but for each of four consecutive days the U.S. dollar lost 75 liras in value.

99) What number in liras represents the change in the value of the U.S. dollar for the four–day period?

100) After the fourth day what was the value of U.S. dollar in liras?

In exercises #101–108, state whether x must be negative or positive for the equation to be true. Do not solve.

101) $-6 \bullet x = -30$ 102) $8 \bullet x = 40$ 103) $-25 \div x = 5$ 104) $x \div -3 = -3$

105) $x \bullet -4 \bullet -3 = -48$ 106) $\dfrac{-70}{x} = 10$ 107) $\dfrac{x}{-8} = -4$ 108) $-7 \bullet x \bullet -1 = 21$

In exercises #109–118, state whether the following statements are True or False.

109) Multiplication and Division are opposites of each other.

110) Equations always remain true as long as you do the exact same thing to both sides of the equation.

111) $-2 \bullet -6 = 12$ is the same as $-2 = \dfrac{(12)}{-6}$

112) $-4 \bullet 8 = -32$ is the same as $-4 = \dfrac{(-32)}{8}$

113) $20 \div -5 = -4$ is the same as $20 = (-4) \bullet (-5)$

114) $\dfrac{-80}{-4} = 20$ is the same as $-80 = (20) \bullet (-4)$

115) $-6 \bullet x = -18$ is the same as $x = -6 \div -18$

116) $x \bullet 4 = -14$ is the same as $x = \dfrac{(-14)}{4}$

117) $\dfrac{x}{18} = -5$ is the same as $x = (-5) \bullet (18)$

118) $-15 \div x = -3$ is the same as $-15 = -3 \bullet x$

Skills Check

1. Solve: –6 – (–5) – 2

2. Solve: –10 – 4 + (–8 – 2) – (3) – (–15)

3. A deep–sea diver was 100 feet below the ocean's surface when he dove another forty feet to observe a rock formation. He then swam upward sixty feet, then dove another eighty feet as he followed a shark. What number represents his elevation now?

4. When Marcie bought stock in the company *A Better Environment for All*, it was worth $18.60 per share. Two weeks later it gained $0.40 in value. The following week it lost – $1.35. During the fourth and fifth week the stock's value climbed $0.25 and $0.50 respectively. What number represents the stock's value per share in relationship to the original price that Marcie paid for it? What was the stock's value per share now?

Answers to Skills Check: 1) –3; 2) –12; 3) –160 ft.; 4) In relationship to its original price, the stock had lost $0.20. Therefore the number that represents the change in value is –$0.20. The stock's current value per share is **$18.40**.

Section 3.4 Multiply and Divide Signed Mixed Numbers & Fractions

Objectives:

• To manipulate the negative sign with fractions and mixed numbers

• To multiply and divide signed mixed numbers and fractions

• To solve for a missing value in a proportion problem

• To set up/solve application problems

Application:

After talking to the owner of a new deli opening next to their business, three office workers decided to invest some money in an effort to raise their incomes. Together they invested $12,000. Christina and Dexter each invested $\frac{1}{5}$ of the money while Sheraz invested the rest. After a year the three had earned back $4,000 of the money they had invested (returned to them proportionately according to the fraction of the amount they had each invested). What numbers represent the investment balance so far for each person?

Vocabulary:

　　***Recognizing the value of a simple fraction** (by simple here we mean that there is just 1 number in the numerator and 1 number in the denominator): In assessing whether a fraction has a negative or a positive value, we must remember that <u>every fraction is a division problem</u>. And a division problem is negative (an odd number of negative signs) or positive (an even number of negative signs) based upon its number of negative signs.

　　Look at these three examples: $-\frac{3}{4}$, $\frac{-3}{4}$, and $\frac{3}{-4}$.

　　Are they the same or different? Well, they are all three–fourths, but are they all the same sign? Let's look.

　　$-\frac{3}{4}$ has the negative sign in front of the fraction, right next to the fractional line. This sign affects the number to its right, that is, the $\frac{3}{4}$. One way of visualizing this fraction is: $-(3 \div 4)$. We can see now that this is a negative value. If we wanted to see what the decimal equivalent of this fraction would be, we would work inside the parenthesis first and get $-(0.75)$. This of course equals -0.75

　　Placing the negative sign directly beside the fractional line as it is in $-\frac{3}{4}$ is a standard way of writing a negative fraction.

The second example of $\dfrac{-3}{4}$ has the negative sign up in the numerator. As a division problem this means: $-3 \div 4$. There is only one negative sign in this division problem so the value is negative. As a decimal we would get -0.75

The third example of $\dfrac{3}{-4}$ has the negative sign in the denominator. As a division problem this means: $3 \div -4$. There is only one negative sign in this division problem so the value is negative. As a decimal we would get -0.75

What we discover is that all three of these fractions have the exact same value. They are all negative (because they all have one—an odd number— of negative signs).

$$-\frac{3}{4} = \frac{-3}{4} = \frac{3}{-4}$$

We want to remember that when we are working on a problem, we can have a negative sign(s) next to the fraction, or possibly in the numerator and/or denominator.
By convention (the accepted norm or habit) in our final answer the negative sign is put either in front of the fraction or in the numerator.

Another example: $\dfrac{-5}{-8}$. This has a positive value because this is a division problem with two negative signs (an even number of negative signs). So, $\dfrac{-5}{-8} = \dfrac{5}{8}$

***Recognizing the value of mixed numbers and improper fractions: **Equivalent mixed number and improper fraction values are always the same sign. In the example of the mixed number of** $-2\dfrac{2}{5}$ **the sign is affecting the number to its right (in this case the entire** $2\dfrac{2}{5}$**).**

$$-2\frac{2}{5} = -\left(2\frac{2}{5}\right) = -\left(\frac{12}{5}\right) = -\frac{12}{5}.$$ If a mixed number is negative its corresponding equivalent as an improper fraction must be negative.

Likewise, if we start with an improper fraction that is negative its corresponding equivalent as a mixed number must be negative.

$$-\frac{5}{3} = -1\frac{2}{3}$$

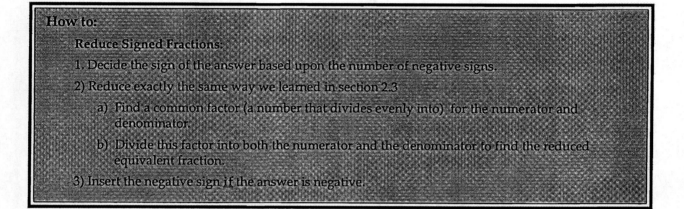

How to:

Reduce Signed Fractions:

1. Decide the sign of the answer based upon the number of negative signs.

2) Reduce exactly the same way we learned in section 2.3

    a) Find a common factor (a number that divides evenly into) for the numerator and denominator.

    b) Divide this factor into both the numerator and the denominator to find the reduced equivalent fraction.

3) Insert the negative sign if the answer is negative.

Example #1: Reduce $\dfrac{-12}{15}$ to lowest terms.

    Step #1: Decide the sign of the answer.

        This fraction (division problem!) has an odd number of negative signs so the <u>answer is negative</u>.

    Step #2: a) Find a common factor for the numerator and denominator.

        3 divides evenly into both 12 and 15

        b) Divide this factor into both the numerator and the denominator.

$$\frac{12}{15} \div \frac{3}{3} = \frac{4}{5}$$

    Step #3: Insert the negative sign if the answer is negative.

        Yes, the <u>answer should be negative</u>.

        Answer: $-\dfrac{4}{5}$

How to:

Multiply Signed Fractions:

1. Decide the sign of the answer based upon the number of negative signs.

2) Multiply exactly the same way we learned in section 2.4

    a) Cancel any single numerator with any single denominator until no more canceling is possible.

    b) Multiply straight across, the numerators together, and then the denominators together.

3) Insert the negative sign <u>if</u> the answer is negative.

Example #2: $-\dfrac{8}{9} \bullet -\dfrac{3}{14}$

Step #1: Decide the sign of the answer.

This multiplication problem has an even number of negative signs so <u>the answer is</u> <u>positive</u>.

Step #2: a) Cancel.

The numerator of 8 and the denominator of 14 have a common factor of 2.

$$-\dfrac{\overset{4}{\cancel{8}}}{9} \bullet -\dfrac{3}{\underset{7}{\cancel{14}}}$$

A second cancellation is possible. The numerator of 3 and the denominator of 9 have a common factor of 3.

$$-\dfrac{\overset{4}{\cancel{8}}}{\underset{3}{\cancel{9}}} \bullet -\dfrac{\overset{1}{\cancel{3}}}{\underset{7}{\cancel{14}}}$$

b) Multiply straight across.

$$-\dfrac{\overset{4}{\cancel{8}}}{\underset{3}{\cancel{9}}} \bullet -\dfrac{\overset{1}{\cancel{3}}}{\underset{7}{\cancel{14}}} = \dfrac{4}{21}$$

Step #3: Insert the negative sign if the answer is negative.

No, the <u>answer is positive</u>.   **Answer:** $\dfrac{4}{21}$

How to:

Divide Signed Fractions:

1. Decide the sign of the answer based upon the number of negative signs.

2) Divide exactly the same way we learned in section 2.4

    a) Decide which fraction is the divisor and take the reciprocal of only the divisor.

    b) The problem now becomes a multiplication of fractions problem. Cancel any single numerator which any single denominator until no more canceling is possible.

    c) Multiply straight across, the numerators together, and then the denominators together.

3) Insert the negative sign <u>if</u> the answer is negative.

Example #3: $\dfrac{-7}{12} \div \dfrac{4}{3}$

Step #1: Decide the sign of the answer.

This division problem has an odd number of negative signs so <u>the answer is negative</u>.

Step #2: a) Take the reciprocal of the divisor

$\dfrac{4}{3}$ is the divisor; its reciprocal is $\dfrac{3}{4}$.

b) Change the problem to multiplication. Cancel.

The problem becomes: $\dfrac{-7}{12} \cdot \dfrac{3}{4}$

The numerator of 3 and the denominator of 12 have a common factor of 3.

$$\dfrac{-7}{\overset{}{\underset{4}{\cancel{12}}}} \cdot \dfrac{\overset{1}{\cancel{3}}}{4}$$

c) Multiply straight across.

$$\dfrac{-7}{\overset{}{\underset{4}{\cancel{12}}}} \cdot \dfrac{\overset{1}{\cancel{3}}}{4} = \dfrac{7}{16}$$

Step #3: Insert the negative sign if the answer is negative.

Yes, the <u>answer should be negative</u>.

Answer: $-\dfrac{7}{16}$

How to:

Multiply & Divide Signed Mixed Numbers:

1. Decide the sign of the answer based upon the number of negative signs.

2) Multiply & Divide exactly the same way we learned in section 2.5

  a) Change all mixed numbers into improper fractions.

  b) Follow the rules for divide and multiply fractions.

3) Insert the negative sign <u>if</u> the answer is negative.

Example #4: $\quad -2\frac{1}{2} \div \left(-\frac{3}{4}\right)$

Step #1: Decide the sign of the answer.

This division problem has an even number of negative signs so <u>the answer is positive</u>.

Step #2: a) Change all mixed numbers into improper fractions.

Rewrite as: $\quad -\frac{5}{2} \div \left(-\frac{3}{4}\right)$

b) Follow rules for division of fractions. Take the reciprocal of the divisor.

Rewrite as: $\quad -\frac{5}{2} \cdot \left(-\frac{4}{3}\right)$

Now follow rules for multiplication of fractions.

Cancel: $\quad -\frac{5}{\underset{1}{\cancel{2}}} \cdot \left(-\frac{\cancel{4}^2}{3}\right) = \frac{10}{3}$

Step #3: Insert the negative sign if the answer is negative.

No, the <u>answer is positive</u>.   **Answer:** $\quad \frac{10}{3}$ or $3\frac{1}{3}$

How to:

Solve for a missing number in an equivalent fractions or a proportion problem:

1. Decide the sign of the answer based upon the number of negative signs.
2. Solve exactly the same way we learned in section 2.1
   a) Multiply the <u>known</u> diagonal pair of numbers (a cross product).
   b) Divide this product by the third known number.
3. Insert the negative sign if the answer is negative.

Example #5: Solve for the value of x in the given proportion (equivalent fractions) problem.

$$\frac{-2}{-7} = \frac{x}{-21}$$

Step #1: Decide the sign of the answer.

We can see that there are an odd number (3) of negative signs in this problem. Because we will only be multiplying and dividing to solve the problem, we know that <u>the answer is negative</u>.

Step #2: a) Multiply the <u>known</u> diagonal pair of numbers.

$$-2 \bullet -21 = +42$$

b) Divide by the third known number.

$$42 \div -7 = -6$$

Step #3: Insert the negative sign if the answer is negative.

Our step–by–step solution correctly yielded a negative answer.

Answer: –6

Sample #1: Solve: $\quad -\frac{3}{8} \bullet \frac{2}{9} \bullet 2\frac{4}{5}$

The <u>answer will be negative</u> because there is only one negative sign (an odd number of signs).

Change all mixed numbers to improper fractions.

Rewrite as: $\quad -\frac{3}{8} \bullet \frac{2}{9} \bullet \frac{14}{5}$

Cancel. $\quad -\frac{\cancel{3}^{1}}{\cancel{8}4} \bullet \frac{\cancel{2}^{1}}{\cancel{9}3} \bullet \frac{14}{5}$

Cancel again, this time with the 4 in the denominator and the 14 in the numerator.

$$-\frac{\cancel{3}^{1}}{\underset{2}{\cancel{\cancel{8}4}}} \bullet \frac{\cancel{2}^{1}}{\cancel{9}3} \bullet \frac{\cancel{14}^{7}}{5}$$

Multiply across. The **answer is:** $\quad -\frac{7}{30}$

■
■   **You try it now:**
■
■   a) $\dfrac{2}{7} \bullet -3\dfrac{2}{3} \bullet -1\dfrac{1}{2}$
■
■
■   b) $-\dfrac{1}{4} \bullet 6 \bullet 1\dfrac{5}{7}$
■

Sample #2: Solve: $-4\dfrac{1}{5} \div \left(-\dfrac{3}{5}\right) \div 1\dfrac{1}{6}$

The <u>answer is positive</u> because there are two negative signs (an even number of signs).

Change all mixed numbers to improper fractions.

Rewrite as: $-\dfrac{21}{5} \div \left(-\dfrac{3}{5}\right) \div \dfrac{7}{6}$

Take the reciprocal(s) of the divisor(s). In this case there are two divisors because there are two values that follow "divided by" symbols.

Rewrite as: $-\dfrac{21}{5} \bullet \left(-\dfrac{5}{3}\right) \bullet \dfrac{6}{7}$

Cancel the 5 and the 5, the 3 and the 6, and the 7 and the 21.

$$-\dfrac{\overset{3}{\cancel{21}}}{\underset{1}{\cancel{5}}} \bullet \left(-\dfrac{\overset{1}{\cancel{5}}}{\underset{1}{\cancel{3}}}\right) \bullet \dfrac{\overset{2}{\cancel{6}}}{\underset{1}{\cancel{7}}}$$

Multiply across. The **answer** is: **6**

■
■   **You try it now:**
■
■   c) $\dfrac{5}{6} \div 6 \div \left(-1\dfrac{1}{6}\right)$
■
■
■
■   d) $-3\dfrac{3}{8} \bullet \left(-2\dfrac{2}{3}\right) \div \left(-1\dfrac{3}{4}\right)$
■

Sample #3: In a robbery an electronics store lost $60,000 in merchandise. $\frac{1}{4}$ of the losses were from stolen TV's. Another $\frac{3}{8}$ of the losses were from missing computers. What number represents the change in the value of the store's inventory of TV's and computers?

The key here is to recognize the form of "a number of another number." This means multiplication.

The number that represents the store's change in the value of its total inventory is − $60,000.

The change in the inventory value of TV's is: $\frac{1}{4}$ *of* − $60,000$.

The change in the inventory value of computers is $\frac{3}{8}$ *of* − $60,000$.

The change in the inventory value of these two items would be found by finding the sum of these two.

Set up: $\left(\frac{1}{4} \cdot \frac{-60,000}{1} \right) + \left(\frac{3}{8} \cdot \frac{-\$60,000}{1} \right)$

$(-\$15,000) + (-\$22,500)$

Answer: −$37,500 was the change in the value of TV/computer inventories.

■ **You try it now:**
■
■   e) The stock of a clothing company barely maintained $\frac{7}{10}$ of it initial value of $22\frac{1}{2}$ per share. What
■   mixed number represents the change in the value of this stock?
■
■   f) Five stores owned by a clothing company announced that together they had lost $1\frac{7}{8}$ million dollars
■   last year. What was the average financial balance for each of these stores (give answer as a fraction of
■   a million dollars)?

Sample #4: An internet company lost $2\frac{3}{4}$ million dollars in a seven–day period. If it continued to lose money at this same rate, what number would represent the company's financial balance after thirty days?

We need to recognize that we have a proportion problem here.

We are given the ratio (relationship) of money to days. $2\frac{3}{4}$ million dollars is lost for every seven days. We can write this ratio as a fraction:

$$\frac{-\$2\frac{3}{4} \text{ million}}{7 \text{ days}}$$

Now complete the proportion (remember, a proportion is two ratios equal to each other).

Proportion Set up: $\dfrac{-\$2\frac{3}{4}\ \text{million}}{7\ \text{days}} = \dfrac{\$x\ \text{million}}{30\ \text{days}}$

First multiply the known diagonal pair of numbers.

$-2\dfrac{3}{4} \bullet 30 \ \Rightarrow$ This becomes: $\ -\dfrac{11}{4} \bullet \dfrac{30}{1}$ which $= \ -\dfrac{165}{2}$

Now divide this value $\left(-\dfrac{165}{2}\right)$ by the third known number (7).

$\left(-\dfrac{165}{2}\right) \div \dfrac{7}{1} \ \Rightarrow$ This becomes: $\left(-\dfrac{165}{2}\right) \bullet \dfrac{1}{7}$ which $= \ -\dfrac{165}{14}$

Answer: The change in the company's financial balance after 30 days would be

$-\$11\dfrac{11}{14}$ **million** .

■ **You try it now:**

g) During an economic recession a small, family–owned, office–support company averaged losses of $\$1\dfrac{1}{8}$ thousand every five working days. If the recession lasted the equivalent of 120 working days, what would the company's financial balance be during this period?

h) The state legislature made an error in calculating the expense of a large water transport system. After the budgeted money for the project was all gone, there was still about $12\dfrac{1}{2}$ weeks of work still to be finished. The project's expenses were about $8\dfrac{2}{3}$ million dollars every four weeks. At that rate the cost for the transport system would be how much more than originally expected?

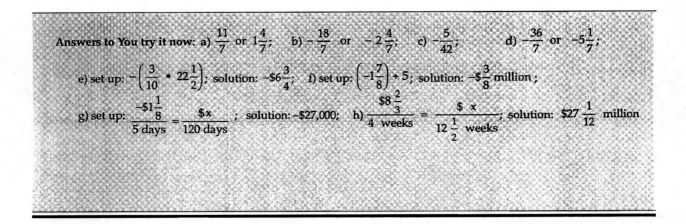

Answers to You try it now: a) $\dfrac{11}{7}$ or $1\dfrac{4}{7}$;   b) $-\dfrac{18}{7}$ or $-2\dfrac{4}{7}$;   c) $-\dfrac{5}{42}$;   d) $-\dfrac{36}{7}$ or $-5\dfrac{1}{7}$;

e) set up: $-\left(\dfrac{3}{10} \bullet 22\dfrac{1}{2}\right)$; solution: $-\$6\dfrac{3}{4}$;   f) set up: $\left(-1\dfrac{7}{8}\right) \div 5$; solution: $-\$\dfrac{3}{8}$ million;

g) set up: $\dfrac{-\$1\frac{1}{8}}{5\ \text{days}} = \dfrac{\$x}{120\ \text{days}}$; solution: $-\$27,000$;   h) $\dfrac{\$8\frac{2}{3}}{4\ \text{weeks}} = \dfrac{\$\ x}{12\frac{1}{2}\ \text{weeks}}$; solution: $\$27\dfrac{1}{12}$ million

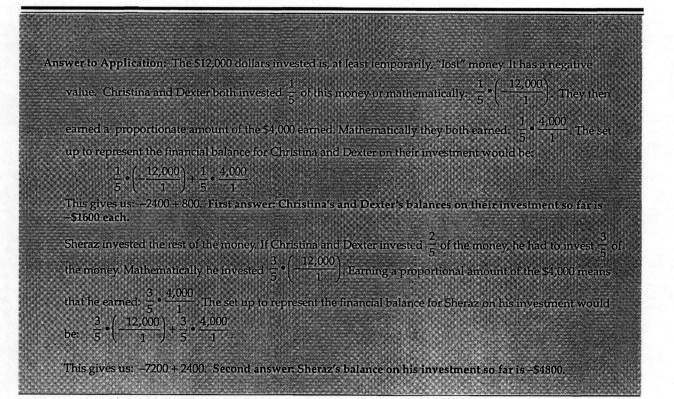

Answer to Application: The $12,000 dollars invested is, at least temporarily, "lost" money. It has a negative value. Christina and Dexter both invested $\frac{1}{5}$ of this money or mathematically: $\frac{1}{5} \bullet \left(-\frac{12,000}{1}\right)$. They then earned a proportionate amount of the $4,000 earned. Mathematically they both earned: $\frac{1}{5} \bullet \frac{4,000}{1}$. The set up to represent the financial balance for Christina and Dexter on their investment would be:

$$\frac{1}{5} \bullet \left(-\frac{12,000}{1}\right) + \frac{1}{5} \bullet \frac{4,000}{1}$$

This gives us: $-2400 + 800$. First answer: Christina's and Dexter's balances on their investment so far is $-\$1600$ each.

Sheraz invested the rest of the money. If Christina and Dexter invested $\frac{2}{5}$ of the money, he had to invest $\frac{3}{5}$ of the money. Mathematically he invested $\frac{3}{5} \bullet \left(\frac{12,000}{1}\right)$. Earning a proportional amount of the $4,000 means that he earned: $\frac{3}{5} \bullet \frac{4,000}{1}$. The set up to represent the financial balance for Sheraz on his investment would be: $\frac{3}{5} \bullet \left(-\frac{12,000}{1}\right) + \frac{3}{5} \bullet \frac{4,000}{1}$.

This gives us: $-7200 + 2400$. Second answer: Sheraz's balance on his investment so far is $-\$4800$.

3.4 Multiply and Divide Signed Mixed Numbers and Fractions Problems

In exercises #1–10, state whether the given expression has a negative or a positive value. Do not solve.

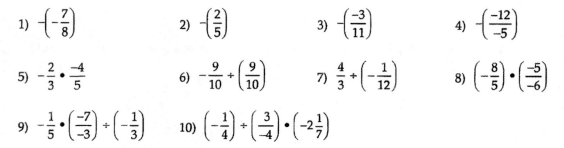

1) $-\left(-\frac{7}{8}\right)$

2) $-\left(\frac{2}{5}\right)$

3) $-\left(\frac{-3}{11}\right)$

4) $-\left(\frac{-12}{-5}\right)$

5) $-\frac{2}{3} \bullet \frac{-4}{5}$

6) $-\frac{9}{10} \div \left(\frac{9}{10}\right)$

7) $\frac{4}{3} \div \left(-\frac{1}{12}\right)$

8) $\left(-\frac{8}{5}\right) \bullet \left(\frac{-5}{-6}\right)$

9) $-\frac{1}{5} \bullet \left(\frac{-7}{-3}\right) \div \left(-\frac{1}{3}\right)$

10) $\left(-\frac{1}{4}\right) \div \left(\frac{3}{-4}\right) \bullet \left(-2\frac{1}{7}\right)$

In exercises #11–17, decide whether each group of expressions all have the same values without solving the problem. Answer yes or no. If your answer is no, identify the letter of the <u>one</u> expression that does not equal the others.

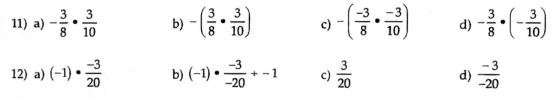

11) a) $-\frac{3}{8} \bullet \frac{3}{10}$

b) $-\left(\frac{3}{8} \bullet \frac{3}{10}\right)$

c) $-\left(\frac{-3}{8} \bullet \frac{-3}{10}\right)$

d) $-\frac{3}{8} \bullet \left(-\frac{3}{10}\right)$

12) a) $(-1) \bullet \frac{-3}{20}$

b) $(-1) \bullet \frac{-3}{-20} \div -1$

c) $\frac{3}{20}$

d) $\frac{-3}{-20}$

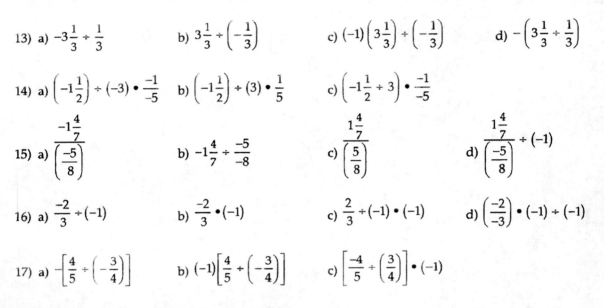

13) a) $-3\frac{1}{3} \div \frac{1}{3}$ b) $3\frac{1}{3} \div \left(-\frac{1}{3}\right)$ c) $(-1)\left(3\frac{1}{3}\right) \div \left(-\frac{1}{3}\right)$ d) $-\left(3\frac{1}{3} \div \frac{1}{3}\right)$

14) a) $\left(-1\frac{1}{2}\right) \div (-3) \bullet \frac{-1}{-5}$ b) $\left(-1\frac{1}{2}\right) \div (3) \bullet \frac{1}{5}$ c) $\left(-1\frac{1}{2} \div 3\right) \bullet \frac{-1}{-5}$

15) a) $\dfrac{-1\frac{4}{7}}{\left(\frac{-5}{8}\right)}$ b) $-1\frac{4}{7} \div \frac{-5}{-8}$ c) $\dfrac{1\frac{4}{7}}{\left(\frac{5}{8}\right)}$ d) $\dfrac{1\frac{4}{7}}{\left(\frac{-5}{8}\right)} \div (-1)$

16) a) $\frac{-2}{3} \div (-1)$ b) $\frac{-2}{3} \bullet (-1)$ c) $\frac{2}{3} \div (-1) \bullet (-1)$ d) $\left(\frac{-2}{-3}\right) \bullet (-1) \div (-1)$

17) a) $-\left[\frac{4}{5} \div \left(-\frac{3}{4}\right)\right]$ b) $(-1)\left[\frac{4}{5} \div \left(-\frac{3}{4}\right)\right]$ c) $\left[\frac{-4}{5} \div \left(\frac{3}{4}\right)\right] \bullet (-1)$

In exercises #18–28, reduce the fractions to their lowest terms.

18) $\frac{-14}{16}$ 19) $\frac{-12}{-9}$ 20) $\frac{22}{4}$ 21) $\frac{-6}{8}$ 22) $\frac{-18}{-23}$

23) $-\frac{98}{63}$ 24) $\frac{-110}{143}$ 25) $-\frac{174}{218}$ 26) $\left(\frac{-(-4)}{-16}\right)$ 27) $\left(\frac{-(-30)}{-(-66)}\right)$

28) $\left(\frac{-(-(-24))}{(-(-49))}\right)$

In exercises #29–40, change any improper fractions into mixed numbers and any mixed numbers into improper fractions.

29) $\frac{-20}{3}$ 30) $-\frac{25}{8}$ 31) $-3\frac{1}{7}$ 32) $4\frac{2}{3}$

33) $-\frac{34}{4}$ 34) $\frac{67}{-9}$ 35) $-\left(6\frac{3}{4}\right)$ 36) $-11\frac{2}{5}$

37) $\frac{-(-133)}{7}$ 38) $-\left(\frac{-(-18)}{-12}\right)$ 39) $-\left(-18\frac{2}{5}\right)$ 40) $\left(-15\frac{40}{80}\right)$

In exercises #41–65, solve for the product or the quotient.

41) $\left(-\frac{1}{4}\right) \bullet \frac{3}{5}$ 42) $\frac{5}{16} \bullet \left(-\frac{8}{11}\right)$ 43) $\frac{2}{7}$ of $\left(-\frac{4}{24}\right)$ 44) $\left(-\frac{1}{8}\right)$ of $\left(-\frac{10}{19}\right)$

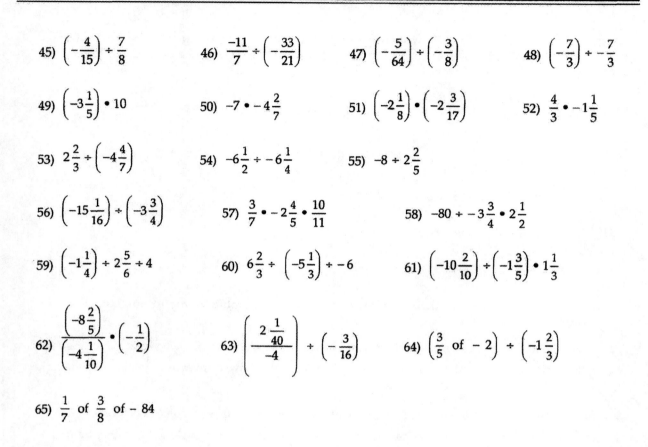

45) $\left(-\dfrac{4}{15}\right) \div \dfrac{7}{8}$ 46) $\dfrac{-11}{7} \div \left(-\dfrac{33}{21}\right)$ 47) $\left(-\dfrac{5}{64}\right) \div \left(-\dfrac{3}{8}\right)$ 48) $\left(-\dfrac{7}{3}\right) \div -\dfrac{7}{3}$

49) $\left(-3\dfrac{1}{5}\right) \bullet 10$ 50) $-7 \bullet -4\dfrac{2}{7}$ 51) $\left(-2\dfrac{1}{8}\right) \bullet \left(-2\dfrac{3}{17}\right)$ 52) $\dfrac{4}{3} \bullet -1\dfrac{1}{5}$

53) $2\dfrac{2}{3} \div \left(-4\dfrac{4}{7}\right)$ 54) $-6\dfrac{1}{2} \div -6\dfrac{1}{4}$ 55) $-8 \div 2\dfrac{2}{5}$

56) $\left(-15\dfrac{1}{16}\right) \div \left(-3\dfrac{3}{4}\right)$ 57) $\dfrac{3}{7} \bullet -2\dfrac{4}{5} \bullet \dfrac{10}{11}$ 58) $-80 \div -3\dfrac{3}{4} \bullet 2\dfrac{1}{2}$

59) $\left(-1\dfrac{1}{4}\right) \div 2\dfrac{5}{6} \div 4$ 60) $6\dfrac{2}{3} \div \left(-5\dfrac{1}{3}\right) \div -6$ 61) $\left(-10\dfrac{2}{10}\right) \div \left(-1\dfrac{3}{5}\right) \bullet 1\dfrac{1}{3}$

62) $\dfrac{\left(-8\dfrac{2}{5}\right)}{\left(-4\dfrac{1}{10}\right)} \bullet \left(-\dfrac{1}{2}\right)$ 63) $\left(\dfrac{2\dfrac{1}{40}}{-4}\right) \div \left(-\dfrac{3}{16}\right)$ 64) $\left(\dfrac{3}{5} \text{ of } -2\right) \div \left(-1\dfrac{2}{3}\right)$

65) $\dfrac{1}{7}$ of $\dfrac{3}{8}$ of -84

In exercises #66–76, solve for the value of "x." If you get a non–integer answer, give your answer in a fractional or mixed number form.

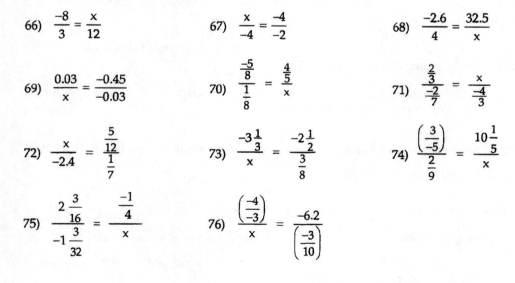

66) $\dfrac{-8}{3} = \dfrac{x}{12}$ 67) $\dfrac{x}{-4} = \dfrac{-4}{-2}$ 68) $\dfrac{-2.6}{4} = \dfrac{32.5}{x}$

69) $\dfrac{0.03}{x} = \dfrac{-0.45}{-0.03}$ 70) $\dfrac{\frac{-5}{8}}{\frac{1}{8}} = \dfrac{\frac{4}{5}}{x}$ 71) $\dfrac{\frac{2}{3}}{\frac{-2}{7}} = \dfrac{x}{\frac{-4}{3}}$

72) $\dfrac{x}{-2.4} = \dfrac{\frac{5}{12}}{\frac{1}{7}}$ 73) $\dfrac{-3\frac{1}{3}}{x} = \dfrac{-2\frac{1}{2}}{\frac{3}{8}}$ 74) $\dfrac{\left(\frac{3}{-5}\right)}{\frac{2}{9}} = \dfrac{10\frac{1}{5}}{x}$

75) $\dfrac{2\frac{3}{16}}{-1\frac{3}{32}} = \dfrac{\frac{-1}{4}}{x}$ 76) $\dfrac{\left(\frac{-4}{-3}\right)}{x} = \dfrac{-6.2}{\left(\frac{-3}{10}\right)}$

In exercises #77–84, translate the following words into math expressions. Use the dot (•) for multiplication and the ÷ symbol for division [the problems with an asterisk (*) need a parenthesis to ensure that order of operations are followed]. Then solve.

77) The product of $\frac{4}{9}$ and $\left(\frac{-5}{-3}\right)$.   78) The quotient of $-1\frac{2}{11}$ and $-3\frac{1}{6}$.   79) $\frac{2}{3}$ of $\frac{-14}{30}$

80) $\frac{-1}{8}$ of -16 81) 5 less than the quotient of 4 and $-\frac{1}{4}$.

*82) The difference of 2 and 6, then times $\frac{-5}{4}$.

*83) The sum of 4 and –7, then divided by $-2\frac{3}{4}$.

84) Subtract 5 from the product of $-\frac{1}{6}$ and –30.

In exercises #85–100: (a) write a mathematical expression (or, if applicable, a proportion) that will solve the problem, and (b) give the solution.

85) Four big–time Wall Street stock brokers, lost a total of $3\frac{5}{8}$ million dollars last week. What was the average financial balance for each of these brokers last week (give answer as a fraction of a million dollars)?

86–88) Because of injuries on the job, Myrtle County calculated that its work force was losing 40,000 hours a week. About $\frac{1}{5}$ of these injuries were office repetitive–stress injuries. The county figured that it lost $\$\frac{1}{8}$ in taxes for every hour someone missed work.

86) How many hours of work were the citizens of Myrtle County missing <u>every week</u> because of office repetitive–stress injuries?

87) How many hours of work were the citizens of Myrtle County losing every week because of injuries <u>other than office repetitive–stress injuries</u>?

88) What number represents the effect on the amount of taxes received in Myrtle County per four week period because of repetitive–stress injuries?

89–90) A new housing subdivision was being built on $20\frac{1}{2}$ acres on the north end of the city. Each new home was to have a property size of $\frac{1}{6}$ of an acre.

89) How many homes were supposed to be built in this subdivision?

90) Instead of building on all $20\frac{1}{2}$ acres, the city insisted that $2\frac{1}{2}$ acres be saved for a new park. If the chief contractor will make $2,000 per house, what number represents the difference in the contractor's profit now that the park will be built?

91) An HMO was sued because of malpractice. After the trial, the HMO was found guilty; it had to pay three–quarters of a million dollars to each of 25 patients. What number represents the financial result of the malpractice suit for the HMO (give answer in a mixed number form)?

92) A runner ran the first 3 miles of a ten–mile race in $16\frac{1}{4}$ minutes. If she maintained this pace, how many minutes would it take to finish the entire race (give the answer in a mixed number form)?

93) Malcolm lost $\$8\frac{3}{10}$ for every 10 minutes that he gambled at the blackjack table. If he continued to lose money at this same rate, what number would represent Malcolm's financial balance for playing blackjack after he had gambled for two hours?

94) A new start–up internet company had lost $4\frac{3}{4}$ million dollars in $2\frac{1}{2}$ years. What was the company's average financial balance per year (give answer in a mixed number form)?

95) A toy store had bought 200 of the new mechanical Godzilla toys—which were predicted to sell rapidly. Unfortunately for the toy store only 20 of the Godzillas sold at the advertised price that earned the store a profit of $12 for each toy. To sell the rest, the store had to take a loss of $\$5\frac{1}{5}$ on every other Godzilla. What was the financial balance of the investment in the Godzilla toys for the store?

96) The state had budgeted 45 million dollars to fight fires last year during the 120–day fire season. 20 million dollars were spent in the first fifty days of the fire season. If fire–fighting money was spent at this same rate for the rest of the fire season, how much more money was spent on fire–fighting last year than budgeted for?

97–98) Studying a herd of caribou in Alaska during the winter, Joaquin weighed one male caribou at 400 pounds. Subsequently the caribou began losing about $6\frac{2}{3}$ pounds per week.

97) What number represents this caribou's change in weight after six weeks?

98) After nine weeks, how much did this caribou weigh when Joaquin put it on a scale?

99) Another caribou had lost $5\frac{7}{10}$ pounds in 4 days. At that same rate, what number represents the caribou's change in weight after 50 days (give answer in a mixed number form)?

100) Doctor Cherub referred 8 patients to the Easy–Off Clinic. All eight of the patients badly needed to lose weight for health reasons. Together in one month the patients lost $99\frac{1}{2}$ pounds. What number represents the average weight change per patient in that month?

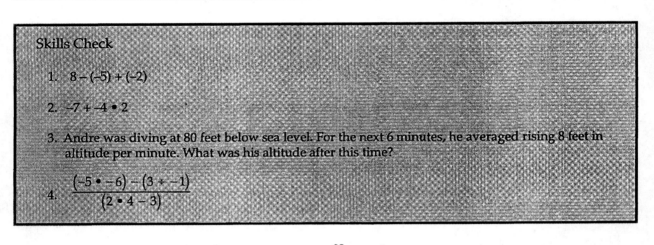

Skills Check

1. $8 - (-5) + (-2)$

2. $-7 + -4 \cdot 2$

3.   Andre was diving at 80 feet below sea level. For the next 6 minutes, he averaged rising 8 feet in altitude per minute. What was his altitude after this time?

4. $\dfrac{(-5 \cdot -6) - (3 \div -1)}{(2 \cdot 4 - 3)}$

Answers to Skills Check: 1) 11;   2) –15;   3) –32 feet;   4) $\dfrac{33}{5}$ or $6\dfrac{3}{5}$

Section 3.5 Combining Signed Mixed Numbers & Fractions

Objectives:

• To translate words into combining expressions

• To combine fractions/mixed numbers using the vertical method

• To combine fractions/mixed numbers using the horizontal method

• To set up/solve combining signed number application problems

Application:

As a wrestler, Anthony always had trouble keeping his weight below 150 pounds so he could compete in the 140–150 pound weight division. Three weeks before a tournament he learned that he needed to lose $3\frac{1}{4}$ pounds to compete in the 140–150 pound weight division. In one week he lost $1\frac{3}{5}$ pounds. During the second week he lost another $2\frac{3}{4}$ pounds, but in the third week he gained back $\frac{2}{3}$ of a pound. Can Anthony compete in the 140–150 pound weight division?

Vocabulary:

***Recognizing different ways of writing a combining fractions problem:** We can write combining problems vertically and horizontally (shown later in the Examples part of this section); we can also display these problems in two different ways horizontally once we have a common denominator.

Examples: $\dfrac{7}{8} - \dfrac{5}{8}$ is the same as: $\dfrac{7-5}{8}$

$-\dfrac{3}{5} + \dfrac{1}{5}$ is the same as: $\dfrac{-3+1}{5}$

$-\dfrac{3}{7} - \dfrac{2}{7}$ is the same as: $\dfrac{-3-2}{7}$

$\dfrac{3}{20} - \dfrac{10}{20}$ is the same as: $\dfrac{3-10}{20}$

***Review of Translation Skills (Words that mean <u>Combining</u>):

Translations that use the addition symbol:

The **sum** of 8 and –12 means:	8 + (–12)
The **total** of –3 and –7 means:	–3 + (–7)
5 **more than** –2 means:	–2 + 5
–7 **increased by** 4 means:	–7 + 4

Translations that use the subtraction symbol:

The **difference** of –4 and –6 means:	–4 – (–6)
–10 **decreased by** 5 means:	–10 – 5
Subtract 6 **from** 15 means:	15 – 6
3 **less than –9 means:	–9 – 3

As mentioned in Section 1.2, we must remember that the order of the numbers is switched when translating the phrases "subtract from" and "less than." Whatever number comes <u>after</u> the word *from* or the words *less than* is what you start with, what comes first.

Look at some more examples:

The **sum** of $-\dfrac{5}{6}$ and $\dfrac{1}{3}$ means:	$-\dfrac{5}{6} + \dfrac{1}{3}$
$\dfrac{3}{4}$ **more than** $1\dfrac{1}{8}$ means:	$1\dfrac{1}{8} + \dfrac{3}{4}$
The **difference** of $-\dfrac{3}{10}$ and $-2\dfrac{1}{4}$ means:	$-\dfrac{3}{10} - \left(-2\dfrac{1}{4}\right)$
Subtract $-\dfrac{1}{2}$ **from** $\dfrac{4}{5}$ means:	$\dfrac{4}{5} - \left(-\dfrac{1}{2}\right)$
$\dfrac{3}{7}$ **less than** $-3\dfrac{1}{3}$ means:	$-3\dfrac{1}{3} - \dfrac{3}{7}$

***Review of the Commutative & Associative Properties (Section 1.6):

The **Commutative Property** recognizes the fact that the answer will be the same when we <u>change the order</u> of the given numbers as long as the problem is either <u>all</u> addition or <u>all</u> multiplication.

Examples: $-5 + 4$ is the same as $4 + -5$

$$5\dfrac{7}{20} + \left(-\dfrac{1}{5}\right) \text{ is the same as } \left(-\dfrac{1}{5}\right) + 5\dfrac{7}{20}$$

$$\dfrac{5}{12} + \left(-\dfrac{1}{6}\right) + \dfrac{2}{3} \text{ is the same as } \dfrac{5}{12} + \dfrac{2}{3} + \left(-\dfrac{1}{6}\right)$$

The **Associative Property** recognizes the fact that the answer will be the same when we <u>change the association of the grouping</u> (which numbers are inside a parenthesis) of numbers as long as the problem is either <u>all</u> addition or <u>all</u> multiplication.

Examples: $\left(-\dfrac{4}{3}+\dfrac{2}{5}\right)+\left(-\dfrac{5}{8}\right)$ is the same as $\left(-\dfrac{4}{3}\right)+\left(\dfrac{2}{5}+-\dfrac{5}{8}\right)$

$-2\dfrac{9}{10}+\left(-1\dfrac{3}{4}+3\dfrac{1}{3}\right)$ is the same as $\left(-2\dfrac{9}{10}+-1\dfrac{3}{4}\right)+3\dfrac{1}{3}$

***Recognizing the same expression written in different ways: **We can always recognize equivalent combining expressions as long as the sign of each value remains the same in each expression.**

$-\dfrac{5}{7}+\dfrac{2}{5}-\dfrac{3}{10}$ or $-\dfrac{5}{7}+\dfrac{2}{5}+\left(-\dfrac{3}{10}\right)$ or $\left(-\dfrac{5}{7}+-\dfrac{3}{10}\right)+\dfrac{2}{5}$ or $\left(-\dfrac{5}{7}-\dfrac{3}{10}\right)+\dfrac{2}{5}$

$2\dfrac{2}{3}-1\dfrac{1}{5}-\dfrac{5}{12}$ or $2\dfrac{2}{3}+\left(-1\dfrac{1}{5}\right)+\left(-\dfrac{5}{12}\right)$ or $2\dfrac{2}{3}+\left(-1\dfrac{1}{5}+-\dfrac{5}{12}\right)$ or $2\dfrac{2}{3}+\left(-1\dfrac{1}{5}-\dfrac{5}{12}\right)$

***Reminder: **When combining, we decide to add or subtract dependent upon whether the signs are the same or different, not because we have an addition or a subtraction symbol.**

How to:

Solve a Combining Signed Fractions problem:

1. Get rid of all double negatives. A double negative becomes a plus.

2. We must have a common denominator, or find one and make an equivalent fraction of each given fraction using this common denominator.

3. If the signs of the values are the same: <u>ADD</u> (the absolute values of the two numbers) and KEEP THE SAME SIGN.

or

If the signs of the values are different: <u>Take the difference</u> (of the absolute values of the two numbers), always subtracting the smaller value from the larger, and KEEP THE SIGN OF THE INITIAL LARGER NUMBER.

Example #1: $-\dfrac{7}{8}+\dfrac{2}{5}$

Step #1: Get rid of all double negatives.

There are no double negatives here. There is nothing to do.

○

Vertical Set up:	Horizontal Set up:

$$-\frac{7}{8}$$

$$+\ \frac{2}{5}$$

$$-\frac{7}{8} + \frac{2}{5}$$

Step #2: Find the common denominator and make equivalent fractions.

The common denominator is 40.

Vertical Method: OR   **Horizontal Method:**

$$-\frac{7}{8} = -\frac{35}{40}$$

$$+\ \frac{2}{5} = \frac{16}{40}$$

$$-\frac{7}{8} + \frac{2}{5}$$

$$-\frac{35}{40} + \frac{16}{40} \ \ or \ \ \frac{-35 + 16}{40}$$

Step #3: The signs of the values are different: <u>**Take the difference**</u> (of the absolute values of the two numbers), always subtracting the smaller value from the larger, and **KEEP THE SIGN** OF THE INITIAL **LARGER NUMBER**.

Take the difference of the absolute values (of the numerators):

$$35 - 16 = 19$$

Keep the sign of the larger number: The larger number is negative so the difference of the numerators gives us -19

Keep the same denominator (40)

$$\text{Answer:} \ -\frac{19}{40}$$

Example #2: $\ -\dfrac{5}{6} - \dfrac{1}{2}$

Step #1: Get rid of all double negatives.

There are no double negatives here. There is nothing to do.

Vertical Set up:	Horizontal Set up:

$$-\frac{5}{6}$$

$$-\ \frac{1}{2}$$

$$-\frac{5}{6} - \frac{1}{2}$$

Step #2: Find the common denominator and make equivalent fractions.

The common denominator is 6.

Vertical Method:			OR	Horizontal Method:

$$-\frac{5}{6} = -\frac{5}{6}$$

$$-\frac{1}{2} = -\frac{3}{6}$$

$$-\frac{5}{6} - \frac{1}{2}$$

$$-\frac{5}{6} - \frac{3}{6} \quad or \quad \frac{-5-3}{6}$$

Step #3: The signs of the values are **the same**: <u>ADD</u> (the absolute values of the two numbers) and **KEEP THE SAME SIGN.**

Add the absolute values (of the numerators): $5 + 3 = 8$

Keep the same sign: The signs were negative so we get –8

Keep the same denominator (6).

We get: $-\frac{8}{6}$ so we still need to reduce.

Answer: $-\frac{4}{3} \quad or \quad -1\frac{1}{3}$

How to:

Solve a Combining Signed Mixed Numbers problem:

1. Get rid of all double negatives. A double negative becomes a plus.

2. We must have a common denominator, or find one and make an equivalent fraction of each given fraction using this common denominator.

3. We now have two possibilities. The signs of the values are either the <u>same or different</u>.

The 1st Possibility: Same Signs—ADDING

Method #1 (vertical) ↔	**Method #2 (horizontal)**
(1) Add the numerators of the fractions.	(1) Change the mixed numbers into improper fractions.
(2) Add the whole numbers last.	(2) Add the numerators of the fractions.

(3) Keep the same sign.

OR

The 2nd Possibility: Different Signs—SUBTRACTING

Method #1 (vertical) ↔	**Method #2 (horizontal)**
(1) Place the largest number value on top.	(1) Change the mixed numbers into improper fractions.
(2) Make sure the top numerator is larger than the numerator of the fraction we are subtracting (If it isn't, borrow 1 or more wholes to make it larger)	(2) Take the difference (of the absolute values of the numbers).
(3) Take the difference (of the absolute values of the numbers).	

Last step: **KEEP THE SIGN OF THE INITIAL LARGER NUMBER.**

Example #3: $5\frac{1}{3} - \left(-2\frac{1}{4}\right)$

Step #1: Get rid of all double negatives.

There is a double negative so we change it to a plus.

Rewrite the problem: $5\frac{1}{3} + 2\frac{1}{4}$

Step #2: Find the common denominator and make equivalent fractions.

The common denominator is 12.

$$5\frac{1}{3} = 5\frac{4}{12} \text{ and } 2\frac{1}{4} = 2\frac{3}{12}$$

Rewrite the problem: $5\frac{4}{12} + 2\frac{3}{12}$

Step #3: The signs are the same so we will add.

Vertical Set up: **Horizontal Set up:**

$5\frac{4}{12}$ $5\frac{4}{12} + 2\frac{3}{12}$

$+ 2\frac{3}{12}$

Step #4: **The Vertical Method:**   OR   **The Horizontal Method:**
Add the fractions first. Then,   Change the mixed numbers into
add the whole numbers.   improper fractions.

$5\frac{4}{12}$ $\frac{64}{12} + \frac{27}{12}$

$+ 2\frac{3}{12}$ Add the numerators (64 + 27 = 91).

$7\frac{7}{12}$

KEEP THE SAME SIGN (in this case, the positive)

Answer: $7\frac{7}{12}$ OR   Answer: $\frac{91}{12}$

Example #4: $-2\dfrac{1}{6} + 1\dfrac{4}{5}$

Step #1: Get rid of all double negatives.

There are no double negatives here. There is nothing to do.

Step #2: Find the common denominator and make equivalent fractions.

The common denominator is 30.

$$-2\dfrac{1}{6} = -2\dfrac{5}{30} \quad \text{and} \quad 1\dfrac{4}{5} = 1\dfrac{24}{30}$$

Rewrite the problem: $-2\dfrac{5}{30} + 1\dfrac{24}{30}$

Step #3: The signs are different so we will take the difference (of the absolute values of the numbers).

Vertical Set up: **Horizontal Set up:**

(make sure the largest value is on top)

$$2\dfrac{5}{30}$$
$$-\ 1\dfrac{24}{30}$$

$$-2\dfrac{5}{30} + 1\dfrac{24}{30}$$

Step #4: **The Vertical Method:**   OR   **The Horizontal Method:**

Subtract the fractions. We can't take 24 from 5 so we must borrow

1 whole $\left(\dfrac{30}{30}\right)$ from the 2 and add

it to $\dfrac{5}{30}$. The problem changes from:

$$\begin{array}{ccc} 2\dfrac{5}{30} & & 1\dfrac{35}{30} \\ & \text{to} & \\ -\ 1\dfrac{24}{30} & & -\ 1\dfrac{24}{30} \\ \hline & & \end{array}$$

Take the difference: $\dfrac{11}{30}$

Change the mixed numbers into improper fractions.

Rewrite and get:

$$\dfrac{-65}{30} + \dfrac{54}{30}$$

Take the difference: $-\dfrac{11}{30}$

KEEP THE SIGN OF THE INITIAL LARGER NUMBER

(in this case, the negative)

Answer: $-\dfrac{11}{30}$ OR   Answer: $-\dfrac{11}{30}$

Sample #1: $-\dfrac{4}{5} - \left(-\dfrac{3}{4}\right) - 2\dfrac{3}{8}$

Get rid of the double negative and rewrite the expression:

$$-\dfrac{4}{5} + \dfrac{3}{4} - 2\dfrac{3}{8}$$

The Vertical Method: OR   **The Horizontal Method:**

(As long as the problem is all combining, it is easiest to add together same signs first)

⇓

There are 2 negative values. Find a common denominator (40) and add.

Change the mixed numbers into improper fractions.

⇓

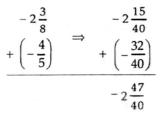

$$-\dfrac{4}{5} + \dfrac{3}{4} - \dfrac{19}{8}$$

⇓

Find a common denominator and rewrite the problem.

Combine this answer with the third value of positive $\dfrac{3}{4}$.

⇓

$$-2\dfrac{47}{40} + \dfrac{3}{4}$$

$$-\dfrac{32}{40} + \dfrac{30}{40} - \dfrac{95}{40} \text{ or } \dfrac{-32 + 30 - 95}{40}$$

Different signs, so take the difference (We can see already that the answer will be negative because that is the larger value) of the absolute values of the numbers.

Combine the numerators.

$$(-32 + 30 - 95) = -97$$

⇓

The denominator stays the same.

$$2\dfrac{47}{40} \Rightarrow 2\dfrac{47}{40}$$
$$-\ \ \dfrac{3}{4} \qquad -\ \dfrac{30}{40}$$
$$\rule{2cm}{0.4pt} \qquad \rule{2cm}{0.4pt}$$
$$2\dfrac{17}{40}$$

KEEP THE SIGN OF THE INITIAL LARGER NUMBER

(in this case, the negative)

Answer: $-2\dfrac{17}{40}$ OR   **Answer:** $-\dfrac{97}{40}$

- **You try it now:**

  a) $-\dfrac{2}{3} - \dfrac{1}{8} - \left(-\dfrac{3}{4}\right)$

  b) $-4\dfrac{1}{5} + 2\dfrac{9}{10} - 1\dfrac{1}{2}$

Sample #2: Find the difference of $-\dfrac{5}{3}$ and $-\dfrac{1}{4}$.

As with any word problem, we must first translate words into math.

We know that the **"difference"** means **"subtract."** Thus the connecting operation between the two values is subtract (–).

The two values are $-\dfrac{5}{3}$ and $-\dfrac{1}{4}$. Insert the connector between the two values and we get the following:

Set up: $-\dfrac{5}{3} - \left(-\dfrac{1}{4}\right)$

We get rid of the double negative and rewrite the problem as: $-\dfrac{5}{3} + \dfrac{1}{4}$

The values are different signs, so we'll take the difference between $\dfrac{5}{3}$ and $\dfrac{1}{4}$, and then keep the sign of the larger value. The larger value is negative, so the answer will be negative.

The Vertical Method:	OR	**The Horizontal Method:**

$$\begin{array}{r}\dfrac{5}{3}\\[2mm]-\dfrac{1}{4}\\\hline\end{array} \Rightarrow \begin{array}{r}\dfrac{20}{12}\\[2mm]-\dfrac{3}{12}\\\hline\dfrac{17}{12}\end{array}$$

$$-\dfrac{5}{3} + \dfrac{1}{4} \Rightarrow -\dfrac{20}{12} + \dfrac{3}{12}$$

$$\Downarrow$$

KEEP THE SIGN OF THE INITIAL LARGER NUMBER

(in this case, the negative)

Answer: $-\dfrac{17}{12}$ *or* $-1\dfrac{5}{12}$ OR   **Answer:** $-\dfrac{17}{12}$ *or* $-1\dfrac{5}{12}$

- **You try it now:**

- c) Find the difference of $-5\frac{2}{7}$ and $-3\frac{3}{5}$.

- d) Subtract $\frac{3}{8}$ from -2.

Sample #3: As a park ranger, one of Sheila's weekly jobs was to measure the change in the water level at the park's pond. Setting a marker at zero on the first day of the month, she returned each week for the next four weeks and recorded the following information. During the first and second weeks the pond's depth decreased by $1\frac{1}{2}$ and $1\frac{4}{5}$ inches respectively. The third week showed a gain of $1\frac{3}{4}$ inches. Finally the fourth week produced a gain of $\frac{1}{10}$ of an inch. What number represents the change in the pond's depth?

To answer this problem we must combine all four of these readings to get the total change. It will be easiest to put the negative readings (the $1\frac{1}{2}$ and the $1\frac{4}{5}$) together and then the positive readings (the $1\frac{3}{4}$ and the $\frac{1}{10}$) together.

Set up: $\left(-1\frac{1}{2} - 1\frac{4}{5}\right) + \left(1\frac{3}{4} + \frac{1}{10}\right)$

Solving Sample #3 by <u>The Vertical Method</u>:

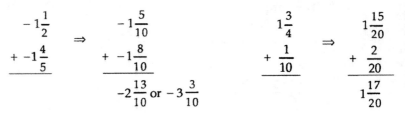

(1) Add the negative values.

$$\begin{array}{r} -1\frac{1}{2} \\ +\,-1\frac{4}{5} \\ \hline \end{array} \Rightarrow \begin{array}{r} -1\frac{5}{10} \\ +\,-1\frac{8}{10} \\ \hline -2\frac{13}{10} \text{ or } -3\frac{3}{10} \end{array}$$

(2) Add the positive values.

$$\begin{array}{r} 1\frac{3}{4} \\ +\,\frac{1}{10} \\ \hline \end{array} \Rightarrow \begin{array}{r} 1\frac{15}{20} \\ +\,\frac{2}{20} \\ \hline 1\frac{17}{20} \end{array}$$

Rewrite the problem: $-3\frac{3}{10} + 1\frac{17}{20}$

We have different signs so take the difference.

$$\begin{array}{r} 3\frac{3}{10} \\ -\,1\frac{17}{20} \\ \hline \end{array} \Rightarrow \begin{array}{r} 3\frac{6}{20} \\ -\,1\frac{17}{20} \\ \hline \end{array}$$

Subtract the fractions first. We can't take 17 from the 6, so we must borrow 1 whole $\left(\dfrac{20}{20}\right)$ from the 3 wholes. Rewrite the problem:

$$
\begin{array}{r}
3\dfrac{6}{20} \\
-\ 1\dfrac{17}{20} \\
\hline
\end{array}
\quad\Rightarrow\quad
\begin{array}{r}
2\dfrac{26}{20} \\
-\ 1\dfrac{17}{20} \\
\hline
1\dfrac{9}{20}
\end{array}
$$

Keep the sign of the larger value (which is negative here).

Answer: $-1\dfrac{9}{20}$ of an inch

Solving Sample #3 by <u>The Horizontal Method</u>:

Set up: $\left(-1\dfrac{1}{2}-1\dfrac{4}{5}\right)+\left(1\dfrac{3}{4}+\dfrac{1}{10}\right)$

Change all mixed numbers to improper fractions. Rewrite the problem:

$$-\dfrac{3}{2}-\dfrac{9}{5}+\dfrac{7}{4}+\dfrac{1}{10}$$

Now rewrite the problem with the common denominator of 20.

$$-\dfrac{30}{20}-\dfrac{36}{20}+\dfrac{35}{20}+\dfrac{2}{20}\quad\text{or}\quad\dfrac{-30-36+35+2}{20}$$

Now combine the numerators: $(-30-36+35+2)\ =\ -29$

The denominator stays the same.

Answer: $-\dfrac{29}{20}$ of an inch

You try it now:

e) Marsha and her running partner Alicia were having a friendly competition to see who could run more in a three week period. In the first week Marsha ran $3\dfrac{3}{8}$ more miles than Alicia. In the second and third week she respectively ran $1\dfrac{4}{5}$ and $1\dfrac{7}{10}$ miles less than Alicia. What number represents the amount of mileage Marsha ran in relation to Alicia?

f) For his Ph.D. research project, Ian was studying a beetle that lived in the foothills of Northern California. The beetle had a unique lifestyle, eating voraciously in the spring and fall, hibernating for a short period in the summer and for about 3 months in the winter. These different periods of activity produced a cyclical weight change in the beetles. On average Ian found that a typical adult beetle lost about $1\frac{1}{8}$ ounces during its winter hibernation. In the next few months it would gain about $\frac{11}{16}$ of an ounce, then lose about $\frac{1}{4}$ of an ounce in the middle of the summer. In the fall it would gain about another $\frac{7}{8}$ ounce. If this was norm, how much weight did an adult beetle gain every year?

Answers to You try it now: a) $-\frac{1}{24}$; b) $-\frac{14}{5}$ or $-2\frac{4}{5}$; c) $-\frac{59}{35}$ or $-1\frac{24}{35}$; d) $-\frac{19}{8}$ or $-2\frac{3}{8}$; e) $-\frac{1}{8}$ mile; f) the average adult beetle gained about $\frac{3}{16}$ of an ounce a year.

Answer to Application: Anthony is currently $3\frac{1}{4}$ pounds over 150. We can think of this as $+3\frac{1}{4}$. He then lost weight. We think of losing as negative $\left(-1\frac{3}{5} \text{ and } -2\frac{3}{4}\right)$. Finally, Anthony gained another $\frac{2}{3}$ of a pound $\left(+\frac{2}{3}\right)$. To see if Anthony weighs 150 pounds or less, we must combine the weight changes and see if we get zero or less.

Set up: $3\frac{1}{4} - 1\frac{3}{5} - 2\frac{3}{4} + \frac{2}{3}$

Let's solve by using the horizontal method. Change the mixed numbers into fractions.

$$\frac{13}{4} - \frac{8}{5} - \frac{11}{4} + \frac{2}{3}$$

Find the common denominator (60) and make equivalent fractions:

$$\frac{195}{60} - \frac{96}{60} - \frac{165}{60} + \frac{40}{60} \text{ or } \frac{195 - 96 - 165 + 40}{60}$$

Combine the numerators; keep the same denominator. We get $\frac{26}{60}$ which reduces to $\frac{13}{30}$.

Answer: Yes, Anthony can wrestle in the 140–150 pound weight division. He weighs $\frac{13}{30}$ of a pound less than 150 pounds.

3.5 Combining Fractions and Mixed Numbers Problems

In exercises #1–5, answer the following questions.

1) State whether the following expression is a double negative or not: $-\left(-1\frac{9}{10}\right)$

2) State whether the following expression is a double negative or not: $-\left(-\frac{11}{100}\right)$

3) State whether the following expression is a double negative or not: $-\frac{1}{5}-\frac{5}{2}$

4) State whether the following expression is a double negative or not: $-2+-\frac{4}{7}$

5) Is a double negative the same as a plus?

In exercises #6–14, state whether the following expressions are True or False. If you are unsure when answering questions #8 – 12, refer to the "How to" box on page 251 to see <u>what process</u> would be followed to get the correct answer.

6) A negative sign changes the value of the number to its right.

7) A plus sign changes the value of the number to its right.

8) We would add to solve the following problem: $-\frac{3}{5}+\frac{5}{12}$

9) We would add to solve the following problem: $-\frac{8}{9}-\frac{2}{3}$

10) We would add to solve the following problem: $-3\frac{1}{6}+\left(-10\frac{3}{8}\right)$

11) We would add to solve the following problem: $-\frac{1}{4}-\left(-\frac{3}{16}\right)$

12) We would add to solve the following problem: $2\frac{3}{7}-\left(-4\frac{3}{4}\right)$

13) When combining two values with different signs, the answer is the sign of the larger number.

14) When combining two values with the same signs, the answer is the sign not given.

In exercises #15–26, state whether the answer to each of the following expressions would be negative or positive. Do not solve the expressions.

15) $3-8$ 　　　　16) $-10+6$ 　　　　17) $-3\frac{1}{10}-\frac{6}{19}$ 　　　18) $-\frac{5}{6}+\left(-\frac{3}{4}\right)$

19) $-8\frac{1}{2}+2\frac{99}{100}$ 　　20) $-4\frac{2}{5}+5\frac{3}{100}$ 　　21) $30-21\frac{3}{4}$ 　　22) $2\frac{5}{8}+(-3)$

23) $-1 - \left(-\dfrac{2}{3}\right)$ 24) $-\dfrac{2}{7} - \left(-3\dfrac{1}{6}\right)$ 25) $3\dfrac{3}{10} - \left(8\dfrac{2}{10}\right)$ 26) $6\dfrac{4}{5} - \left(4\dfrac{11}{12}\right)$

In exercises #27–38, identify the letter of the one expression that is different from the others. Do not solve.

27) a) $-\dfrac{7}{10} + \dfrac{5}{10}$ b) $\dfrac{-7 + 5}{10}$ c) $\dfrac{-(7 + 5)}{10}$ d) $\dfrac{(-7 + 5)}{10}$

28) a) $\dfrac{4 - 6}{5}$ b) $\dfrac{4}{5} + \left(\dfrac{-6}{5}\right)$ c) $\dfrac{4}{5} - \dfrac{6}{5}$ d) $\dfrac{4}{5} - \left(\dfrac{-6}{5}\right)$

29) a) $\dfrac{7 - 3 - 2}{11}$ b) $\dfrac{7 - (3 - 2)}{11}$ c) $\dfrac{7 - 3}{11} + \left(-\dfrac{2}{11}\right)$ d) $\dfrac{7}{11} - \dfrac{3}{11} - \dfrac{2}{11}$

30) a) $-\dfrac{4}{7} - \dfrac{5}{7} + \left(-\dfrac{6}{7}\right)$ b) $\dfrac{-(4 + 5) - 6}{7}$ c) $\dfrac{-4 - 5 - 6}{7}$ d) $\dfrac{-4 - 5 + 6}{7}$

31) a) $1\dfrac{3}{4} - \left(-1\dfrac{1}{8}\right)$ b) $1\dfrac{3}{4} - 1\dfrac{1}{8}$ c) $1\dfrac{1}{8} + 1\dfrac{3}{4}$ d) $1\dfrac{3}{4} + 1\dfrac{1}{8}$

32) a) $-3\dfrac{1}{10} - 3\dfrac{1}{10}$ b) $3\dfrac{1}{10} + 3\dfrac{1}{10}$ c) $-3\dfrac{1}{10} + \left(-3\dfrac{1}{10}\right)$ d) $\left(-3\dfrac{1}{10}\right) \bullet 2$

33) a) $-3 + -6$ b) $-6 + -3$ c) $-(3 + 6)$ d) $-(3) + (6)$

34) a) $4 - 7 - 3$ b) $4 + 7 - 3$ c) $4 + 7 + (-3)$ d) $(4 + 7) - 3$

35) a) $\dfrac{1}{2} - \dfrac{3}{5}$ b) $-\dfrac{3}{5} + \dfrac{1}{2}$ c) $+\left(\dfrac{1}{2} - \dfrac{3}{5}\right)$ d) $-\dfrac{1}{2} + \left(\dfrac{3}{5}\right)$

36) a) $2\dfrac{1}{4} - 1\dfrac{7}{12}$ b) $-\left(2\dfrac{1}{4} - 1\dfrac{7}{12}\right)$ c) $-1\dfrac{7}{12} + 2\dfrac{1}{4}$ d) $+\left(2\dfrac{1}{4} - 1\dfrac{7}{12}\right)$

37) a) $-\dfrac{7}{3} + \dfrac{4}{5} + \left(\dfrac{-2}{9}\right)$ b) $\dfrac{4}{5} + \left(-\dfrac{7}{3}\right) + \left(\dfrac{-2}{9}\right)$ c) $\dfrac{4 - 7 - 2}{5 + 3 + 9}$ d) $\left(-\dfrac{7}{3} + \dfrac{4}{5}\right) - \dfrac{2}{9}$

38) a) $\left(-\dfrac{8}{5} - \dfrac{2}{3}\right) - \dfrac{5}{6}$ b) $-\dfrac{8}{5} + \left(-\dfrac{2}{3}\right) + \left(-\dfrac{5}{6}\right)$ c) $\left(-\dfrac{2}{3} + \dfrac{-8}{5}\right) - \dfrac{5}{6}$ d) $\dfrac{5}{6} + \dfrac{-2}{3} + \dfrac{-8}{5}$

In exercises #39–72, solve.

39) $-\dfrac{1}{4} - \dfrac{3}{4}$ 40) $\dfrac{3}{8} - \dfrac{5}{8}$ 41) $-\dfrac{1}{2} + \dfrac{2}{3}$ 42) $-\dfrac{4}{5} - \dfrac{1}{4}$

43) $-\dfrac{3}{11} + \left(-\dfrac{2}{5}\right)$ 44) $-\dfrac{1}{8} + \left(-\dfrac{2}{3}\right)$ 45) $\dfrac{2}{7} - \left(-\dfrac{1}{3}\right)$ 46) $\dfrac{3}{5} - \left(-\dfrac{3}{4}\right)$

47) $-\dfrac{1}{2} - \left(-\dfrac{5}{6}\right)$ 48) $-\dfrac{7}{10} - \left(-\dfrac{5}{9}\right)$ 49) $-\dfrac{1}{5} - \dfrac{3}{2} - \dfrac{3}{4}$ 50) $\dfrac{3}{8} - \dfrac{1}{2} - \dfrac{2}{4}$

51) $-\dfrac{3}{5} - \dfrac{3}{10} + \dfrac{3}{25}$ 52) $-\dfrac{2}{7} + \left(-\dfrac{4}{5}\right) - \dfrac{1}{10}$ 53) $-\dfrac{4}{3} + \dfrac{1}{8} - \dfrac{1}{2}$ 54) $-\dfrac{1}{9} + \dfrac{2}{3} - \dfrac{1}{6}$

55) $\dfrac{7}{10} - \dfrac{3}{4} + \dfrac{1}{2}$ 56) $\dfrac{7}{8} - 1 + \dfrac{1}{6}$ 57) $-\dfrac{1}{10} + \dfrac{1}{100} + \dfrac{1}{1000}$ 58) $-1\dfrac{1}{2} - 1\dfrac{1}{4}$

59) $-1\dfrac{2}{5} + 1\dfrac{1}{3}$ 60) $2\dfrac{3}{5} - 4\dfrac{1}{2}$ 61) $-5\dfrac{1}{10} + \left(-3\dfrac{2}{6}\right)$ 62) $6\dfrac{2}{8} - \left(-1\dfrac{3}{8}\right)$

63) $4\dfrac{3}{7} - \left(-2\dfrac{1}{2}\right)$ 64) $-3\dfrac{3}{4} - \left(-1\dfrac{1}{4}\right)$ 65) $-6 - \left(-3\dfrac{2}{9}\right)$ 66) $8 - \left(2\dfrac{4}{11}\right)$

67) $-3\dfrac{1}{5} + \left(6\dfrac{2}{3}\right)$ 68) $-4\dfrac{7}{8} + 5\dfrac{1}{4}$ 69) $-2\dfrac{5}{9} + \left(10\dfrac{1}{3}\right)$ 70) $-3\dfrac{2}{3} - 2\dfrac{1}{4} + 4\dfrac{11}{12}$

71) $-3\dfrac{2}{5} + 5\dfrac{1}{4} - 1\dfrac{3}{10}$ 72) $3 + \left(-4\dfrac{2}{3}\right) - 1\dfrac{2}{6}$

In exercises #73–84, translate the following words into math expressions. Then solve.

73) The sum of $\dfrac{3}{8}$ and $-\dfrac{1}{3}$.

74) The difference of $\dfrac{3}{8}$ and $-\dfrac{1}{3}$.

75) $\dfrac{3}{4}$ more than $-1\dfrac{1}{5}$.

76) 4 less than $-2\dfrac{1}{7}$.

77) $-\dfrac{5}{4}$ increased by $\dfrac{2}{3}$.

78) Subtract $-\dfrac{1}{3}$ from $\dfrac{1}{6}$.

79) Subtract $-\dfrac{2}{5}$ from $-\dfrac{1}{10}$.

80) Subtract $1\dfrac{1}{2}$ from $\dfrac{5}{8}$.

81) The difference of $-\dfrac{3}{5}$ and $\dfrac{3}{5}$.

82) The difference of $-3\dfrac{2}{3}$ and $-1\dfrac{3}{4}$.

83) The total of $-8\dfrac{1}{3}$ and $2\dfrac{2}{3}$.

84) The total of $2\dfrac{1}{4}$, $-1\dfrac{3}{8}$ and $-\dfrac{5}{6}$.

In exercises #85–88: (a) write a mathematical expression that will solve the problem, and (b) give the solution.

85) When Oliver became ill with dengue fever, his temperature increased by $2\dfrac{3}{4}$ of a degree in the morning, then another 2 degrees in the next few hours. Only after taking some medication, did his temperature drop about $\dfrac{4}{5}$ of a degree before sunset. What mixed number represents the change in Oliver's body temperature that day?

86) A parent corporation announced the year's earning for three of the companies that it owned. Company A earned $3\frac{2}{5}$ million dollars; Company B lost $1\frac{1}{4}$ million, and Company C lost $2\frac{1}{2}$ million. What amount represents the corporation's profit/loss from these companies?

87–88) A computer monitored the altitude of a newly launched weather balloon. In one hour it gained $2\frac{1}{4}$ thousand feet. In the second and third hours respectively the balloon lost $\frac{1}{2}$ thousand feet and $1\frac{1}{3}$ thousand feet.

87) What number represents the change in the altitude of the weather balloon in the three–hour period (give answer as a fraction of a thousand feet)?

88) What number represents the change in the altitude of the weather balloon in actual feet (give answer as a mixed number)?

For exercise #89 – 94: The profits for four companies (Companies A, B, C, and D) are posted on the number line below.   Use the information provided on the number line to answer questions #89–94.

The values above represent the **number of millions of dollars** in profit each company made last year.

For #89–92, no set up is necessary (solution only).

89) What number represents the financial balance for Company A last year (give answer as a fraction of a million dollars)?

90) What number represents the financial balance for Company A last year in actual dollars?

91) What number represents the financial balance for Company C last year (give answer as a mixed number of a million dollars)?

92) What number represents the financial balance for Company C last year in actual dollars?

For #93–94: (a) write a mathematical expression that will solve the problem, and (b) give the solution.

93) What was the overall financial balance for the companies A and B combined (give answer as a fraction of a million dollars)?

94) What was the financial balance for the four companies last year in actual dollars?

95–100) Look at the graph below.

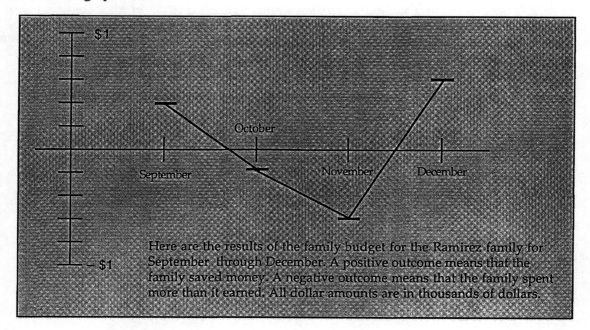

Here are the results of the family budget for the Ramirez family for September through December. A positive outcome means that the family saved money. A negative outcome means that the family spent more than it earned. All dollar amounts are in thousands of dollars.

95) What was the budget balance for the Ramirez family for September (give answer as a fraction of a thousand dollars)?

96) What was the budget balance for the Ramirez family for September in actual dollars?

97) What was the budget balance for the Ramirez family for November (give answer as a fraction of a thousand dollars)?

98) What was the budget balance for the Ramirez family for November in actual dollars?

For #99–100, give: (a) write a mathematical expression that will solve the problem, and (b) give the solution.

99) What was the overall budget balance for the Ramirez family for all four months (give answer as a fraction of a thousand dollars)?

100) What was the overall budget balance for the Ramirez family for all four months in actual dollars?

101) After investing in the *We're Really Fast* digital service company, Megan watched the value of the company's stock carefully. In a four–week period it moved as shown in the chart below. Draw a graph where the vertical number line represents the value of the stock per share above or below the original price she paid for it (make the amount between each dash be $\$\frac{1}{4}$). Zero would mean that the stock is selling for the same price as that which Megan paid for it. The horizontal number line will show the four weeks after she purchased the stock. Plot (by drawing a darkened circle) the data in the chart below and then connect with a line the changing value of the stock from its opening (week 0) through the end of week 4.

End of the Week	Change in value of the We're Really Fast stock per share
Week #1	$-\$1\frac{1}{2}$
Week #2	$+\$\frac{3}{4}$
Week #3	$-\$\frac{1}{4}$
Week #4	$+\$1\frac{1}{4}$

In exercises #102–106, state whether the following statements are True or False.

102) $-\frac{4}{9} - \frac{1}{4} = -\frac{25}{36}$ is the same as $-\frac{4}{9} = -\frac{25}{36} + \frac{1}{4}$

103) $-\frac{2}{5} + \frac{1}{3} = -\frac{1}{15}$ is the same as $\frac{1}{3} = -\frac{1}{15} - \frac{2}{5}$

104) $-1\frac{1}{2} + 2\frac{3}{8} = \frac{7}{8}$ is the same as $-1\frac{1}{2} = \frac{7}{8} + 2\frac{3}{8}$

105) $-\frac{3}{7} + 2\frac{2}{3} = -2\frac{5}{21}$ is the same as $-2\frac{5}{21} - 2\frac{2}{3} = -\frac{3}{7}$

106) $\frac{1}{10} - \frac{3}{4} = -\frac{13}{20}$ is the same as $-\frac{13}{20} - \frac{1}{10} = -\frac{3}{4}$

In exercises #107–112, solve for the value of x.

107) $\frac{6}{7} - \frac{4}{3} = x$

108) $x = -3 - \frac{7}{10}$

109) $x - \frac{2}{3} = -4$

110) $x + 1\frac{2}{5} = -3\frac{1}{4}$

111) $-4\frac{1}{4} + x = -3\frac{5}{7}$

112) $-1\frac{1}{12} + x = -5$

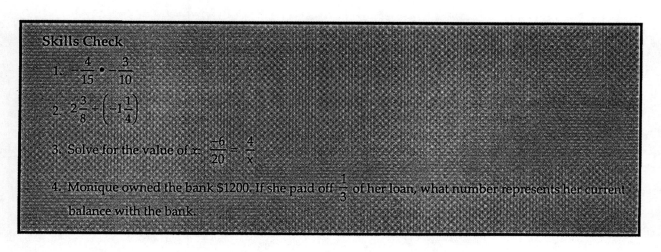

Skills Check

1. $-\dfrac{4}{15} \cdot -\dfrac{3}{10}$

2. $2\dfrac{3}{8} \div \left(-1\dfrac{1}{4}\right)$

3. Solve for the value of x: $\dfrac{-6}{20} = \dfrac{4}{x}$

4. Monique owned the bank $1200. If she paid off $\dfrac{1}{3}$ of her loan, what number represents her current balance with the bank.

Answers to Skills Check: 1) $\dfrac{2}{25}$;   2) $-\dfrac{19}{10}$ *or* $-1\dfrac{9}{10}$;   3) $-\dfrac{40}{3}$ *or* $-13\dfrac{1}{3}$; 4) Monique still owed the bank, so her balance is negative. The answer would be –$800.

Section 3.6 Order of Operations and a Review of Some Other Ideas and Processes within the System of Rational Numbers

Objectives:

- To solve order of operations problems with various rational numbers
- To review many concepts and computation skills from units #1–3
- To set up/solve various rational number application problems

Application:

When Jim signed on as a crew member on a fishing vessel, he was told that he would receive a base salary of $100 dollars per day for a 5-day trip, plus he and the other four crew members would each get credited for $\frac{1}{10}$ of the profit (or loss) after all expenses (including the salaries of the crew) were paid. General expenses for the trip were $1,000. They caught $3\frac{1}{4}$ thousand pounds of fish and were able to sell it for $1.20 per pound. How much money did Jim earn from this trip?

Vocabulary:

> ***Knowing the Scheme to Solve all Signed Number Expressions:** We need to remind ourselves that the one guiding principle to solving any expression is to <u>always</u> follow the order of operations (PEMDAS—section 1.6). Beyond this, we also need to be able to look at any problem (or a part of a larger problem) and recognize if we have either a **combining problem** <u>or</u> a **multiplication/division problem**.

> Once we have identified a problem as combining or multiplication/division, we have a very different process to follow. It is our responsibility to: (1) identify the problem type correctly and then, (2) follow the correct process. In the picture below the "Grand Canyon" represents <u>the split between the two processes</u> and emphasizes the <u>importance of keeping them forever separated</u>.

> The Scheme: **<u>ALWAYS</u> follow the ORDER of OPERATIONS!**

> 1st Priority: **Label each of the operations in a problem as either a combining <u>or</u> a multiplication/division problem.**

> 2nd Priority: **Follow the process below for multiplication/divison**

> 3rd Priority: **Follow the process below for combining.**

> In General: **Remember that the sign <u>always</u> affects the value to its right.**

The Grand Canyon approach to solving signed number expressions.

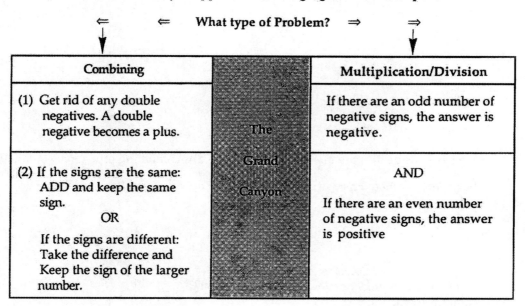

⇐   ⇐   **What type of Problem?**   ⇒   ⇒

Combining	The Grand Canyon	Multiplication/Division
(1) Get rid of any double negatives. A double negative becomes a plus.		If there are an odd number of negative signs, the answer is negative.
(2) If the signs are the same: ADD and keep the same sign. OR If the signs are different: Take the difference and Keep the sign of the larger number.		AND If there are an even number of negative signs, the answer is positive

Because the Order of Operations is not a new concept, there are no example problems in this section to show new concepts. The sample problems give the opportunity to explore longer and more complex order of operations problems.

Sample #1: $-6 - 4(2 + (-3) \cdot 4)$

We have an order of operations problem.

We work inside the parenthesis first. There are 2 parentheses, so we look at the innermost parenthesis first, which is: (–3). There is no operation to solve inside this parenthesis, so we look to the larger parenthesis: (2 + (–3) • 4). Here we have a combining operation and multiplication. We must first:

Solve the multiplication: $-6 - 4(2 + \underline{(-3) \cdot 4})$

⇓

Now finish the work inside the parenthesis: $-6 - 4(\underline{2 + -12})$

⇓

Next, we are left with only two operations, a combining operation and multiplication. $-6 \underline{- 4(-10)}$

We must do the multiplication (–4 • –10):   ⇓

Solve the combining: $\underline{-6 + 40}$

Answer: **34**

You try it now:

a) $5 - 6 \bullet 3\,(-4 - 1)$

b) $4 \bullet -7 + 20 \div -5 - 1$

Sample #2: $\dfrac{1}{3} - \dfrac{4}{5}\left(-2\dfrac{1}{2} + \dfrac{3}{4}\right)$

We have an order of operations problem.

We work inside the parenthesis first. Let's solve this combining problem by using the horizontal method. First we change $-2\dfrac{1}{2}$ to its equivalent fraction form of $-\dfrac{5}{2}$.

We get: $\dfrac{1}{3} - \dfrac{4}{5}\left(-\dfrac{5}{2} + \dfrac{3}{4}\right)$

$\Downarrow$

We rewrite the fractions inside the parenthesis using the common denominator of 4; now we combine them: $\dfrac{1}{3} - \dfrac{4}{5}\left(\dfrac{-10}{4} + \dfrac{3}{4}\right)$

$\Downarrow$

Next, we are left with only two operations, a combining operation and multiplication.

We must do the multiplication $\left[-\dfrac{4}{5}\left(-\dfrac{7}{4}\right)\right]$: $\dfrac{1}{3} - \dfrac{4}{5}\left(-\dfrac{7}{4}\right)$

$\Downarrow$

$\dfrac{1}{3} + \dfrac{7}{5}$

Solve the combining:

Answer: $\dfrac{26}{15}$ *or* $1\dfrac{11}{15}$

You try it now:

c) $-\dfrac{1}{5} + \dfrac{1}{4} \div 3 - \dfrac{1}{2}$

d) $-\dfrac{3}{4} \div 1\dfrac{3}{4} - \dfrac{3}{8}$

Sample #3: $\dfrac{\left(-\dfrac{1}{4} - 1\dfrac{1}{2}\right)}{\left(-2\dfrac{1}{8} + 1\dfrac{1}{3}\right)}$

We have an order of operations problem here. This problem may, at first glance, look very complicated, but remember that every fraction is a division problem. This problem is the

same as: $\left(-\dfrac{1}{4} - 1\dfrac{1}{2}\right) \div \left(-2\dfrac{1}{8} + 1\dfrac{1}{3}\right)$. Really, all we are doing here is solving the top part of

the problem and the bottom part separately and then dividing the two answers.

So, if this is an order of operations problem, we solve inside the parentheses first.

Solve inside the parenthesis in the numerator:

$\left(-\dfrac{1}{4} - 1\dfrac{1}{2}\right)$ becomes $\left(-\dfrac{1}{4} - \dfrac{3}{2}\right)$ which becomes $\left(-\dfrac{1}{4} - \dfrac{6}{4}\right)$ which equals: $-\dfrac{7}{4}$

Solve inside the parenthesis in the denominator:

$\left(-2\dfrac{1}{8} + 1\dfrac{1}{3}\right)$ becomes $\left(\dfrac{-17}{8} + \dfrac{4}{3}\right)$ which becomes $\left(\dfrac{-51}{24} + \dfrac{32}{24}\right)$; it equals: $-\dfrac{19}{24}$

We now have the following problem:

$\dfrac{\left(\dfrac{-7}{4}\right)}{\left(\dfrac{-19}{24}\right)}$ which is the same as: $\left(\dfrac{-7}{4}\right) \div \left(\dfrac{-19}{24}\right)$

Answer: $\dfrac{42}{19}$ *or* $2\dfrac{4}{19}$

You try it now:

e) $-2\dfrac{1}{4} + \dfrac{3}{4} \cdot 1\dfrac{1}{5}$

f) $\dfrac{3}{7} \div 1\dfrac{2}{5} - \dfrac{1}{7}$

Sample #4: $\dfrac{2}{x} - \dfrac{5}{x} - \left(-\dfrac{4}{x}\right)$

We recognize that we have a combining problem. To combine fractions we will need a common denominator—We already have it! The variable x is our common denominator.

So we need to follow the process for combining signed numbers. First we get rid of any double negatives.

$$\dfrac{2}{x} - \dfrac{5}{x} \underbrace{- \left(-\dfrac{4}{x}\right)}$$

$$\Downarrow$$

Now we combine the numerators.

$$\dfrac{2}{x} - \dfrac{5}{x} + \dfrac{4}{x}$$

Answer: $\dfrac{1}{x}$

You try it now:

g) $-\dfrac{4}{x} - \left(-\dfrac{3}{x}\right) - \dfrac{2}{x}$

h) $-\left(\dfrac{7}{m} - \dfrac{5}{m}\right) - \dfrac{1}{m}$

Answers to You try it now: a) 95;   b) -33;   c) $-\dfrac{37}{60}$;   d) $-\dfrac{45}{56}$;   e) $-\dfrac{27}{20}$ or $-1\dfrac{7}{20}$;   f) $\dfrac{8}{49}$ g) $-\dfrac{3}{x}$;   h) $-\dfrac{3}{m}$.

Answer to Application: First we can establish the fact that Jim will be paid in two different ways: (1) by salary, and (2) by $\dfrac{1}{10}$ of the profit (or loss). Our conceptual set up will be:

(money earned by salary) + (money earned by calculating $\dfrac{1}{10}$ of the trip's profit or loss)

Money Jim earned by salary: ($100 per day for 5 days). That is: $(100 \cdot 5)$

Money Jim earned by calculating $\dfrac{1}{10}$ of the profit: First we find how much money the entire trip made, that is, we find the difference between its earnings and its expenses.

Earnings from the trip: $3\dfrac{1}{4}$ thousand lb. sold at $1.20 per lb. That is: $\left(3\dfrac{1}{4} \text{ thousand} \cdot 1.20\right)$

Expenses of the trip: $1,000 plus 5 crew members each getting paid $100 per day for 5 days. That is:
$[\,1000 + (5)(100)(5)\,]$

Total profit from the trip: (Earnings) − (Expenses)

$$\text{Profit} = \left(3\dfrac{1}{4} \text{ thousand} \cdot 1.20\right) - [\,1000 + (5)(100)(5)\,]$$

Finally, Jim will get "$\frac{1}{10}$ of" the profits. We know that this means "$\frac{1}{10}$ times."

We return again now to our original conceptual set up:

(money earned by salary) + (money earned by calculating $\frac{1}{10}$ of the profit or loss)

Set up: $(100 \cdot 5) + \frac{1}{10} \cdot \left(\left(3\frac{1}{4} \text{ thousand} \cdot 1.20 \right) - [1000 + (5)(100)(5)] \right)$

Solve by following the order of operations. In this problem it is probably easiest to change the mixed number of $3\frac{1}{4}$ (thousand) to its decimal form of 3.25 (thousand) or 3250 pounds.

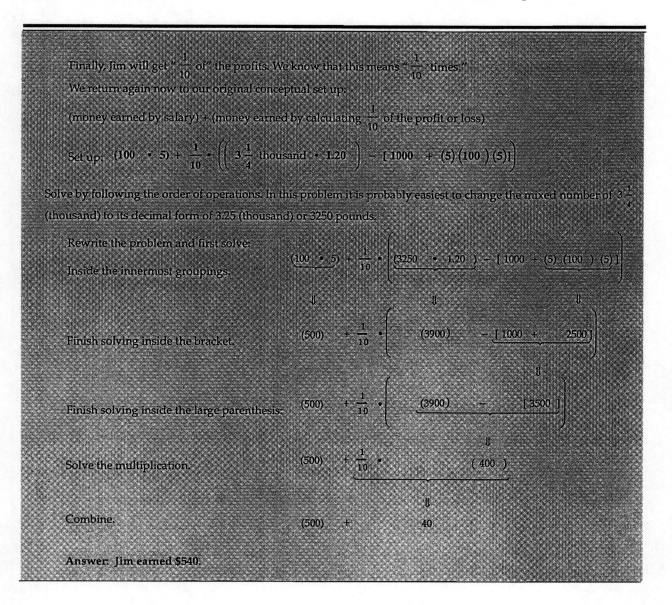

Rewrite the problem and first solve:

Inside the innermost groupings.

$(100 \cdot 5) + \frac{1}{10} \cdot \left((3250 \cdot 1.20) - [1000 + (5)(100)(5)] \right)$

Finish solving inside the bracket.

$(500) + \frac{1}{10} \cdot \left((3900) - [1000 + 2500] \right)$

Finish solving inside the large parenthesis:

$(500) + \frac{1}{10} \cdot \left((3900) - [3500] \right)$

Solve the multiplication.

$(500) + \frac{1}{10} \cdot (400)$

Combine.

$(500) + 40$

Answer: Jim earned $540.

3.6 Order of Operations and Other Review Problems

In exercises #1-47, solve by following the order of operations.

1) $-3 + 4 \bullet -3$

2) $8 - 5 \bullet 2$

3) $6 + -4(-2 - 2)$

4) $-10 - 10(6 - 3 \bullet 3)$

5) $4 - 10 \div -2$

6) $-3 - 8 \div -4$

7) $3 \bullet -2\left[-2\left(80 \div -4 -1\right)\right]$

8) $14 + (-4)\left[8 - 6 \div 2\right]$

9) $4 - 4 - (-3)$

10) $-5 - (-5) - 2$

11) $4 - 4 - (-3)(-4)$

12) $-5 - (-5)(-2)$

13) $-15.8 - (-3.5)$

14) $-3.4 - (-117.06) + 0.24$

15) $11.6 - 2.8 \div 0.4$

16) $-32.4 - 8.4 \div - 16.8$

17) $\dfrac{5}{8} - \dfrac{3}{8} \bullet \dfrac{4}{9}$

18) $\dfrac{2}{3} - \dfrac{5}{3} \bullet 3$

19) $\dfrac{4}{7} + \dfrac{1}{2} \div \left(-\dfrac{1}{3}\right)$

20) $-\dfrac{2}{5} + \dfrac{3}{10} \div \dfrac{-3}{4}$

21) $\dfrac{1}{4} - \left(-\dfrac{4}{3}\right) + \dfrac{1}{2}$

22) $-\dfrac{1}{10} - \left(-\dfrac{1}{5}\right) - \dfrac{3}{30}$

23) $-\dfrac{3}{8} - \left(\dfrac{1}{5} + \dfrac{2}{3} \bullet \dfrac{-9}{10}\right)$

24) $\dfrac{4}{5} - \left(-\dfrac{4}{5}\right) \div \dfrac{4}{25}$

25) $-\dfrac{2}{11} - \left(-\dfrac{1}{2}\right) \bullet - 4$

26) $6 - \left(-\dfrac{3}{4} \bullet \dfrac{3}{4}\right)$

27) $-\dfrac{1}{3} - \left(\dfrac{4}{3} \div \dfrac{8}{3}\right)$

28) $3\dfrac{1}{5} + \dfrac{4}{5} \bullet 1\dfrac{1}{7}$

29) $-2\dfrac{1}{4} - 1\dfrac{1}{4} + 1\dfrac{7}{8}$

30) $-1\dfrac{3}{8} + 2\left(-\dfrac{3}{4} - 1\right)$

31) $-3 - 3\dfrac{1}{3}\left(6\dfrac{1}{6} - \dfrac{1}{6} \div \dfrac{-1}{2}\right)$

32) $-5\dfrac{1}{10} \div \dfrac{3}{5}\left(\dfrac{1}{8} \bullet \dfrac{1}{2} + \dfrac{7}{16}\right)$

33) $\dfrac{\left(-1\dfrac{1}{5} + \dfrac{3}{5}\right)}{\left(-\dfrac{2}{3} - \dfrac{2}{3}\right)}$

34) $\dfrac{\left(\dfrac{3}{7} - 1\dfrac{2}{5}\right)}{\left(-\dfrac{1}{7} + \dfrac{2}{7}\right)}$

35) $\dfrac{8 \div -\dfrac{1}{4}}{-(-2)}$

36) $\dfrac{-(-(-3))}{-3 + \dfrac{1}{3}}$

37) $\dfrac{-\dfrac{1}{5} + \dfrac{1}{5} - \left(-\dfrac{2}{3}\right)}{4 \div 9}$

38) $\dfrac{2 - \dfrac{1}{5}}{-7 - 3\dfrac{1}{4}}$

39) $\dfrac{8\dfrac{1}{10} - 9\dfrac{2}{3}}{0}$

40) $\dfrac{0}{\dfrac{1}{7} - 2\dfrac{1}{4}}$

41) $\dfrac{3}{x} - \dfrac{3}{x}$

42) $\dfrac{3}{x} - \dfrac{5}{x}$

43) $\dfrac{-11 - 6}{x}$

44) $\dfrac{-4 - (-2)}{m}$

45) $\dfrac{\left(\dfrac{1}{2}\right)}{x} + \dfrac{\left(\dfrac{1}{2}\right)}{x}$

46) $\dfrac{5}{r} - \dfrac{7}{r} - \left(-\dfrac{3}{r}\right)$

47) $-\dfrac{2}{x} + \left(\dfrac{10}{x}\right) - \left(\dfrac{1}{x}\right)$

In exercises #48-53, give the answer as a fraction or a mixed number.

48) $3.3 + \left(-2\dfrac{2}{5}\right)$

49) $-12.7 - \left(1\dfrac{1}{4}\right)$

50) $-2.4 + 1.3 \cdot \dfrac{2}{3}$

51) $-3\dfrac{1}{8} - 1.75 \div \dfrac{3}{8}$

52) $100\dfrac{2}{3} \cdot 0.01 - \dfrac{7}{50}$

53) $\left(-8.23 - 4\dfrac{3}{7}\right) \div 0$

In exercises #54-59, give the answer as a decimal. If the answer runs beyond the hundredths place, round to the nearest hundredths.

54) $-7.47 - 3\dfrac{3}{8}$

55) $-2\dfrac{4}{5} - (-2.80)$

56) $-6\dfrac{1}{16} + 2.9$

57) $-4\dfrac{1}{3} + 2.\overline{6}$

58) $-11 - \left(-3\dfrac{6}{9}\right)$

59) $-2\dfrac{1}{4} \cdot -1.3 \div 0.1$

In exercises #60-67: (a) write a mathematical statement that will solve the problem, and (b) give the solution.

60) At a large elementary school there were three fifth-grade classes. One teacher had 23 students, a second had 28, and the third had 27 students. What was the ratio of teachers to students?

61) When the state's budget of 98 billion dollars was passed, 18 billion went for education. What was the ratio of money spent on education to that spent on all other matters?

62) Biologists studying the population of crickets in a farming community counted 800 crickets on one-third of an acre. If this same ratio of crickets to land remained constant throughout the area, how many crickets would there be on an $8\dfrac{1}{2}$ acre piece of farmland?

63) In a small town a survey showed that three out of every five adults read at least one book every month. If there are 570 adults in the town, how many read at least one book a month?

64-67) In the city of Summerville, 20,000 people voted during the last election. There were three main candidates for mayor, here to be labeled as candidates A, B, and C. Candidate A received 5,000 votes; Candidate B received 4500 votes; Candidate C received 6800 votes, and six others received the rest of the votes.

64) What fraction of the votes did Candidate C receive?

65) Written as a fraction, what was the probability that someone cast a vote for Candidate B?

66) Written as a fraction, what was the probability that someone cast a vote for one of the other 6 candidates?

67) What was the average number of votes received by each of the other six candidates (round to the nearest whole)?

In exercises #68-71 prime factor each number. If the number is prime, simply write the word "prime" for your answer.

68) 300   69) 154   70) 845   71) 207

In exercises #72-75, find the GCF of the given numbers.

72) 49 and 91   73) 48 and 180   74) 14 and 39   75) 30, 63, and 105

76) Is 181 a multiple of 3?

77) What is the eleventh multiple of 7?

In exercises #78-81, find the LCM of the given numbers:

78) 6 and 30   79) 10 and 42   80) 8, 12, and 16   81) 5, 6, and 8

In exercises #82-91, state whether the following statements are True of False.

82) $\frac{11}{4} \geq 2.75$ 　　　 83) $-2\frac{1}{5} \geq -2\frac{1}{4}$ 　　 84) $\frac{2}{3} \leq 0.\overline{6}$ 　　　 85) $4.3 \geq 4\frac{1}{3}$

86) $-2 \geq 0.02$ 　　　 87) $5.031 \leq 5\frac{31}{100}$ 　　　 88) $6 \div -7 > \frac{-6}{-7}$

89) $4 + \left(-\frac{3}{8}\right) < 4 - \left(-\frac{3}{8}\right)$ 　　 90) $|-5| + -5 = -|5| - (-5)$ 　 91) $\frac{3}{4} - \left|-\frac{1}{2}\right| = -\left|\frac{1}{4}\right|$

In exercises #92-102: (a) write a mathematical expression that will solve the problem, and (b) give the solution.

92) Derrick ran 8.4 miles on both Tuesday and Thursday last week. He ran $4\frac{1}{2}$ miles less on Wednesday than the distance he averaged running on Saturday and Sunday. On Saturday he ran 11 miles and he ran $6\frac{1}{4}$ miles on Sunday. How many miles did Derrick run last week?

93) In the video game *The Princess*, the princess had to travel the unknown lands and collect as many treasures as she could to earn points. She earned 20 points for finding a magical staff and 60 points for a golden crown before she lost $\frac{1}{5}$ of her points when she was robbed by bandits. Next, she found three dragon eggs, each worth 100 points. When the princess thought all was good, she came across a tax collector, who made her surrender $\frac{1}{4}$ of her current points. How many points did the princess have now?

94) When a drought hit a farmer in the Midwest, he estimated that he would lose about $5\frac{1}{2}$ thousand dollars from his wheat crop and about triple that amount from his corn crop. He only managed to earn a little money, about $1\frac{3}{8}$ thousand from his livestock. What number represents this farmer's financial balance this year (give answer as a mixed number of a thousand dollars)?

95-96) Over an eight-week period earlier this year a new Information Technology company posted a balance of -$12,000,000.

95) What was the average balance per week?

96) What was the average balance per day (round to the nearest dollar)?

97-98) At a resort near Yosemite, the normal income per day for the 31 days of July was $15,000. When a fire closed roads and threatened homes, the resort took in only $\frac{3}{10}$ of its norm for the last 10 days of the month.

97) Because of the fire, how much money, less than its norm, did the resort collect in July?

98) What was the resort's income this July?

99) A retailer had agreed to buy 10,000 feet of lumber at the price of $0.55 per foot from a mill. If the retailer was originally billed $550, was he charged the correct amount of money? If not, how much was he overcharged or undercharged?

100) Another retailer had bought 5,000 feet of lumber at $0.52 per foot. Unfortunately a fire destroyed 2,000 feet of the lumber, and $\frac{1}{2}$ of the rest was damaged by water. If the retailer had to sell the damaged wood at $0.32 a foot and sold the good wood for $0.77 a foot, what number represents the retailer's financial balance on the lumber which he purchased?

101-102) A judge fined four companies a total of $\frac{9}{10}$ of a million dollars. Each company was fined the same amount.

101) How much money did each company have to pay (give answer as a fraction of a million dollars)?

102) How much money did each company have to pay in actual dollars?

In exercises #103-108, answer the following questions.

103) 4 weeks is how many hours?

104) 3.6 yards is how many inches?

105) 6 minutes is how much of a week?

106) $4\frac{1}{3}$ inches is how much of a foot?

107) $1\frac{1}{5}$ years (non leap-year) is how many days?

108) 5 ounces is how much of a ton (2000 pounds)?

109) Round $125.3\overline{7}$

   a) to the nearest whole   b) to the tenths place   c) to the hundredths place

   d) to the thousandths place   e) to the tens place   f) to the thousands place

In exercises #110-126, tell whether the given statements are True or False. Do not solve.

110) $2.16 - 84.33 = -82.17$ is the same as $2.16 = -82.17 + 84.33$

111) $\frac{1}{3} \bullet -22 = -7\frac{1}{3}$ is the same as $\frac{1}{3} = -7\frac{1}{3} \div -22$

112) $(4 \bullet x) \bullet 6 = 4 \bullet (x \bullet 6)$

113) $(-8) + 6.23 + (-90.052) = (-8) + (-90.052) + 6.23$

114) $\frac{1}{8}$ of x is the same as $x \div 8$ 115) $\dfrac{\frac{1}{x}}{y}$ is the same as $1 \div \frac{x}{y}$ 116) $x \bullet (-1) = -x$

117) $\frac{r}{-1} = -r$ 118) $a - a = 0$

119) Subtract x from y is the same as: $y - x$

120) Take the difference of x and $-y$ is the same as: $x - (-y)$

121) A prime number has only 2 factors.

122) $\frac{b}{b}$ is equal to one whole unless b has the value of only one specific number.

123) $500\,(0.01)$ is the same as $500 \bullet \frac{1}{100}$

124) $30 \div 0.001$ is the same as $30 \div \frac{1}{1000}$ which is the same as $30 \bullet 1000$

125) Assuming that x is a positive integer, we can say that $\frac{x+1}{x}$ has a greater value than $\frac{x}{x}$.

126) $\frac{a}{m} - \frac{b}{m}$ is the same as $\frac{a-b}{m}$

Skills Check

1. True or False: $\frac{3}{5} - \frac{4}{5}$ is the same as $\frac{3-4}{5}$

2. $1\frac{1}{4} - 2\frac{1}{6}$

3. Find the difference of $-\frac{2}{3}$ and $-\frac{3}{5}$.

4. Subtract $-4\frac{1}{10}$ from 8.

Answers to Skills Check: 1) True: 2) $-\frac{11}{12}$; 3) $-\frac{1}{15}$; 4) $12\frac{1}{10}$

Chapter 4 Exponents

Section 4.1 Understand & Evaluate Exponential Expressions

Objectives:

- To recognize equivalent expressions in factored, simplified, and evaluated forms
- To evaluate exponential expressions (when the base is within a parenthesis or not)
- To solve order of operation problems with exponents

Application:

Looking through his microscope in a state biology lab, Joaquin isolated four viruses of a type new to the area. After studying the viruses for the next two days, he discovered that these microorganisms doubled in population every hour. How many viruses were there after 2 hours? After 5 hours? After 12 hours? After 24 hours?

Vocabulary:

Exponent or Power—An **exponent** or a **power** (these two words have the same meaning) tells us how many times to multiply a base number by itself. The exponent is raised above and to the right of the base number.

Examples: 2^3 where the 2 is the base and the 3 is the exponent.

2^3 means $2 \cdot 2 \cdot 2$ which equals 8.

$(-3)^4$ where the -3 is the base and the 4 is the exponent.

$(-3)^4$ means $(-3) \cdot (-3) \cdot (-3) \cdot (-3)$ which equals 81.

Squared—To say that a base number is **"squared"** is to mean that it has an exponent of 2. The expression "three squared" means 3^2.

Cubed—To say that a base number is **"cubed"** is to mean that it has an exponent of 3. The expression "five cubed" means 5^3.

**Three Ways to Represent the Value of an Exponential Expression

Factored Form—The factored form of an expression shows all the factors individually that make up a number value. For example, the factored form of the number 20 could be $2 \cdot 2 \cdot 5$.

Simplified or Exponential Form—The simplified or exponential form of an expression is the same as the factored form, <u>except</u> we use exponents whenever we can. 20 in simplified form would be $2^2 \cdot 5$.

Evaluated Form—The **evaluated form** of an expression is its actual solution, a single-number answer. The evaluated form of the expression $2^2 \cdot 5$ would be 20.

Here are a few more expressions which all have the same value.

Factored Form	Simplified or Exponential Form	Evaluated Form
$3 \cdot 3 \cdot 4 \cdot 4 \cdot 7$	$3^2 \cdot 4^2 \cdot 7$	1008
$5 \cdot 5 \cdot 5 \cdot \frac{1}{4} \cdot \frac{1}{4}$	$5^3 \cdot \left(\frac{1}{4}\right)^2$	$\frac{125}{16}$
$(-2) \cdot (-2) \cdot (-2) \cdot 6 \cdot 6$	$(-2)^3 \cdot 6^2$	-288

**Using a Calculator to Evaluate Exponential Expressions

When working with exponents, we only need to use a calculator when evaluating expressions. Here are two important keys to know:

(1) The "**squared**" key look like this: $\boxed{x^2}$ We would use the squared key if we were asked to evaluate (solve) an expression such as 21^2. Punch 21 on our calculator, then the $\boxed{x^2}$ button. The answer of 441 appears.

Try these on your calculator to make sure you get the correct answer.

$$14^2 = 196 \qquad\qquad 50^2 = 2500$$

(2) The "**exponent**" key can have a different icon on different calculators, but is usually either $\boxed{x^y}, \boxed{y^x}$, or $\boxed{\wedge}$. The last symbol is called a caret. We would use the exponent key if we were asked to evaluate (solve) an expression such as 3^5.

It's good to think of the exponent key as meaning "**raised to the power of**." To solve 3^5, punch the 3, then the exponent key, then the five, and finally the equal sign. The sentence that we have just put into the calculator would be "3 raised to the power of 5 equals—" And the answer is 243.

We can also put a long multiplication sequence—like $2^3 \cdot 3^2 \cdot 12^3$ —into our calculators.

Try these on your calculator to make sure you get the correct answer.

$$2^{10} = 1024 \qquad\qquad 7^4 = 2401 \qquad\qquad 2^3 \cdot 3^2 \cdot 12^3 = 124{,}416$$

***2 Exponent Rules

(1) **Every base number raised to the power of one is itself.**

Examples: $\quad 3^1 = 3 \qquad\qquad (-8)^1 = -8 \qquad\qquad \left(\frac{2}{5}\right)^1 = \frac{2}{5}$

In fact, every number has a power of one unless it is shown differently. An exponent of one simply recognizes that a number is itself.

(2) Every non-zero number raised to the power of zero has a value of 1.

Examples: $3^0 = 1$ $(-8)^0 = 1$ $\left(\dfrac{2}{5}\right)^0 = 1$

We will prove this second rule of exponents in the next section. Accept that it is true until then.

**Note: Zero raised to any power is still zero.

***All <u>bases which are negative numbers and fractions must be put inside a parenthesis</u> when an exponent is raised above them.

If a negative or a fractional base is not inside a parenthesis, it can yield a different evaluated answer. Before evaluating any exponential expression, we need to ask ourselves: "<u>What does the exponent affect?</u>" Look at the following examples.

$(-3)^2$ The exponent of 2 is <u>raised above the parenthesis</u>, meaning that it affects everything (in this case the minus sign and the number) inside that parenthesis.

$(-3)^2$ in factored form is $(-3) \cdot (-3)$. The evaluated answer is 9.

-3^2 The exponent of 2 is <u>raised above the base of 3</u>, meaning that it affects <u>only</u> the three and <u>not</u> the sign.

-3^2 in factored form is $-(3 \cdot 3)$. The evaluated answer is -9.

$\left(\dfrac{1}{3}\right)^2$ The exponent of 2 is <u>raised above the parenthesis</u>, meaning that it affects every thing (in this case the numerator and the denominator) inside that parenthesis.

$\left(\dfrac{1}{3}\right)^2$ in factored form is $\dfrac{1}{3} \cdot \dfrac{1}{3}$. The evaluated answer is $\dfrac{1}{9}$.

$\dfrac{1^2}{3}$ The exponent of 2 is <u>raised above the base of 1</u>, meaning that it affects <u>only</u> the 1 (the numerator) and <u>not</u> the 3 (the denominator).

$\dfrac{1^2}{3}$ in factored form is $\dfrac{(1 \cdot 1)}{3}$. The evaluated answer is $\dfrac{1}{3}$.

We see that we can get very different solutions, dependent upon whether a negative or fractional number is inside a parenthesis or not.

***Knowing the Sign of the Answer to an Exponential Expression with a Negative Base**

This follows the same rule that we applied when multiplying and dividing signed numbers. If there are an odd number of negative signs, the answer is negative. If there are an even number of negative signs, the answer is positive.

If the exponent above a negative base (that is, the negative base is inside a parenthesis) is odd, then the answer is negative.

If the exponent above a negative base (that is, the negative base is inside a parenthesis) is even, then the answer is positive.

Examples:

$(-5)^3$ This expression means $(-5) \cdot (-5) \cdot (-5)$. There are 3 negative signs (an odd number) so the answer is negative.

$(-4)^6$ This expression means $(-4) \cdot (-4) \cdot (-4) \cdot (-4) \cdot (-4) \cdot (-4)$. There are 6 negative signs (an even number) so the answer is positive.

We should always be able to look at a basic exponential expression and know whether the evaluated answer will be negative or positive.

We should never have to put a negative sign into our calculators when evaluating an exponential expression. **Don't surrender signed number skills to a calculator!**

How to:

Evaluate an Exponential Expression:

1. See what the exponent is affecting—identify the base.
2. Identify whether the answer will be negative or positive.
3. Multiply the base by itself the number of times of the exponent.

Example #1: Evaluate -2^6.

Step #1: See what the exponent is affecting—identify the base.

The exponent is affecting the 2. The 2 is the base. This means that the negative sign is unaffected by the exponent.

So, -2^6 is the same as $-(2)^6$

Step #2: Identify whether the answer will be negative or positive.

2^6 will be positive. Then, the negative sign will still be there out front. The **answer must be negative**.

Step #3: Multiply the base by itself the number of times of the exponent.

$-(2)^6$ means $-(2 \bullet 2 \bullet 2 \bullet 2 \bullet 2 \bullet 2)$

Using a calculator, we get $-(64)$

Answer: -64

Example #2: Evaluate $\left(-\dfrac{2}{3}\right)^3$.

Step #1: See what the exponent is affecting—identify the base.

The exponent is raised above the parenthesis, so it is affecting both the negative sign <u>and</u> the number. It is affecting the $-\dfrac{2}{3}$. The $-\dfrac{2}{3}$ is the base.

Step #2: Identify whether the answer will be negative or positive.

$\left(-\dfrac{2}{3}\right)^3$ means $\left(-\dfrac{2}{3}\right)$ will be multiplied by itself 3 times. There are an odd number of negative signs. The **answer must be negative.**

Step #3: Multiply the base by itself the number of times of the exponent.

$\left(-\dfrac{2}{3}\right)^3$ means $\left(-\dfrac{2}{3}\right) \bullet \left(-\dfrac{2}{3}\right) \bullet \left(-\dfrac{2}{3}\right)$ or $\dfrac{(-2 \bullet -2 \bullet -2)}{(3 \bullet 3 \bullet 3)}$

Answer: $-\dfrac{8}{27}$

How to:

Solve an Order of Operations problem (with exponents):

1. Do any work inside a parenthesis first.

2. Do any exponent work.

3. Do any multiplication and division (working left to right).

4. Do any addition and subtraction.

Example #3: Evaluate $(-3)^4 \bullet (-2)^3$

We can see that this is an order of operations (PEMDAS) problem. We have 3 operations in this problem, the exponent of 4, the multiplication symbol, and the exponent of 3.

Step #1: Do any work inside a parenthesis.

There are two parentheses, but no work to do inside them. There are simply negative numbers inside the parentheses.

Step #2: Do any exponent work.

See what the exponent(s) is affecting—identify the base(s).

The exponent of 4 is raised above the parenthesis, so it is affecting both the sign <u>and</u> the number.

$(-3)^4$ will be positive because there are 4 negative signs. We work this out and get positive or plus 81.

The exponent of 3 is raised above the parenthesis, so it is affecting both the sign <u>and</u> the number.

$(-2)^3$ will be negative because there are 3 negative signs. We work this out and get negative (or subtract) 8.

So here is our exponent work: $(-3)^4 \bullet (-2)^3$

Step #3: Do any multiplication or division. $81 \bullet (-8)$

A positive times a negative is a negative. -648

Answer: -648

Example #4: Evaluate $(2.4)^2 - 3^2 - (-4)^2$

We can see that this is an order of operations (PEMDAS) problem. We have 5 operations in this problem. There are 3 exponents and two subtraction (combining) signs.

Step #1: Do any work inside a parenthesis.

There are two parentheses, but no work to do inside them.

Step #2: Do any exponent work.

See what the exponent(s) is affecting—identify the base(s).

The first exponent of 2 is raised above the parenthesis which holds the positive value of 2.4 $(2.4)^2$ will be positive. We work this out and get positive 5.76

The second exponent of 2 is raised above the 3, so it is <u>not</u> affecting the sign. 3^2 will be positive. We work this out and get positive 9.

The third exponent of 2 is raised above the parenthesis, so it is affecting both the sign <u>and</u> the number. $(-4)^2$ will be positive because there are 2 negative signs. We work this out and get positive 16.

So here is our exponent work: $\underbrace{(2.4)^2}$ – $\underbrace{3^2}$ – $\underbrace{(-4)^2}$

(Bring down the subtraction symbols: ⇓)   ⇓   ⇓

Step #3: Do any multiplication or division.   ⇓   ⇓

There is none.

$\underbrace{5.76 \ – \ 9 \ – \ (16)}$

Step #4: Do any addition or subtraction.

Follow the combining rules.   –19.24

Answer: –19.24

Sample #1: Evaluate: $-(10)^2 \ + \ \left[\ 5 \ \bullet \ 10^2 \ \bullet \ \left(\dfrac{3}{5}\right)^3 \right]$

In this order of operations problem, we have 2 grouping symbols, the brackets—[ ]—and the parentheses. There is no work to do inside the parentheses, so we must solve inside the brackets.

In the brackets there are 4 operations, 2 exponents and 2 multiplication signs.

We must solve the exponents first. $-(10)^2 \ + \ \left[\ 5 \ \bullet \ \underline{10^2} \ \bullet \ \underline{\left(\dfrac{3}{5}\right)^3} \right]$

Now we finish the work inside the bracket. $-(10)^2 \ + \ \left[\ \underbrace{5 \ \bullet \ 100 \ \bullet \ \dfrac{27}{125}} \right]$

⇓

Now we still need to solve the: $-(10)^2$. $-(10)^2 \ + \ [108]$

There is a subtraction sign and an exponent.

We must evaluate the exponent first. The exponent affects the 10. $-\underbrace{(10)^2} \ + \ [108]$

The subtraction sign affects the 100. $-(100) \ + \ [108]$

This leaves us with a final combining problem of $-100 \ + \ [108]$. $\underbrace{-100 \ + \ [108]}$

Answer: 8

■ **You try it now:**

a) $-5^3 - (-3)^2 - 2^4$

b) $-(7)^2 - \left[3 \cdot (2.5)^2 - \left(\dfrac{3}{2}\right)^2 \right]$

Sample #2: With an appropriate breeding program and protection, game wardens believed that they could save their rhinoceros population at a Wildlife Refuge Park in Africa. There were currently only 6 rhinoceroses, but biologists created a 20-year plan that would double the rhino population every 5 years. If this plan succeeded, how many rhinos would be in the park after 20 years?

We start by recognizing that right now (at year zero) there are 6 rhinos. If the rhino population is going to double every 5 years as planned, that would mean that the rhino population would double 4 times (20 years divided by 5) in the 20-year period.

Look at what would happen to the rhino population:

> Starting population: 6 rhinos
> After 1st 5-year period: $6 \cdot 2 = 12$ rhinos
> After 2nd 5-year period: $12 \cdot 2 = 24$ rhinos
> After 3rd 5-year period: $24 \cdot 2 = 48$ rhinos
> After 4th 5-year period: $48 \cdot 2 = 96$ rhinos

Of course this is the long way to solve this problem.

If we know that doubling means to multiply by 2, then the total number of rhinos after 20 years would be the original 6 multiplied by 2 (doubled) four times, or $2 \cdot 2 \cdot 2 \cdot 2$. In fact, after 20 years, the total number of rhinos would be $6 \cdot 2 \cdot 2 \cdot 2 \cdot 2$. Now take advantage of our knowledge of exponents.

> Set up: $6 \cdot 2^4$
>
> Follow order of operations: $6 \cdot \underline{2^4}$
>
> $\underbrace{6 \cdot 16}$

> **Answer:**   96 rhinos would live in the park after 20 years.

■ **You try it now:**

c) At age 20, Elena had $5,000 dollars. She could buy a new car or make a financial investment in her future. She decided to invest her money after seeing that one financial company over the last 50 years had averaged tripling their investors' money every 10 years. If this rate of return remained true for Elena, how much money would she have at the age of 40? At age 60?

d) In a science fiction movie, a cuddly little 3-pound creature escapes from an alien spacecraft and wanders onto a farm in Iowa, where a lonely child finds it and takes it into her house. (Now, after the opening 10 minutes, it's time for the Director to alter the sweet "doggie" to alien monster!). This creature eats literally almost anything and almost constantly. In fact it doubles its weight every day. How much would the creature weigh after a week? After two weeks?

Answers to You try it now: a) –150 ; b) –65.5 ; c) At age 40, after 20 years, Elena would have $\left(\$5{,}000 \bullet 3^2\right)$ a total of $45,000. At age 60, after 40 years, Elena would have $\left(\$5{,}000 \bullet 3^4\right)$ a total of $405,000; d) After 1 week the creature would weigh $\left(3 \bullet 2^7\right)$ 384 pounds. After 2 weeks the creature would weigh $\left(3 \bullet 2^{14}\right)$ 49,152 pounds.

Answer to Application: Joaquin initially had 4 viruses under his microscope. After one hour this population would have doubled (4 • 2), so there would have been 8 viruses. In the second hour, this population would have doubled again (8 • 2), so there would have been 16 viruses after two hours.

What we are witnessing here is what is called exponential growth, where the increase is made through repeated multiplication, and not through repeated addition. Look at what we've learned so far.

Time Zero = 4 viruses

After 1 hour = (4 • 2) or 8 viruses (which is the same as $4 \bullet 2^1$ organisms)

After 2 hours = (4 • 2 • 2) or 16 viruses (which is the same as $4 \bullet 2^2$ organisms)

After 3 hours = (4 • 2 • 2 • 2) or 32 viruses (which is the same as $4 \bullet 2^3$ organisms)

We can recognize a pattern here. After each succeeding hour in which the population doubles our exponent above our base of 2 will increase by 1.

So, after 5 hours there would be 4 • 2^5 or **128 viruses.**

After 12 hours there would be 4 • 2^{12} or **16,384 viruses.**

After 24 hours there would be 4 • 2^{24} or **67,108,864 viruses.**

4.1 Evaluating Exponential Expression Problems

In exercises #1-15, tell what value the exponent of 3 affects.

1) 8^3 2) 4^3 3) $(-5)^3$ 4) $(-7)^3$ 5) -2^3

6) -10^3 7) $-(3)^3$ 8) $-(20)^3$ 9) $(2.61)^3$ 10) -3.4^3

11) $\left(\dfrac{3}{4}\right)^3$ 12) $\left(-\dfrac{2}{11}\right)^3$ 13) $-\left(-\dfrac{1}{4}\right)^3$ 14) $\dfrac{5^3}{6}$ 15) $\dfrac{-3^3}{8}$

In exercises #16-30, tell whether this expression has a negative or positive value. Do not solve.

16) $(-3)^4$ 　　　17) $(-7)^5$ 　　　18) $(-11)^3$ 　　　19) $(-1)^{24}$ 　　　20) $\left(-\frac{1}{8}\right)^{10}$

21) $\left(-\frac{2}{3}\right)^7$ 　　22) -7^2 　　　23) -10^4 　　　24) -5^9 　　　25) $-(6)^4$

26) $-(4)^{13}$ 　　27) $-(-2)^3$ 　　28) $-(-2.75)^6$ 　　29) $-(1.6)^4$ 　　30) $-\left(\frac{1}{6}\right)^7$

In exercises # 31-39, write the given exponential expression in simplified (exponential) form (remember to use parenthesis as necessary.

31) $2 \bullet 2 \bullet 5 \bullet 7 \bullet 7$ 　　　　　32) $3 \bullet 3 \bullet 3 \bullet 3 \bullet 3$ 　　　　　33) $-4 \bullet -4 \bullet -5 \bullet -5 \bullet -5$

34) $\frac{2}{3} \bullet \frac{2}{3} \bullet \frac{2}{3} \bullet \frac{2}{3}$ 　　35) $\frac{3}{8} \bullet \frac{3}{8} \bullet -\frac{4}{5} \bullet -\frac{4}{5} \bullet -\frac{4}{5}$ 　　36) $\frac{1}{5} \bullet -\frac{1}{2} \bullet -\frac{1}{2} \bullet \frac{1}{5}$

37) $x \bullet x \bullet x \bullet y \bullet y$ 　　　　38) $x \bullet y \bullet y \bullet z \bullet z$ 　　　　39) $-x \bullet -x \bullet -x \bullet -x$

In exercises #40-48, write the given exponential expression in factored form.

40) $2^3 \bullet 3^2$ 　　　　　　41) $5^4 \bullet 7^2$ 　　　　　　42) -7^2

43) -3^4 　　　　　　　44) $(-2)^2 \bullet (-5)^3$ 　　　　45) $(-2)^3 \bullet 3^2 \bullet (-7)^2$

46) $(3.1)^1 \bullet (-5.7)^2$ 　　47) $\left(\frac{4}{5}\right)^2 \bullet \left(-\frac{1}{3}\right)^2$ 　　48) $-\left(\frac{1}{2}\right)^4$

In exercises #49-60, write the given exponential expression in evaluated form.

49) 3^4 　　　　50) $3^2 \bullet 5^2$ 　　　51) $(8.6)^3$ 　　　52) $2^5 \bullet (-3)^2 \bullet 7^3$

53) $(-2)^4$ 　　　54) $(-5)^3$ 　　　55) $-(10)^2$ 　　　56) $-(6)^3$

57) $\left(\frac{3}{4}\right)^3$ 　　58) $\left(\frac{1}{7}\right)^2 \bullet \left(\frac{5}{2}\right)^2$ 　　59) $-\left(\frac{1}{10}\right)^3$ 　　60) $-\left(-\frac{3}{5}\right)^2$

In exercises #61-67, decide whether each group of expressions all have the same value. Answer yes or no. If your answer is no, identify the letter of the one expression that does not equal the others.

61) a) 3^5 　　　　　b) $3 \bullet 5$ 　　　　c) $3^3 \bullet 3 \bullet 3$ 　　　d) $(3)^5$

62) a) $(3)^6$ 　　　　b) 3^6 　　　　c) $3 \bullet 6$ 　　　　d) $3^3 \bullet 3^3$

63) a) $(10)^2$ 　　　b) $(-10)^2$ 　　　c) $-(10)^2$ 　　　d) $(2 \bullet 5)^2$

64) a) $-3 \bullet -3 \bullet -3$ 　　b) $(-3)^3$ 　　　c) $(-3)^2 \bullet -3$ 　　d) $-(3)^3$

65) a) $\left(-\dfrac{1}{4}\right)^3$ b) $-\dfrac{1}{4} \bullet -\dfrac{1}{4} \bullet -\dfrac{1}{4}$ c) $\dfrac{(-1 \bullet -1 \bullet -1)}{(4 \bullet 4 \bullet 4)}$ d) $\dfrac{(1 \bullet 1 \bullet 1)}{(-4 \bullet -4 \bullet -4)}$

66) a) $\left(\dfrac{-5}{6}\right)^2$ b) $-\left(\dfrac{5}{6}\right)^2$ c) $-\left(\dfrac{-5}{6}\right)^2$ d) $-\left(\dfrac{5}{6} \bullet \dfrac{5}{6}\right)$

67) a) $\left(\dfrac{6.2}{3}\right)^2$ b) $\dfrac{(6.2)^2}{3^2}$ c) $(6.2)^2 \div 3^2$ d) $\dfrac{(6.2 \bullet 6.2)^1}{(-3)^2}$

In exercises #68-79, translate the following words into math expressions. <u>Use exponents</u> whenever you can. Do not solve.

68) Five cubed

69) Ten squared

70) 7 multiplied by itself five times.

71) 10 multiplied by itself 4 times.

72) x multiplied by itself 3 times.

73) Two to the third, then four more

74) Four squared, then 3 less

75) The difference of two cubed and three to the fifth.

76) $\dfrac{1}{8}$ of the expression of five to the sixth power

77) x squared plus y to the third

78) Find the difference of a cubed and b cubed.

79) Subtract x cubed from y to the fifth.

In exercises #80-100, solve the following order of operations problems.

80) $2^2 + 3^4$

81) $2^5 - \left(5^2\right)$

82) $8^2 \div 2^6$

83) $7 + 4 \bullet 11^2$

84) $6 + 3 \bullet 9^2$

85) $5 - 2^3 + 3^0$

86) $9 - 3^2 \bullet 5$

87) $(-4)^3 - (-1)^4$

88) $(-7)^2 - (-2)^4$

89) $-4^2 + (-2)^3$

90) $-6^2 + (-3)^2$

91) $-(5)^2 + \left(7 - 3^3 \div 9\right)$

92) $-(-2)^2 + \left(2 - 2^3 \div 2\right)$

93) $(3.1)^2 \div (-0.2)^3$

94) $\left[(4.2)^3 - 4.088\right] \div \left(3^2 - 2^3\right)$

95) $3 - 7^1 \left[2\left(4 - (-2)^4\right)\right]$

96) $-(5)^2 + 4\left[2 \bullet 4^2 \bullet \left(\dfrac{3}{4}\right)^2\right]$

97) $\left(-\dfrac{3}{2}\right)^3 + \left(\dfrac{1}{4}\right)^3 - \left(-\dfrac{3}{8}\right)$

98) $\dfrac{2}{3} - \dfrac{1}{3} \bullet \left(\dfrac{2}{5}\right)^2 \bullet (-5)^2$

99) $6^1 \div (-50)^0 - (1)^{10}$

100) $20^0 - 5^1 + (1)^6$

In exercises #101-106: (a) translate the following words into math expressions (use exponents whenever you can), and (b) give the solution.

101) Take the number 5, then double it three times.

102) Take the number 7, then double it three times.

103) Take the number 80, then triple it four times.

104) Take the number 1000, then triple it six times.

105) Start with $5,000; double it four times.

106) Start with $1; double it every day for 3 weeks.

In exercises #107-114: (a) write a mathematical expression that will solve the problem, and (b) give the solution.

107-108) Scientists from the World Health Organization studied a new type of flu virus in a laboratory. They discovered that the virus population doubled every 30 minutes.

107) If 100 of these flu viruses were isolated in a lab at the start of an experiment, how many viruses would there be in 4 hours?

108) When Vicki went to work, her son was starting to feel ill. Unbeknownst to her, 1000 of these flu viruses were living in her home. According to the scientists at the World Health Organization, how many of these viruses would be in Vicki's house when she arrived home 8 hours later?

109) When Jeff invested $30,000 dollars in a new company, he hoped that this money would double every 5 years for the next fifteen years. If his hope came true, how much money would Jeff have after 15 years?

110) A small company made a profit of $70,000 last year. If the company repeated this four more times, how much money did the company make in 5 years?

111) In another investment, Jeff hoped to earn $5,000 a year for 15 years. If his hope came true, how much money would Jeff have earned from this investment?

112) A new type of tomato started to be grown in California in 1996. In that first year, 1996, only 50 acres of the tomatoes were planted. However, in the next five years, the number of acres where these tomatoes were planted was tripled every year. How many acres were used to grow this type of tomato in the year 2001, the sixth year it was grown in the state?

113-114) When a mosquito infestation in Florida became a health hazard, an attempt was made to wipe out many of the insects by introducing huge numbers of dragonflies that preyed on the mosquitoes. Health officials and entomologists monitored an area that they estimated to support a million mosquitoes. Over a four week period, they discovered that the existing mosquito population decreased $\frac{1}{4}$ every week (that is, only $\frac{3}{4}$ as many mosquitoes were alive at the end of the week than there had been at the beginning of that week).

113) How many mosquitoes were alive in this area after the first week of the dragonfly introduction?

114) How many mosquitoes were alive in this area after the fourth week of the dragonfly introduction (round to the nearest thousand)?

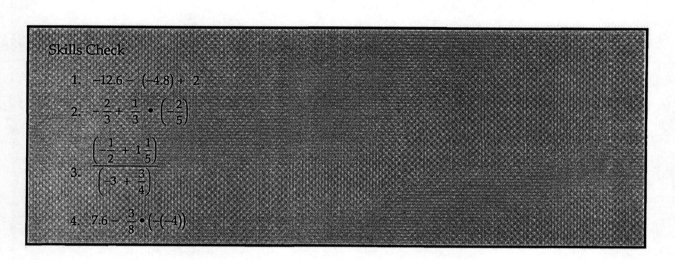

Skills Check

1. $-12.6 - (-4.8) + 2$

2. $-\dfrac{2}{3} + \dfrac{1}{3} \cdot \left(-\dfrac{2}{5}\right)$

3. $\dfrac{\left(-\dfrac{1}{2} + 1\dfrac{1}{5}\right)}{\left(-3 + \dfrac{3}{4}\right)}$

4. $7.6 - \dfrac{3}{8} \cdot \left(-(-4)\right)$

· Answers to Skills Check: 1) -10.2 ;   2) $-\dfrac{4}{5}$;   3) $-\dfrac{14}{45}$;   4) 6.1

Section 4.2 Manipulate Exponential Expressions

Objectives:

• To multiply exponential expressions with the same bases

• To divide exponential expressions with the same bases

• To get rid of negative exponents

• To recognize equivalent exponential expressions

Application:

Scientists identified two types of bacteria. Curious to discover which bacteria could thrive better in a temperate climate, they took 3 viruses of each type and isolated them in a room. After 10 hours the scientists observed that the Type A bacteria tripled its population every hour, while the Type B bacteria managed to triple its population only every 2 hours. If the ratio of bacteria A to bacteria B was $\frac{1}{1}$ or 1:1 $\left(\frac{3 \; \text{Type} \; \text{A} \; \text{bacteria}}{3 \; \text{Type} \; \text{B} \; \text{bacteria}} \right)$ at the start of the experiment, what was the ratio after 10 hours?

Vocabulary:

Negative Exponent—A **Negative Exponent** mathematically is a reciprocal function. It means that we **take the reciprocal of the base**, which then changes the sign of the negative exponent to positive. It is often easy to remember the phrase "**jump the line.**"

A base number with a negative exponent in the numerator jumps the fractional line and ends up in the denominator with a positive exponent.

Example: $4^{-2} = \frac{1}{4^2}$

A base number with a negative exponent in the denominator jumps the fractional line and ends up in the numerator with a positive exponent.

Example: $\frac{1}{3^{-2}} = 3^2$

In the first example of 4^{-2}, the 4 is the base and the −2 is the exponent. The whole number of 4 has a denominator of 1, so when we take the reciprocal of the 4, we end up with the fraction of $\frac{1}{4}$. The exponent is still raised above 4, but it has become positive.

Look at the following equivalent expressions. As we move left to right, check and make sure that we can <u>see why each successive expression is the same</u>.

$$4^{-2} = \left(\frac{4}{1}\right)^{-2} = \frac{(4)^{-2}}{(1)^{-2}} = \frac{(1)^2}{(4)^2} = \frac{1}{(4)^2} = \frac{1}{16}$$

$4^{-2} = \left(\frac{4}{1}\right)^{-2}$ is true because 4 and $\frac{4}{1}$ are the same.

$\left(\frac{4}{1}\right)^{-2} = \frac{(4)^{-2}}{(1)^{-2}}$ is true because the exponent is raised above the parenthesis and

therefore affects both the numerator and the denominator.

$\frac{(4)^{-2}}{(1)^{-2}} = \frac{(1)^2}{(4)^2}$ is true because in following the reciprocal process to get rid of

negative exponents, the base of 4 ends up in the denominator and the base of 1 ends up in the numerator.

$\frac{(1)^2}{(4)^2} = \frac{1}{(4)^2}$ is true after evaluating the $(1)^2$. In fact the number 1 raised to

any power is equal to 1.

$\frac{1}{(4)^2} = \frac{1}{16}$ is true after evaluating the $(4)^2$.

In the second example of $\frac{1}{3^{-2}}$, the 3 is the base and the -2 is the exponent. Ultimately, when we take the reciprocal of the base, we end up with this base number (the 3) up in the numerator with a positive exponent (the 2). The quick and easy way to rewrite this expression is: $1 \cdot 3^2$, which of course equals the simplified answer of 3^2 or the evaluated answer of 9.

It is always true that we can simply "jump the line" as shown in this example above, but let's look at the step-by-step process below that shows how we actually arrived at our action and answer. As we move left to right, check and make sure that we can <u>see why each successive expression is the same</u>.

$$\frac{1}{3^{-2}} = 1 \div 3^{-2} = 1 \div \left(\frac{3}{1}\right)^{-2} = 1 \div \left(\frac{(3)^{-2}}{(1)^{-2}}\right) = 1 \div \left(\frac{(1)^2}{(3)^2}\right) =$$

$$1 \div \left(\frac{1}{3^2}\right) = 1 \cdot \left(\frac{3^2}{1}\right) = 3^2 = 9$$

$\frac{1}{3^{-2}} = 1 \div 3^{-2}$ is true as this is just rewriting the division problem using

the $\div$ symbol.

$1 \div 3^{-2} = 1 \div \left(\frac{3}{1}\right)^{-2}$ is true because 3 and $\frac{3}{1}$ are the same.

$1 \div \left(\dfrac{3}{1}\right)^{-2} = 1 \div \left(\dfrac{(3)^{-2}}{(1)^{-2}}\right)$ is true because the exponent is raised above the

parenthesis and therefore affects both the numerator and the denominator.

$1 \div \left(\dfrac{(3)^{-2}}{(1)^{-2}}\right) = 1 \div \left(\dfrac{(1)^{2}}{(3)^{2}}\right)$ is true because in following the reciprocal process

to get rid of negative exponents, the base of 3 ends up in the denominator and the base of 1 ends up in the numerator.

$1 \div \left(\dfrac{(1)^{2}}{(3)^{2}}\right) = 1 \div \left(\dfrac{1}{3^{2}}\right)$ is true after evaluating the $(1)^{2}$.

$1 \div \left(\dfrac{1}{3^{2}}\right) = 1 \cdot \left(\dfrac{3^{2}}{1}\right)$ is true because we just took the reciprocal of

the divisor.

$1 \cdot \left(\dfrac{3^{2}}{1}\right) = 3^{2}$ because anything multiplied by 1 is itself.

$3^{2} = 9$ after we evaluate the exponent expression.

*** Remember: The Negative Exponent is **NOT** a negative number. **It is simply a reciprocal function. The original example of** $\dfrac{1}{3^{-2}}$ **does not, and we see, did not signify a negative value.**

How to:

Simplify the Multiplication of Exponential Expressions with the Same Bases:

1. Identify the same bases and add the exponents.

***Remember: The base(s) don't change.

Example #1: Simplify the expression: $2^{4} \cdot 2^{3} \cdot 3^{5} \cdot 3$

Step #1: Identify the same bases and add the exponents.

2^{4} and 2^{3} have the same base of 2. We add the exponents and get $2^{(4 + 3)} = 2^{7}$.

3^{5} and 3 have the same base of 3. We add the exponents (remember that 3 is the same as 3^{1}) and get $3^{(5 + 1)} = 3^{6}$.

Answer: $2^{7} \cdot 3^{6}$ We are done. The directions asked us to simplify the expression, not to evaluate it.

If we aren't sure why this process for multiplying same bases works, let's look at the expression in factored form. $2^4 \cdot 2^3 \cdot 3^5 \cdot 3$ would be:

$$(2 \cdot 2 \cdot 2 \cdot 2) \cdot (2 \cdot 2 \cdot 2) \cdot (3 \cdot 3 \cdot 3 \cdot 3 \cdot 3) \cdot (3)$$

Now we certainly wouldn't want to write out expressions like this regularly (ugh!), but by counting the numbers here we can see that, in fact 2 is multiplied by itself 7 times and 3 is multiplied by itself 6 times.

How to:

Simplify the Division of Exponential Expressions with the Same Bases:

1. Identify the same bases and subtract the exponents.

   In this unit of the book, we will always subtract the exponent in the denominator from the exponent in the numerator. Therefore, our initial answer to any division of same bases problem will have the base in the numerator.

***Remember: The base(s) don't change.**

Example #2: Simplify the expression: $\dfrac{3^5}{3^2}$

Step #1: Identify the same bases and subtract the exponents.

3^5 and 3^2 have the same base of 3. We subtract the exponent in the denominator from the exponent in the numerator and get $3^{(5-2)} = 3^3$

Answer: 3^3 We are done. The directions asked us to simplify the expression, not to evaluate it.

If we aren't sure why this process for dividing same bases works, let's look at the expression in factored form. $3^5 \div 3^2$ would be:

$$\frac{(3 \cdot 3 \cdot 3 \cdot 3 \cdot 3)}{(3 \cdot 3)} \quad \text{We can cancel.} \quad \frac{(3 \cdot 3 \cdot 3 \cdot 3 \cdot 3)}{(3 \cdot 3)}$$

Again, we wouldn't want to write out problems like this on a regular basis, but the visual here clearly shows that after canceling we are left with $\dfrac{3^3}{1}$ or just 3^3.

Example #3: Simplify the expression: $\dfrac{4^3}{4^3}$

Step #1: Identify the same bases and subtract the exponents.

4^3 and 4^3 have the same base of 4. We subtract the exponent in the denominator from the exponent in the numerator and get $4^{(3-3)} = 4^0$.

We learned in the last section that any non-zero number raised to the power of zero equals 1. Thus, the answer here is **1**.

This example is a proof of the zero-power rule. It is a recognition that any value divided by itself (in this case $4^3 \div 4^3$) equals 1.

Answer: 1   We are done. Whenever we get an answer to the power of zero or the power of 1, our simplified and evaluated answers are the same.

How to:

Get rid of a Negative Exponent:

1. Take the reciprocal of the base.

2. Change the sign of the exponent.

Example #4: Simplify by getting rid of the negative exponent: $(-2)^{-3}$

Step #1: Take the reciprocal of the base.

In this example, the -2 is the base and the -3 is the exponent. The whole number of -2 has a denominator of 1, so when we take the reciprocal of the -2, we end up with the fraction of $\dfrac{1}{(-2)}$.

Step #2: Change the sign of the exponent.

The exponent is still raised above the -2, but it changes from negative to positive.

Answer: $\dfrac{1}{(-2)^3}$

We are done. The question is simplified. Notice that <u>we got rid of the negative exponent,</u> <u>not</u> the negative base.

Below is a breakdown of the step-by-step process to get to the answer. Moving left to right, check and make sure that you can see why each successive expression is the same.

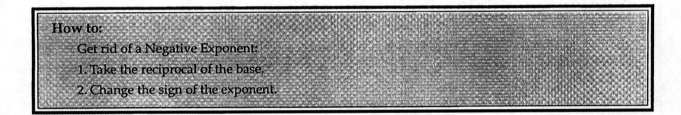

$$(-2)^{-3} \;=\; \left(\frac{-2}{1}\right)^{-3} \;=\; \frac{(-2)^{-3}}{(1)^{-3}} \;=\; \frac{(1)^3}{(-2)^3} \;=\; \frac{1}{(-2)^3}$$

<u>If</u> we had been asked to evaluate this expression, our final steps would have looked like the following:

$$\frac{1}{(-2)^3} \;=\; \frac{1}{-8} \;=\; -\frac{1}{8}$$

How to:

Simplify an Exponential Expression:

1. Follow any exponent rules for multiplying or dividing same bases.

2. Get rid of any negative exponents.

Example #5: Simplify: $\dfrac{3^4 \cdot 5^2}{3 \cdot 5^4 \cdot 7^{-3}}$

Step #1: Follow any exponent rules for multiplying or dividing same bases.

We first recognize that we have all multiplication and division. Therefore we can look for any same bases.

3^4 and 3^1 are same bases. We have division of same bases, so we subtract the exponent in the denominator from the exponent in the numerator. $3^{(4-1)}$ becomes 3^3. This answer is in the numerator.

5^2 and 5^4 are same bases. We have division of same bases, so we subtract the exponent in the denominator from the exponent in the numerator. $5^{(2-4)}$ becomes 5^{-2}. This answer is in the numerator.

Our problem now looks like: $\dfrac{3^3 \cdot 5^{-2}}{7^{-3}}$

Step #2: Get rid of any negative exponents.

We get rid of any negative exponents by taking the reciprocal of the base. Therefore, the 5^{-2} in the numerator will become 5^2 in the denominator. The 7^{-3} in the denominator will become 7^3 in the numerator.

Let's take another visual look at what is happening when we take the reciprocal of a base. Consider each base number as if it were its own fraction.

$$\frac{3^3}{1} \cdot \frac{5^{-2}}{1} \cdot \frac{1}{7^{-3}} \quad \text{becomes} \quad \frac{3^3}{1} \cdot \frac{1}{5^2} \cdot \frac{7^3}{1}$$

Multiply the numerators together, then the denominator.

Answer: $\dfrac{3^3 \cdot 7^3}{5^2}$ We are done. This is the simplified answer.

Sample #1: Simplify and evaluate: $\dfrac{7^2}{7^{-3}}$

Recognize this as division of same bases. We need to subtract exponents.

Look what happens here!!

$\dfrac{7^2}{7^{-3}}$ becomes $7^{(2 - {-3})}$. We end up with a double negative.

This then becomes $7^{(2 + 3)}$.

Simplified Answer: 7^5

Now get into the habit of evaluating the expression <u>from</u> the simplified answer.

Evaluated Answer: 16,807

You try it now:

a) Simplify and evaluate: $\dfrac{3^7 \bullet 3^{-3}}{3^{-2}}$

b) Simplify and evaluate: $\dfrac{11^{-3}}{11^{-2}}$

Sample #2: Simplify and evaluate: $\dfrac{4^6 \bullet 5 \bullet 3^{-2}}{4^2 \bullet 5^2 \bullet 4^4}$

Visually it may help to write each "same base" as its own fraction. $\dfrac{4^6}{4^2 \bullet 4^4} \bullet \dfrac{5}{5^2} \bullet \dfrac{3^{-2}}{1}$

Simplify the same bases (working out the rules for multiplication/division of same bases). $\dfrac{1}{1} \bullet \dfrac{5^{-1}}{1} \bullet \dfrac{3^{-2}}{1}$

Get rid of any negative bases. $\dfrac{1}{1} \bullet \dfrac{1}{5^1} \bullet \dfrac{1}{3^2}$

Simplified Answer: $\dfrac{1}{3^2 \bullet 5}$ Now, evaluate from this answer.

Evaluated Answer: $\dfrac{1}{45}$

*** When we evaluate a simplified answer where the only remaining factors are in the denominator, it is important to remember the factor of 1 in the numerator.

You try it now:

c) Simplify and evaluate: $\dfrac{2^5 \bullet 6^{-2}}{2^5}$

d) Simplify and evaluate: $\dfrac{3^{-3} \bullet 5^{-4}}{3^{-4} \bullet 5^3}$

Sample #3: Simplify and evaluate: $\left(\dfrac{3}{5}\right)^5 \bullet \left(\dfrac{2}{3}\right)^2$

Recognize that the exponents are raised above the parentheses, so they affect "everything" (the numerators and the denominators).

We can rewrite this as: $\dfrac{3^5}{5^5} \bullet \dfrac{2^2}{3^2}$

Now rewrite as: $\dfrac{2^2}{1} \bullet \dfrac{3^5}{3^2} \bullet \dfrac{1}{5^5}$

Simplified Answer: $\dfrac{2^2 \bullet 3^3}{5^5}$ Evaluated Answer: $\dfrac{108}{3125}$

You try it now:

e) Simplify and evaluate: $\left(\dfrac{1}{2}\right)^3 \bullet \left(\dfrac{2}{7}\right)^3$

f) Simplify and evaluate: $\left(\dfrac{4}{5}\right)^5 \bullet 5^6$

Sample #4: The small town of Hamilton had a population of 5,000 and a water system that could support 8,000 people. The ratio of the town's population to the number of people which the water system could support was $\dfrac{(5{,}000 \ \ \text{people})}{(\text{water for } 8{,}000 \ \ \text{people})}$ which reduces to the ratio of $\dfrac{(5 \ \ \text{people})}{(\text{water for every 8 people})}$ (A ratio is also sometimes expressed in the following form: 5:8). In the next 20 years, Hamilton saw its population double every 4 years. During the same period, its water system's capacity doubled every 5 years. After 20 years what was the ratio of the town's (city's!) population to the number of people which the water system could support?

First, we need to figure out how many people will live in Hamilton in 20 years. Right now (at year zero) there are 5000 people. If the population is going to double every 4 years, that would mean that the population would double five times (20 years divided by 4) in the 20-year period.

Doubling means to multiply by two. If we are doubling 5 times, we can represent this as 2^5. The population of Hamilton in 20 years will be: $5{,}000 \bullet 2^5$.

Second, we need to figure out how many people the water supply will support in 20 years. Right now the water system supports 8,000 people. If the water system's capacity will double every 5 years, that would mean that it would double four times (20 years divided by 5) in the 20-year period.

Doubling means to multiply by 2. If we are doubling 4 times, we can represent this as 2^4. The water system of Hamilton in 20 years will be able to support the following number of people: $8,000 \cdot 2^4$.

The ratio after 20 years now becomes: $\dfrac{\left(5,000 \cdot 2^5 \text{ people}\right)}{\left(\text{water for } 8,000 \cdot 2^4 \text{ people}\right)}$ ***

We cancel the 5,000 with the 8,000 by dividing both values by 1000. We recognize the division of same bases with $\dfrac{2^5}{2^4}$ and get 2^1 or 2.

We rewrite the ratio as: $\dfrac{\left(5 \cdot 2 \text{ people}\right)}{\left(\text{water for every } 8 \cdot 1 \text{ people}\right)}$

Reduce to lowest terms to get the **Answer**: $\dfrac{\left(5 \text{ people}\right)}{\left(\text{water for every 4 people}\right)}$

***If we evaluate the expression of $\dfrac{\left(5,000 \cdot 2^5 \text{ people}\right)}{\left(\text{water for } 8,000 \cdot 2^4 \text{ people}\right)}$, we see that in raw

numbers the ratio is $\dfrac{160,000 \text{ people}}{\text{water for } 128,000 \text{ people}}$. The town (city) of Hamilton does not have an adequate water supply for 32,000 people.

You try it now:

g) A biotechnology company had 30 employees in 1996 and made a profit of $90,000. This meant that the company made a $3,000 profit per employee ($90,000 ÷ 30). In the next 6 years the company saw its profits triple every year. The number of employees tripled every 2 years. After 6 years what was the profit per employee?

h) A 200,000 acre forest was infected with a tree-killing fungus. When biologists initially discovered the fungus, only 10 acres of the forest were infected. At this time (year zero) we start with the ratio of:

$\dfrac{\left(10 \text{ infected acres}\right)}{\left(200,000 - 10 \text{ uninfected acres}\right)}$ which gives us $\dfrac{\left(10 \text{ infected acres}\right)}{\left(199,990 \text{ uninfected acres}\right)}$ which reduced gives us a

ratio of: $\dfrac{\left(1 \text{ infected acre}\right)}{\left(\text{for every } 19,999 \text{ uninfected acres}\right)}$. However, for the next 10 years the amount of the

infected forest land doubled every year. After 10 years what was the ratio of infected acres of forest to uninfected acres of forest (you don't need to reduce your answer)?

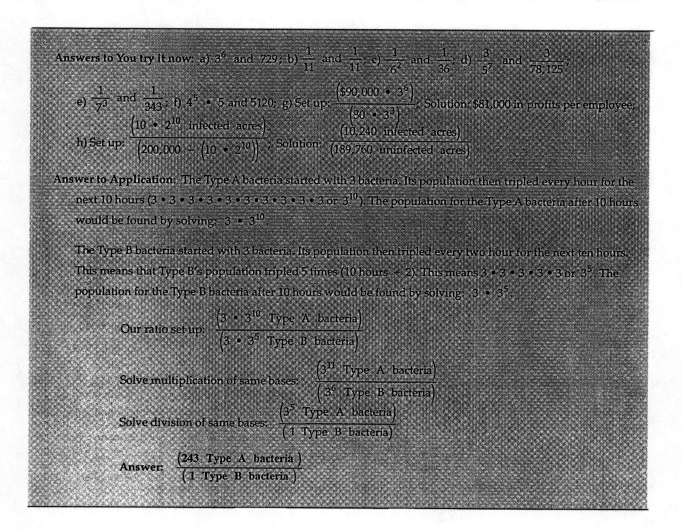

Answers to You try it now: a) 3^6 and 729; b) $\frac{1}{11}$ and $\frac{1}{11}$; c) $\frac{1}{6^2}$ and $\frac{1}{36}$; d) $\frac{3}{5^7}$ and $\frac{3}{78,125}$;

e) $\frac{1}{7^3}$ and $\frac{1}{343}$; f) $4^5 \cdot 5$ and 5120; g) Set up: $\frac{(\$90,000 \cdot 3^5)}{(30 \cdot 3^2)}$; Solution: $81,000 in profits per employee;

h) Set up: $\frac{(10 \cdot 2^{10} \text{ infected acres})}{(200,000 - (10 \cdot 2^{10}))}$; Solution: $\frac{(10,240 \text{ infected acres})}{(189,760 \text{ uninfected acres})}$

Answer to Application: The Type A bacteria started with 3 bacteria. Its population then tripled every hour for the next 10 hours ($3 \cdot 3 \cdot 3 \cdot 3 \cdot 3 \cdot 3 \cdot 3 \cdot 3 \cdot 3 \cdot 3$ or 3^{10}). The population for the Type A bacteria after 10 hours would be found by solving: $3 \cdot 3^{10}$.

The Type B bacteria started with 3 bacteria. Its population then tripled every two hour for the next ten hours. This means that Type B's population tripled 5 times (10 hours ÷ 2). This means $3 \cdot 3 \cdot 3 \cdot 3 \cdot 3$ or 3^5. The population for the Type B bacteria after 10 hours would be found by solving: $3 \cdot 3^5$.

Our ratio set up: $\frac{(3 \cdot 3^{10} \text{ Type A bacteria})}{(3 \cdot 3^5 \text{ Type B bacteria})}$

Solve multiplication of same bases: $\frac{(3^{11} \text{ Type A bacteria})}{(3^6 \text{ Type B bacteria})}$

Solve division of same bases: $\frac{(3^5 \text{ Type A bacteria})}{(1 \text{ Type B bacteria})}$

Answer: $\frac{(243 \text{ Type A bacteria})}{(1 \text{ Type B bacteria})}$

4.2 Manipulating Exponential Expression Problems

In exercises #1-12, identify which rule of exponents still needs to be done to simplify the expression. Your answer is either (1) multiplication of same bases, (2) division of same bases, or (3) eliminating the negative exponent.

1) $\frac{5^3 \cdot 5}{3^2}$

2) $\frac{3^3 \cdot 3^2}{5^2}$

3) $\frac{3^3 \cdot 2^2}{3^2}$

4) $\frac{7^3 \cdot 4^5}{4^3}$

5) $\frac{(-3)^3 \cdot 5^5}{(-3)^2}$

6) $\frac{(-2)^3 \cdot (-2)^5}{(7)^2}$

7) $\frac{3^{-3} \cdot 2^2}{5^2}$

8) $\frac{5^3 \cdot (-5)^2}{7^{(-2)}}$

9) $\frac{x^3 \cdot y^2}{x^2}$

10) $\frac{a^3 \cdot b^{-4}}{c^2}$

11) $\frac{x^3 \cdot y^5}{y^2}$

12) $\frac{(-x)^4 \cdot (-x)^2}{y^3}$

In exercises #13–24, state whether the value of each given expression has a negative or positive value. Do not solve.

13) 3^{-1}

14) $(-3)^1$

15) $(-4)^2$

16) $(-7)^3$

17) 5^{-1}

18) 5^{-2}

19) 2^{-7}

20) $\left(\dfrac{1}{3}\right)^{-1}$

21) $\left(\dfrac{1}{3}\right)^{-4}$

22) -3^2

23) $(-5)^{-1}$

24) $(-7)^{-2}$

In exercises #25–68, simplify the following expressions. The expression will be simplified when you have completed the three rules of exponents we have learned—multiplication of same bases, division of same bases, and getting rid of a negative exponent. Do not evaluate.

25) $7^3 \bullet 7^4$

26) $5^2 \bullet 5^2$

27) $2^5 \bullet 5^2 \bullet 2^3$

28) $3^7 \bullet 2^2 \bullet 3^3$

29) $2^3 \bullet 2^{-1}$

30) $7^{-3} \bullet 7^5$

31) $3^2 \bullet 3^{-2} \bullet 7^2$

32) $11^{-2} \bullet 3^2 \bullet 11^3$

33) 2^{-3}

34) 9^{-2}

35) $2^{-3} \bullet 2^2$

36) $5^{-4} \bullet 5^{-2}$

37) $\dfrac{3^3}{10^2}$

38) $\dfrac{2^7}{5^2}$

39) $\dfrac{7^5}{7^3}$

40) $\dfrac{11^8}{11^2}$

41) $\dfrac{4^3}{4^3}$

42) $\dfrac{7^5}{7^5}$

43) $\dfrac{(-5)^3}{(-5)^3}$

44) $\dfrac{(-2)^9}{(-2)^9}$

45) $\dfrac{4^{-2}}{4^5}$

46) $\dfrac{3^{-4}}{3^2}$

47) $\dfrac{2^{-1}}{2^{-2}}$

48) $\dfrac{5^{-3}}{5^{-1}}$

49) $\dfrac{15^0}{15^{-5}}$

50) $\dfrac{2^{-3}}{2^0}$

51) $\dfrac{2^6 \bullet 3^5}{2^{-2} \bullet 3}$

52) $\dfrac{2 \bullet 7^3}{2^{-2} \bullet 7}$

53) $\dfrac{5^3 \bullet 6^3}{5^2 \bullet 6^3}$

54) $\dfrac{3^4 \bullet 5^3}{3^4 \bullet 5^{-2}}$

55) $\dfrac{3^{-2} \bullet 9^3}{3^4 \bullet 9}$

56) $\dfrac{2^2 \bullet 11^{-3}}{2^4 \bullet 11^{-5}}$

57) $\dfrac{3 \bullet 5^{-7}}{3^4 \bullet 5^{-3}}$

58) $\dfrac{2^{-3} \bullet 3^{-4} \bullet 5}{2^3 \bullet 3^{-2} \bullet 5^3}$

59) $\dfrac{2^{-3} \bullet 5^{-4} \bullet 7}{2^{-3} \bullet 3^{-2} \bullet 11^3}$

60) $\dfrac{2^{-3} \bullet 3 \bullet 5^{-4}}{3^{-3} \bullet 3^{-2} \bullet 5}$

61) x^{-2}

62) y^{-3}

63) $\dfrac{x^7}{x^3}$

64) $\dfrac{a^{-5}}{a^3}$

65) $a^4 \bullet a$

66) $x^3 \bullet x^2$

67) $\dfrac{x^{-3} \bullet y}{x^2 \bullet y^{-2}}$

68) $\dfrac{x^5 \bullet y^{-1} \bullet z^{-2}}{x^2 \bullet y^{-3} \bullet z}$

In exercises #69–82, decide whether each group of expressions all have the same value. Answer yes or no. If your answer is no, identify the letter of the one expression that does not equal the others.

69) a) $\dfrac{5^7}{5^3}$ b) $5^{(7\ -\ 3)}$ c) $\dfrac{1}{5^4}$ d) 5^4

70) a) $\dfrac{3^5}{3^2}$ b) $\dfrac{3^5}{1} \bullet \dfrac{1}{3^2}$ c) $\dfrac{3^5}{1} \bullet \dfrac{3^{-2}}{1}$ d) 3^3

71) a) $2^3 \bullet 2^5$ b) $2^{(3\ -\ 5)}$ c) $2^{(3\ +\ 5)}$ d) $\dfrac{2^3}{1} \bullet \dfrac{1}{2^{-5}}$

72) a) $7^{(-2\ +\ 6)}$ b) $\dfrac{7^{-2}}{7^{-6}}$ c) $7^{-2} \bullet 7^6$ d) 7^4

73) a) $\dfrac{8^5}{8^{-2}}$ b) $\dfrac{8^5}{1} \bullet \dfrac{1}{8^{-2}}$ c) $8^{[5\ -\ (-2)]}$ d) $\dfrac{8^5}{1} \bullet \dfrac{8^2}{1}$

74) a) $\dfrac{3^{-2}}{3^5}$ b) $3^{[-2\ -\ 5]}$ c) 3^{-7} d) $\dfrac{1}{3^7}$

75) a) $7^2 \bullet 7^{-5}$ b) $7^{(2\ +\ -5)}$ c) 7^{-3} d) $\dfrac{1}{7^3}$

76) a) $4^{-4} \bullet 4$ b) $4^{(-4\ +\ 1)}$ c) 4^{-3} d) $\dfrac{1}{4^{-3}}$

77) a) $\dfrac{2^{-3}}{5^{-3}}$ b) $\dfrac{2^{-3}}{1} \bullet \dfrac{1}{5^{-3}}$ c) $\dfrac{1}{2^3} \bullet \dfrac{5^3}{1}$ d) $2^3 \bullet 5^3$

78) a) $\dfrac{7^{-5}}{11^{-5}}$ b) $\dfrac{7^{-5}}{1} \bullet \dfrac{1}{11^{-5}}$ c) $\dfrac{1}{7^5} \bullet \dfrac{11^5}{1}$ d) $\dfrac{11^5}{7^5}$

79) a) $\left(\dfrac{2}{5}\right)^3$ b) $\left(\dfrac{2^3}{5^3}\right)$ c) $\dfrac{2^3}{1} \bullet \dfrac{1}{5^3}$ d) $\left(\dfrac{2 \bullet 2 \bullet 2}{5 \bullet 5 \bullet 5}\right)$

80) a) $\left(\dfrac{3}{7}\right)^{-2}$ b) $\left(\dfrac{3^2}{7^2}\right)$ c) $\dfrac{3^2}{1} \bullet \dfrac{1}{7^2}$ d) $\dfrac{1}{3^{-2}} \bullet \dfrac{7^{-2}}{1}$

81) a) $\left(\dfrac{2}{3}\right)^{-3}$ b) $\dfrac{2^{-3}}{1} \bullet \dfrac{1}{3^{-3}}$ c) $\dfrac{1}{2^3} \bullet \dfrac{3^{-3}}{1}$ d) $\dfrac{3^3}{2^3}$

82) a) $\left(\dfrac{1}{5}\right)^{-4}$ b) $\dfrac{1^{-4}}{5^{-4}}$ c) $\dfrac{5^4}{1^4}$ d) $\left(\dfrac{5}{1}\right)^4$

In exercises #83–102: (a) simplify the expression (all answers must be given using positive exponents), and (b) give the evaluated solution.

83) $7^3 \cdot 7^2$

84) $5^2 \cdot 5^{-5}$

85) $3 \cdot 3^{-7}$

86) $\dfrac{3^4}{3^2}$

87) $\dfrac{11^{-5}}{11^{-2}}$

88) $\dfrac{6^3}{6^4}$

89) 3^{-4}

90) $\dfrac{1}{5^{-2}}$

91) $\dfrac{2^3 \cdot 3^3}{2^5 \cdot 3^{-2}}$

92) $\dfrac{2^{-2} \cdot 5^3}{2 \cdot 5^2}$

93) $\dfrac{3^{-2} \cdot 7^{-1}}{3^4 \cdot 7}$

94) $\dfrac{3^0 \cdot 5^{-2}}{3^3 \cdot 5^2}$

95) $\dfrac{2^3 \cdot 5^3 \cdot 2}{3^3 \cdot 5^2}$

96) $\dfrac{2^{-7} \cdot 3^{-2} \cdot 11}{3^{-2} \cdot 11^2 \cdot 11^{-1}}$

97) $\dfrac{(-2)^3}{(-2)^{-2}}$

98) $\dfrac{(-3)^2}{(-3)^6}$

99) $\left(\dfrac{2}{3}\right)^2 \cdot \left(\dfrac{2}{5}\right)^3$

100) $\left(\dfrac{1}{4}\right)^3 \cdot \left(\dfrac{4}{3}\right)^2$

101) $\left(\dfrac{5}{2}\right)^3 \cdot \left(\dfrac{2}{3}\right)^{-2}$

102) $\left(\dfrac{3}{7}\right)^{-3} \cdot \left(\dfrac{7}{3}\right)^1$

In exercises #103–112: (a) write a mathematical expression or proportion that will solve the problem, and (b) give the solution.

103–107) Two third-world countries slowly improved their economies over four decades. In 1960 Country X had an economic output of 3 million dollars while Country Y produced 2 million dollars worth of goods and services. Over the next 40 years, Country X doubled its economic output every 5 years. During this same period Country Y tripled its economic output every 8 years.

103) In 1960 what was the ratio of Country X's economic output to that of Country Y's output?

104) What was the actual dollar amount of economic output for Country X forty years later?

105) What was the actual dollar amount of economic output for Country Y forty years later?

106) After forty years what was the ratio of Country X's economic output to that of Country Y's output (you don't need to reduce this ratio)?

107) After forty years, how much money worth of goods and services did Country X produce for every one dollar that Country Y produced (round answer to the nearest cent)?

108–113) Thirty years ago a small country had a population of 5 million people and produced enough food to feed 6 million people. Over the next thirty years, the population doubled every fifteen years while the country tripled the amount of food it could produce.

108) What was the population of this country after thirty years?

109) How many people could the country's food production feed after thirty years?

110) What was the ratio of the country's population to the amount of people it could feed thirty years later?

111) How many people could this country feed to every 100 of its citizens when it had a population of 5 million?

112) How many people can this country feed out of every 100 of its citizens thirty years later?

113) After 30 years, what percentage of this country's citizens can be fed by the amount of food produced by the country?

114–116) When another mosquito infestation gripped several counties in Florida, two different methods were tested to eliminate the insects. The state chose two separate test areas that were each estimated to support mosquito populations of about 10,000,000. One area was sprayed with chemicals. Over a four-week period, they discovered that the chemicals decreased the existing mosquito population by $\frac{1}{5}$ every week (only $\frac{4}{5}$ as many mosquitoes were alive at the end of each week than there had been at the beginning of the week). In a second area a tiny fish that preys on mosquito larvae (egg hatchlings) was introduced into as many watery areas as reasonable. It was discovered that in this area the existing mosquito population decreased by $\frac{1}{10}$ every week (only $\frac{9}{10}$ as many mosquitoes were alive at the end of each week than there had been at the beginning of the week).

114) How many mosquitoes were alive after four weeks in the area treated by chemicals (round to the nearest hundred thousand)?

115) How many mosquitoes were alive after four weeks in the area planted with the tiny fish (round to the nearest hundred thousand)?

116) During the week after the 4-week testing period, health experts estimated that every one hundred thousand mosquitoes in both test areas would make three people ill. They also estimated that the chemical which was sprayed would make about 75 people ill in that test area. If this was true would more people become ill during the week after the testing period in the test area sprayed by chemicals or the test area where the fish were introduced?

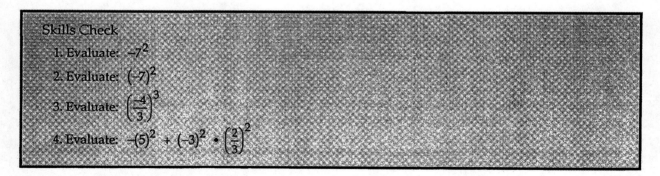

Skills Check

1. Evaluate: -7^2

2. Evaluate: $(-7)^2$

3. Evaluate: $\left(\dfrac{-4}{3}\right)^3$

4. Evaluate: $-(5)^2 + (-3)^2 \cdot \left(\dfrac{2}{3}\right)^2$

Answers to Skills Check: 1) -49; 2) 49; 3) $\dfrac{-64}{27}$ or $-2\dfrac{10}{27}$; 4) -21

Section 4.3 More Exponential Expression Manipulations

Objectives:

- To simplify exponential expressions with a power raised to a power
- To simplify exponential expressions to their prime bases
- To simplify and evaluate exponential expressions involving all the rules of exponents.

Application:

While studying a rare mold in the forests of the Northeast, it was discovered that a particular bacteria was always present. In fact, it was learned that the number of this bacteria was mathematically consistent, existing (in the thousands) at about square the number of pounds of this mold. In one acre of land scientists estimated that about 3 pounds of this rare mold existed when they first discovered it. However, over the next 10 years this amount doubled every two years. After this 10-year period, about how many of this particular type of bacteria lived on this acre of land?

Vocabulary:

Power Raised to a Power—The phrase **power raised to a power** refers to an exponent raised above a base that already includes an exponent.

Examples: $\left(2^3\right)^2$ where the 2^3 is the base inside the parenthesis and the 2 is the power or exponent raised above this base.

$\left(5^{-2}\right)^4$ where the 5^{-2} is the base inside the parenthesis and the 4 is the power or exponent raised above this base.

$\left(2^3\right)^2$ means $2^3 \bullet 2^3$ which means $2^{(3+3)}$ which means $2^6 = 64$

$\left(5^{-2}\right)^4$ means $5^{-2} \bullet 5^{-2} \bullet 5^{-2} \bullet 5^{-2}$ which means $5^{(-2+-2+-2+-2)}$ which means 5^{-8} which means $\dfrac{1}{5^8} = \dfrac{1}{390,625}$

The easiest and quickest way to **simplify a power raised to a power expression** is to multiply **the exponents**.

$$\left(2^3\right)^2 = 2^{(3 \bullet 2)} = 2^6 \qquad\qquad \left(5^{-2}\right)^4 = 5^{(-2 \bullet 4)} = 5^{-8}$$

***Recognizing the Different Meanings of Expressions with different operations inside a parenthesis:

(1) Multiplication inside a parenthesis:

$(2 \cdot 3)^2$ means $(2 \cdot 3) \cdot (2 \cdot 3)$ which gives the simplified answer of $2^2 \cdot 3^2$

In fact, in moving from $(2 \cdot 3)^2$ to $2^2 \cdot 3^2$, <u>we have just witnessed the rule of power raised to a power working</u>. Another way of looking at this original problem is to recognize that every value has a power of 1 unless otherwise indicated.

$(2 \cdot 3)^2$ means $(2^1 \cdot 3^1)^2$. Because the exponent of 2 is raised above the parenthesis this means that it affects "everything" inside the parenthesis, in this case both 2^1 and 3^1. By writing in the exponents of 1, we can see that we do have "power to a power." Therefore, we multiply the exponents.

$(2^1 \cdot 3^1)^2$ means $2^{(1 \cdot 2)} \cdot 3^{(1 \cdot 2)}$ which means $2^2 \cdot 3^2$ which means $4 \cdot 9 = 36$

(2) Division inside a parenthesis:

$(2 \div 3)^2$ means $(2 \div 3) \cdot (2 \div 3)$ or $\left(\dfrac{2}{3}\right) \cdot \left(\dfrac{2}{3}\right)$ which gives the simplified answer of $2^2 \div 3^2$ or $\dfrac{2^2}{3^2}$

In fact, in moving from $(2 \div 3)^2$ to $2^2 \div 3^2$ or $\dfrac{2^2}{3^2}$, <u>we have just witnessed the rule of power raised to a power working</u>. Another way of looking at this original problem is to recognize that every value has a power of 1 unless otherwise indicated.

$(2 \div 3)^2$ means $(2^1 \div 3^1)^2$. Because the exponent of 2 is raised above the parenthesis this means that it affects "everything" inside the parenthesis, in this case both 2^1 and 3^1. By writing in the exponents of 1, we can see that we do have "power to a power." Therefore, we multiply the exponents.

$(2^1 \div 3^1)^2$ means $2^{(1 \cdot 2)} \div 3^{(1 \cdot 2)}$ which means $2^2 \div 3^2$ or $\dfrac{2^2}{3^2}$ which means $4 \div 9 = \dfrac{4}{9}$

(3) Addition inside a parenthesis:

$(2 + 3)^2$ means $(2 + 3) \cdot (2 + 3)$ which means $(5) \cdot (5) = 25$

It is important to see that **the rule of "power raised to a power"** <u>does not apply to a base of addition</u> inside a parenthesis. It doesn't work mathematically.

$(2 + 3)^2$ means $(2^1 + 3^1)^2$, but <u>does not equal</u> $2^2 + 3^2$ because if we evaluated this expression we would get $4 + 9 = 13$—which is <u>incorrect</u>!!

(4) Subtraction inside a parenthesis:

$(2 - 3)^2$ means $(2 - 3) \cdot (2 - 3)$ which means $(-1) \cdot (-1) = 1$

It is important to see that **the rule of "power raised to a power"** <u>does not apply to a base of</u> <u>subtraction</u> inside a parenthesis. It doesn't work mathematically.

$(2-3)^2$ means $\left(2^1 - 3^1\right)^2$, <u>but does not equal</u> $2^2 - 3^2$ because if we evaluated this expression we would get $4 - 9 = -5$—which is <u>incorrect</u>!!

From the examples above we can see that it is **mathematically correct to apply the rule of power to a power to <u>only</u>: (1) a single base, <u>or</u> (2) a base where the numbers are connected by either multiplication or division.**

The rule of **power to a power does not work with base numbers connected by addition or subtraction.** Bases connected by addition or subtraction must be solved by following the order of operations for now.

How to:

Simplify an Exponential Expression with a power raised to a power.

1. Multiply the exponents.

***Remember: The base(s) doesn't change.

Example #1: Simplify the expression: $\left(2^3\right)^4 \cdot \left(5^2\right)^3$

Step #1: Multiply the exponents.

$$2^{(3 \cdot 4)} \cdot 5^{(2 \cdot 3)}$$

Answer: $2^{12} \cdot 5^6$

To get a visual of what we have done, here are equivalencies:

$\left(2^3\right)^4$ means $2^3 \cdot 2^3 \cdot 2^3 \cdot 2^3$. Following the rule of multiplication of same bases (add the exponents), we get 2^{12}.

$\left(5^2\right)^3$ means $5^2 \cdot 5^2 \cdot 5^2$. Following the rule of multiplication of same bases (add the exponents), we get 5^6.

Example #2: Simplify the expression: $\left(\left(3^2\right)^4\right)^3$

Step #1: Multiply the exponents.

Here we actually have a power raised to a power raised to another power.

Work one power to a power at a time, working inside out. First solve $\left(3^2\right)^4$ to get 3^8.

Our problem now looks like: $\left(3^8\right)^3$

Solve the remaining power to a power.

Answer: 3^{24}

How to:

Simplify all Exponential Expressions.

1. Follow the exponent rule of power raised to a power.

2. Follw the exponent rules for multiplication & division of same bases.

3. Follow the exponent rule to get rid of any negative exponents.

Example #3: Simplify the expression: $\dfrac{\left(3^4\right)^3}{\left(3^2\right)^5}$

Step #1: Follow the exponent rule of power to a power.

We identify two "power to a power" examples.

$\left(3^4\right)^3$ becomes 3^{12} after multiplying the exponents.

$\left(3^2\right)^5$ becomes 3^{10} after multiplying the exponents.

The problem now looks like: $\dfrac{3^{12}}{3^{10}}$

Step #2: Follow the exponent rules for multiplication & division of same bases.

We identify the "division of same bases" which tells us to subtract the exponent in the denominator from the exponent in the numerator.

$\dfrac{3^{12}}{3^{10}}$ is the same as $3^{(12-10)}$

The problem now looks like: 3^2

Step #3: Follow the exponent rule to get rid of any negative exponents.

There are no negative exponents. We are finished.

Answer: 3^2

Example #4: Simplify the expression: $\dfrac{\left(2^2 \bullet 3^{-3}\right)^3}{2^{-5} \bullet \left(3^2\right)^2}$

Step #1: Follow the exponent rule of power to a power.

We identify three "power to a power" examples.

In the numerator the exponent of 3 is raised above the parenthesis, thus <u>affecting</u> <u>both</u> 2^2 and 3^{-3}.

$\left(2^2 \bullet 3^{-3}\right)^3$ is the same as $\left(2^2\right)^3 \bullet \left(3^{-3}\right)^3$. We get $2^6 \bullet 3^{-9}$ after multiplying the exponents.

In the denominator $\left(3^2\right)^2$ becomes 3^4 after multiplying the exponents.

The problem now looks like: $\dfrac{2^6 \bullet 3^{-9}}{2^{-5} \bullet 3^4}$

Step #2: Follow the exponent rules for multiplication & division of same bases.
We identify two "division of same bases" examples, so we must subtract the exponents in the denominators from the exponents in the numerators.

$\dfrac{2^6}{2^{-5}}$ is the same as $2^{(6 - -5)}$ which equals $2^{(6 + 5)}$ which is 2^{11}

$\dfrac{3^{-9}}{3^4}$ is the same as $3^{(-9 - 4)}$ which equals 3^{-13}

The problem now looks like: $2^{11} \bullet 3^{-13}$

Step #3: Follow the exponent rule to get rid of any negative exponents.
We identify one negative exponent. We must take the reciprocal of the base.

3^{-13} becomes $\dfrac{1}{3^{13}}$

The problem now looks like: $\dfrac{2^{11}}{1} \bullet \dfrac{1}{3^{13}}$

Multiply across to get: $\dfrac{2^{11}}{3^{13}}$

We are done. We have completed all the rules of exponents.

Answer: $\dfrac{2^{11}}{3^{13}}$

How to:

Simplify all Exponential Expressions to Prime Bases:

1. Change all non-prime bases to prime numbers (use exponents as necessary).
2. Follow the exponent rule of power raised to a power.
3. Follow the exponent rules for multiplication & division of same bases.
4. Follow the exponent rule to get rid of any negative exponents.

Example #5: Simplify the expression to prime bases: 4^3

Step #1: Change all non-prime bases to prime numbers (use exponents as necessary).

The base of 4 is not prime. We prime factor it and get 2^2. Now replace the 4 in the expression with the 2^2.

The problem now looks like: $\left(2^2\right)^3$

Step #2: Follow the exponent rule of power to a power.

$\left(2^2\right)^3$ becomes 2^6 after multiplying the exponents.

No other rules of exponents exist. We are done.

Answer: 2^6

Sample #1: Simplify the expression: $\dfrac{(5+2)^3}{(8-1)^2}$

Being asked to simplify this expression, we look for any rules of exponents. Remember: the rule of "power raised to a power" <u>does not apply to a base of addition or subtraction</u> inside a parenthesis. It doesn't work mathematically.

We must follow order of operations, solving what is inside each parenthesis first.

In the numerator $(5+2)^3 = (7)^3$ In the denominator $(8-1)^2 = \left(7^2\right)$

The problem now looks like: $\dfrac{7^3}{7^2}$. Now solve division of same bases.

Answer: 7

You try it now:

a) Simplify the expression: $(5-3)^5$

b) Simplify the expression: $\dfrac{(1+2)^5}{(4-1)}$

Sample #2: Simplify and evaluate the expression: $\dfrac{3^{-8} \cdot 7^3 \cdot 7^{-5}}{\left(3^2\right)^{-3} \cdot 7^{-1}}$

Simplify the expression first.

In the numerator the multiplication of same bases expression of $7^3 \cdot 7^{-5}$ equals 7^{-2}.

In the denominator the power to a power expression of $\left(3^2\right)^{-3}$ becomes 3^{-6}.

The problem now looks like: $\dfrac{3^{-8} \cdot 7^{-2}}{3^{-6} \cdot 7^{-1}}$

We now solve the division of same bases: $\qquad \dfrac{3^{-8}}{3^{-6}} = 3^{\left(-8 - -6\right)} = 3^{-2}$

$$\dfrac{7^{-2}}{7^{-1}} = 7^{\left(-2 - -1\right)} = 7^{-1}$$

The problem now looks like: $3^{-2} \cdot 7^{-1}$

Get rid of negative exponents: $3^{-2} \cdot 7^{-1} = \dfrac{1}{3^2} \cdot \dfrac{1}{7}$

Simplified Answer: $\dfrac{1}{3^2 \cdot 7}$ $\qquad$ **Evaluated Answer:** $\dfrac{1}{63}$

■ **You try it now:**

c) Simplify and evaluate the expression: $\dfrac{2^{-5} \cdot 5^3}{2^{-3} \cdot 5}$

d) Simplify and evaluate the expression: $\dfrac{2^3 \cdot 3^{-5}}{2 \cdot 3^{-2} \cdot 2^4 \cdot 5}$

Sample #3: Simplify the expression to prime bases. Then evaluate. $\dfrac{\left(27^2\right)^3}{\left(3^{-2}\right)^{-10}}$

Make all the bases prime:

In the numerator: $27 = 3^3$ $\qquad$ In the denominator 3 is prime already.

Rewrite the problem: $\dfrac{\left(\left(3^3\right)^2\right)^3}{\left(3^{-2}\right)^{-10}}$

Simplify using the power to a power rule:

In the numerator: $\left(\left(3^3\right)^2\right)^3 = 3^{18}$ $\qquad$ In the denominator: $\left(3^{-2}\right)^{-10} = 3^{20}$

Rewrite the problem: $\dfrac{3^{18}}{3^{20}} \quad \Rightarrow \quad \dfrac{3^{18}}{3^{20}} = 3^{(18-20)} = 3^{-2} = \dfrac{1}{3^2}$

Simplified Answer: $\dfrac{1}{3^2}$ Evaluated Answer: $\dfrac{1}{9}$

■ **You try it now:**

e) Simplify the expression to prime bases. Then evaluate. $\dfrac{8^4}{4^{-2}}$

f) Simplify the expression to prime bases. Then evaluate. $\dfrac{5^3 \bullet 25^2}{\left(25^2\right)^3}$

Sample #4: Simplify the expression to prime bases. Then evaluate. $(36)^3$

First prime factor the base of 36. This is $2^2 \bullet 3^2$.

Rewrite the problem: $\left(2^2 \bullet 3^2\right)^3$

Simplify using the power to a power rule: $\left(2^2\right)^3 \bullet \left(3^2\right)^3$

Simplified Answer: $2^6 \bullet 3^6$ Evaluated Answer: 46,656

■ **You try it now:**

g) Simplify the expression to prime bases. Then evaluate. $(15)^4$

h) Simplify the expression to prime bases. Then evaluate. $(126)^3$

Answers to You try it now: a) 2^5; b) 3^4; c) $\dfrac{5^2}{2^2}$; and $\dfrac{25}{4}$ d) $\dfrac{1}{2^2 \bullet 3^3 \bullet 5}$ and $\dfrac{1}{540}$; e) 2^{16} and 65,536;

f) $\dfrac{1}{5^5}$ and $\dfrac{1}{3125}$; g) $3^4 \bullet 5^4$ and 50,625; h) $2^3 \bullet 3^6 \bullet 7^3$ and 2,000,376

Answer to Application: There was 3 pounds of this rare mold initially (year zero). Over the next 10 years it doubled every two years (or doubled 5 times). Therefore, after 10 years there would be $3 \bullet 2^5$ number of pounds of mold.

We are told that a bacteria existed (in the thousands) in a number that was square the number of pounds of mold. Therefore, to find the number of bacteria we must square the number of pounds of mold.

The set up would be: $\left(3 \bullet 2^5\right)^2$ Solving power to a power would give us $3^2 \bullet 2^{10} = 9216$

Remember, the number of bacteria is in the thousands, so we must multiply 9216 by 1000.

Answer: 9,216,000 of this bacteria

4.3 More Exponential Expression Problems

In exercises #1-12, decide whether each group of expressions all have the same value. Answer yes or no. If your answer is no, identify the one letter of the expression that does not equal the others. There is nothing to solve.

1) a) $(4 \cdot 7)^3$ b) $\left(4^3 \cdot 7^3\right)$ c) $(28)^3$ d) $\left(4^3\right) \cdot (7)^3$

2) a) $(2 \cdot 5)^4$ b) $2^4 \cdot 5^4$ c) $10 \cdot 10 \cdot 10 \cdot 10$ d) $(10)^4$

3) a) $(5+3)^2$ b) $\left(5^2 + 3^2\right)$ c) $(8)^2$ d) $(5+3)(5+3)$

4) a) $(9-4)^3$ b) $(5)^3$ c) $9^3 - 4^3$ d) $(9-4)(9-4)(9-4)$

5) a) $\left(\dfrac{2^5}{5^5}\right)$ b) $(2 \div 5)^5$ c) $\left(\dfrac{2}{5}\right)^5$ d) $\left(\dfrac{2^1}{5}\right)^5$

6) a) $(4 \div 3)^2$ b) $\left(\dfrac{4}{3}\right)^2$ c) $\left(\dfrac{4}{3}\right)\left(\dfrac{4}{3}\right)$ d) $\dfrac{4^2}{3^2}$

7) a) $(3-7)^2$ b) $\left(3^2 - 7^2\right)$ c) $(-4)^2$ d) $(-4)(-4)$

8) a) $(7)^2$ b) $(2+5)^2$ c) $2^2 + 5^2$ d) $(2+5)(2+5)$

9) a) 9^2 b) $\left(3^2\right)^2$ c) $3^2 \cdot 3^2$ d) 3^4

10) a) $\left(2^2\right)^5$ b) 4^5 c) $2 \cdot 10$ d) 2^{10}

11) a) 16^{-2} b) $\left(4^2\right)^{-2}$ c) $\dfrac{1}{4^4}$ d) 4^{-4}

12) a) 25^{-3} b) $\dfrac{1}{25^3}$ c) $\left(5^2\right)^{-3}$ d) $\dfrac{1}{5^6}$

In exercises #13-56, simplify the following expressions. The expression is simplified when you have completed all possible rules of exponents that you have learned (multiplication and division of same bases, power to power, and eliminating negative exponents).

13) $3^2 \cdot \left(3^3\right)^4$ 14) $5^3 \cdot \left(5^2\right)^3$ 15) $\left(2^2\right)^5 \cdot \left(7^2\right)^{10}$ 16) $\left(11^3\right)^1 \cdot \left(17^2\right)^4$

17) $\left(2^{-1}\right)^3 \cdot \left(2^3\right)^3$

18) $\left(7^2\right)^5 \cdot \left(7^3\right)^{-2}$

19) $\left(\left(5^3\right)^2\right)^2$

20) $\left(\left(10^2\right)^3\right)^5$

21) $\left(3^6\right)^{-2}$

22) $\left(5^3\right)^{-3}$

23) $\left(4^{-1}\right)^0$

24) $\left(7^0\right)^{-4}$

25) $\left(\left(3^{-2}\right)^2\right)^3$

26) $\left(\left(6^5\right)^{-3}\right)^2$

27) $\dfrac{\left(2^3\right)^5}{\left(2^2\right)^3}$

28) $\dfrac{\left(11^4\right)^3}{\left(11^3\right)^3}$

29) $\dfrac{\left(5^2\right)^3}{\left(5^5\right)^2}$

30) $\dfrac{\left(3^{-2}\right)^{-4}}{\left(3^2\right)^6}$

31) $\left(7^2\right)^2 \div \left(7^5\right)^{-1}$

32) $\left(4^7\right)^2 \div \left(4^{-2}\right)^2$

33) $\left((-2)^2\right)^3 \div \left((-2)^{-1}\right)^{-2}$

34) $\left((-8)^{-2}\right)^4 \div \left((-8)^{-3}\right)^4$

35) $\dfrac{\left(3 \cdot 11^3\right)^2}{3 \cdot 11^4}$

36) $\dfrac{\left(5^2 \cdot 7^3\right)^3}{5^3 \cdot 7^4}$

37) $\dfrac{\left(2^3 \cdot 3\right)^4}{2^2 \cdot \left(3^{-2}\right)^3}$

38) $\dfrac{\left(2 \cdot 5^2\right)^4}{2^3 \cdot \left(5^{-2}\right)^2}$

39) $\dfrac{\left(7^2 \cdot 11^{-1}\right)^2}{\left(7^{-3} \cdot 11^3\right)^{-2}}$

40) $\dfrac{\left(2 \cdot 3^2 \cdot 5^{-2}\right)^2}{\left(2^2 \cdot 3^2 \cdot 5\right)^3}$

41) $\dfrac{\left(5^2 \cdot 7^{-2}\right)^2}{\left(2^2 \cdot 5^3 \cdot 7^{-1}\right)^2}$

42) $\dfrac{(4+1)^3}{(7-2)^2}$

43) $\dfrac{(3-1)^3}{(5-3)^3}$

44) $\dfrac{(8-5)^3}{(2+1)^5}$

45) $\dfrac{(11+2)^7}{(10-(-3))^4}$

46) $\dfrac{x^3}{x}$

47) $\dfrac{a^2}{a^5}$

48) $\dfrac{b^3 \cdot b}{b^2}$

49) $\dfrac{x \cdot y^3}{x \cdot y}$

50) $\dfrac{\left(x^2\right)^3}{x^4}$

51) $\dfrac{\left(m^2\right)^5}{m^{-4}}$

52) $\dfrac{r^4}{\left(r^{-2}\right)^{-3}}$

53) $\dfrac{\left(x^3\right)^{-3} \cdot \left(y^{-1}\right)^3}{\left(x^2 \cdot y\right)^{-2}}$

54) $\dfrac{\left(m^0\right)^3 \cdot \left(n^3\right)^2}{m^3 \cdot \left(n^2\right)^4}$

55) $\left(\left(x^3\right)^{-2}\right)^5$

56) $\left(\left(y^{-1}\right)^{-2}\right)^3$

In exercises #57-68, simplify the following expressions to prime bases.

57) 16

58) 625

59) 9^3

60) 8^2

61) $\left(4^3\right)^3$

62) $\left(27^2\right)^2$

63) $(14)^2$

64) $(50)^3$

65) $\left(3^2 \cdot 6\right)^3$

66) $\dfrac{\left(4^3\right)^2}{(10)^3}$

67) $(5+4)^2$

68) $(2+7)^3$

In exercises #69-88, evaluate the following expressions. If the answer is not an integer, give the answer in fractional form, __not__ decimal form.

69) $(4-3)^3$

70) $(7-2)^3$

71) $(6+4)^3$

72) $(10+2)^2$

73) $2+3(2^2 \cdot 5)^2$

74) $3+4(3^2 \cdot 7^2)^2$

75) $(3+2)^{-3}$

76) $(8-5)^{-4}$

77) $(2-4)^3$

78) $(3-8)^2$

79) $\left(\dfrac{3}{8}\right)^{-2}$

80) $\left(\dfrac{4}{5}\right)^{-2}$

81) $\left(\dfrac{3^2}{2}\right)^{-2}$

82) $\left(\dfrac{1}{5^2}\right)^{-1}$

83) $(3^2 \cdot 5)^{-3}$

84) $(2 \cdot 3^3)^{-2}$

85) $(-2)^{-1}$

86) $(-5)^{-2}$

87) $(-3)^{-3}$

88) $(-2)^{-3}$

In exercises #89-94: (a) write an exponential expression that will solve the problem, and (b) give the solution.

89-91) A new virus in the shape of a perfect cube (that is its height, length, and width are all the same) was discovered. For every nanometer (one billionth of a meter) in height, the overall size (the space it takes up measured in cubic nanometers) of the virus was the cube of that height. When the virus was originally isolated it had a height of 50 nanometers. Over the next 24 hours the height of the virus doubled every six hours.

89) What was the overall size (measured in cubic nanometers) of the virus when a scientist first discovered it?

90) What was the height (measured in nanometers) of the virus after 24 hours?

91) What was the overall size(measured in cubic nanometers) of the virus after 24 hours?

92-94) When a small neighborhood dairy farm with 15 cows began to increase its number of cows, a bacteria also increased in numbers. In fact, it was discovered that within a square mile of the dairy that the number of a particular bacteria (in the thousands) existed at about square the number of cows. Over a period of 5 years the number of cows doubled each year.

92) How many of this particular bacteria existed when the dairy farm had only 15 cows?

93) How many cows were at the dairy after five years?

94) How many of this particular bacteria existed at the dairy after five years?

In exercises #95-100, translate the following words into math expressions. Use exponents whenever you can. Do not solve.

95) Three squared, all raised to the third power

96) Five squared, all raised to the fourth power

97) Two cubed, then squared

98) Three squared, then cubed

99) The entire quantity of x squared plus y, all raised to the fifth power.

100) The entire quantity of x cubed minus y, all raised to the third power.

In exercises #101-108, state whether the following statements are True or False.

101) $5 + 2^3 = 13$ is the same as $5 = 13 - 2^3$

102) $6 - 4^5 = -1018$ is the same as $6 = -1018 + 4^5$

103) $3^4 - 2^5 = 49$ is the same as $3^4 = 49 - 2^5$

104) $2^6 + 3^3 = 91$ is the same as $2^6 = 91 + 3^3$

105) $3^3 - 2^5 = -5$ is the same as $-2^5 + 5 = -3^3$

106) $2^4 + 7^3 = 259$ is the same as $-259 = -2^4 - 7^3$

107) $x^2 + y^3 = 68$ is the same as $x^2 = 68 - y^3$

108) $x^3 - y = 122$ is the same as $x^3 = 122 - y$

In exercises #109-116, write an equivalent equation which changes any given addition statement to a subtraction statement or any given subtraction statement to an addition statement. There is nothing to solve here.

109) $3^2 - 4 = 5$ 110) $4^3 + 7 = 71$ 111) $3^5 + 486 = 3^6$ 112) $4^3 - 28 = 6^2$

113) $x^2 - y^2 = z^2$ 114) $a^2 + b^2 = c^2$ 115) $-m - n = -p$ 116) $-r + (-s) = -t$

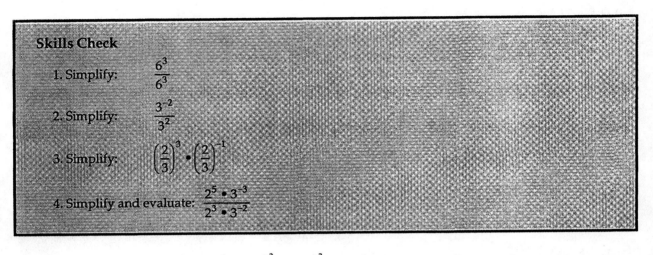

Skills Check

1. Simplify: $\dfrac{6^3}{6^3}$

2. Simplify: $\dfrac{3^{-2}}{3^2}$

3. Simplify: $\left(\dfrac{2}{3}\right)^3 \bullet \left(\dfrac{2}{3}\right)^{-1}$

4. Simplify and evaluate: $\dfrac{2^5 \bullet 3^{-3}}{2^3 \bullet 3^{-2}}$

Answers to Skills Check: 1) 1;   2) $\dfrac{1}{3^4}$;   3) $\dfrac{2^2}{3^2}$;   4) $\dfrac{2^2}{3}$ and $\dfrac{4}{3}$

| Section 4.4 | Scientific Notation, Squares and Square Roots, and the Pythagorean Theorem |

Objectives:

• To find equivalents between scientific notation and standard number notation

• To recognize the differences between squares and square roots

• To solve for the square root of a number

• To apply the Pythagorean theorem

Application:

A college professor introduced her students to nanotechnology, the science of working with the very small (manipulating and controlling atoms). A nanometer is one billionth of a meter in width (a meter is $\approx$ 39.37 inches). Some researchers are now already manipulating atoms (it takes about 3 atoms to make a distance of 1 nanometer). If a scientist strung together 6,000 atoms, approximately how much of a meter is this written in both scientific notation and standard number form?

Vocabulary:

Irrational Numbers—The system of irrational numbers consists of any number that in its decimal form does not terminate and also does not repeat in any pattern. While $0.\overline{3}$ does not terminate, it does repeat forever in a pattern, so it is rational. An example of an irrational number would be 2.67294756...(on and on without repeating a pattern).

Real Numbers—The system of real numbers consists of all rational numbers (see 3.1) and all irrational numbers.

***Understanding Base 10 with exponents: First, let's take an inventory of what we already know. $10^0 = 1$ because any non-zero number to the zero power equals 1. $10^1 = 10$ because any number to the power of 1 equals itself.

In reality, the only difference between the values of 1 (or 1.0) and 10 (or 10.0) is the placement of the decimal point. To move from the value of 1 to the value of 10 we only have to move the decimal point 1 place to the right.

In Base 10, <u>our reference point is</u> $10^0 = 1$ or just <u>1</u>.

To solve for the value of any Base-10 number other than our reference point of 1, look at the exponent above Base 10 and move the decimal point from the reference point: (1) the number of times, and (2) the direction as told by the exponent.

A positive exponent tells us to move the decimal point to the right (the movement is to a larger number).

A negative exponent tells us to move the decimal point to the left (the movement is to a smaller number).

Examples:

10^2 is the same as our reference point of 10^0 or 1, except we must move the decimal point 2 places to the right. 1 becomes 100

10^3 is the same as our reference point of 10^0 or 1, except we must move the decimal point 3 places to the right. 1 becomes 1000

10^5 is the same as our reference point of 10^0 or 1, except we must move the decimal point 5 places to the right. 1 becomes 100,000

10^{-1} is the same as our reference point of 10^0 or 1, except we must move the decimal point 1 place to the left. 1 becomes 0.1

10^{-2} is the same as our reference point of 10^0 or 1, except we must move the decimal point 2 places to the left. 1 becomes 0.01

10^{-4} is the same as our reference point of 10^0 or 1, except we must move the decimal point 4 places to the left. 1 becomes 0.0001

Scientific Notation—Scientific Notation expresses the value of a number in the form of "**A Number** multiplied by a **Base-10 Number**." In this form or notation, the first number must be greater than or equal to ($\geq$) 1 and less than ($<$) 10. The exponent raised above the Base-10 Number tells us how many places and the direction in which we move the decimal point from its location in the first number.

Examples:

<u>Scientific Notation</u>	=	<u>Standard Number Notation</u>
5.6×10^2	=	560

This is true because the positive exponent of 2 above the Base-10 number tells us to move the decimal in 5.6 two places to the right.

7.2×10^{-3}	=	0.0072

This is true because the negative exponent of 3 above the Base-10 number tells us to move the decimal in 7.2 three places to the left.

Scientific Notation is especially handy when representing either very, very large numbers (as, for example, in discussing the distances within our solar system and the universe) and very, very small numbers (as, for example, when discussing distances and sizes at the level of atoms or even smaller). Here are two more examples, which are certainly easier to write in scientific notation.

$$4.03 \times 10^{11} \qquad = \qquad 403{,}000{,}000{,}000$$

$$8.5 \times 10^{-9} \qquad = \qquad 0.0000000085$$

***Understanding Squares and Square Roots:** We have already learned that the square of any number (negative or positive) is positive. Both $(5)^2$ and $(-5)^2$ equal a positive 25.

In fact, we need to understand two truths here: (1) any number multiplied by itself gives us a positive product, and (2) any positive product found by multiplying a number by itself must have 2 answers, or two square roots, 1 negative and 1 positive.

Let's look at some examples:

$(x)^2 = 16$ To solve for the unknown number, we ask ourselves: **What value multiplied by itself gives us the product of 16?**

The <u>answer</u> for the value of x <u>is</u> positive 4 because $(4)^2 = 16$.

The <u>answer</u> for the value of x <u>is also</u> negative 4 because $(-4)^2 = 16$

Every square (in this case the 16) has two square roots (in this case the 4 and the -4). The 4 and the -4 are called square roots because they are the root numbers beneath the square that make the equation true.

$(x)^2 = \dfrac{4}{9}$ To solve for the unknown number, we ask ourselves: **What value multiplied by itself gives us the product of $\dfrac{4}{9}$?**

The <u>answer</u> for the value of x <u>is</u> positive $\dfrac{2}{3}$ because $\left(\dfrac{2}{3}\right)^2 = \dfrac{4}{9}$.

The <u>answer</u> for the value of x <u>is also</u> negative $\dfrac{2}{3}$ because $\left(-\dfrac{2}{3}\right)^2 = \dfrac{4}{9}$

Every square (in this case the $\dfrac{4}{9}$) has two square roots (in this case the $\dfrac{2}{3}$ and the $-\dfrac{2}{3}$).

$(x)^2 = -25$ Is this possible? Can we multiply any real number by itself and get a negative answer? No. The answer here is that there is **no real number solution.**

$\sqrt{}$ is the symbol which is called the **radical sign** (radical!!—as in potentially an irrational number!!) <u>or</u> the **square root symbol**. It means "the <u>positive</u> square root."

When we see a number inside a radical sign or the square root symbol, we must ask ourselves: **What <u>positive number</u> times itself equals the value inside the radical sign?**

Let's look at some examples:

$\sqrt{36}$ = ?? To solve for the positive square root of 36, we ask ourselves: what positive number multiplied by itself equals 36?

> ***The answer is <u>only</u> a positive 6 and <u>not</u> a negative 6 because by definition this symbol asks for the positive square root.

$\sqrt{\dfrac{25}{49}}$ = ?? To solve for the positive square root of $\dfrac{25}{49}$, we ask ourselves: what positive number multiplied by itself equals $\dfrac{25}{49}$?

> ***The answer is <u>only</u> a positive $\dfrac{5}{7}$ and <u>not</u> a negative $\dfrac{5}{7}$ because by definition this symbol asks for the positive square root.

$\sqrt{-64}$ = ?? To solve for the positive square root of -64, we ask ourselves: what positive number multiplied by itself equals -64?

> ***There is no real number that we can multiply by itself to get a negative value. The answer is **no real number solution.**

***Using a calculator to evaluate the square root of a number:

On our calculators the square root or radical key looks like: $\sqrt{}$ or $\sqrt{x}$. In most scientific calculators, we input the number inside the radical first and then hit the square root key.

Test your calculator and make sure you get the following answers:

$\sqrt{25}$ = 5 $\sqrt{81}$ = 9 $\sqrt{289}$ = 17

perfect square—A **perfect square** is a number which is the product of a whole number multiplied by itself. The 3 examples above—the numbers 25, 81, and 289—are all perfect squares.

Here are the first ten perfect squares: 1, 4, 9, 16, 25, 36, 49, 64, 81, 100
They are perfect squares because:

1 • 1 = 1	3 • 3 = 9	5 • 5 = 25	7 • 7 = 49	9 • 9 = 81
2 • 2 = 4	4 • 4 = 16	6 • 6 = 36	8 • 8 = 64	10 • 10 = 100

The square root of any number that is not a perfect square is an irrational number—a decimal number that continues forever and never repeats.

Examples of irrational numbers:

$$\sqrt{2} = 1.4142235... \qquad \sqrt{15} = 3.8729833...$$

right triangle—A **right triangle** is a triangle that has a right angle (90°), which is identified by a box (see picture below).

hypotenuse—The **hypotenuse** is the side of a right triangle which is <u>opposite the right angle</u>. It is the longest side of the triangle.

Pythagorean Theorem—The **Pythagorean Theorem** is a mathematical process that allows us to find the lengths of the sides of a right triangle. It is true that: (the length of one side squared) plus (the length of a second side squared) is equal to (the length of the hypotenuse squared).

The formula used is: $a^2 + b^2 = c^2$

In the formula: <u>a</u> is the length of one side, <u>b</u> is the length of a second side, and <u>c</u> is the length of the hypotenuse. After labeling the hypotenuse as "c," it doesn't matter which of the other two sides are labeled as "a" or "b."

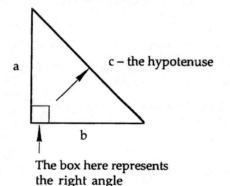

The box here represents
the right angle

How to:

Change a Value in Standard Number Form to Scientific Notation:

1. Rewrite the given number so that the decimal point is placed to the right of the first non-zero number (this creates a value of ≥ 1 and < 10).

2. Insert the "multiply by a base 10." This is "x 10."

3. Put the exponent above this base 10 which moves the decimal point in the number we just created: (1) the correct direction, and (2) the number of places to get us back to (or equal to) the given number in standard number form.

Example #1: Change 6500 to scientific notation.

  Step #1: Rewrite the given number so that the decimal point is placed to the right of the first non-zero number (this creates a value of ≥ 1 and < 10)

  6.5 (**Notice**: we <u>do not write zeros at the end of a number</u>.

  We are trying to write numbers in a shorter way!)

  Step #2: Insert the "multiply by a base 10." This is "x 10."

  6.5 x 10

  Step #3: Put the exponent above the base 10.

  Look at the decimal point in the number we have created: 6.5

  Now look at where it is in the given number of 6500—after the last zero.

  To get us from 6.5 back to 6500, we have to move the decimal point three places to the right.

  Therefore: the exponent above the base 10 must be positive 3.

  Answer: 6.5×10^{3}

Example #2: Change .02083 to scientific notation.

  Step #1: Rewrite the given number so that the decimal point is placed to the right of the first non-zero number (this creates a value of ≥ 1 and < 10)

  2.083 (**Notice**: we must write <u>all</u> the non-zero digits in the first part of a scientific notation. In this case the zero between the 2 and the 8 must be included.)

  Step #2: Insert the "multiply by a base 10." This is "x 10."

  2.083 x 10

  Step #3: Put the exponent above the base 10.

  Look at the decimal point in the number we have created: 2.083

  Now look at where it is in the given number of .02083

  To get us from 2.083 back to .02083, we have to move the decimal point two places to the left.

  Therefore: the exponent above the base 10 must be negative 2.

  Answer: 2.083×10^{-2}

> **How to:**
>
> **Change a Value in Scientific Notation to Standard Number Form:**
>
> 1. Locate the decimal point in the first part of the scientific notation.
> 2. Move the decimal point the number of places and the direction as indicated by the exponent above the base 10.

Example #3: Change 4.0785×10^3 to standard number form.

Step #1: Locate the decimal point in the first part of the scientific notation.

4.0785 The decimal point is to the right of the 4.

Step #2: Move the decimal point the number of places and the direction as indicated by the exponent above the base 10.

The exponent above the base 10 is positive, so we will be moving the decimal point to the right (going to a bigger number). We will move it 3 places to the right.

Answer: 4078.5

Example #4: Change 7×10^{-6} to standard number form.

Step #1: Locate the decimal point in the first part of the scientific notation.

7 is a whole number. The decimal point is to the right of the 7.

Step #2: Move the decimal point the number of places and the direction as indicated by the exponent above the base 10.

The exponent above the base 10 is negative, so we will be moving the decimal point to the left (going to a smaller number). We will move it 6 places to the left.

Answer: 0.000007

Sample #1: Solve: (a) $(x)^2 = 49$ (b) $x = \sqrt{49}$

(a) What number multiplied by itself equals 49?

7 multiplied by itself gives us 49

-7 multiplied by itself gives us 49

Every square has 2 roots, one negative and one positive.

Answer: (a) x = 7 and -7

(b) The symbol $\sqrt{}$ means "the positive square root"

Therefore, the question here is "<u>what positive number</u> multiplied by itself equals 49? Only positive 7.

Answer: (b) x = 7

- **You try it now:**

    a) Solve: (1) $(x)^2 = 64$ (2) $x = \sqrt{64}$

    b) Solve: (1) $(x)^2 = \dfrac{16}{25}$ (2) $x = \sqrt{\dfrac{16}{25}}$

Sample #2: Evaluate the expression of $\sqrt{30}$. Round the answer to the nearest thousandths place if the answer isn't a perfect square.

First we look to see if 30 is a perfect square. In other words, is there a number multiplied by itself that equals 30.

$5 \times 5 = 25$ and $6 \times 6 = 36$

The answer is somewhere between 5 and 6.

Go ahead and use your calculator. Take the square root of 30.

30 is not a perfect square. The answer is the irrational number of 5.477225575....(on and on). Round to the thousandths.

Answer: 5.477

- **You try it now:**

    c) Evaluate the expression of $\sqrt{70}$. Round to the thousandths.

    d) Evaluate the expression of $\sqrt{150}$. Round to the nearest whole number.

Sample #3: Evaluate the expression: $-\sqrt{\dfrac{9}{121}} - \dfrac{2}{11}$

First we must solve inside the square root symbol. The positive square root of $\dfrac{9}{121}$ is $\dfrac{3}{11}$. The negative sign in front of the square root symbol is still there.

Rewrite the problem as: $-\dfrac{3}{11} - \dfrac{2}{11}$

Combine same signs: $-\dfrac{5}{11}$

Answer: $-\dfrac{5}{11}$

- **You try it now:**

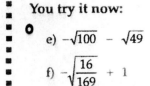

    e) $-\sqrt{100} - \sqrt{49}$

    f) $-\sqrt{\dfrac{16}{169}} + 1$

Sample #4: A once relatively weak flu virus began to spread throughout the state after a group of these viruses mutated into a new form. If there were about 6200 of these stronger viruses originally, how many viruses existed after 8 hours if the virus population increased tenfold (ten times as many!) each hour? Give your answer in scientific notation and standard number form.

We start with 6200 viruses.

This population will increase by the product of 10 each hour. Because this will happen 8 times (8 hours), we can see that the increase can be represented by "multiplying by 10^8."

The number of viruses will be found by multiplying 6200×10^8

To give an answer in scientific notation, first look at the 6200. In scientific notation this would be 6.2×10^3

So: $\underline{6200} \times 10^8$ is the same as: $6.2 \times 10^3 \times 10^8$

Simplify multiplication of same bases: $6.2 \times 10^3 \times 10^8$

We get: 6.2×10^{11}

Answer in scientific notation: 6.2×10^{11} viruses

Answer in standard number form: 620,000,000,000 viruses

■ **You try it now:**

g) During an outbreak of a fungus that threatened to kill millions of trees in the state, scientists discovered that a microorganism that carried the disease was increasing by a factor of ten (multiplying tenfold!) every month. In March there were an estimated 2.6 million of these microorganisms in an area being studied. How many microorganisms would there be in 6 months? Give the answer in scientific notation and standard number form.

h) Recognizing that the state needed to save more water in its reservoirs, it began a five-month plan of diverting water into one reservoir that currently had a surface area of 20 square miles. The plan was to increase the surface area of the reservoir by $\frac{1}{10}$ (0.1) its size each month (important: this means that after each succeeding month there would be $\frac{11}{10}$ (1.1) times as much surface area as the previous month). If the plan succeeded what was the surface area of the lake after five months? Give the answer in standard number form (round the answer to the nearest square mile).

Sample #5: A building is 100 feet in height. It also has an antenna directly in the center of the top of the building which rises another 40 feet into the air. If the distance from the center of the first floor of the building to the base of the cable is 200 feet, what is the length of the cable (the dotted line in the picture) that stretches from the top of the antenna on the building to the ground? Round answer to the nearest foot.

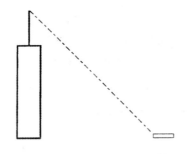

First, we must recognize that we have a right triangle here. Side "c" or the hypotenuse is the cable. The height of the building plus the antenna $(100 + 40$ feet$)$ could be labeled as side "a" and the distance along the ground from the center of the building to the base of the cable $(200$ feet$)$ could be labeled as side "b."

Write down the Pythagorean theorem: $\qquad a^2 + b^2 = c^2$

Substitute the values of the known sides: $\quad (100 + 40)^2 + (200)^2 = c^2$

Solve the left-hand side of the equation: $\quad 19,600 + 40,000 = c^2$

$$59,600 = c^2$$

At this point, if you look at this equation, we can see that if we are trying to solve for the value of "c" we are asking ourselves:

What value multiplied by itself equals 59,600?

We solve this equation by doing the same thing to both sides of the equation—in this case, taking the square root of both sides.

Rewrite the equation: $\quad \sqrt{59,600} = \sqrt{c^2}$

The square root of c^2 is just c. Then, using your calculator, get the square root of 59,600.

We now get: $\qquad 244.1311... = c$

Round to the nearest whole value:

Answer: The **cable is 244 feet long**.

- **You try it now:**

- i) If the two shorter sides of a right triangle are 9 and 18 yards respectively, what is the length of the hypotenuse (round the answer to the nearest whole)?

- j) When televisions are sold, the diagonal across the front screen is the size of the television. What is the screen size of the television below (round to the nearest whole)?

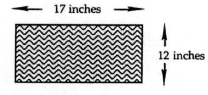

← 17 inches →

12 inches

Answers to You try it now: a) (1) $x = 8$ and -8; (2) $x = 8$; b) (1) $x = \frac{4}{5}$ and $-\frac{4}{5}$; (2) $x = \frac{4}{5}$; c) 8.367;

d) 12; e) -17; f) $\frac{9}{13}$; g) 2.6×10^{12} and $2,600,000,000,000$ microorganisms; h) 32 square miles;
i) 20 yards; j) 21 inches.

Answer to Application: We are told that 3 atoms are about 1 nanometer in length. So, first we find out how many nanometers there are in 6,000 atoms. $6,000 \div 3$ tells us that the string of atoms is about 2000 nanometers in length.

We are also told that a single nanometer is one billionth of a meter, exactly 0.000000001 of a meter. We can write this in scientific notation as 10^{-9} meters.

We can discover how many meters 2000 nanometers is by multiplying: 2000×10^{-9}

We know that 2000 is the same as 2×10^3 Rewrite the expression: $2 \times 10^3 \times 10^{-9}$

Simplify the same bases: $2 \times \underline{10^3 \times 10^{-9}}$ $\Rightarrow$ We get: 2×10^{-6}

Answer in scientific notation: 2×10^{-6} meters
Answer in standard number form: 0.000002 meters

4.4 Scientific Notation, Squares, Square Roots, & Pythagorean Theorem Problems

In exercises #1-12, answer the following questions.

1) What are the two characteristics of an irrational number?

2) Is 3.421 a rational or irrational number?

3) Is $5.\overline{6}$ a rational or irrational number?

4) Is $8.41892\overline{4}$ a rational or irrational number?

5) Is $\dfrac{3}{4}$ a rational or irrational number?

6) In analyzing the value of Base 10, does the number become larger or smaller as the exponent becomes larger?

7) In scientific notation, what does a positive exponent above the Base 10 tell us to do to the decimal point of the given number?

8) In scientific notation, what does a negative exponent above the Base 10 tell us to do to the decimal point of the given value.

9) When rewriting a number given in standard number form into scientific notation, the first part of the scientific notation has a value which is ≥ 1 and less than what value?

10) What symbol means "the positive square root of?"

11) How many answers are there when we evaluate the expression of $\sqrt{x}$ where x is a particular positive value?

12) If y is a specific positive number how many answers are there for the value of x in the expression of $(x)^2 = y$?

In exercises #13-22, decide whether each group of expressions all have the same value. Answer yes or no. If your answer is no, identify the letter of the one expression that is different from the others.

13) a) 0.001 b) $\dfrac{1}{1000}$ c) 10^{-3} d) $\dfrac{1}{10^3}$

14) a) 10 b) 10^1 c) $\dfrac{1}{10}$ d) $\dfrac{10}{1}$

15) a) 1000 b) 10×10^2 c) 10^3 d) $\dfrac{1000}{1}$

16) a) 0.01 b) 10^{-3} c) $\dfrac{1}{100}$ d) 10^{-2}

17) a) 0.1 b) 10^1 c) $\dfrac{1}{10}$ d) 10^{-1}

18) a) 100   b) $\dfrac{1}{10^{-2}}$ c) 10^2 d) 1×10^2

19) a) 1,000,000   b) 1×10^6 c) $\dfrac{1}{10^6}$ d) $10^{-2} \times 10^8$

20) a) 0.00001   b) $\dfrac{1}{10^3} \times \dfrac{1}{100}$ c) 10^{-5} d) $\dfrac{1}{100,000}$

21) a) 0.01   b) 10^{-2} c) $\dfrac{1}{100}$ d) 1×10^2

22) a) 1   b) 10^0 c) 1^1 d) 1^0

In exercises #23-32, write the given values in order from the largest to the smallest.

23) 0.01, 0.001, and 10^{-1}

24) 0.1, $\dfrac{1}{100}$, and 10^0

25) 10^0, 10^1, and 10^{-2}

26) 10^{-1}, 10^1, and 10^2

27) 10, $\dfrac{1}{10}$, 10^{-2}, and 1

28) $\dfrac{1}{100}$, 10^{-3}, $\dfrac{1}{10^{-2}}$, and 0.1

29) 0.001, $\dfrac{1}{10^2}$, $\dfrac{10}{1^5}$, and 1

30) 10^4, 1000, $\dfrac{1}{10^{-2}}$, and 10^{-5}

31) $\left(10^{-2}\right)^{-1}$, $\dfrac{10}{10^{-2}}$, 10×10^{-2}, and $\dfrac{1}{10^2}$

32) $\left(10^{-3}\right)^{-1}$, $\dfrac{1}{10^3}$, $\dfrac{10^{-1}}{10^{-1}}$, $10^4 \times 10^{-1}$

In exercises #33-44, rewrite the following expressions in standard number form.

33) 2.4×10^3 34) 3.71×10^1 35) 0.4×10^5

36) 0.97×10^7 37) 5.83×10^{-1} 38) 9.103×10^{-3}

39) 6×10^{-3} 40) 4×10^4 41) 0.82×10^{-3}

42) 42.7×10^{-2} 43) 7×10^1 44) 5×10^0

In exercises #45-65, rewrite the following expressions in scientific notation.

45) 1800   46) 22,000,000   47) 10,500

48) 1,003,000   49) 0.84   50) 0.0006

51) 0.00405   52) 0.0000031   53) 15

54) 7   55) 3   56) 26

57) 0.000000625   58) 0.0005002   59) 7,205,000,000,000

60) $\dfrac{3}{10,000}$

61) $\dfrac{1}{100,000}$

62) $\dfrac{1}{10^{-3}}$

63) $\dfrac{7}{10^{-4}}$

64) $\dfrac{1}{10^2}$

65) $\dfrac{1}{10^5}$

In exercises #66-77, solve for __all__ the values of x in both parts (a) and (b). If there is no correct answer, write "no real number solution."

66) (a) $(x)^2 = 4$ (b) $x = \sqrt{4}$

67) (a) $(x)^2 = 9$ (b) $x = \sqrt{9}$

68) (a) $(x)^2 = 100$ (b) $x = \sqrt{100}$

69) (a) $(x)^2 = 169$ (b) $x = \sqrt{169}$

70) (a) $(x)^2 = 625$ (b) $x = \sqrt{625}$

71) (a) $(x)^2 = 900$ (b) $x = \sqrt{900}$

72) (a) $(x)^2 = \dfrac{121}{36}$ b) $x = \sqrt{\dfrac{121}{36}}$

73) (a) $(x)^2 = \dfrac{25}{144}$ (b) $x = \sqrt{\dfrac{25}{144}}$

74) (a) $(x)^2 = -81$ (b) $x = \sqrt{-81}$

75) (a) $(x)^2 = -\dfrac{16}{121}$ (b) $x = \sqrt{-\dfrac{16}{121}}$

76) (a) $(x)^2 = \dfrac{225}{1600}$ (b) $x = \sqrt{\dfrac{225}{1600}}$

77) (a) $(x)^2 = \dfrac{576}{81}$ (b) $x = \sqrt{\dfrac{576}{81}}$

In exercises #78-93, evaluate the following expressions. Round the answer to the nearest thousandths place __only__ if the answer is an irrational number.

78) $\sqrt{56.25}$

79) $\sqrt{27.04}$

80) $\sqrt{50}$

81) $\sqrt{29}$

82) $-\sqrt{25} - 4$

83) $-\sqrt{64} + 6$

84) $\sqrt{121} - 11$

85) $\sqrt{1} + \sqrt{4}$

86) $\sqrt{\dfrac{4}{36}} - \dfrac{1}{6}$

87) $\sqrt{\dfrac{49}{81}} - \left(\dfrac{2}{3}\right)$

88) $-\sqrt{\dfrac{4}{9}} - \left(-\dfrac{4}{9}\right)$

89) $-\sqrt{\dfrac{121}{16}} + 1$

90) $\sqrt{9} - 9^2$

91) $4^2 - \sqrt{4}$

92) $-\sqrt{10} - \sqrt{25}$

93) $\sqrt{70} - \sqrt{49}$

In exercises #94-105, (a) write a mathematical expression that will solve the problem, and (b) give the solution. Some problems, as stated below, do not need a set up.

94-96) Light travels at the speed of 186,000 miles per second.

94) Represent the speed of light (in miles per second) in scientific notation (no set up is needed).

95) Represent the speed of light (in miles per hour) in scientific notation __and__ standard notation. This problem requires (a) setup and (b) mph in both scientific notation and standard notation)

96) The distance around the earth at the equator is about 25,000 miles. If you could travel at the speed of light, about how many times could you circle the earth in one second (round your answer to the nearest tenth)?

97-99) In astronomy, a parsec is a unit of distance that is equivalent to the distance that light travels in 3.26 years. This is the same as 3.09×10^{13} kilometers.

97) Write the number of kilometers in a parsec in standard number form (no set up is needed).

98) How many kilometers are in a light year? Give the answer in scientific notation, rounding the number in the first part of the notation to the thousandths place.

99) The nearest star to the planet earth is Alpha Centauri, which is about 4.3 light years away. How many kilometers is this? Give the answer in scientific notation, rounding the number in the first part of the notation to the thousandths place.

100) One meter is approximately 39.37 inches. A micrometer is one-millionth of a meter. How many inches (or, more accurately, how much of an inch) is a micrometer? Write the answer in scientific notation and standard number form (no set up is needed).

101) A nanometer is one-billionth of a meter. How many inches (or, more accurately, how much of an inch) is a nanometer? Write the answer in scientific notation and standard number form (no set up is needed).

102) A panic spread through a federal science lab when scientists reported that a vial with 1000 deadly viruses was stolen. Classified as Top Secret, the government did not immediately release the name of the virus in the theft. One scientist did state that this virus, if contained in an ideal environment, could multiply by a factor of 10 (ten times as many) every hour. How many viruses might there be after 12 hours? Give the answer in scientific notation and standard number form (no set up is needed).

103-104) In a science fiction movie, the earth was being pulled upward away from its magnetic core. The earth was actually being slowly stretched outward, becoming bigger and bigger. The earth's diameter is approximately 7,900 miles. The diameter was being enlarged by $\frac{1}{100}$ its size each day (important: this means that after each succeeding day the diameter would be $\frac{101}{100}$ (1.01) times as large as it had been the previous day).

103) How many miles would the size of the earth's diameter be after 10 days (round to the nearest mile)?

104) How many miles would the size of the earth's diameter be after 20 days (round to the nearest mile)?

105) In another science fiction movie, the earth was collapsing inward on itself, our wonderful round ball shrinking into a denser and denser state. The earth's diameter is approximately 7,900 miles. If the diameter was losing $\frac{1}{10}$ of its remaining distance every month (that is it kept only $\frac{9}{10}$ of its remaining distance each month), what was the earth's diameter after five months?

In exercises #106-112, solve for the hypotenuse. First, (a) write a set up which shows the Pythagorean theorem with the numbers taking the place of the "a" and "b" variables; and (b) give the solution. If the solution is an irrational number, round to the thousandths place.

106) In a right triangle, the two known sides are 6 feet and 8 feet respectively. What is the length of the longest side—the hypotenuse?

107) In a right triangle, the two known sides are 15 meters and 20 meters respectively. What is the length of the longest side—the hypotenuse?

108)
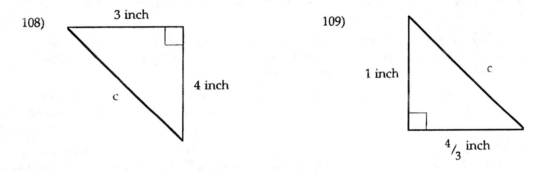

109)

110) A pasture is in the shape of a right triangle. It has one side that is $\frac{5}{6}$ of a mile and a second side that is 2 miles. If the missing side is the hypotenuse, what is the length of the third side?

111) The four bases of a baseball field make up a perfect square. If each side of this square is 90 feet, what is the diagonal distance across the square (round answer to the nearest whole foot)?

112) A skating rink, in the shape of a rectangle, had a length of 100 yards. Its width was one-half of its length. What was the diagonal distance across the skating rink?

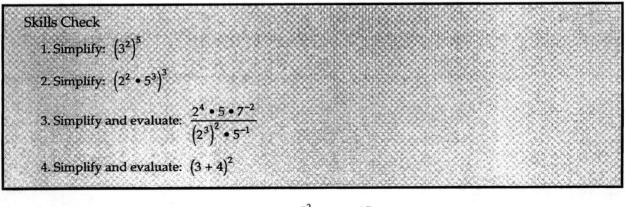

Skills Check

1. Simplify: $\left(3^2\right)^5$

2. Simplify: $\left(2^2 \cdot 5^3\right)^3$

3. Simplify and evaluate: $\dfrac{2^4 \cdot 5 \cdot 7^{-2}}{\left(2^3\right)^2 \cdot 5^{-1}}$

4. Simplify and evaluate: $\left(3 + 4\right)^2$

Answers to Skills Check: 1) 3^{10}; 2) $2^6 \cdot 5^9$; 3) $\dfrac{5^2}{2^2 \cdot 7^2}$ and $\dfrac{25}{196}$; 4) 7^2 and 49.

Chapter 5   Geometry

Section 5.1 Perimeter and Area of the Four Common Geometric Shapes

Objectives:

• To learn important geometry vocabulary

• To solve for the perimeters of squares, rectangles, triangles, and circles

• To solve for the areas of squares, rectangles, triangles, and circles

Application:

A farmer had a rectangular piece of land that was $\frac{1}{4}$ of a mile (440 yards) in width and a thousand yards in length. If the land could successfully support 1 sheep on a strip of land 50 yards by 50 yards, how many sheep could the farmer support on his land?

Vocabulary:

parallel lines—**Parallel lines** are lines that reside on the same plane (picture a sheet of paper) and extend in the exact same direction, thus never crossing each other.

Examples:

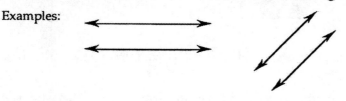

Perpendicular lines—**Perpendicular lines** are lines that cross or intersect each other and create four right angles (90° angles).

Example:

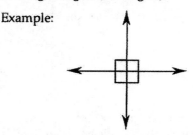

In everyday conversation we talk about streets that are **parallel** (running in the same direction, but never crossing) and **perpendicular** (running in opposite directions as vertical and horizontal lines do; these meet/cross at intersections).

vertex—A **vertex** is the point of intersection of the two sides of an angle.

the vertex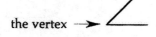

two-dimensional objects—**Two-dimensional objects** are flat objects. They have two dimensions—length and width, but no height. Picture a sheet of paper—a **two-dimensional object** which has only length and width (no height) versus a book which has length, width, and also height. A book is a three-dimensional shape. We will look at three-dimensional objects in section 5.4. In the next three sections we will be working with two-dimensional or flat objects.

Perimeter—The **perimeter** of an object is the distance around the outside of a two-dimensional object. It is measured in what is called **linear units** because the perimeter can be represented by a line that represents a particular distance.

Area—The **area** of an object is the space inside a two-dimensional object (in fact it is the space inside a perimeter). It is measured in **square units** (space can't be measured by a line!). We actually measure how many squares of a certain size would fit into this object.

Example of Visualizing the Perimeter and Area of a Shape:

Notice that each "block" is a square that has a length of 1 ft. and a width of 1 ft.

3 ft

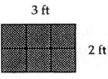

2 ft

We can see that the **perimeter** (a walk around the outside of the shape: 3 + 2 + 3 + 2) is **10 feet**.

The space inside the perimeter is made up of 6 squares that each have 1 ft. in length and 1 ft. in width. The **area** (the space inside the perimeter) is therefore 6 square ft.

***Answers to area problems are <u>always</u> given in square units. There are two correct notations for writing square units—**sq. units** <u>or</u> **units**^{2}.

Example: 50 square feet could be written as: 50 sq. ft. or 50 ft.^{2}

4 Regular Two-Dimensional Geometric Shapes

rectangle—A **rectangle** is a four-sided figure where opposite sides are parallel and of equal length. It has four 90° angles.

square—A **square** is a special type of rectangle. It is a rectangle in which the lengths of all four sides are the same.

triangle—A **triangle** is a three-sided figure. The height of a triangle is found by drawing a perpendicular line from the base of the triangle to its opposite vertex. Look at the three triangles below and the identified height of each object.

Notice that the height of the first triangle (a right triangle) is actually one of its sides. In the third triangle the height is actually measured outside the triangle itself.

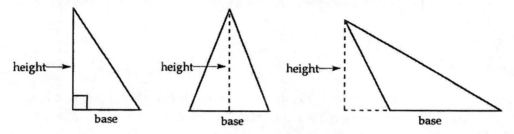

circle—A **circle** is an enclosed curved line which is always the same distance from the center point of a circle.

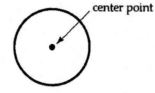

Important parts of a circle:

radius—The **radius** is the distance (a line) from the center point of the circle to the edge of the circle.

diameter—The **diameter** is the distance (a line) from a point on the edge of a circle to a point on the opposite edge of the circle (the line passes through the center point).

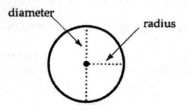

It is important that we know the <u>relationship between the radius and the diameter</u>. **The radius is equal to** $\frac{1}{2}$ **"of" the diameter.** This is the same as saying the radius is equal to the diameter divided by 2.

We should know/understand these formulas where "r" is the radius and "d" is the diameter.

$$r = \frac{1}{2} \cdot d \qquad r = \frac{d}{2}$$

If we are given the length of the diameter, we can find the length of the radius by taking $\frac{1}{2}$ of that diameter <u>or</u> dividing that diameter by two.

If the diameter is 10 inches, then substitute the value of 10 for the "d" in one of the formulas—either

$$r = \frac{1}{2} \bullet d \qquad \text{or} \qquad r = \frac{d}{2}.$$

$$r = \frac{1}{2} \bullet 10 \qquad\qquad r = \frac{10}{2}$$

$$r = 5 \text{ inches} \qquad\qquad r = 5 \text{ inches}$$

It is also true to say that **the diameter is twice (two times) the length of the radius.** We need to know/understand this formula: $d = 2 \bullet r$

If we are given the radius, we can find the diameter by multiplying the radius by 2.

If the radius is 3.5 feet, then substitute the value of 3.5 for the "r" in the formula.

$$d = 2 \bullet r$$

$$d = 2 \bullet 3.5$$

$$d = 7 \text{ feet}$$

circumference—The **circumference** is the perimeter of a circle.

pi—Pi is the ratio of the length of the circumference to the length of the diameter. The circumference is always **pi** times longer than the diameter.

The symbol for **pi** is π.

Pi is actually an irrational number that continues forever without repeating in a pattern (3.141592...), but we give it an approximate value when solving various problems. The value of π as a decimal is approximately 3.14; its approximate value as a fraction is $\frac{22}{7}$.

The result of a problem will differ slightly dependent upon whether we use the decimal or fractional value of π in a problem.

Example: Find the circumference of a circle with a diameter of 14 feet.

Well, we know that the circumference is π times the length of the diameter. In fact this gives us the circumference formula of $C = \pi \bullet d$.

Using 3.14 for π	Using $\frac{22}{7}$ for π
$C = \pi \bullet d$	$C = \pi \bullet d$
$C = 3.14 \bullet 14$	$C = \frac{22}{7} \bullet \frac{14}{1}$
$C = \mathbf{43.96}$ **ft.**	$C = \mathbf{44}$ **ft.**

Both answers are correct. When we do problems, we must always follow directions that tell us to use 3.14 or $\frac{22}{7}$ for π.

***Converting large Improper Fractions on the Calculator**: If the calculator we are using doesn't change an improper fraction into a mixed number, we will want to know the following process.

Example: Change $\frac{869}{32}$ to a mixed number.

(1) Divide the numerator by the denominator (869 ÷ 32) in the calculator. We get 27.15625. The ".15625" tells us that there are <u>some parts left over</u>. We don't know what this fraction is, but we do know that the mixed number which is equal to $\frac{869}{32}$ has 27 wholes.

We now know this: $\frac{869}{32} = 27\frac{?}{32}$

(2) To get the number of parts left over (the new numerator) multiply the whole number by the denominator (27 • 32). We find out that the 27 wholes use up 864 parts. Subtract this from the 869 parts that we started with (869 - 864) and we see that there are still 5 parts left over.

Answer: $27\frac{5}{32}$

Do the following examples to make sure you can change improper fractions to mixed numbers on the calculator.

Ex: $\frac{1839}{15} = 122\frac{9}{15}$ which of course needs to reduced to $122\frac{3}{5}$

Ex: $\frac{14682}{51} = 287\frac{45}{51}$

The Process for Solving <u>All</u> Perimeter and Area Problems is written in the "How to" box that follows. It is the <u>only</u> process you need to know and follow.

How to:

Solve Perimeter and Area Problems:

1. Identify the figure (draw a picture if necessary).

2. Find/Write the formula.

3. Substitute the number value(s) for the variable(s).

4. Solve and give the answer using the appropriate measurement (perimeter answers in linear units and area answers in square units).

Example #1: Find the perimeter and the area of the rectangle below.

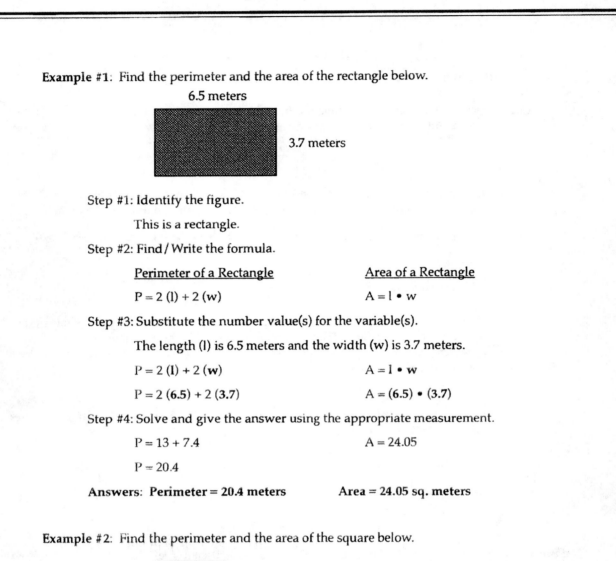

6.5 meters

3.7 meters

Step #1: Identify the figure.

This is a rectangle.

Step #2: Find / Write the formula.

Perimeter of a Rectangle   Area of a Rectangle

$P = 2\,(l) + 2\,(w)$ $A = l \bullet w$

Step #3: Substitute the number value(s) for the variable(s).

The length (l) is 6.5 meters and the width (w) is 3.7 meters.

$P = 2\,(l) + 2\,(w)$ $A = l \bullet w$

$P = 2\,(6.5) + 2\,(3.7)$ $A = (6.5) \bullet (3.7)$

Step #4: Solve and give the answer using the appropriate measurement.

$P = 13 + 7.4$ $A = 24.05$

$P = 20.4$

Answers: Perimeter = 20.4 meters   Area = 24.05 sq. meters

Example #2: Find the perimeter and the area of the square below.

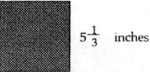

$5\frac{1}{3}$ inches

Step #1: Identify the figure.

This is a square.

Step #2: Find / Write the formula.

Perimeter of a Square   Area of a Square

$P = 4\,(s)$ $A = s^2$

Step #3: Substitute the number value(s) for the variable(s).

The length of a side (s) is $5\frac{1}{3}$ inches..

$P = 4\,(s)$ $A = s^2$

$P = 4\left(5\frac{1}{3}\right)$ $A = \left(5\frac{1}{3}\right)^2$

Step #4: Solve and give the answer using the appropriate measurement.

$P = \frac{4}{1}\,\bullet\,\frac{16}{3}$ $A = 5\frac{1}{3}\,\bullet\,5\frac{1}{3}$

$P = \frac{64}{3}$ or $21\frac{1}{3}$ $A = \frac{16}{3}\,\bullet\,\frac{16}{3}$

$A = \frac{256}{9}$ or $28\frac{4}{9}$

Answers: **Perimeter** = $21\frac{1}{3}$ inches   **Area** = $28\frac{4}{9}$ sq. inches

Example #3: Find the perimeter and the area of the triangle below.

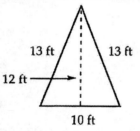

13 ft   13 ft

12 ft

10 ft

Step #1: Identify the figure.

This is a triangle.

Step #2: Find / Write the formula.

Perimeter of a Triangle   **Area of a Triangle**

$P = s_1 + s_2 + s_3$ $A = \frac{1}{2}\,\bullet\,b\,\bullet\,h$

Step #3: Substitute the number value(s) for the variable(s).

The lengths of the three   The base (b) is 10 feet and
sides are 10, 13, and 13 feet   the height (h) is 12 feet.
respectively.

$$P = s_1 + s_2 + s_3 \qquad\qquad A = \frac{1}{2} \cdot b \cdot h$$

$$P = 10 + 13 + 13 \qquad\qquad A = \frac{1}{2} \cdot \frac{10}{1} \cdot \frac{12}{1}$$

Step #4: Solve and give the answer using the appropriate measurement.

$$P = 36 \qquad\qquad A = \frac{1}{\overset{}{\underset{1}{2}}} \cdot \frac{\overset{5}{\cancel{10}}}{1} \cdot \frac{12}{1}$$

$$A = \frac{60}{1}$$

Answers: **Perimeter = 36 feet**   **Area = 60 sq. feet**

Example #4: Find the perimeter (circumference) and the area of the circle below.

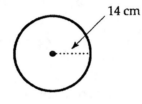

14 cm

Step #1: Identify the figure.

      This is a circle.

Step #2: Find / Write the formula.

     <u>Circumference of a Circle</u>   <u>Area of a Circle</u>

        $C = \pi \cdot d$ $A = \pi \cdot r^2$

Step #3: Substitute the number value(s) for the variable(s).

     Use $\frac{22}{7}$ for π.

     If the radius equals 14 centi-   The radius is 14 centimeters.

     meters, the diameter must be $A = \pi \cdot r^2$

     double this (d = 2 • r) or 28 cm. $A = \frac{22}{7} \cdot (14)^2$

     $C = \pi \cdot d$

     $C = \frac{22}{7} \cdot \frac{28}{1}$

Step #4: Solve and give the answer using the appropriate measurement.

$$C = \frac{22}{\underset{1}{\cancel{7}}} \cdot \frac{\overset{4}{\cancel{28}}}{1} \qquad\qquad A = \frac{22}{7} \cdot \frac{14}{1} \cdot \frac{14}{1}$$

$$C = 88 \qquad\qquad A = \frac{22}{\underset{1}{\cancel{7}}} \cdot \frac{\overset{2}{\cancel{14}}}{1} \cdot \frac{14}{1}$$

$$A = 616$$

Answers: Circumference = 88 cm.   Area = 616 sq. cm.

Sample #1: An isosceles triangle has two equal sides. If the equal sides are both 8 feet and the perimeter of the triangle is thirty feet, what is the length of the third side?

This problem deals with perimeter. The three sides must add up to 30. If we know the lengths of two of the sides, we can subtract these from the total distance of the perimeter to get the length of the third side.

Concept Set up: $(\text{Perimeter}) - (s_1 + s_2)$

Substitute the Values for the perimeter, s_1 and s_2: $30 - (8 + 8)$

Answer: 14 feet

You try it now:

a) One side of a triangle is $4\frac{1}{3}$ meters. A second side is $2\frac{1}{2}$ meters. If the perimeter of the triangle is 9 meters, what is the length of the third side?

b) If a right triangle has a height of 3 feet and a base of 4 feet, what is the length of the third side (use the Pythagorean Theorem)? What is the perimeter of the triangle?

Sample #2: A new bike path was created in the shape of a rectangle just to the west of a city. It had a length of 6.2 miles and a width of 5.3 miles. If 4 miles of the path was unpaved, what fraction of the pathway was paved? What percentage of the pathway was paved (round to the nearest tenth of a percent)? What is the ratio of paved to unpaved miles of the pathway?

To find out what fraction (and what percentage) of the pathway was paved, we have to first find the total distance of the pathway—in this case the perimeter of this rectangle.

Formula for Perimeter of a Rectangle: $P = 2(l) + 2(w)$

Substitute the given values: $P = 2(6.2) + 2(5.3)$

Solve: $P = 12.4 + 10.6$

                               $P = 23$ miles

Now, to answer the first question: what fraction of the path is paved?

The concept here is $\dfrac{\text{part}}{\text{whole}}$ where the part is the paved miles and the whole is the total miles.

Concept Set up: $\dfrac{\#\ \text{of paved miles}}{\#\ \text{of miles}}$

We get the miles paved by taking the total miles (23) and subtracting the number of miles that are unpaved.

Number Set up: $\dfrac{23 - 4}{23}$ **1st Answer:** $\dfrac{19}{23}$ of the path is paved

We can get the percentage of the pathway that is paved by converting the fraction $\left(\dfrac{19}{23}\right)$ into a percent.

Convert a fraction to a percent by either:

Changing the fraction   or   Changing the fraction to a decimal
directly to a percent: first, and then converting to a percent.

Multiply by 100:

$\dfrac{19}{23} \bullet \dfrac{100}{1} = \dfrac{1900}{23} = 82.608...\%$ $19 \div 23 = 0.82608...$

Fraction to a decimal: $\dfrac{\text{numerator}}{\text{denominator}}$

Decimal to a percent: Multiply by 100:

$0.82608... (100) = 82.608...\%$

Round to the nearest tenth.

2nd Answer: 82.6% of the path is paved

To answer the third question, we simply provide the information we already know. The ratio of paved miles of road (19) to unpaved miles of road (4) is 19:4.

3rd Answer (in fractional form): $\dfrac{19\ \text{miles paved}}{4\ \text{miles unpaved}}$

■ **You try it now:**

c) A rectangular piece of property had a length of 70 yards and a width of 50 yards. One width of the property and 20 yards of one length were bordered by a stone wall. The rest of the property was enclosed by a wooden fence. What fraction of the property's border was enclosed by the stone wall? What percent of the border was enclosed by the stone wall (round to the nearest whole percent)? What is the ratio of stone wall to wooden fencing?

d) A new fountain, surrounded by a circular pond, was installed in a downtown park. Every three feet along the circular rim of the pond a marble mythological creature (mostly nymphs and fauns) decorate the structure. If the pond has a diameter of $10\frac{1}{2}$ feet, how many creatures decorate the pond's rim (use $\frac{22}{7}$ for π)?

Sample #3: A building contractor purchased a piece of land which was 1000 feet in length and 450 feet in width. If she knew that she could build a house for every 15,000 sq. feet of land, how many homes could she build?

First we see that this problem deals with space. We must find the area of this piece of rectangular land.

Formula for the Area of a Rectangle: $A = l \cdot w$

Substitute the given values: $A = 1000 \cdot 450$

Solve: $A = 450,000$ sq. ft.

To find out how many houses will be built, we take the **total area** (450,000 sq. ft) and **divide it by the area needed for each house** (15,000 sq. ft).

Set up: $\dfrac{450,000}{15,000} = 30$

Answer: 30 houses would be built.

- **You try it now:**

e) A museum had hired a contractor to put in new tile in the front hall of the museum. The rectangular hall had a length of 150 feet and a width of 90 feet. If each tile which the contractor would lay was 2 feet by 3 feet, how many tiles would be needed to complete the job?

f) A painter painted a room (4 walls and a flat ceiling) where each wall was a square that had a side of 10 feet. If he knew that he would use a gallon of paint for each 250 sq. ft that he painted, how many gallons of paint would he need to finish the job?

Sample #4: A sprinkler sprayed water $4\frac{1}{2}$ meters outward in a circular pattern. How much space did the sprinkler cover (give answer as a mixed number)? $\frac{3}{4}$ of the area watered was lawn and $\frac{1}{4}$ of the area watered was rock landscaping. What was the size of the area where water was being wasted?

First, we recognize that we are dealing with the space (**area**) of a circle (the spraying of water). We must find the area of the land being watered (use $\frac{22}{7}$ for π).

Formula for the Area of a Circle: $A = \pi \cdot r^2$

Substitute the given values: $A = \dfrac{22}{7} \cdot \left(4\frac{1}{2}\right)^2$

Solve:

$$A = \frac{22}{7} \cdot \frac{9}{2} \cdot \frac{9}{2}$$

$$A = \frac{\overset{11}{\cancel{22}}}{7} \cdot \frac{9}{\underset{1}{\cancel{2}}} \cdot \frac{9}{2}$$

$$A = \frac{891}{14}$$

Convert $\frac{891}{14}$ to a mixed number. 14 goes into 891 a total of 63 whole times with a

remainder of 9.   So: $\frac{891}{14} = 63\frac{9}{14}$

1st Answer: $63\frac{9}{14}$ **sq. meters** is the area watered by the sprinkler.

The second question asks how much land is watered uselessly (wasted!). This wasted watering is the area that is the rock landscaping—which is $\frac{1}{4}$ of the total area.

We know that: $\frac{1}{4}$ of $63\frac{9}{14}$ sq. m. of land is being watered wastefully.

A number of another number tells us that we have multiplication.

Set up: $\frac{1}{4} \cdot 63\frac{9}{14}$

Solve: $\frac{1}{4} \cdot \frac{891}{14}$

$\frac{891}{56} = 15\frac{51}{56}$

2nd Answer: $15\frac{51}{56}$ **sq. m.** of land is watered wastefully.

■ **You try it now:**

g) A pond has a radius of $15\frac{1}{2}$ feet. During a cold spell, $\frac{1}{3}$ of the pond froze over with a coating of ice. How many square feet of the pond's surface were frozen (give answer as a mixed number)? Use $\frac{22}{7}$ for π in this problem.

h) At a picnic a circular birthday cake with a diameter of 21 inches was left unprotected on a table. Within an hour 4150 ants were crawling on the top surface of the cake. How many ants were there per square inch of cake (round answer to the nearest ant)? Use 3.14 for π in this problem.

Answers to You try it now: a) Set up: $9 - \left(4\frac{1}{3} + 2\frac{1}{2}\right)$; Solution: $2\frac{1}{6}$ meters; b) First, use the Pythagorean Theorem to find the third side of the triangle $\Rightarrow a^2 + b^2 = c^2$. This tells us that $c = 5$. Now use the perimeter formula $(P = s_1 + s_2 + s_3)$. Set up: $P = 3 + 4 + 5$; Solution: 12 feet; c) First find the perimeter of the rectangle $[P = 2(l) + 2(w)] \Rightarrow P = 2(70) + 2(50)$. The perimeter is 240 yards. 1st Set up: $\dfrac{50 + 20}{2\,(70) + 2\,(50)}$ or $\dfrac{50 + 20}{240}$; 1st Solution: $\dfrac{7}{24}$ of border is made of stone; 2nd Solution: 29%; 3rd Solution: $\dfrac{7 \text{ ft. stone wall}}{17 \text{ feet wooden fencing}}$ d) First find the circumference of the circle $(C = \pi \cdot d) \Rightarrow C = \dfrac{22}{7} \cdot 10\frac{1}{2}$. The circumference is 33 feet. Set up: $33 \div 3$.

Solution: 11 creatures; e) First find the area of the hall $A = l \cdot w \Rightarrow A = 150 \cdot 90$. The area of the hall is 13,500 sq. ft. Now find the area of a tile $A = l \cdot w \Rightarrow A = 2 \cdot 3$. The area of a tile is 6 sq. ft. Set up: $\dfrac{13500}{6}$; Solution: 2250 tiles; f) First find the area of a wall $A = s^2 \Rightarrow A = (10)^2$. The area of one wall is 100 sq. ft. There are 4 walls and the ceiling which are all identical areas. Set up: $\dfrac{(5 \cdot 100)}{250}$; Solution: 2 gallons of paint; g) First find the area of the circle $\left(A = \pi \cdot r^2\right) \Rightarrow A = \dfrac{22}{7} \cdot \left(15\frac{1}{2}\right)^2 \Rightarrow A = \dfrac{22}{7} \cdot \dfrac{31}{2} \cdot \dfrac{31}{2} \Rightarrow A = \dfrac{10571}{14}$. The area of the circle is $755\frac{1}{14}$ sq. ft. Set up: $\dfrac{1}{3} \cdot 755\frac{1}{14}$; Solution: $251\frac{29}{42}$ sq. ft. of pond is frozen; h) First find the area of the circle $\left(A = \pi \cdot r^2\right) \Rightarrow A = 3.14 \cdot (10.5)^2 \Rightarrow A = 346.185$. The area of the circle is 346.185 sq. inches. Set up: $4150 \div 346.185$; Solution: 12 ants per sq. inch.

Answer to Application: To find out how many sheep the farmer can successfully support, we first need to know how many square yards of land he has available and how many square yards of land he needs per sheep.

First, find the area of the land. The length is 440 yards and the width is 1000 yards.

Area of a Rectangle: $A = l \cdot w$

$A = 1000 \cdot 440$

Area of the land: 440,000 sq. yards.

Second, find the area needed per sheep. Each sheep needs an area 50 yards by 50 yards.

Area of a Rectangle: $A = l \cdot w$

$A = 50 \cdot 50$

Area of land that a sheep needs: 2500 sq. yards.

Finally, divide the total amount of land by the area of land each sheep needs.

Set up: $440,000 \div 2500$

Solution: **176 sheep** could be supported on the farmer's land.

5.1 Perimeter and Area Problems for the Common Geometric Shapes

In exercises #1-10, answer True or False.

1) Parallel lines never cross (intersect) each other.

2) Perpendicular lines cross (intersect) and create 4 right angles.

3) A right angle is the same as a 90° angle.

4) The angle formed at the vertex of a rectangle is a 90° angle.

5) Area is measured in linear units.

6) Area is the space inside a two-dimensional object.

7) A two-dimensional object has three dimensions—length, width, and height.

8) A square is a special type of rectangle where all 4 sides have the same length.

9) Area is the space inside a perimeter.

10) Perimeter is measured in linear units because it measures the distance (a line) around the outside of a flat object.

In exercises #11-13, draw a line that identifies the height of each triangle.

11) 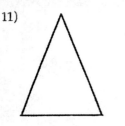   12) 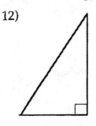   13)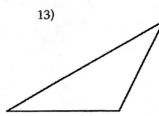

14) Draw a line that identifies the radius.   15) Draw a line that identifies the diameter.

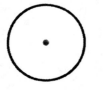

16) Draw a line inside the rectangle that is the hypotenuse for two right triangles.

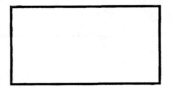

In exercises #17-36, answer the following questions.

17) The height of a triangle is measured from the base of a triangle to <u>what</u> (be exact)?

18) What is the word for the distance from the center point of a circle to a point on the circle's edge?

19) What do we call the perimeter of a circle?

20) Pi is a ratio between what two things?

21) The diameter is double what?

22) The radius is $\frac{1}{2}$ of what?

23) Area is measured in what kind of units?

24) If the perimeter of a square is 4 feet, what is the area of the square?

25) If the radius is 5 feet, what is the diameter?

26) If the diameter is 5 feet, what is the radius?

27) If the diameter is $7\frac{3}{4}$ meters, what is the radius?

28) If the radius is $7\frac{3}{4}$ meters, what is the diameter?

29) If the area of a circle is 50 square feet, what is $\frac{1}{5}$ of the circle's area?

30) If the area of a circle is 72 square yards, what is $\frac{3}{4}$ of the circle's area?

31-33) A trail around a lake is 2000 yards. 600 yards of the trail are dirt and 1400 yards are paved.

31) What fraction of the trail is paved?

32) What percentage of the trail is paved?

33) What is the ratio of paved to unpaved yards of the trail?

34-36) A park of 100,000 square feet includes a softball field that is 35,000 square feet.

34) What fraction of the park consists of the softball field?

35) What percentage of the park consists of the softball field?

36) What is the ratio of land covered by the softball field to park land that is not covered by the softball field?

In exercises #37-42, convert the given improper fraction to a mixed number.

37) $\dfrac{929}{18}$ 38) $\dfrac{1084}{21}$ 39) $\dfrac{1472}{24}$ 40) $\dfrac{1995}{38}$ 41) $\dfrac{18264}{259}$ 42) $\dfrac{23172}{341}$

In exercises #43-52, solve for the perimeter of the given shape. Remember to follow this process: first, find and write the formula, then substitute the number values for the variables, and last, solve the problem.

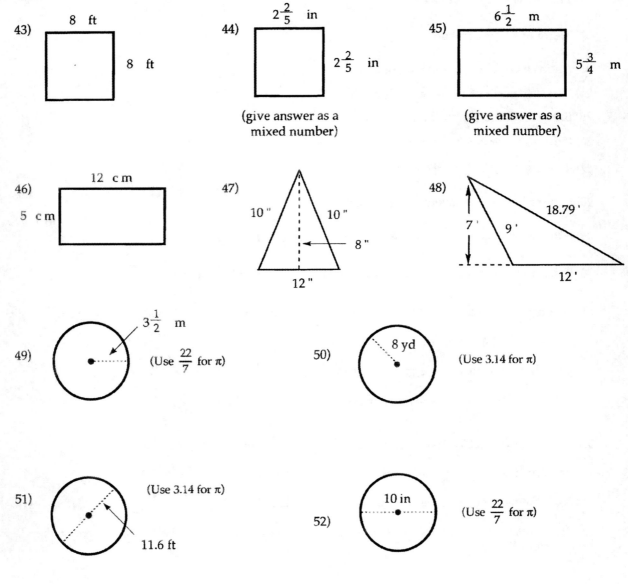

43) 8 ft, 8 ft

44) $2\frac{2}{5}$ in, $2\frac{2}{5}$ in
(give answer as a mixed number)

45) $6\frac{1}{2}$ m, $5\frac{3}{4}$ m
(give answer as a mixed number)

46) 12 cm, 5 cm

47) 10 ", 10 ", 8 ", 12 "

48) 7 ', 9 ', 18.79 ', 12 '

49) $3\frac{1}{2}$ m (Use $\frac{22}{7}$ for π)

50) 8 yd (Use 3.14 for π)

51) (Use 3.14 for π) 11.6 ft

52) 10 in (Use $\frac{22}{7}$ for π)

In exercises #53-62, solve for the area of the given shape. Remember to follow this process: first, find and write the formula, then substitute the number values for the variables, and last, solve the problem.

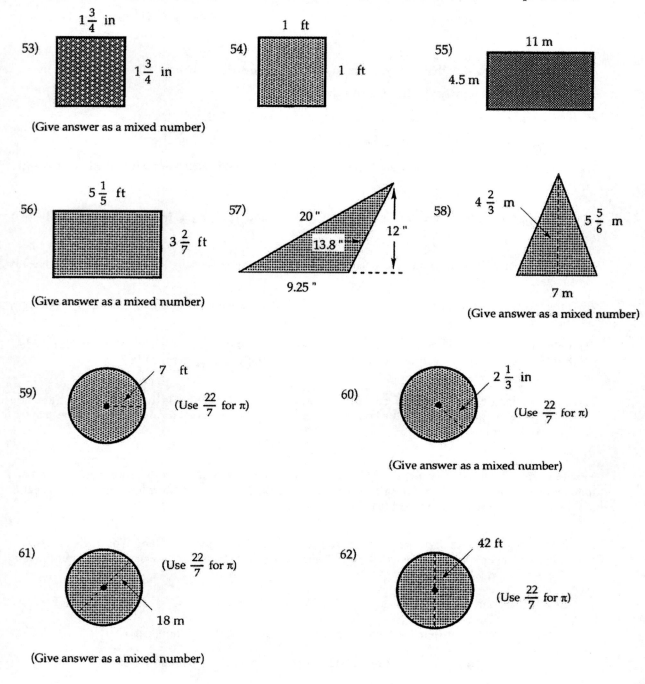

53) $1\frac{3}{4}$ in

(Give answer as a mixed number)

54) 1 ft

55) 11 m, 4.5 m

56) $5\frac{1}{5}$ ft, $3\frac{2}{7}$ ft

(Give answer as a mixed number)

57) 20 ", 13.8 ", 12 ", 9.25 "

58) $4\frac{2}{3}$ m, $5\frac{5}{6}$ m, 7 m

(Give answer as a mixed number)

59) 7 ft (Use $\frac{22}{7}$ for π)

60) $2\frac{1}{3}$ in (Use $\frac{22}{7}$ for π)

(Give answer as a mixed number)

61) (Use $\frac{22}{7}$ for π), 18 m

(Give answer as a mixed number)

62) 42 ft (Use $\frac{22}{7}$ for π)

In exercises #63-72: (a) write a mathematical expression using the given numbers that will solve the problem, and (b) give the solution. Draw figures and label them if it helps you visualize the shape.

63) A triangle has a perimeter of 22 inches. One side is 8 inches and a second side is 5 inches. What is the length of the third side?

64) A triangle has one side that is $7\frac{1}{2}$ inches and a second side of 5.25 inches. If the perimeter of the triangle is 20 inches, what is the length of the third side?

65) If the perimeter of a square is 20 meters, what is the length of each side?

●66) If the perimeter of a square is 4.8 miles, what is the length of each side?

67) If two opposite sides of a rectangle add up to 30 feet, what is the length of each of the two opposite sides?

68) If two opposite sides of a rectangle add up to $14\frac{3}{4}$ centimeters, what is the length of each of the two opposite sides?

69) If the diameter has a distance of x, what expression would represent the radius (the set up is the only answer).

70) If the radius has a distance of x, what expression would represent the diameter (the set up is the only answer).

71) If a right triangle has a height of six feet and a base of eight feet, what is the length of the third side (hint: the set up is substituting the known values into the Pythagorean formula)?

72) If a right triangle has a height of 4.5 yards and a base of 7.2 yards, what is the length of the third side (hint: the set up is substituting the known values into the Pythagorean formula)? Round the answer to the nearest tenths place.

In exercises #73-93, you will first need to solve for any perimeter or area that will be needed as a part of a setup to answer a question. Then: (a) write a mathematical expression using numbers that will solve the problem for many of these setups, and (b) give the solution.

73-75) A rectangular piece of property was surrounded by a picket fence. The length of the property was eighty feet and the width was 110 feet. The front length of the fence was painted red and the rest was painted white.

73) What fraction of the fence was painted red?

74) What percent of the fence was painted red (round to the nearest whole percent)?

75) What is the ratio of the feet of fence painted red to feet of fence painted white?

76-78) A farmer grew corn on a rectangular piece of land that was 30 yards long and 20 yards wide. She also grew broccoli on a triangular piece of land which had a base of 10 yards and a height of 8 yards.

76) What fraction of these two pieces of land were used to grow broccoli?

77) What percent of these two pieces of land were used to grow broccoli?

78) What is the ratio of the area of land used to grow broccoli to the area used to grow corn?

79-81) A circular swimming pool has a diameter of 28 feet. The space inside the outer edge of the pool (occupying about 154 square feet of space) had a depth of 3 feet. The rest of the pool was 8 feet in depth.

79) What fraction of the pool's area had a depth of 3 feet (Use $\frac{22}{7}$ for π)?

80) What percent of the pool's area had a depth of 3 feet (Use $\frac{22}{7}$ for π)?

81) What is the ratio of the pool's area that has a depth of 3 feet to the area that has a depth of 8 feet?

82-84) For his art class, Ryan visited a museum exhibition titled "Geometry in Modern Paintings." One painting consisted of only triangles. One long, thin triangle at the top of the painting represented a cloud. The top or the base of the triangle was 20 centimeters across and painted in luminescent silver. The two downward leaning sides, each 12 centimeters long, were dark purple lines.

82) What fraction of the cloud was lined in silver?

83) What percent of the cloud was lined in silver?

84) What is the ratio of the centimeters of cloud lined in silver to centimeters lined in purple?

85) In another part of this painting one small bright red triangle had a base of 4 centimeters and a height of 8 centimeters. The triangle was cracked like a broken window and divided into 9 equal-sized, smaller triangles. What is the area of one of these smaller triangles (give answer as a mixed number)?

86) Marisa decided to fence in a triangular piece of her property to stop deer from eating her plants. Two sides were 10 yards each and the third side was 12 yards. If she would need a fence post every 2 yards, how many posts would she need to buy?

87) A square piece of property measuring 60 feet to a side needs to be sodded. Sod is sold in strips (rolls) that are 3 feet by 6 feet. How many rolls of sod does a homeowner need delivered so he can cover his property (Remember to add 10% more strips to make up for the mistakes he might make)?

88) Children created a large quilt titled "People Important To Us" for a school project. When finished, the quilt was forty feet in length and twelve feet in width. Each section of the quilt (1.25 feet in length and 0.75 feet in width) held a picture of a person. How many people were represented on the quilt?

89-90) A circular green on a golf course had a radius of 16 feet (192 inches). There were 300 blades of grass per square inch of the green. $\frac{1}{5}$ of the green's edge was lined with sand bunkers.

89) How many feet of the green's perimeter are lined with sand bunkers (Use 3.14 for π and round the answer to the nearest whole foot)?

90) How many blades of grass make up the green (Use 3.14 for π)?

91) In a compromise worked out between government officials, environmentalists, and builders, a land management plan was created for a slice of land 8 miles by 30 miles in the Sierra foothills. 200 square miles of the land was to remain a wilderness area with no construction. On the rest of the land developers could build 1 house on every half acre. How many homes could the developers build (1 square mile = 640 acres)?

92-93) A developer bought a piece of land 2000 by 1000 feet. $\frac{3}{8}$ of the land needed to be reserved for roads and a park area.

92) How many square feet of land could be developed?

93) The land which could be developed was zoned to allow for a maximum of 5 homes per acre. What is the most homes the developer could build here (1 acre = 43,560 sq. ft)? Round the answer to the nearest whole house.

Skills Check

1. What is the value of 10^{-4}?

2. Write 6,257,000 in scientific notation.

3. Write the values in order from the largest to the smallest: 0.1, 10^0, $\frac{1}{1000}$, and $\frac{10}{1^{10}}$

4. Solve for all the values of x in both parts (a) and (b).

   (a) $(x)^2 = 64$ (b) $x = \sqrt{64}$

Answers to Skills Check: 1) 0.0001; 2) 6.257 × 10^6; 3) $\frac{10}{1^{10}}$, 10^0, 0.1, $\frac{1}{1000}$; 4) (a) x = 8 and − 8; (b) x = 8

Section 5.2 Finding the Perimeters of Irregular Shapes

Objectives:

- To recognize relationships between different shapes and parts within a shape
- To create formulas to find specific distances
- To solve for the perimeters of irregular shapes

Application:

A contractor was asked by an exclusive resort to give a price estimate on the cost of rimming the resort's pool with marble. Knowing the cost of the material and the time it would take to install it, the contractor figured that he would charge $125 per foot of the pool's rim. The resort sent the contractor a blueprint (pictured below) of the uniquely shaped pool. What was the contractor's estimated cost for the job (use $\frac{22}{7}$ for)?

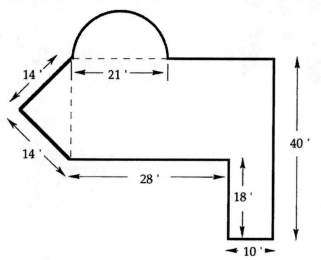

Vocabulary:

> trapezoid—A **trapezoid** is a four-sided shape in which only one pair of opposite sides are parallel.
>
> Examples of trapezoids:

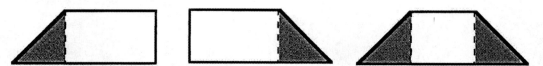

> If we look at each of these examples take note of 2 important facts: (1) only one pair of sides is parallel, and (2) a trapezoid consists of 1 rectangle <u>and</u> 1 or 2 triangles.

parallelogram—A **parallelogram** is a four-sided shape in which opposite sides are both parallel <u>and</u> of equal length.

Examples of parallelograms:

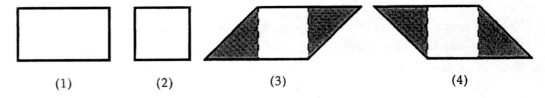

(1)   (2)   (3)   (4)

By definition, both rectangles and squares (examples #1 and #2) ar e specific types of parallelograms. By convention, however, we tend to use the term of parallelogram for the slanted shapes of #3 and #4 above (pictur e a rectangle after an elephant has sat upon it).

Looking at a "slanted" parallelogram, we can see that it consists of a rectangle <u>and</u> 2 triangles. Look at the progression below to see how we can manipulate a parallelogram to create a rectangle.

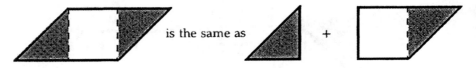

is the same as   +

By moving this triangular piece of the parallelogram on the left to the opposite end of the figure, we create a rectangle.

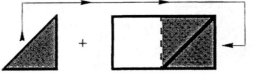

+

Half circle or a **semicircle**—A **half circle** or a **semicircle** is exactly that! It is half the way around the circumference of the circle.

We talk about two different types of half circles—an <u>**open**</u> **half circle** and a <u>**closed**</u> **half circle**.

Let's look at the following differences:

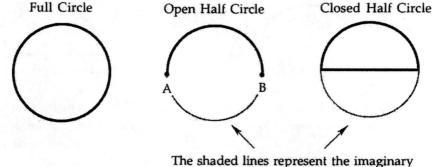

Full Circle   Open Half Circle   Closed Half Circle

The shaded lines represent the imaginary
completions of the full circles

An **open half circle** is a distance, not a true perimeter. It is exactly $\frac{1}{2}$ of the circumference (the distance from Pt. A to Pt. B following the arc of the circle).

A **closed half circle** is a true perimeter because it is the distance around an enclosed shape. It is exactly the same as an open half circle, except it **also has the diameter that closes the open half circle.**

Let's make sure that we understand the relationships among a full circle, an open half circle, and a closed half circle.

If a full circle has a circumference of 22 feet, we would obtain the distance of an open half circle by taking $\frac{1}{2}$ "of" this 22. Mathematically, this would be $\frac{1}{2} \bullet \frac{22}{1}$ or **11 feet.**

As for the distance around the closed half circle, it would have to be exactly the same as the open half circle (11 feet) **plus the diameter.** If we are told that the diameter is 7 feet, we would get the distance of the closed half circle by adding the diameter of 7 to the distance of the half circle (11 feet). Mathematically, we solve 11 + 7 to get **18 feet.**

Let's look at these differences in the formulas below. If the diameter for each given shape is 7 feet, what are their respective distances?

To find the circumference of a full circle, we already know to use the regular circumference formula.

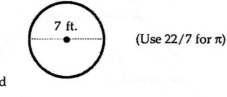

7 ft.   (Use 22/7 for π)

Write the formula: $C = \pi \bullet d$

Substitute: $C = \frac{22}{7} \bullet \frac{7}{1}$

Solve: $C = \textbf{22 feet}$

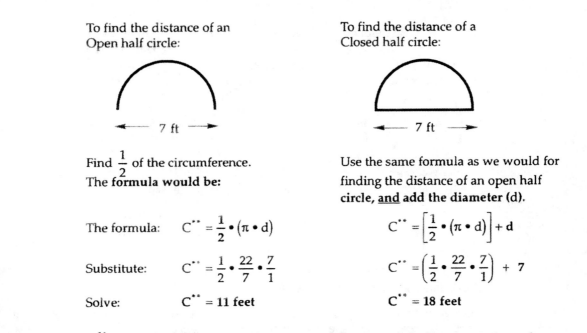

To find the distance of an
Open half circle:

To find the distance of a
Closed half circle:

7 ft

7 ft

Find $\frac{1}{2}$ of the circumference.
The **formula would be:**

Use the same formula as we would for
finding the distance of an open half
circle, **and add the diameter (d).**

The formula: $C^{**} = \frac{1}{2} \cdot (\pi \cdot d)$

$C^{**} = \left[\frac{1}{2} \cdot (\pi \cdot d)\right] + d$

Substitute: $C^{**} = \frac{1}{2} \cdot \frac{22}{7} \cdot \frac{7}{1}$

$C^{**} = \left(\frac{1}{2} \cdot \frac{22}{7} \cdot \frac{7}{1}\right) + 7$

Solve: $C^{**} = 11$ feet

$C^{**} = 18$ feet

C^{**} – The asterisks are placed here to note that we aren't finding a true circumference
(distance around a full circle) in these problems.

How to:

Solve for the Perimeter of an Irregular Shape:

1. Identify the shape and/or parts of the perimeter (draw a picture and trace the outside if
   necessary).

2. Find/Create the formula (using any given variables).

3. Substitute the number value(s) for the variable(s).

4. Solve and give the answer in linear units.

Example #1: Find the perimeter of the shape below. We know that $s_2 = s_4$.

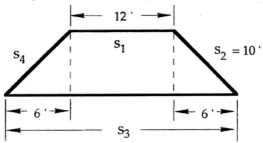

Step #1: Identify the shape and/or parts of the perimeter.

The shape is a trapezoid (consisting of 1 rectangle and 2 triangles).

Step #2: Find/Create the formula (using any given variables).

The perimeter is the 4 labeled sides added together.

$P = s_1 + s_2 + s_3 + s_4$

Step #3: Substitute the number value(s) for the variable(s).

We are given that $s_1 = 12$ and that $s_2 = 10$. If s_2 and s_4 are equal to each other, that means that s_4 must also equal 10.

Now we only have to calculate the length of s_3. This last side of the trapezoid consists of three parts (the bases of the two triangles <u>and</u> a side of the rectangle). The base of each triangle is given as 6 feet long. The rest of the trapezoid's base must be 12 feet because its opposite side (the opposite side of the rectangle) is given as 12 feet. $s_3 = (6 + 12 + 6)$

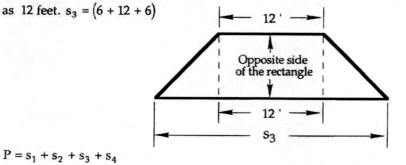

$P = s_1 + s_2 + s_3 + s_4$

$P = 12 + 10 + (6 + 12 + 6) + 10$

Step #4: Solve and give the answer in linear units.

$P = 12 + 10 + (24) + 10$

$P = 56$

Answer: 56 feet

Example #2: Find the perimeter (We are really measuring a distance, not a perimeter here because the object is not enclosed) of the shape below (use $\frac{22}{7}$ for π).

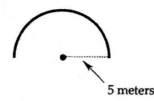

5 meters

Step #1: Identify the shape and/or parts of the perimeter.

In this case the distance we are looking for is half the circumference.

Step #2: Find/Create the formula (using any given variables).

We know the formula for the circumference $\left(C = \pi \cdot d\right)$. To find half of this we can either multiply by $\frac{1}{2}$ or divide by 2

$$C = \frac{1}{2} \cdot \left(\pi \cdot d\right) \ \text{ or } \ \frac{\left(\pi \cdot d\right)}{2}$$

Let's use the formula of $C = \frac{1}{2} \cdot \left(\pi \cdot d\right)$.

Step #3: Substitute the number value(s) for the variable(s).

We are told to use $\frac{22}{7}$ for π. We are given that the radius equals 5 meters. The diameter is double the radius, so the diameter must equal 10 meters.

$$C = \frac{1}{2} \cdot \left(\pi \cdot d\right)$$

$$C = \frac{1}{2} \cdot \left(\frac{22}{7} \cdot \frac{10}{1}\right)$$

Step #4: Solve and give the answer in linear units.

$$C = \frac{110}{7}$$

$$C = 15\frac{5}{7}$$

Answer: $15\frac{5}{7}$ **meters**

Example #3: Find the perimeter of the shape below. The diameter equals $4\frac{1}{2}$ inches (use $\frac{22}{7}$ for π).

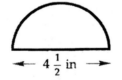

$$\longleftarrow \ 4\frac{1}{2} \ \text{in} \ \longrightarrow$$

Step #1: Identify the shape and/or parts of the perimeter.

In this case the distance we are looking for is a closed half circle—half the circumference (an open half circle) plus the diameter that closes the half circle.

Step #2: Find/Create the formula (using any given variables).

Visually we can picture this perimeter as:

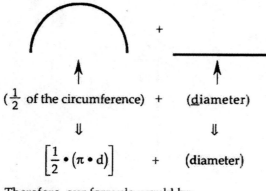

$(\frac{1}{2}$ of the circumference) + (diameter)

$\Downarrow$ $\Downarrow$

$\left[\frac{1}{2} \bullet (\pi \bullet d) \right]$ +   (diameter)

Therefore, our formula would be:

$$P = \left[\frac{1}{2} \bullet (\pi \bullet d) \right] + d$$

Step #3: Substitute the number value(s) for the variable(s).

We are told to use $\frac{22}{7}$ for π. We are given that the diameter equals $4\frac{1}{2}$ inches.

$$P = \left[\frac{1}{2} \bullet (\pi \bullet d) \right] + d$$

$$P = \left[\frac{1}{2} \bullet \left(\frac{22}{7} \bullet 4\frac{1}{2} \right) \right] + 4\frac{1}{2}$$

Step #4: Solve and give the answer in linear units.

$$P = \left[\frac{1}{2} \bullet \left(\frac{22}{7} \bullet \frac{9}{2} \right) \right] + 4\frac{1}{2}$$

$$P = \left[\frac{99}{14} \right] + 4\frac{1}{2}$$

$$P = \left[7\frac{1}{14} \right] + 4\frac{1}{2}$$

$$P = \left[7\frac{1}{14} \right] + 4\frac{7}{14}$$

$$P = 11\frac{8}{14} = 11\frac{4}{7}$$

Answer: $11\frac{4}{7}$ inches

Example #4: Find the perimeter of the shape below. All measurements are given in centimeters.

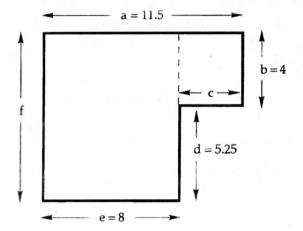

Step #1: Identify the shape and/or parts of the perimeter.

The perimeter is the distance around the outside of this 6-sided figure. One way to visualize this shape is as two rectangles—created here by the dotted line inside the shape.

Step #2: Find/Create the formula (using any given variables).

The perimeter is the 6 labeled sides added together.

P = a + b + c + d + e + f

Step #3: Substitute the number value(s) for the variable(s).

We are given the following information: Side $\underline{a}$ = 11.5 centimeters; side $\underline{b}$ = 4 centimeters; side $\underline{d}$ = 5.25 centimeters; and side $\underline{e}$ = 8 centimeters.

Let's substitute these known values into our formula.

P = a + b + c + d + e + f

P = 11.5 + 4 + c + 5.25 + 8 + f

To solve for the perimeter we still need to calculate the lengths of sides $\underline{c}$ and $\underline{f}$.

Calculating the length of side $\underline{c}$:

Picture this perimeter as a fence around a piece property. We could pick up and move the side $\underline{c}$ of fencing, so it is next to side $\underline{e}$, right? See the diagram below which moves the side $\underline{c}$ downward.

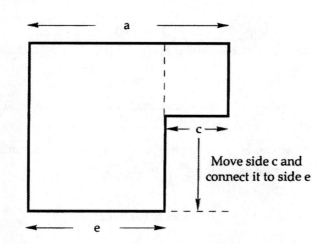

We can see from the picture above that: (side a) = (side e + side c). We are assuming here that the sides e and c together form a side of a rectangle that is opposite side a.

We can now calculate for side c: (side c) = (side a − side e)

We can write this as: $c = (a - e)$

Substitute: $c = (11.5 - 8)$

Side c = 3.5 centimeters

Now, we still need to calculate for the length of side f. This time let's pick up and move the side d of fencing, so it is next to side b. See the diagram below which moves the side d to the right.

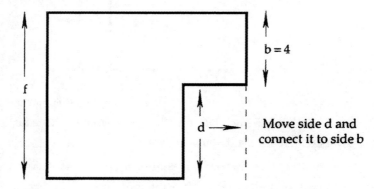

We can see from the picture above that: (side f) = (side b + side d). Again we are making an assumption that the sides b and d together form a side of a rectangle that is opposite side f.

We can now calculate for side f: (side f) = (side b + side d)

We can write this as: $f = (b + d)$

Substitute: $f = (4 + 5.25)$

Side f = 9.25 centimeters

Now we can make the full substitution into the formula.

$P = 11.5 + 4 + 3.5 + 5.25 + 8 + 9.25$

Step #4: Solve and give answer in linear units.

$P = 41.5$

Answer: 41.5 centimeters

*** A HELPFUL SHORT CUT!! We could have "moved fences" first and created a single big rectangle. Look at the diagram below.

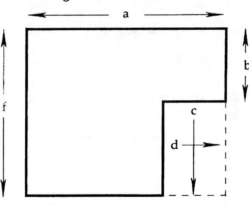

We can now find the perimeter of this rectangle by using the common formula of: $P = 2(l) + 2(w)$. Remember it is okay to do what we have just done because **we are still measuring the same distance** of fence.

The length of this big rectangle is the same as side a: 11.5 cm.

The width of this big rectangle is the same as side f: 9.25 cm.

The formula: $P = 2(l) + 2(w)$

Substitute: $P = 2(11.5) + 2(9.25)$

Solve: $P = 23 + 18.5$

Answer: **41.5 centimeters**

Sample #1: A circular piece of pie was cut into four equal pieces. If the radius of the pie was 6 inches, what was the perimeter of one of the pieces of pie when it was served (use $\frac{22}{7}$ for π)? Draw a picture of what we have.

Whole Pie   One Piece of the Pie

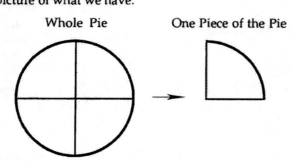

Looking at the single piece of pie, we can visualize the perimeter as consisting of three parts—an arc that is $\frac{1}{4}$ of the circumference and two radii (radii is the plural of radius).

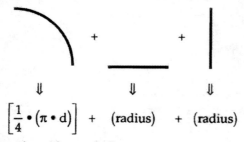

$$\left[\frac{1}{4} \bullet (\pi \bullet d)\right] \quad + \quad (\text{radius}) \quad + \quad (\text{radius})$$

Therefore, our formula would be:

$$P = \left[\frac{1}{4} \bullet (\pi \bullet d)\right] + r + r \quad \underline{\text{or}} \quad P = \left[\frac{1}{4} \bullet (\pi \bullet d)\right] + 2r$$

Let's use the second formula. Before we substitute, identify again the fact that the radius = 6 inches; therefore the diameter = 12 inches.

The formula: $\quad P = \left[\frac{1}{4} \bullet (\pi \bullet d)\right] + 2r$

Substitution: $\quad P = \left[\frac{1}{4} \bullet \left(\frac{22}{7} \bullet \frac{12}{1}\right)\right] + 2(6)$

Solve: $\quad P = \left[\frac{66}{7}\right] + 12$

$\quad P = \left[9\frac{3}{7}\right] + 12$

$\quad P = 21\frac{3}{7}$

Answer: $\quad 21\frac{3}{7}$ inches

You try it now:

a) A circular garden was divided into three equal segments (shown in the picture below). If the
diameter of the garden was $7\frac{1}{2}$ yards, what was the perimeter of the part of the garden where
roses were grown (use $\frac{22}{7}$ for π)?

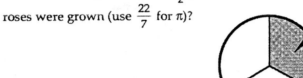

b) If the parallelogram below was to lose the shaded area, what would be the perimeter of the
newly created shape (we will need to use the Pythagorean Theorem before we can answer this
question)?

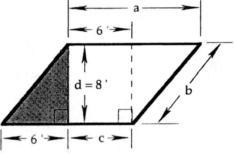

Sample #2: At a local elementary school, community volunteers created a miniature basketball court
for first and second graders. The basketball "key" (shown below) was outlined in bright
yellow paint. What was the perimeter of this shape (use $\frac{22}{7}$ for)?

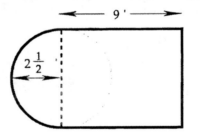

We can define this irregular shape as a half circle plus a rectangle. Before we create a
formula, however, let's be careful and remind ourselves that <u>the only distances</u> of the half
circle and the rectangle <u>that we are concerned with are the distances that make up the
outside of the given shape</u> (We are <u>not concerned</u> with the parts of these two shapes that
are not a part of the actual outside of this irregular shape).

Visually, we are solving for the following:

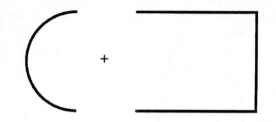

In fact, we are solving for the distance of an open half circle (not closed!) plus three sides (2 lengths and 1 width) of the rectangle (not four sides!).

Concept: (an open half circle)   +   (2 lengths + 1 width)

                             ⇓   ⇓

Formula Set up: $P = \left[\dfrac{1}{2} \bullet (\pi \bullet d)\right]$ + $[2(l) + w]$

Find the Values of the variables:

We have to substitute for 3 unknown variables here—the <u>d</u>iameter, the <u>l</u>ength of the rectangle and the <u>w</u>idth of the rectangle.

We are given the radius of $2\frac{1}{2}$ ft; therefore, the <u>d</u>iameter is 5 ft.

The <u>l</u>ength of the rectangle is given as 9 ft.

The <u>w</u>idth of the rectangle is not provided. However, we did figure out that the diameter of the circle is 5 ft—and, in fact, by looking at the picture again we can see that the diameter is one of the widths of the rectangle. The <u>w</u>idth of the rectangle is 5 ft.

Substitute: $P = \left[\dfrac{1}{2} \bullet \left(\dfrac{22}{7} \bullet \dfrac{5}{1}\right)\right] + [2(9) + 5]$

Solve: $P = \left[\dfrac{55}{7}\right] + [23]$

                $P = \left[7\,\dfrac{6}{7}\right] + [23]$

                $P = 30\,\dfrac{6}{7}$

Answer: $30\,\dfrac{6}{7}$ ft.

You try it now:

c) Find the perimeter of the race track (use $\frac{22}{7}$ for π).

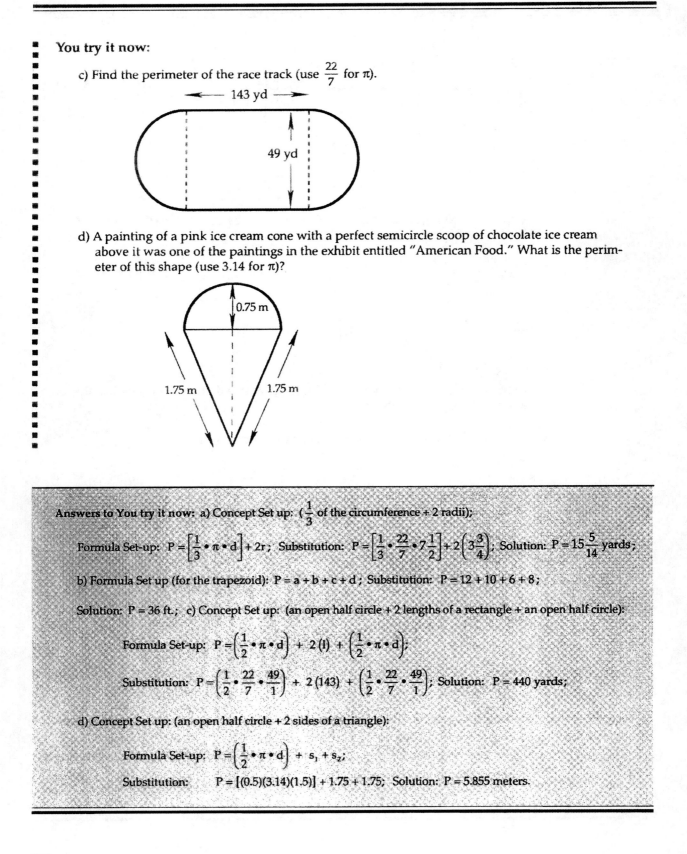

d) A painting of a pink ice cream cone with a perfect semicircle scoop of chocolate ice cream above it was one of the paintings in the exhibit entitled "American Food." What is the perimeter of this shape (use 3.14 for π)?

Answers to You try it now: a) Concept Set up: ($\frac{1}{3}$ of the circumference + 2 radii);

Formula Set-up: $P = \left[\frac{1}{3} \bullet \pi \bullet d\right] + 2r$; Substitution: $P = \left[\frac{1}{3} \bullet \frac{22}{7} \bullet 7\frac{1}{2}\right] + 2\left(3\frac{3}{4}\right)$; Solution: $P = 15\frac{5}{14}$ yards;

b) Formula Set up (for the trapezoid): $P = a + b + c + d$; Substitution: $P = 12 + 10 + 6 + 8$;

Solution: $P = 36$ ft.; c) Concept Set up: (an open half circle + 2 lengths of a rectangle + an open half circle):

Formula Set-up: $P = \left(\frac{1}{2} \bullet \pi \bullet d\right) + 2\,(l) + \left(\frac{1}{2} \bullet \pi \bullet d\right)$;

Substitution: $P = \left(\frac{1}{2} \bullet \frac{22}{7} \bullet \frac{49}{1}\right) + 2\,(143) + \left(\frac{1}{2} \bullet \frac{22}{7} \bullet \frac{49}{1}\right)$; Solution: $P = 440$ yards;

d) Concept Set up: (an open half circle + 2 sides of a triangle):

Formula Set-up: $P = \left(\frac{1}{2} \bullet \pi \bullet d\right) + s_1 + s_2$;

Substitution: $P = [(0.5)(3.14)(1.5)] + 1.75 + 1.75$; Solution: $P = 5.855$ meters.

Answer to Application: To know how much the contractor would charge we must first know the perimeter of the pool. Walking a finger around the outside of this shape, we can see that the perimeter consists of the following:

(2 sides of a triangle) +   (an open half circle)   +   (5 pieces of rest of the irregular pool)

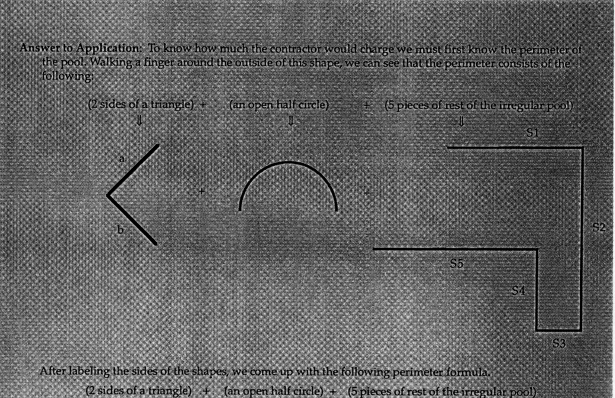

After labeling the sides of the shapes, we come up with the following perimeter formula.

(2 sides of a triangle)   +   (an open half circle) +   (5 pieces of rest of the irregular pool)

$$\Downarrow \qquad\qquad \Downarrow \qquad\qquad \Downarrow$$

Formula: $P = (\text{side a} + \text{side b}) + \left(\frac{1}{2} \cdot \pi \cdot d\right) + (s_1 + s_2 + s_3 + s_4 + s_5)$

Substitute the known values into the formula. We know that both side a and side b equal 14 feet. The diameter of the half circle is 21 feet. We are given that $s_2 = 40$ ft; $s_3 = 10$ ft; $s_4 = 18$ ft; and $s_5 = 28$ ft. We only have to solve for s_1. If we recognize that $s_1 + 21$ must be equal to $s_3 + s_5$ because they makeup opposite sides of a rectangle, we can solve for s_1. $s_3 + s_5$ are equal to 38 ft. Thus, s_1 must equal $38 - 21$. In fact, $s_1 = 17$ ft.

Substitution: $P = (14 + 14) + \left(\frac{1}{2} \cdot \frac{22}{7} \cdot \frac{21}{1}\right) + (17 + 40 + 10 + 18 + 28)$

Solve: $P = (28) + (33) + (113)$

$P = 174$ ft

Now we can find the price estimate for the job by multiplying by the $125 per foot.

Set up: 174 (125)

Solution: $21,750

<u>5.2 Perimeter Problems for Irregular Shapes</u>

In exercises #1-10, answer the following questions.

1) What is the word for the line that encloses an open half circle?

2) If an open half circle which is 22 feet in length has a radius of 7 feet, what would the perimeter of this half circle be if it were enclosed?

3) If an open half circle which is $16\frac{1}{2}$ meters in length has a radius of $5\frac{1}{4}$ meters, what would the perimeter of this half circle be if it were enclosed?

4) If a closed half circle with a radius of $3\frac{1}{2}$ inches has a perimeter of 18 inches, what would the distance of this half circle be if it were open?

5) If a closed half circle with a radius of 14 inches has a perimeter of 72 inches, what would the distance of this half circle be if it were open?

6) If opposite sides of a parallelogram equal 18 feet together, what is the length of one of these sides of the parallelogram?

7) If opposite sides of a parallelogram equal 11.25 feet together, what is the length of one of these sides of the parallelogram?

8) Could the answer to a perimeter problem be 200 sq. inches? Answer yes or no and explain why or why not?

9) A trapezoid has a perimeter of 94 centimeters. One of its sides has a length of 28 centimeters. If the other three sides of the trapezoid have the same length, what is the length of one of the other sides?

10) A trapezoid has a perimeter of 37.5 centimeters. One of its sides has a length of 14.2 centimeters. If the other three sides of the trapezoid have the same length, what is the length of one of the other sides?

In exercises #11-21, use the picture below to either select the variable that identifies the object in question, or write an expression using <u>only</u> the given variables that represents each item below. Use π if necessary.

11) The radius

12) The diameter

13) The height of the triangle (if <u>e</u> is the base)

14) The length of side <u>a</u>

15) The length of side <u>d</u>

16) The length of side <u>e</u>

17) The perimeter of the rectangle

18) The perimeter of the triangle

19) The distance of the open half circle.

20) The distance of the closed half circle.   21) The distance around the outside of this irregular object.

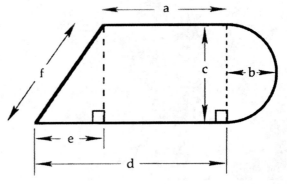

In exercises #22-29, use the picture below to either select the side that identifies the object in question, or write an expression using <u>only</u> the given sides that represents each item below.

22) Side 5 + Side 3

23) Side 2 + Side 4

24) Side 6 - Side 4

25) Side 1 - Side 5

26) Side 1

27) Side 6

28) Side 3

29) Side 4

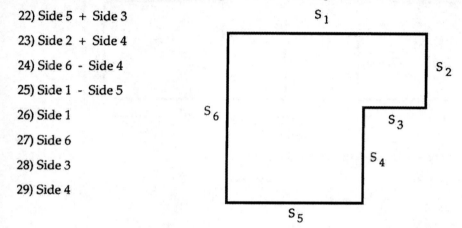

In exercises #30-32, choose the formula from the list below that corresponds to the perimeter of each of the following shapes.

$$P = \frac{\pi \cdot d}{2} + d \qquad P = \frac{\pi \cdot r^2}{2} \qquad P = \frac{\pi \cdot d}{2} \qquad P = \pi \cdot d \qquad P = \pi \cdot r^2 + d$$

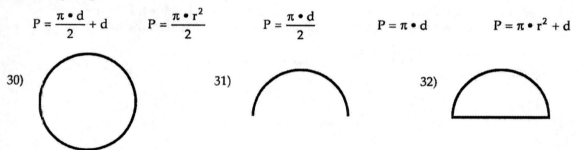

30)   31)   32)

In exercises #33-38, answer yes or no as to whether the given formula would solve for the perimeter of the figure below (in the formulas below, d = diameter and r = radius).

33) $P = \left(\frac{\pi \cdot d}{2} + d \right) + 2(a) + 2(b)$

34) $P = \left(\frac{\pi \cdot d}{2} + d \right) + (a + b + c)$

35) $P = \left(\frac{\pi \cdot d}{2} \right) + (a + b + c)$

36) $P = \left(\frac{\pi \cdot d}{2} \right) + 2a + b$

37) $P = (\pi \cdot r) + 2c + b$

38) $P = (\pi \cdot r) + 3(a)$

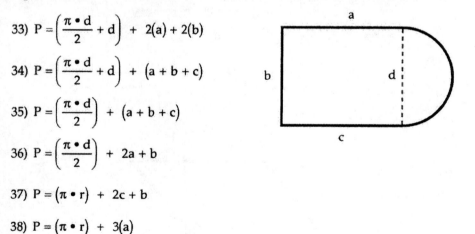

39) State yes or no as to whether the given pair of shapes have the same perimeter.

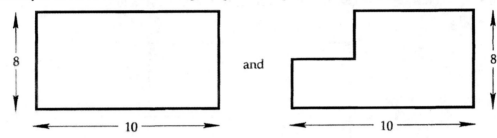

40) State yes or no as to whether the given lines have the same distance.

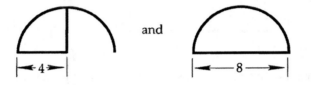

In exercises #41-60: (a) write a formula using the given variables that will solve for the perimeter (or distance) of the given shape, (b) show the substitution (no solving yet!), and (c) the solution.

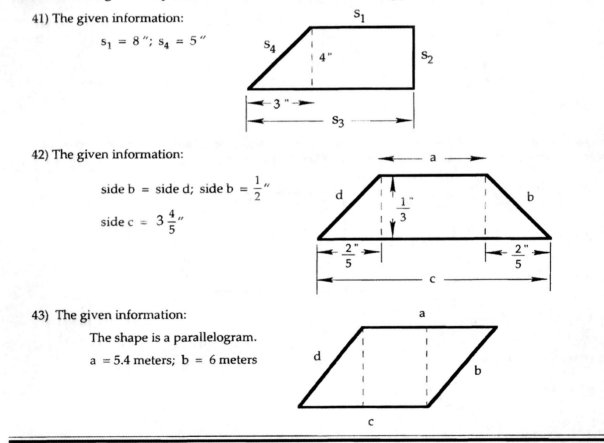

41) The given information:

$s_1 = 8\ ''$; $s_4 = 5\ ''$

42) The given information:

side b = side d; side b = $\frac{1}{2}''$

side c = $3\frac{4}{5}''$

43) The given information:

The shape is a parallelogram.

a = 5.4 meters; b = 6 meters

44) The given information:
The shape is a parallelogram.

$s_1 = 4\frac{1}{3}$ yards; $s_2 = 2$ yards

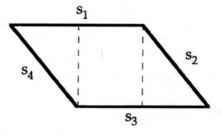

45) The given information:

$d = 7$ miles; use $\frac{22}{7}$ for π

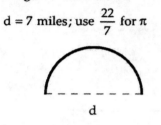

46) The given information:

$d = 4.5$ feet; use 3.14 for π

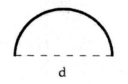

47) The given information:

$r = 1\frac{3}{4}$ feet; use $\frac{22}{7}$ for π

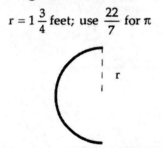

48) The given information:

$r = 9$ feet; use $\frac{22}{7}$ for π

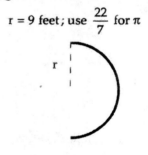

49) The given information:

$d = 14$ centimeters; use $\frac{22}{7}$ for π

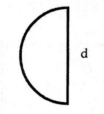

50) The given information:

$d = 10\frac{1}{2}$ inches; use $\frac{22}{7}$ for π

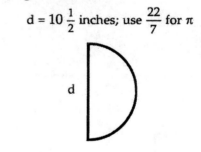

51) The given information:

$r = 4\frac{2}{3}$ inches; use $\frac{22}{7}$ for π

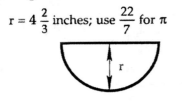

52) The given information:

$r = 5$ centimeters; use 3.14 for π

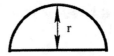

53) The given information:

$l = 10$ feet; $w = 14$ feet; use $\frac{22}{7}$ for π

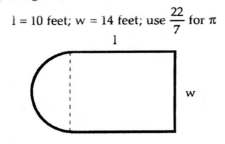

54) The given information:

$b = 3$ feet; $r = 1\frac{1}{4}$ feet; use $\frac{22}{7}$ for π

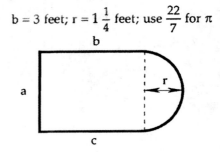

55) The given information:

$a = 6.25$ feet; $r = 3.8$ feet; use 3.14 for π

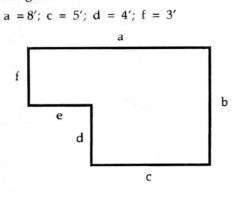

(round answer to nearest whole)

56) The given information:

$a = 6\frac{3}{4}$ inches; $d = 2\frac{3}{4}$ inches; use $\frac{22}{7}$ for π

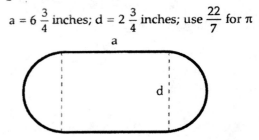

57) The given information:

$a = 8'$; $c = 5'$; $d = 4'$; $f = 3'$

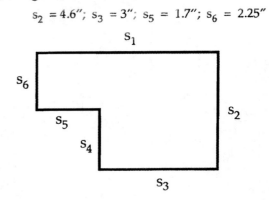

58) The given information:

$s_2 = 4.6''$; $s_3 = 3''$; $s_5 = 1.7''$; $s_6 = 2.25''$

59) The given information:

$s_1 = 6"$; $s_2 = 1\frac{2}{5}"$; $s_4 = 2\frac{2}{3}"$; $s_5 = 4\frac{1}{3}"$

60) The given information:

$b = 20'$; $c = 22'$; $e = 38'$; $f = 50'$

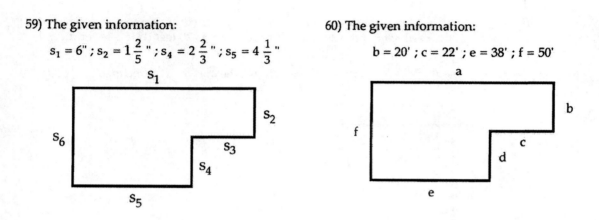

In exercises #61-67: (a) write a formula using variables that will solve for the perimeter of the given shape, (b) show the substitution (no solving yet!), and (c) give the solution.

61) If a cake was cut exactly in half vertically (where the dotted line is), what would the perimeter of the shaded piece be?

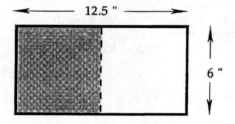

62) If a cake was cut exactly in half diagonally (where the dotted line is), what would the perimeter of the shaded piece be?

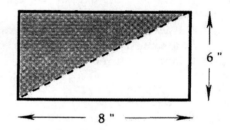

63) If a cake in the shape of a parallelogram was cut where the dotted line is, what would the perimeter of the shaded piece be?

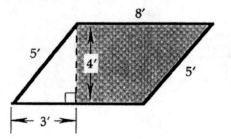

64) If a cake was cut exactly in half (where the dotted line is), what would the perimeter of the shaded piece be (use $\frac{22}{7}$ for π)?

65) A circular pizza was cut into 8 equal pieces. If the radius of the pizza was 8 inches, what was the perimeter of one of the pieces of pizza (use $\frac{22}{7}$ for π)?

66) In the newly built City Hall, a large window in the shape of a half circle lay above the doors entering the building. What was the perimeter of this window if its radius was 20 feet (Use 3.14 for π)?

67) Find the perimeter of the shape below. Use $\dfrac{22}{7}$ for π and give the answer as a decimal.

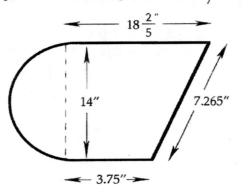

In exercises #68-71, solve the problems.

68) Both runners ("A" and "B") start the foot race at their designated points as illustrated in the diagram below. Runner A must run along the outside perimeter of the track while Runner B runs along the inside perimeter. If both runners end the race at the same finish line, would they both have run the same distance. Answer Yes or No. If the answer is "No," tell which runner went a farther distance and by how much.

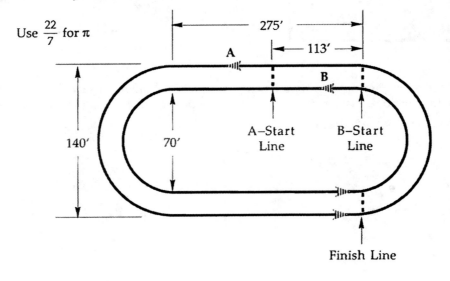

69) An apartment manager wants to install a new fence around his odd—shaped pool area. If it costs $9.50 per foot of eight-foot-high fencing, how much would it cost to put up a new fence?

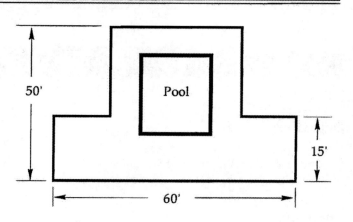

70) A hippie-to-yuppie-to-dot-com millionaire had a jeweler make a circular brooch (with a diameter of $3\frac{1}{2}$ centimeters) with a peace symbol for his daughter. The rim of the brooch as well as the peace symbol itself were formed by diamonds. If there were 8 diamonds per centimeter (and each diamond cost $1200), what was the value of the diamonds on the brooch?

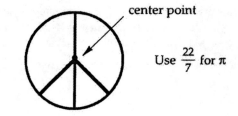

Use $\frac{22}{7}$ for π

71) An architect (seeing the window design for the City Hall in problem #66) decided upon an even larger glass area for a governmental building he was going to build (see the picture below). The shaded area is the glass while the clear area is the doors into the building. What is the perimeter of the glass area?

Use $\frac{22}{7}$ for π

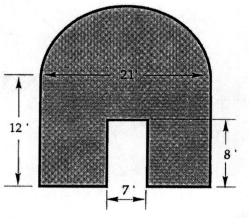

Skills Check

1. If the diameter is x, what expression represents the radius?

2. If the radius is x, what expression represents the diameter?

3. If a triangle has a height of 3.25 meters and a base of 7 meters, what is the area of the triangle?

4. A community garden is a rectangular piece of land, 80 feet by 400 feet. If it is divided into parcels of 10 feet by 20 feet, how many garden parcels are available for people to use?

Answers to Skills Check: 1) $\frac{x}{2}$; 2) 2 • x; 3) Area = 11.375 sq. meters; 4) 160 parcels.

Section 5.3 Finding the Areas of Irregular Shapes

Objectives:

- To recognize shapes within shapes
- To create formulas to find specific areas
- To solve for the area of irregular shapes

Application:

After State safety regulators inspected a public pool, the pool attendant was told that he needed to post the recommended safety maximum number of people allowed in this pool at one time (see the pool below). If the law says that the maximum capacity for a pool is one person for every 40 square feet, how many people could legally be in the pool at one time (use $\frac{22}{7}$ for π)? Round answer to the nearest whole person.

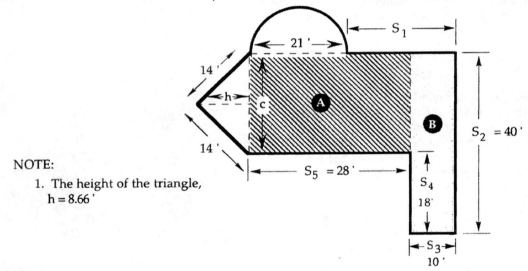

NOTE:
  1. The height of the triangle,
     $h = 8.66'$

Vocabulary:

> **More on Trapezoids and Parallelograms:** The **parallel sides** of trapezoids and parallelograms are called the **bases** of these shapes. The **height** of a trapezoid or a parallelogram is **found by drawing a perpendicular line from one base to its opposite base.**
>
> Look at the trapezoids and parallelograms below. The opposite parallel bases are labeled as b_1 and b_2; the heights are the dotted lines.

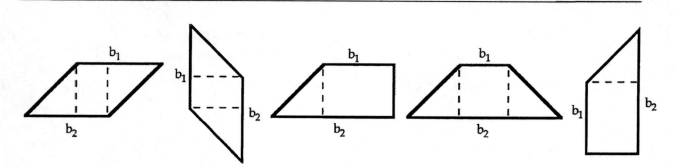

Finding the Area of a Half Circle: When finding the perimeter of a half circle, the distance was different whether the half circle was open or closed (by the diameter). When finding area, however, it doesn't matter if the half circle (or any other shape) is open or closed. Look at the examples below—the shaded region (the area) is the same!

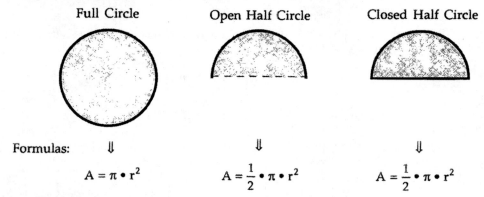

Full Circle   Open Half Circle   Closed Half Circle

Formulas: ⇓   ⇓   ⇓

$$A = \pi \cdot r^2 \qquad A = \frac{1}{2} \cdot \pi \cdot r^2 \qquad A = \frac{1}{2} \cdot \pi \cdot r^2$$

***Reminder: All area measurements are given in <u>square units</u>!!

How to:

Solve for the Area of an Irregular Shape:

1. Identify the shape and/or shapes within shapes of a given area (darken over certain areas if it helps us see shapes).

2. Find/Create the formula (using any given variables).

3. Substitute the number value(s) for the variable(s).

4. Solve and give the answer in square units.

Example #1: Find the area of the shape below.

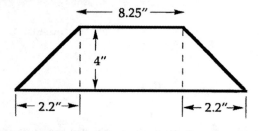

Step #1: Identify the shape and/or shapes within shapes of a given area.

The shape is 4-sided and has only 1 pair of parallel sides. It is a trapezoid.

Step #2: Find/Create the formula (using any given variables).

Formula: $A = \dfrac{1}{2} \bullet \left(b_1 + b_2\right) \bullet h$

Step #3: Substitute the number value(s) for the variable(s).

The bases $\left(b_1 + b_2\right)$ are the parallel sides.

b_1 is given as 8.25"

b_2 is found by adding the given lengths of the bottom parallel side.

$b_2 = \left(2.2 + 8.25 + 2.2\right)$ or 12.65"

The height is the distance of a perpendicular line between these 2 bases. The height is given as 4".

$$A = \dfrac{1}{2} \bullet \left(b_1 + b_2\right) \bullet h$$

Substitution: $A = \dfrac{1}{2} \bullet \left(8.25 + 12.65\right) \bullet 4$

Step #4: Solve and give answer in square units.

$$A = \dfrac{1}{2} \bullet \left(20.9\right) \bullet 4$$
$$A = 41.8$$

Answer: 41.8 sq. inches

Example #2: Find the area of the shape below (use $\dfrac{22}{7}$ for π).

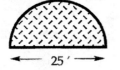

$\longleftarrow$ 25' $\longrightarrow$

Step #1: Identify the shape and/or shapes within shapes of a given area.

The shape is a half circle.

Step #2: Find/Create the formula (using any given variables).

The formula for a full circle is: $A = \pi \bullet r^2$. Now we must find " $\dfrac{1}{2}$ of this space."

Formula: $A = \dfrac{1}{2} \bullet \pi \bullet r^2$

Step #3: Substitute the number value(s) for the variable(s).

The diameter is given as 25 feet. Therefore the radius is $12\frac{1}{2}$ feet. We are told to use $\frac{22}{7}$ for π.

$$A = \frac{1}{2} \bullet \pi \bullet r^2$$

Substitution: $A = \frac{1}{2} \bullet \frac{22}{7} \bullet \left(12\frac{1}{2}\right)^2$

Step #4: Solve and give answer in square units.

$$A = \frac{1}{2} \bullet \frac{22}{7} \bullet \frac{25}{2} \bullet \frac{25}{2}$$

$$A = \frac{6875}{28}$$

$$A = 245\frac{15}{28}$$

Answer: $245\frac{15}{28}$ sq. feet

Example #3: Find the area of the shape below.

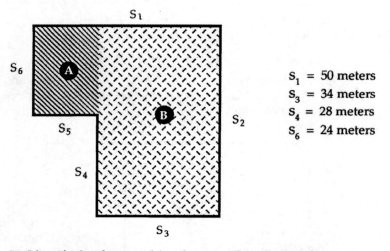

$S_1 = 50$ meters
$S_3 = 34$ meters
$S_4 = 28$ meters
$S_6 = 24$ meters

Step #1: Identify the shape and/or shapes within shapes of a given area.

The shape is an irregular figure that consists of 2 rectangles (labeled here as Rectangle $\underline{A}$ and Rectangle $\underline{B}$.

We will solve this area problem using two different methods:

First: **Finding the solution through <u>Addition</u>.**

Step #2: Find/Create the formula (using any given variables).

Formula Concept: (Area of Rectangle A) + (Area of Rectangle B)

Variable Formula: $A = (s_5 \cdot s_6) + (s_2 \cdot s_3)$

Step #3: Substitute the number value(s) for the variable(s).

s_6 is given as 24 meters

s_5 must be equal to $(s_1 - s_3)$ or (50 - 34). Thus, s_5 is 16 meters

s_3 is given as 34 meters

s_2 must be equal to $(s_4 + s_6)$ or (28 + 24). Thus, $s_2 = 52$ meters

$$A = (s_5 \cdot s_6) + (s_2 \cdot s_3)$$

Substitution: $A = (16 \cdot 24) + (52 \cdot 34)$

Step #4: Solve and give answer in square units.

$$A = (384) + (1768)$$

$$A = 2152$$

Answer: 2152 sq. meters

Now, let's **find the solution through <u>Subtraction</u>.**

Step #2: Find/Create the formula (using any given variables).

Instead of visualizing this irregular shape as the 2 rectangles <u>A</u> and <u>B</u>, we could picture the figure as one large rectangle by drawing imaginary extensions to sides 3 and 6 (see the dotted lines below).

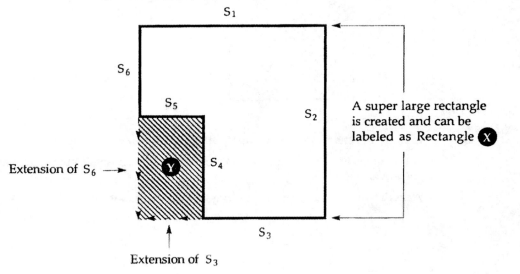

Now let's look at the labels of these newly created rectangles: (1) Rectangle $\underline{Y}$ (the shaded area above), and (2) Rectangle $\underline{X}$, the super-large rectangle that includes the original irregular shape $\underline{\text{and}}$ the Rectangle $\underline{Y}$.

Now we can find the area of the original irregular shape through subtraction.

Formula Concept: (Area of Rectangle X) - (Area of Rectangle Y)

Variable Formula: $A = (s_1 \bullet s_2) - (s_4 \bullet s_5)$

Step #3: Substitute the number value(s) for the variable(s).

s_1 is given as 50 meters

s_2 must be equal to $(s_4 + s_6)$ or $(28 + 24)$. Thus, $s_2 = 52$ meters

s_4 is given as 28 meters

s_5 must be equal to $(s_1 - s_3)$ or $(50 - 34)$. Thus, $s_5 = 16$ meters

$$A = (s_1 \bullet s_2) - (s_4 \bullet s_5)$$

Substitution: $A = (50 \bullet 52) - (28 \bullet 16)$

Step #4: Solve and give answer in square units.

$$A = (2600) - (448)$$

$$A = 2152$$

Answer: 2152 sq. meters

We can successfully use either the addition or subtraction method to solve for the area of this shape.

Sample #1: A stained glass window (pictured to the right), made 300 years ago, was valued at $28,350. What was the value per square foot?

First, we must discover the area of this irregular shape. We can see that the figure consists of a half circle and a rectangle.

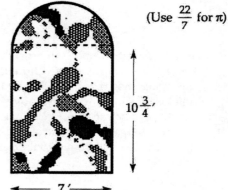

(Use $\frac{22}{7}$ for π)

$10\frac{3}{4}\,'$

$\longleftarrow 7' \longrightarrow$

Formula Concept: A = (Area of the half circle) + (Area of the rectangle)
                                              ⇓   ⇓

Variable Formula: $A = \left(\frac{1}{2} \bullet \pi \bullet r^2\right) + (l \bullet w)$

The diameter is 7 feet so the radius is $3\frac{1}{2}$ feet.

Substitution: $A = \left[\dfrac{1}{2} \cdot \dfrac{22}{7} \cdot \left(3\,\dfrac{1}{2}\right)^2 \right] + \left(10\,\dfrac{3}{4} \cdot 7\right)$

Solve: $A = \left[\dfrac{1}{2} \cdot \dfrac{22}{7} \cdot \dfrac{7}{2} \cdot \dfrac{7}{2} \right] + \left(\dfrac{43}{4} \cdot 7\right)$

                     $A = \left[\dfrac{77}{4} \right] + \left(\dfrac{301}{4}\right)$

                     $A = \dfrac{378}{4}$

The area of the window is 94.5 sq. feet

Set up to find the cost per sq. foot: $28,350 \div 94.5$

Answer: **$300 per sq. foot**

You try it now:

a) A high school put new sod on the area inside the track oval pictured below. If the cost of the sod was $30 per sq. yard, how much did it cost to sod the field (Use 3.14 for π)?

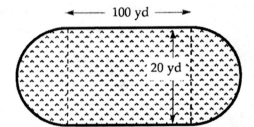

b) In a surrealist painting, an artist used geometric shapes to represent a vulture flying over a decaying civilization watching mindless television shows. If the artist averaged 12 strokes per square centimeter of canvas that she painted, how many strokes did it take to paint the vulture (round to the nearest whole)?

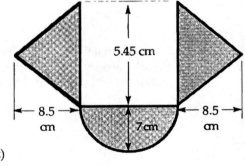

(Use $\dfrac{22}{7}$ for π)

Sample #2: On a piece of farmland, a farmer maintained an orchard (the shaded area of the figure below) of apple trees. He also kept a semicircular pond as a water resource (the unshaded region). If he grew 4 trees for every 25 square yards of his orchard, how many apples trees did the farmer have (round to the nearest whole)?

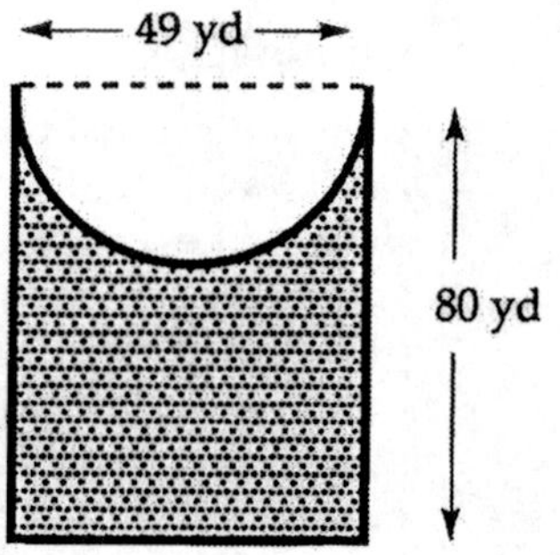

First, we need to know the area of his orchard. We can see that the property is a rectangle with a half circle cut out of it.

(Use $\frac{22}{7}$ for π)

Formula Concept: A = (Area of the rectangle) − (Area of the half circle)

$$\Downarrow \qquad\qquad \Downarrow$$

Variable Formula:
The diameter is 49 yards so the radius is $24\frac{1}{2}$ yards.

$$A = \left(l \bullet w\right) \quad - \quad \left(\frac{1}{2} \bullet \pi \bullet r^2\right)$$

Substitution:

$$A = \left(80 \bullet 49\right) \quad - \quad \left(\frac{1}{2} \bullet \frac{22}{7} \bullet \left(24\frac{1}{2}\right)^2\right)$$

Solve:

$$A = \left(3920\right) \quad - \quad \left(\frac{1}{2} \bullet \frac{22}{7} \bullet \frac{49}{2} \bullet \frac{49}{2}\right)$$

$$A = \left(3920\right) \quad - \quad \left(\frac{3773}{4}\right)$$

$$A = \left(3920\right) \quad - \quad \left(943.25\right)$$

$$A = 2976.75$$

The area of the orchard is 2976.75 square yards.

One way to find the answer now would be to recognize the ratio we were given (4 trees to every 25 square yards) and set up a proportion.

Set up to find the number of trees: $\dfrac{4\ \text{trees}}{25\ \text{sq. yards}} = \dfrac{x\ \text{trees}}{2976.75\ \text{sq. yards}}$

$$= 476.28 \text{ trees. Now round.}$$

Answer: 476 apple trees

■ **You try it now:**

c) At an amusement park, one can take a ride around the *Pirate Island*. The island is shaped like a parallelogram and is surrounded by a circular body of water (the shaded area below). For every 800 square meters of water, the park allows 3 boats in the Pirate Lake. What is the maximum number of boats that could be in the lake at one time (round to the nearest whole)?

(Use 3.14 for π)

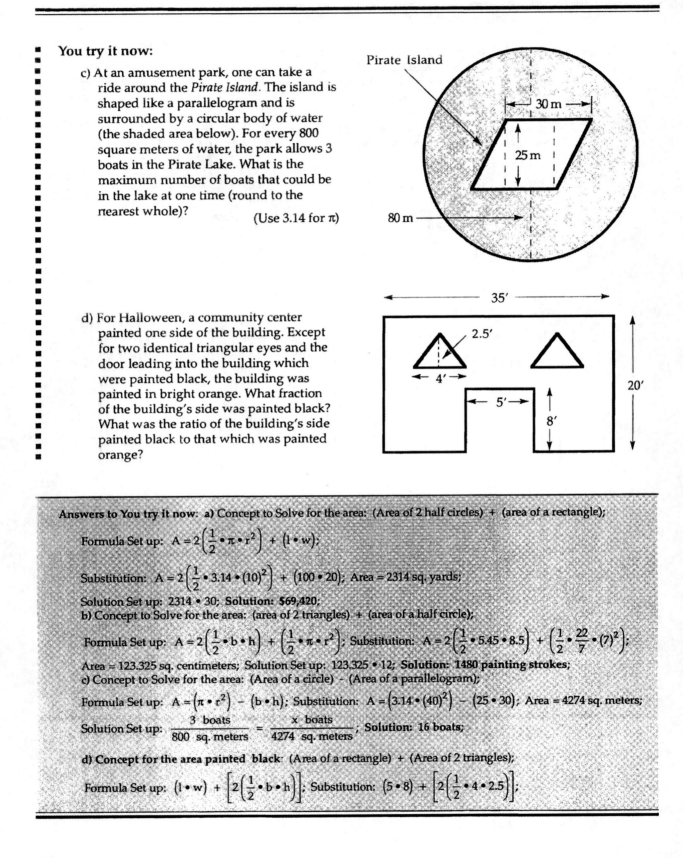

d) For Halloween, a community center painted one side of the building. Except for two identical triangular eyes and the door leading into the building which were painted black, the building was painted in bright orange. What fraction of the building's side was painted black? What was the ratio of the building's side painted black to that which was painted orange?

Answers to You try it now: a) Concept to Solve for the area: (Area of 2 half circles) + (area of a rectangle);

Formula Set up: $A = 2\left(\frac{1}{2} \bullet \pi \bullet r^2\right) + (l \bullet w)$;

Substitution: $A = 2\left(\frac{1}{2} \bullet 3.14 \bullet (10)^2\right) + (100 \bullet 20)$; Area = 2314 sq. yards;

Solution Set up: 2314 • 30; **Solution: $69,420;**
b) Concept to Solve for the area: (area of 2 triangles) + (area of a half circle);

Formula Set up: $A = 2\left(\frac{1}{2} \bullet b \bullet h\right) + \left(\frac{1}{2} \bullet \pi \bullet r^2\right)$; Substitution: $A = 2\left(\frac{1}{2} \bullet 5.45 \bullet 8.5\right) + \left(\frac{1}{2} \bullet \frac{22}{7} \bullet (7)^2\right)$;

Area = 123.325 sq. centimeters; Solution Set up: 123.325 • 12; **Solution: 1480 painting strokes;**
c) Concept to Solve for the area: (Area of a circle) - (Area of a parallelogram);

Formula Set up: $A = \left(\pi \bullet r^2\right) - (b \bullet h)$; Substitution: $A = \left(3.14 \bullet (40)^2\right) - (25 \bullet 30)$; Area = 4274 sq. meters;

Solution Set up: $\dfrac{3 \text{ boats}}{800 \text{ sq. meters}} = \dfrac{x \text{ boats}}{4274 \text{ sq. meters}}$; **Solution: 16 boats;**

d) Concept for the area painted black: (Area of a rectangle) + (Area of 2 triangles);

Formula Set up: $(l \bullet w) + \left[2\left(\frac{1}{2} \bullet b \bullet h\right)\right]$; Substitution: $(5 \bullet 8) + \left[2\left(\frac{1}{2} \bullet 4 \bullet 2.5\right)\right]$;

Area painted black = 50 sq. feet. Concept for the total area of the side of the building: (Area of a rectangle);
Formula Set up: $(l \cdot w)$; Substitution: $(35 \cdot 20)$; Total area painted = 700 sq. feet;
Concept for the Area painted orange: (Total painted area) - (Area painted black); Set up: 700 - 50;

Area painted orange = 650 sq. feet; Solutions: $\frac{1}{14}$ of the building is painted black; the ratio is:
$\frac{1 \text{ sq. ft. painted black}}{13 \text{ sq. ft. painted orange}}$.

Answer to Application: To know how many people can legally be in the pool at one time, we must first know the area of the pool. One way of envisioning the pool is to see it as 4 distinct shapes.

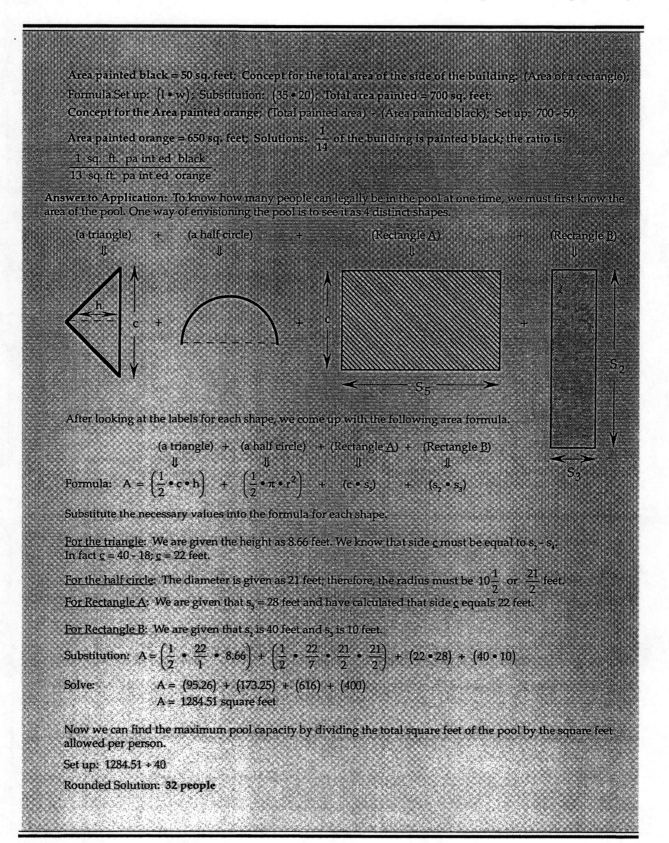

After looking at the labels for each shape, we come up with the following area formula.

$$\text{(a triangle)} + \text{(a half circle)} + \text{(Rectangle A)} + \text{(Rectangle B)}$$

Formula: $A = \left(\frac{1}{2} \cdot c \cdot h\right) + \left(\frac{1}{2} \cdot \pi \cdot r^2\right) + (c \cdot s_5) + (s_2 \cdot s_3)$

Substitute the necessary values into the formula for each shape.

<u>For the triangle:</u> We are given the height as 8.66 feet. We know that side c must be equal to s_2 - s_1. In fact $c = 40 - 18$; $c = 22$ feet.

<u>For the half circle:</u> The diameter is given as 21 feet; therefore, the radius must be $10\frac{1}{2}$ or $\frac{21}{2}$ feet.

<u>For Rectangle A:</u> We are given that $s_5 = 28$ feet and have calculated that side c equals 22 feet.

<u>For Rectangle B:</u> We are given that s_2 is 40 feet and s_3 is 10 feet.

Substitution: $A = \left(\frac{1}{2} \cdot \frac{22}{1} \cdot 8.66\right) + \left(\frac{1}{2} \cdot \frac{22}{7} \cdot \frac{21}{2} \cdot \frac{21}{2}\right) + (22 \cdot 28) + (40 \cdot 10)$

Solve: $A = (95.26) + (173.25) + (616) + (400)$
                $A = 1284.51$ square feet

Now we can find the maximum pool capacity by dividing the total square feet of the pool by the square feet allowed per person.

Set up: $1284.51 \div 40$

Rounded Solution: 32 people

5.3 Area Problems for Irregular Shapes

In exercises #1-12: (a) write a mathematical expression that will solve the problem, and (b) give the solution.

1-6) A farmer grows spinach on 50 acres of his land and broccoli on 80 acres. In a year the farmer earns $600 per acre growing spinach and $450 per acre growing broccoli.

   1) On what fraction of this land does he grow spinach?

   2) On what percentage of this land (round to the nearest whole percent) does he grow spinach?

   3) What is the ratio of the amount of land used to grow spinach to the amount of land used to grow broccoli?

   4) How much money does the farmer currently earn in a year?

   5) Overall, what is the average amount of money the farmer makes per acre of his farmed land (round answer to the nearest cent)?

   6) If he stopped growing broccoli on 20 acres and instead planted spinach, how much more money would he make per year if prices remained steady?

7-12) The city of Pleasantville had a population of 80,000 people and an area of 20 square miles.

   7) If the city boundaries were in the shape of a rectangle and its length and width were each a whole number of miles, what are the three different dimensions (length by width) which the city could have (no set up is necessary)?

   8) How many people are there per square mile of the city?

   9) If $\frac{1}{4}$ of the city was park and recreation areas, how many people were there per square mile in the rest of the city (round answer to the nearest whole person) ?

   10) How many people are there per acre of the entire city (640 acres = 1 square mile)?

   11) If the city's population grew 20%, how many people would there be per acre of the entire city?

   12) If the city's population grew 20%, how many people would there be per acre of land not including the park and recreation areas?

13) State yes or no as to whether the given pair of shapes have the same area.

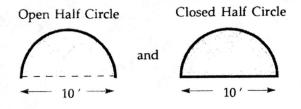

Open Half Circle   Closed Half Circle

and

10 '   10 '

14) State yes or no as to whether the given pair of shapes have the same area.

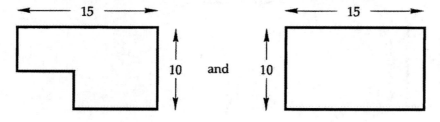

15) State yes or no as to whether the given shaded regions have the same area.

Note: length a ≠ length b.

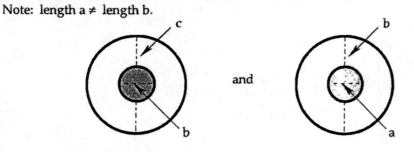

16) State yes or no as to whether the given pair of shapes have the same area.

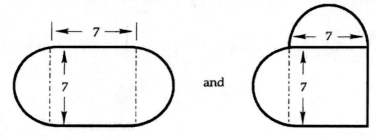

17) State yes or no as to whether the given pair of shapes have the same area. We know that side a ≠ side b.

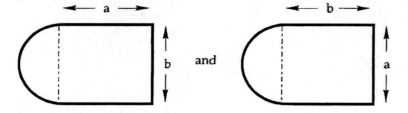

18) State yes or no as to whether the given pair of shapes have the same area. We know that side x = side y.

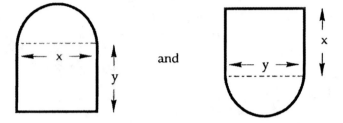

and

In exercises #19-38, state yes or no whether the given formula would solve for the area of each shape below. When working with circles, the variable "d" is used for the diameter and the variable "r" is used for the radius.

19-21)

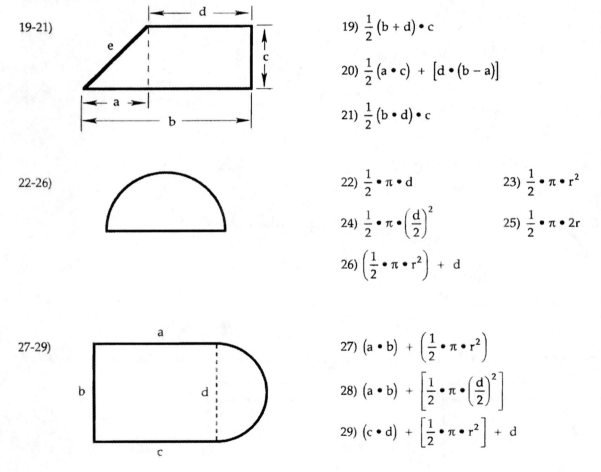

19) $\frac{1}{2}(b + d) \bullet c$

20) $\frac{1}{2}(a \bullet c) + [d \bullet (b - a)]$

21) $\frac{1}{2}(b \bullet d) \bullet c$

22-26)

22) $\frac{1}{2} \bullet \pi \bullet d$ 23) $\frac{1}{2} \bullet \pi \bullet r^2$

24) $\frac{1}{2} \bullet \pi \bullet \left(\frac{d}{2}\right)^2$ 25) $\frac{1}{2} \bullet \pi \bullet 2r$

26) $\left(\frac{1}{2} \bullet \pi \bullet r^2\right) + d$

27-29)

27) $(a \bullet b) + \left(\frac{1}{2} \bullet \pi \bullet r^2\right)$

28) $(a \bullet b) + \left[\frac{1}{2} \bullet \pi \bullet \left(\frac{d}{2}\right)^2\right]$

29) $(c \bullet d) + \left[\frac{1}{2} \bullet \pi \bullet r^2\right] + d$

30-34)

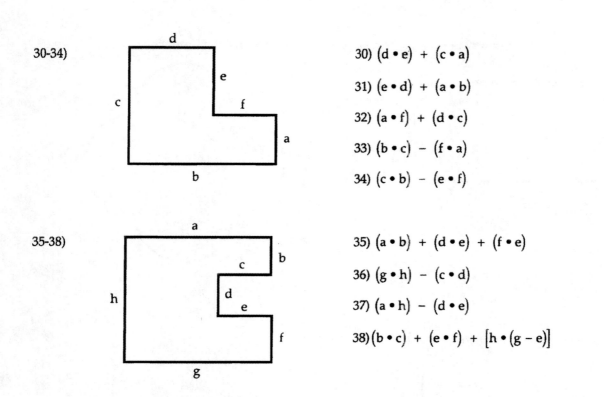

30) $(d \bullet e) + (c \bullet a)$

31) $(e \bullet d) + (a \bullet b)$

32) $(a \bullet f) + (d \bullet c)$

33) $(b \bullet c) - (f \bullet a)$

34) $(c \bullet b) - (e \bullet f)$

35-38)

35) $(a \bullet b) + (d \bullet e) + (f \bullet e)$

36) $(g \bullet h) - (c \bullet d)$

37) $(a \bullet h) - (d \bullet e)$

38) $(b \bullet c) + (e \bullet f) + \left[h \bullet (g - e) \right]$

In exercises #39-48: (a) write a formula using the given variables that would solve for the area of each of the shapes below, and (b) show the substitution (no solving yet!), and (c) the solution. Use "d" for the diameter of any formula and "r" for the radius of any formula.

39) The given information: $s_1 = 10'$; $s_2 = 7'$

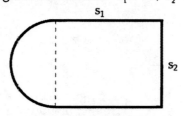

(use $\dfrac{22}{7}$ for π and give answer as a mixed number)

40) The given information: $a = 25'$; $b = 8.3'$

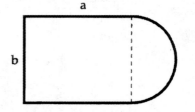

(use 3.14 for π and round answer to the nearest whole foot)

41) The given information: x = 22 meters; y = 14 meters

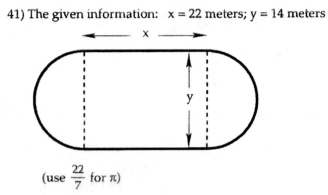

(use $\frac{22}{7}$ for π)

42) The given information: $a = 2\frac{4}{5}''$

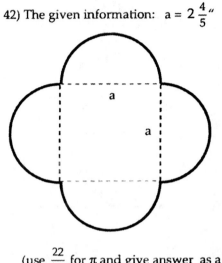

(use $\frac{22}{7}$ for π and give answer as a mixed number)

43) The given information: $s_1 = 4.3''$

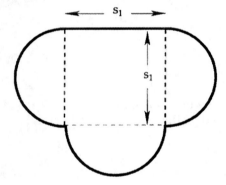

(use 3.14 for π and round answer to the nearest whole inch)

44) The given information:

a = 15 cm; c = 10 cm; c = d; e = 8 cm

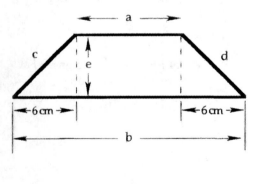

45) The given information:

$s_1 = 8\frac{3}{4}''$; $s_2 = 5''$; $s_2 = s_3$; $s_4 = 6\frac{1}{4}''$

(give answer as a mixed number)

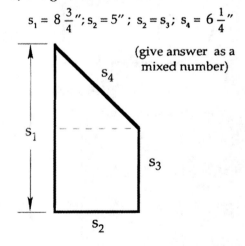

46) Use the <u>Addition Method</u> to set up and solve.

The given information: a = 20'
c = 8'
d = 7'
f = 8'

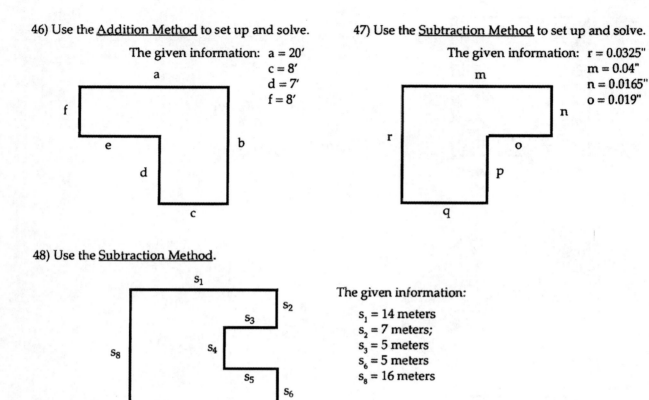

47) Use the <u>Subtraction Method</u> to set up and solve.

The given information: r = 0.0325"
m = 0.04"
n = 0.0165"
o = 0.019"

48) Use the <u>Subtraction Method</u>.

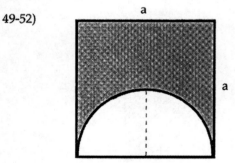

The given information:

s_1 = 14 meters
s_2 = 7 meters;
s_3 = 5 meters
s_6 = 5 meters
s_8 = 16 meters

In exercises #49-64, state yes or no whether the given concept or formula would solve for the area of each <u>shaded region</u> below. The variable "d" is used for the diameter and the variable "r" is used for the radius.

49-52)

49) (Area of a square) - (Area of a half circle)

50) $\left(a^2\right) - \left(\dfrac{1}{2} \bullet \pi \bullet d\right)$

51) $\left(a^2\right) - \left(\dfrac{1}{2} \bullet \pi \bullet r^2\right)$

52) $\left(a^2\right) - \left(\dfrac{1}{2} \bullet \pi \bullet \left(\dfrac{d}{2}\right)^2\right)$

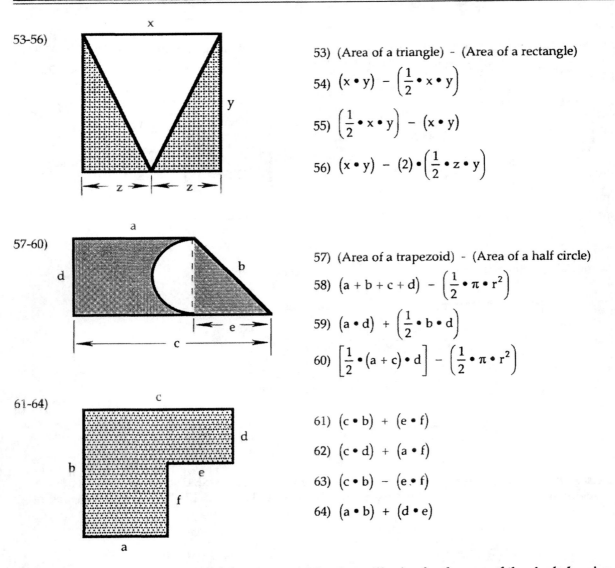

53-56)

53) (Area of a triangle) - (Area of a rectangle)

54) $(x \cdot y) - \left(\dfrac{1}{2} \cdot x \cdot y\right)$

55) $\left(\dfrac{1}{2} \cdot x \cdot y\right) - (x \cdot y)$

56) $(x \cdot y) - (2) \cdot \left(\dfrac{1}{2} \cdot z \cdot y\right)$

57-60)

57) (Area of a trapezoid) - (Area of a half circle)

58) $(a + b + c + d) - \left(\dfrac{1}{2} \cdot \pi \cdot r^2\right)$

59) $(a \cdot d) + \left(\dfrac{1}{2} \cdot b \cdot d\right)$

60) $\left[\dfrac{1}{2} \cdot (a + c) \cdot d\right] - \left(\dfrac{1}{2} \cdot \pi \cdot r^2\right)$

61-64)

61) $(c \cdot b) + (e \cdot f)$

62) $(c \cdot d) + (a \cdot f)$

63) $(c \cdot b) - (e \cdot f)$

64) $(a \cdot b) + (d \cdot e)$

In exercises #65-70: (a) write a formula using variables that will solve for the area of the shaded region, (b) show the substitution (so solving yet!), and (c) give the solution.

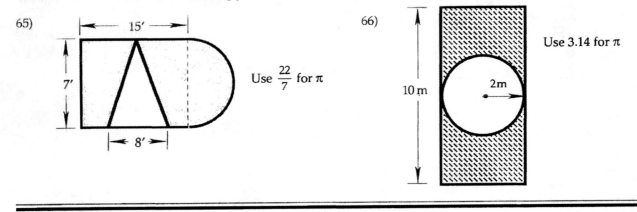

65)

7′   15′   Use $\dfrac{22}{7}$ for π

8′

66)

10 m   2m   Use 3.14 for π

67) Use 3.14 for π

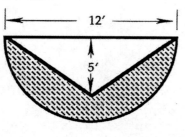

68) Use $\frac{22}{7}$ for π. Each small circle has a diameter of $4\frac{2}{3}$ centimeters.

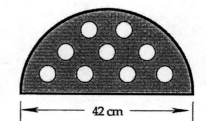

69) The small shapes inside the figure are all squares with a side of 2 feet.

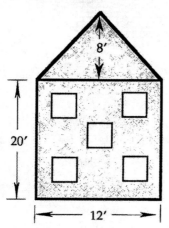

70)

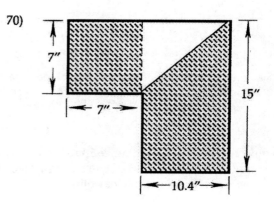

In exercises #71-90, solve the problems.

71-74) A circular field was divided into 4 equally sized parts. One part was made into a baseball field, one part became a new parking lot, and two parts were turned into a pond/wetland space for biology/ecology students to have as a resource for science projects.

71) What is the area of the baseball field (use 3.14 for π and round the answer to the nearest whole)?

72) 20% of the new parking area was to be earthen areas with trees and flowering bushes. How much would it cost to pave the parking lot if the price was $0.48 per square foot (round answer to the nearest dollar)?

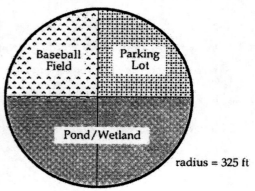

73) What percent of the circular field became a pond/wetland space?

74) One acre is equal to 43,560 square feet. How many acres is the new wetland area (round the answer to the nearest tenth)?

75-76) A circular planter has a brick pathway around it. The width of the path is $3\frac{1}{2}$ feet and the radius of the planter is $2\frac{1}{2}$ feet.

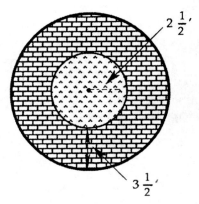

75) What is the square footage of the pathway itself (use $\frac{22}{7}$ for π)?

76) If each brick ($\frac{1}{4}$ of a foot by $\frac{1}{2}$ of a foot) cost $2, how much did it cost to make the brick pathway? Don't forget to add an extra 5% to your cost for broken bricks and errors.

77-79) A corporation rented office space. It usually rented space for $12 per square foot per year. It currently rented all three stories of one building (each floor had dimensions of 120 feet by 80 feet) to the same high-tech company at a discount.

77) If the high tech company currently paid a total rent of $302,400 per year for the office space, how much was it paying per square foot of office each year?

78) What was the high tech company's discount per square foot per year from the normal $12 per square foot per year?

79) What was the monthly office-space rental bill for the high-tech company?

80-81) On a piece of land 1 square mile in area, $\frac{1}{5}$ of the land is covered by a lake. Another $\frac{1}{2}$ of the land is covered by houses. The remaining land is an old apple orchard.

80) How many acres of land are covered by the lake (640 acres = 1 square mile)?

81) How many acres of land are covered by the apple orchard (640 acres = 1 square mile)?

82-88) In the section of farmland below, the shaded region is the area in which grapes are grown for wine; the unshaded region is the area where peaches are grown.

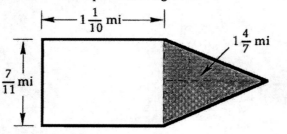

82) On how many acres of land are grapes grown (640 acres = 1 square mile)?

83) On how many acres of land are peaches grown (640 acres = 1 square mile)?

84) On what fraction of this land are peaches grown (you do <u>not</u> need to reduce)?

85) On what percent of this land are peaches grown?

86) If the grapes create a profit of $800 dollars a year per acre, what is the profit made from growing grapes every year?

87) If the peaches create a profit of $90 a year per acre, what is the profit made from growing peaches every year?

88) If the landowner stopped growing peaches on 50 acres of land and instead planted grapes, how much more money would the landowner make per year if the prices remained steady?

89-90 To estimate the cost of the paint necessary to paint <u>two</u> coats on the building below (front and back plus both sides), the painter knew that he would first have to calculate the total area that he needed to paint. To do this he would have to calculate the total surface area and then subtract the area of the windows and the front and back doors from this area. The paint he was using cost $18 a gallon; each gallon covered 400 square feet.

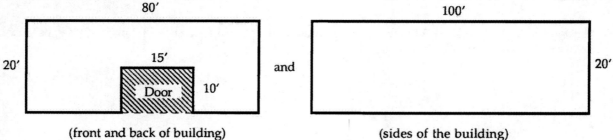

(front and back of building)   (sides of the building)

89) The painter estimated that the area of all the building's windows was 1440 square feet. What is the total area of the building that he would need to paint (the answer includes both coats of paint)?

90) How much would the paint cost?

Skills Check

1. If a closed half circle has a diameter of 14 meters and a perimeter of 36 meters, what would be the distance of the half circle if it were open?

   Use the shapes below for questions 2 and 3:

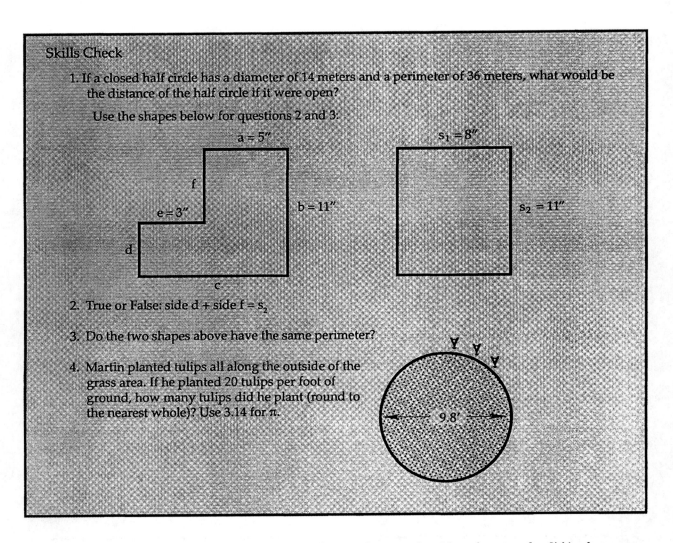

2. True or False: side d + side f = s_2

3. Do the two shapes above have the same perimeter?

4. Martin planted tulips all along the outside of the grass area. If he planted 20 tulips per foot of ground, how many tulips did he plant (round to the nearest whole)? Use 3.14 for π.

Answers to Skills Check: 1) 22 meters; 2) Yes, these make opposite sides of a retangle; 3) Yes, because we can move sides; 4) 615 tulips.

Section 5.4 Finding the Volumes of Three-dimensional Shapes

Objectives:

- To recognize the relationships between shapes and formulas
- To create formulas to find specific volumes
- To solve for the volumes of cubes, rectangular boxes, triangular prisms, cylinders, cones, spheres, and pyramids

Application:

In the diagram of the pool below, the shaded areas have a depth of eight feet, the triangular area has a depth of 3 feet, and the semicircular area, where there are diving boards, has a depth of 14 feet. If hoses are filling the pool at the rate of 5000 gallons an hour, how many hours will it take to fill the pool (7.48 gallons = 1 cubic foot)? Round answer to the nearest tenth of an hour.

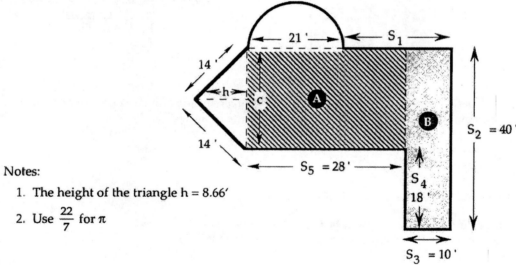

Notes:

1. The height of the triangle h = 8.66'

2. Use $\dfrac{22}{7}$ for π

Vocabulary:

> **Three-dimensional objects**—Three-dimensional objects are objects that have height or depth. In our geometry study so far we have been working with two-dimensional objects—flat objects that have only a width and a length. **Three-dimensional objects** have <u>width</u>, <u>length</u>, and <u>height</u>.

> **Volume**—The **volume** of an object is the space inside a three-dimensional object. It is measured in **cubic units** (space that has height can't be measured in square units which are flat!). We actually measure how many cubes of a certain size would fit into an object.

A good way to visualize a cube is to picture a square (say 1 foot by 1 foot) on the floor. Now put your hand on the floor in the middle of this square. Raise your hand up one foot off the ground. Imagine the shape that you have just created—you have given the square a height of 1 foot. In fact we have created a cube—a cubic foot which has a length of 1 foot, a width of 1 foot, and a height of 1 foot.

Example of Visualizing the Volume of a Shape:

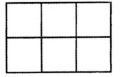

Here we have a flat shape. Multiplying the length times the width (2 • 3) gives us an <u>area of 6 square feet.</u>

Now give the object a height of 3 feet.

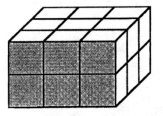

Now we have a three-dimensional shape. Multiplying the <u>length</u> times the <u>width</u> times the <u>height</u> (2 • 3 • 3) gives us a <u>volume of 18 cubic feet</u>. 18 cubes (each 1 ft. x 1 ft. x 1 ft) make up this shape.

***Answers to volume problems are always given in cubic units. There are two correct notations for writing cubic units—**cub. units or units^3**.

Example: 18 cubic feet could be written as: 18 cub. ft. or 18 ft.^{3}

Regular Three-Dimensional Geometric Shapes

rectangular box—A **rectangular box** has a rectangle as its base that has been given height by extending the perimeter upwards at a 90° angle from this rectangular base. An example of a rectangular box is a shoe box.

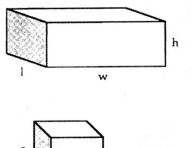

cube—A **cube** is a special type of rectangular box. It has a square as its base that has been given height. An example of a cube is a sugar cube.

cylinder—A **cylinder** has a circle as its base that has been given height by extending the perimeter upwards at a 90° angle from this circular base. An example of a cylinder is a soft drink can.

triangular prism—A **triangular prism** has a triangle as its base that has been given height by extending the perimeter upwards at a 90° angle from this triangular base. One example of a triangular prism can be seen in the way some camping tents are set up.

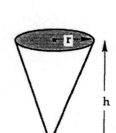

cone—A **cone's** base is a circle; it also has a height that is vertical (90°) to the center point of the circular base. Unlike a cylinder, however, the surface of the cone that extends upward from the circumference does not move upward at a 90° angle from the circumference. It moves both upward and inward to a meeting point, the peak of the cone. Examples of a cone are a street cone or a pointed party hat.

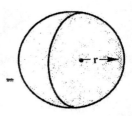

sphere—A **sphere** is a shape that is created from a center point and moving outward (infinite radii) the same distance in all directions. Examples of a sphere are a ball and the earth.

pyramid—A common **pyramid** is a shape that has a square base whose height is created by moving the perimeter upward and inward to a point.

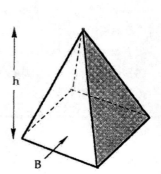

***Understanding Volume Formulas:** If we look at the volume formulas for the shapes above, we can find the area formula for the flat part of that figure's shape. In reality, to find the volume for these common geometric shapes, we are simply **multiplying the Base** (that is the <u>area of the flat surface</u>) **by the "height"** (that is the volume gained by the height increase over the Bases's area).

<u>Shape</u> $\Downarrow$	<u>Volume formula</u> $\Downarrow$	=	<u>Area formula</u> $\Downarrow$	x	<u>Height</u> $\Downarrow$
rectangular box	$V = l \bullet w \bullet h$	=	$(l \bullet w)$	$\bullet$	h
cube	$V = s^3$	=	s^2	$\bullet$	s
cylinder	$V = \pi \bullet r^2 \bullet h$	=	$(\pi \bullet r^2)$	$\bullet$	h
triangular prism	$V = \mathbf{B} \bullet h$	=	$\mathbf{B}$	$\bullet$	h
cone	$V = \frac{1}{3} \bullet \pi \bullet r^2 \bullet h$	=	$(\pi \bullet r^2)$	$\bullet$	$\frac{1}{3} \bullet h$
sphere	$V = \frac{4}{3} \bullet \pi \bullet r^3$	=	$(\pi \bullet r^2)$	$\bullet$	$\frac{4}{3} \bullet r$
pyramid	$V = \frac{1}{3} \bullet \mathbf{B} \bullet h$	=	$\mathbf{B}$	$\bullet$	$\frac{1}{3} \bullet h$

***Notice that the <u>capital</u> **B**'s in the formulas for the volumes of a triangular prism and a pyramid refer to the <u>areas of those bases,</u> not their sides.

The Process for Solving <u>All</u> Volume Problems is written in the "How to" box that follows. As with Area and Perimeter, it is the only process that we need to follow.

How to:

Solve Volume Problems:

1. Identify the figure (draw a picture if it helps).

2. Find/Write the formula.

3. Substitute the number value(s) for the variable(s).

4. Solve and give the answer in cubic units.

Example #1: Which shape below has a greater volume (use $\frac{22}{7}$ for π)?

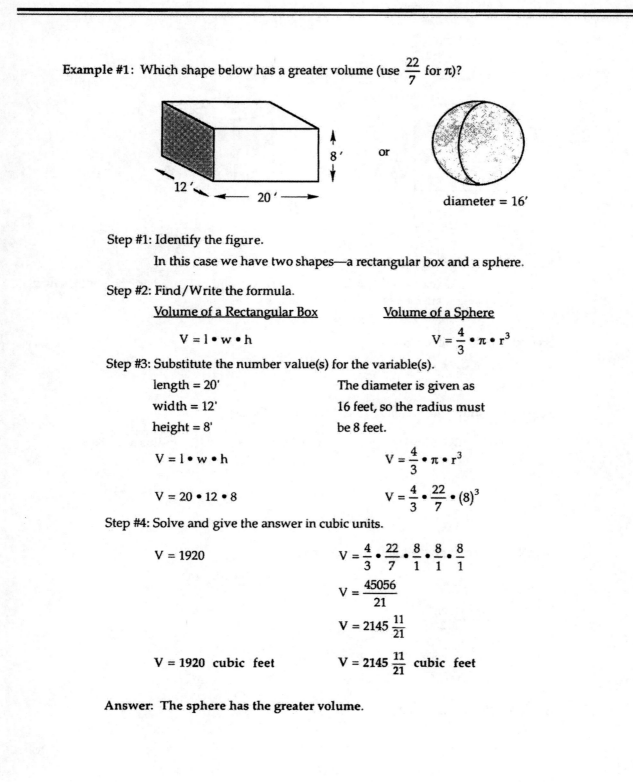

8'

or

diameter = 16'

12'

20'

Step #1: Identify the figure.

In this case we have two shapes—a rectangular box and a sphere.

Step #2: Find/Write the formula.

<u>Volume of a Rectangular Box</u>   <u>Volume of a Sphere</u>

$$V = l \bullet w \bullet h$$ $$V = \frac{4}{3} \bullet \pi \bullet r^3$$

Step #3: Substitute the number value(s) for the variable(s).

length = 20'   The diameter is given as

width = 12'   16 feet, so the radius must

height = 8'   be 8 feet.

$$V = l \bullet w \bullet h$$ $$V = \frac{4}{3} \bullet \pi \bullet r^3$$

$$V = 20 \bullet 12 \bullet 8$$ $$V = \frac{4}{3} \bullet \frac{22}{7} \bullet (8)^3$$

Step #4: Solve and give the answer in cubic units.

$$V = 1920$$ $$V = \frac{4}{3} \bullet \frac{22}{7} \bullet \frac{8}{1} \bullet \frac{8}{1} \bullet \frac{8}{1}$$

$$V = \frac{45056}{21}$$

$$V = 2145\frac{11}{21}$$

$$V = 1920 \text{ cubic feet}$$ $$V = 2145\frac{11}{21} \text{ cubic feet}$$

Answer: The sphere has the greater volume.

Example #2: Which shape below has a greater volume (use $\frac{22}{7}$ for π)?

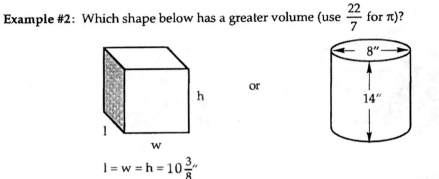

$l = w = h = 10\frac{3}{8}''$

Step #1: Identify the figure.

In this case we have two shapes—a cube (a rectangular box where the width, length, and height are the same) and a cylinder.

Step #2: Find/Write the formula.

Volume of a Cube   Volume of a Cylinder

$V = s^3$ $V = \pi \cdot r^2 \cdot h$

Step #3: Substitute the number value(s) for the variable(s).

side $= 10\frac{3}{8}$ inches   The diameter is 8", so the radius must be 4".

                                 The height $= 14$".

$V = s^3$ $V = \pi \cdot r^2 \cdot h$

$V = \left(10\frac{3}{8}\right)^3$ $V = \frac{22}{7} \cdot 4^2 \cdot 14$

Step #4: Solve and give the answer in cubic units.

$V = \frac{83}{8} \cdot \frac{83}{8} \cdot \frac{83}{8}$ $V = \frac{22}{7} \cdot \frac{4}{1} \cdot \frac{4}{1} \cdot \frac{14}{1}$

$V = \frac{571787}{512}$

$V = 1116\frac{395}{512}$ $V = 704$

$V = 1116\frac{395}{512}$ cubic inches $V = 704$ cubic inches

Answer: The cube has the greater volume.

Example #3: Which shape below has a greater volume (use 3.14 for π)?

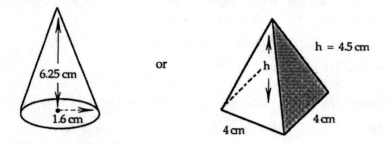

or

Step #1: Identify the figure.

In this case we have two shapes—a cone and a pyramid.

Step #2: Find/Write the formula.

<u>Volume of a Cone</u>

$$V = \frac{1}{3} \cdot \pi \cdot r^2 \cdot h$$

<u>Volume of a Pyramid</u>

$$V = \frac{1}{3} \cdot B \cdot h$$

Step #3: Substitute the number value(s) for the variable(s).

The radius is given as 1.6 cm.
The height = 6.25 cm.

The sides of the Base are the same
(both 4 cm.); therefore, the area of the
Base = (4 • 4) = 16 sq. cm.
The height = 4.5 cm.

$$V = \frac{1}{3} \cdot \pi \cdot r^2 \cdot h$$

$$V = \frac{1}{3} \cdot 3.14 \cdot (1.6)^2 \cdot 6.25$$

$$V = \frac{1}{3} \cdot B \cdot h$$

$$V = \frac{1}{3} \cdot (4 \cdot 4) \cdot 4.5$$

Step #4: Solve and give the answer in cubic units.

$$V = 16.74\overline{6}$$

$$V = 16.74\overline{6} \text{ cubic cm.}$$

$$V = 24$$

$$V = 24 \text{ cubic cm.}$$

Answer: The pyramid has the greater volume.

Sample #1: A hiker set up his one-person tent (see below). He
estimated that his body and all his equipment filled
up about 40% of the tent. What is the volume of the
tent that is filled with air?

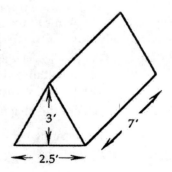

First we need to identify this 3-dimensional object. The figure is a triangular prism. To find out how much of the volume of this prism is filled with air, we must find the total volume and subtract 40% of that volume.

Concept Set up: (Volume of Triangular Prism) - (40% of Prism)

Formula Set up: (B • h) - [40% • (B • h)]

Substitution: The **B** is the area of the triangular Base. That area formula is $\left(\frac{1}{2} \cdot b \cdot h\right)$

where b is the base of the two-dimensional triangle (2.5 ft.) and h is the height of that two-dimensional triangle (3 ft.). The **h** in the formula for the triangular prism is the height of the prism (7 ft).

Substitution: $\left[\left(\frac{1}{2} \cdot 2.5 \cdot 3\right) \cdot 7\right] - \left\{(.40)\left[\left(\frac{1}{2} \cdot 2.5 \cdot 3\right) \cdot 7\right]\right\}$

Solve: [26.25] - {(.40) [26.25]}

(26.25) - (10.5)

Answer: **15.75 cubic feet** of the tent is filled with air.

You try it now:

a) A pair of shoes inside a shoe box take up $\frac{3}{8}$ of the space inside the rectangular box. If the height of the box is $6\frac{3}{4}$ inches, the width is 6 inches, and the length is 12 inches, what is the volume of the shoe box that is filled with air (round answer to the nearest whole)?

b) At only four years of age Lydia showed an interest in building. Her parents bought her a set of plastic building blocks from which Lydia built a solid pyramid. The base of the pyramid was a perfect square with a length of 8 inches. The height of the pyramid was 6 inches. If 35% of the volume of this pyramid was built from red blocks, what volume of the pyramid was constructed of other-colored blocks?

Sample #2: After cutting the angel food cake into 6 equal pieces, Christina's father served her the first piece because it was her birthday. What was the volume of the remaining cake (use 3.14 for π)?

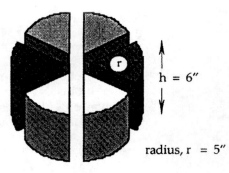

One way to view this problem is to see it as a shape within a shape. The cake itself is a cylinder and we are cutting out or subtracting $\frac{1}{6}$ of this shape.

One warning here: the $\frac{1}{6}$ of the cake is <u>not</u> a triangular prism because one of its side is an arc, <u>not</u> a straight line.

Concept Set up: (Volume of a cylinder) - ($\frac{1}{6}$ of the cylinder's volume)

Formula Set up: $V = \left(\pi \bullet r^2 \bullet h\right) - \left[\frac{1}{6} \bullet \left(\pi \bullet r^2 \bullet h\right)\right]$

Substitution: $V = \left(3.14 \bullet (5)^2 \bullet 6\right) - \left[\frac{1}{6} \bullet \left(3.14 \bullet (5)^2 \bullet 6\right)\right]$

Solve: $V = (471) - \left[\frac{1}{6} \bullet (471)\right]$

                    $V = (471) - \left[78\frac{1}{2}\right]$

                    $V = 392\frac{1}{2}$

Answer: $392\frac{1}{2}$ **cubic inches**

You try it now:

c) In the bowl illustrated to the right, Martha had made a
   jello mold. In the jello were 120 whole cranberries, each
   with a radius of $\frac{3}{4}$ of a centimeter. What was the
   volume of the jello without the cranberries?

   (use 3.14 for π)

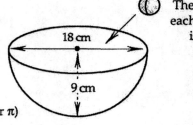

The radius of
each cranberry
is 3/4 cm

18 cm

9 cm

d) At a store that sold fine candy, a new creation was a
   cubic inch in size. It consisted of dark chocolate sur-
   rounding a cone-shaped creamy inside. The diameter of
   the base of the creamy chocolate was $\frac{4}{5}$ of an inch; the
   height of the cone was $\frac{7}{8}$ of an inch. What was the
   volume of the dark chocolate (use $\frac{22}{7}$ for π)?

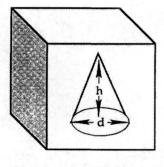

The dimensions of the cone:

   h = $\frac{7''}{8}$ and d = $\frac{4''}{5}$

Answers to You try it now: a) Concept Set up: (Volume of Rectangular Box) - (Volume of Shoes);

Formula Set up: $(l \cdot w \cdot h) - \left[\frac{3}{8} \cdot (l \cdot w \cdot h)\right]$; Substitution: $\left(12 \cdot 6 \cdot 6\frac{3}{4}\right) - \left[\frac{3}{8} \cdot \left(12 \cdot 6 \cdot 6\frac{3}{4}\right)\right]$;

Solution (rounded to the nearest whole): **304 cubic inches;**
b) Concept Set up: (Volume of Pyramid) - (Volume of red blocks);

Formula Set up: $\left(\frac{1}{3} \cdot B \cdot h\right) - \left[35\% \cdot \left(\frac{1}{3} \cdot B \cdot h\right)\right]$;

Substitution: $\left(\frac{1}{3} \cdot (8 \cdot 8) \cdot 6\right) - \left[(.35) \cdot \left(\frac{1}{3} \cdot (8 \cdot 8) \cdot 6\right)\right]$; **Solution: 83.2 cubic inches;**

c) Concept Set up: (Volume of $\frac{1}{2}$ a sphere) - [Volume of 120 cranberries (spheres)];

Formula Set up: $\frac{1}{2} \cdot \left(\frac{4}{3} \cdot \pi \cdot r^3\right) - \left[120\left(\frac{4}{3} \cdot \pi \cdot r^3\right)\right]$;

Substitution: $\frac{1}{2} \cdot \left(\frac{4}{3} \cdot 3.14 \cdot (9)^3\right) - \left[120\left(\frac{4}{3} \cdot 3.14 \cdot \left(\frac{3}{4}\right)^3\right)\right]$;

Solution: 1314.09 cubic cm; d) Concept Set up: (Volume of a Cube) - (Volume of a Cone);

Formula Set up: $s^3 - \left(\frac{1}{3} \cdot \pi \cdot r^2 \cdot h\right)$; Substitution: $(1)^3 - \left(\frac{1}{3} \cdot \frac{22}{7} \cdot \left(\frac{2}{5}\right)^2 \cdot \frac{7}{8}\right)$;

Solution: $\frac{64}{75}$ **of a cubic inch.**

Answer to Application: To know how long it would take for the pool to fill with water, we must first know the volume of the pool and the number of gallons which it holds. To find the total volume it is easiest to look at this figure as four distinct shapes and find the volume for each of the following:

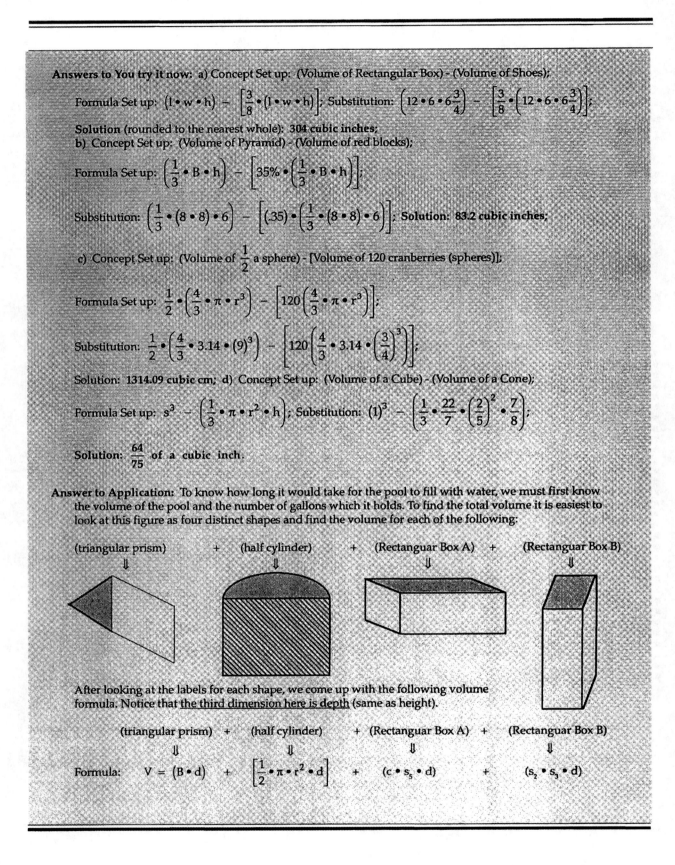

(triangular prism)   +   (half cylinder)   +   (Rectanguar Box A) +   (Rectanguar Box B)
  ⇓   ⇓   ⇓   ⇓

After looking at the labels for each shape, we come up with the following volume formula. Notice that <u>the third dimension here is depth</u> (same as height).

(triangular prism) +   (half cylinder)   + (Rectanguar Box A) +   (Rectanguar Box B)
  ⇓   ⇓   ⇓   ⇓

Formula: $V = (B \cdot d)$ + $\left[\frac{1}{2} \cdot \pi \cdot r^2 \cdot d\right]$ + $(c \cdot s_5 \cdot d)$ + $(s_2 \cdot s_3 \cdot d)$

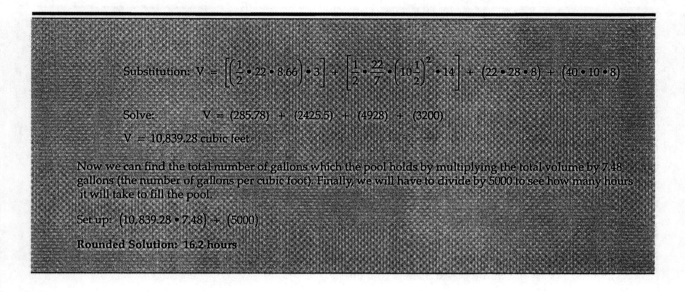

Substitution: $V = \left[\left(\dfrac{1}{2} \cdot 22 \cdot 8.66\right) \cdot 3\right] + \left[\dfrac{1}{2} \cdot \dfrac{22}{7} \cdot \left(10\dfrac{1}{2}\right)^2 \cdot 14\right] + (22 \cdot 28 \cdot 8) + (40 \cdot 10 \cdot 8)$

Solve: $V = (285.78) + (2425.5) + (4928) + (3200)$

$V = 10,839.28$ cubic feet

Now we can find the total number of gallons which the pool holds by multiplying the total volume by 7.48 gallons (the number of gallons per cubic foot). Finally, we will have to divide by 5000 to see how many hours it will take to fill the pool.

Set up: $(10,839.28 \cdot 7.48) \div (5000)$

Rounded Solution: 16.2 hours

5.4 Volume Problems

In exercises #1-10, answer the following questions.

1) A cylinder and a cone have the same radius and the same height. Now look at the volume formulas for these two shapes. The cone has what fraction of the cylinder's volume?

2) A cube and a pyramid have the same <u>Base</u> (area) and the same height. Now look at the volume formulas for these two shapes. Which figure will have a greater volume?

3) Why is volume measured in cubic units and not square units?

4) Is a cube a rectanglar box?

5) We know that $y > x$. Which will have a greater volume: a cube with a side of "x" length or a rectanglar box which has the distance of "x" for both its length and width and a height of distance "y"?

6) We know that $a > b$. Which will have a greater volume: a cube with a side of "a" length or a rectanglar box which has the distance of "a" for its length and width and a height of distance "b"?

7) If the height of a triangular prism is 6 feet, is it true that the number representing the volume of this prism would be 6 times larger than the number representing the area of the triangular base of the prism?

8) If the height of a cone is 6 feet, is it true that the number representing the volume of this figure would be 6 times larger than the number representing the area of the circular base of the cone?

9) If the height of a pyramid is 6 feet, is it true that the number representing the volume of this pyramid would be 6 times larger than the number representing the area of the square base of the pyramid?

10) If the height of a rectangular box is 6 feet, is it true that the number representing the volume of this rectangular box would be 6 times larger than the number representing the area of the rectangular base of the box?

In exercises #11-31, solve for the volume of the following figures.

11) A cube with a height of 1 foot?

12) A cube with a height of $\frac{1}{2}$ of an inch?

13) A cube with a length of 2 feet?

14) A rectangular box with a length of 8 feet, a width of 10 feet, and a height of 12 feet.

15) A rectangular box with a length of $3\frac{2}{3}$ feet, a width of 5 feet, and a height of $4\frac{1}{4}$ feet.

16) A rectangular box with a length of 2.8 feet, a width of 5.25 feet, and a height of 8 feet.

17) A triangular prism where the two measurements of the triangular base are a base of 7 meters and a height of 5 meters. The height of the prism itself is 20 meters.

18) A triangular prism where the two measurements of the triangular base are a base of $2\frac{1}{2}$ meters and a height of $1\frac{1}{3}$ meters. The height of the prism itself is $4\frac{1}{5}$ meters.

19) A triangular prism where the two measurements of the triangular base are a base of 4.8 meters and a height of 11 meters. The height of the prism itself is 8 meters.

20) A cylinder with a radius of 14 centimeters and a height of 30 centimeters. Use $\frac{22}{7}$ for π.

21) A cylinder with a radius of $8\frac{2}{3}$ meters and a height of 21 meters. Use $\frac{22}{7}$ for π.

22) A cylinder with a diameter of 4.7 centimeters and a height of 9 centimeters. Use 3.14 for π.

23) A cone with a diameter of its base of 11 yards and a height of 21 yards. Use $\frac{22}{7}$ for π.

24) A cone with a diameter of its base of $3\frac{1}{2}$ feet and a height of 8 feet. Use $\frac{22}{7}$ for π.

25) A cone with a radius of its base of 15 inches and a height of 60 inches. Use 3.14 for π.

26) A sphere with a radius of 3 feet? Use $\frac{22}{7}$ for π.

27) A sphere with a radius of $4\frac{1}{2}$ feet? Use $\frac{22}{7}$ for π.

28) A sphere with a diameter of 60 feet? Use 3.14 for π.

29) A pyramid where a side of its base is 8 yards; the height of the pyramid itself is 12 yards.

30) A pyramid where a side of its base is $10\frac{1}{2}$ meters; the height of the pyramid itself is $8\frac{3}{5}$ meters.

31) A pyramid where the side of its base is 25 yards; the height of the pyramid itself is 18.5 yards.

In exercises #32-55, solve the problems.

32) The water tower to the right is 75% filled. How many gallons of water are currently in the tower (7.48 gallons ≈ 1 cubic ft.)? Use $\frac{22}{7}$ for π and round the answer to the nearest thousand gallons.

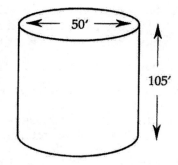

33) A canal connecting a lake to a river was being built in Russia. When completed the canal would be 2 miles long, 300 feet wide and 50 feet deep. How many cubic feet of water would the canal hold when completed? (5280 feet = 1 mile)

34-36) The earth and sun are spheres. The earth has a diameter of about 7927 miles at the equator. The sun has a diameter of 875,000 miles.

34) What is the approximate volume of the earth? Give the answer in scientific notation (round the first part of the scientific notation to the nearest tenth; as an example an answer of 2.78045×10^8 would be given as 2.8×10^8).

35) What is the approximate volume of the sun? Give the answer in scientific notation (round the first part of the scientific notation to the nearest tenth; as an example an answer of 2.78045×10^8 would be given as 2.8×10^8).

36) How many times larger is the sun than the earth (round to the nearest whole)?

37-38) One ice cream parlor served *The Giant Cone*, a dessert for two that consisted of an ice cream cone (see the picture) completely filled with ice cream. Bill and Bonnie ordered *The Giant Cone*—stuffed with three super scoops of Rocky Road and 2 scoops of Mint Chocolate Chip.

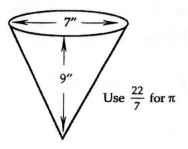

37) How many cubic inches of ice cream are served in *The Giant Cone*?

38) How many cubic inches of Rocky Road ice cream were served in *The Giant Cone* ordered by Bill and Bonnie?

39) One side of the square base of the great pyramid at Giza, Egypt is 720 feet; its height is 480 feet. What is the volume of this massive wonder of the world?

40-41) When wrapped inward, a deadly virus is the shape of a cube with a side of 0.0000016 inches.

40) What is the volume of one of these viruses? Give answer in scientific notation.

41) How many of these viruses could fit in a salt shaker which is 2 cubic inches in size? Give the answer in scientific notation and standard number form (round the first part of the scientific notation to the nearest tenth).

42-43) Marine biologists were studying an area of the Pacific Ocean south of the Hawaiian Islands. They were looking at a piece of ocean about 5 miles wide, 12 miles long, and with an ocean depth that averaged about 3 miles. Within a week they were able to estimate the shark population at 600.

42) Looking only at the ocean's surface, how many sharks were there per square mile?

43) How many sharks were there per cubic mile (round answer to the nearest tenth)?

44) Find the volume of a rectangular solid that has a length double its height and a height that is double its width. The width of the rectangle is equal to the edge of a cube that has a volume of 1 in³.

45) If a cone and a sphere share the same radius of 2 inches, what is the volume of the space inside the sphere not occupied by the cone?

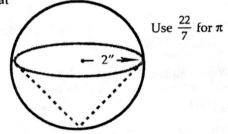

Use $\frac{22}{7}$ for π

46-48) Three tennis balls fit in a cylindrical can, one on top of the other. The top and bottom of the can each touch a ball and the edge of the balls touch the sides of the can. The radius of a tennis ball is 1.25 inches.

46) What is the volume of the can (round the answer to the nearest tenth)?

47) What is the volume of a fifth of a tennis ball (round answer to the nearest tenth)?

48) What is the volume of the can not occupied by the tennis balls (round the answer to the nearest tenth)?

r = 1.25 in

49) A rectangular aquarium has a base which is 20" x 15" and a height of 12". A 1.5 inch layer of rock covers the aquarium's bottom and it is decorated with 2 identical pyramids. The pyramids sit on the rock bottom, have square bases with sides of 3 inches and heights of 5 inches. What is the volume of the aquarium which is occupied by water?

50) A resort has a rectangular pool that is 100 feet long, 70 feet wide, and 6 feet deep. In the middle of the pool is an island the shape of a rectangular solid which has a length and width of 20 feet and a height of 7 feet (that is, it rises a foot above the level of the water). How many gallons of water are needed to fill the pool (1 cubic foot of water = 7.48 gallons)?

51-55 Melinda won a contract to grow cantaloupes for a canned fruit company on two acres of land. The company agreed to pay her $.03 per cubic inch of fruit. Melinda studied her options. She could grow a small cantaloupe that has an average diameter of 4.5 inches or a giant cantaloupe that has a 6.5 inch diameter. Both cantaloupes have a $\frac{1}{4}$ inch thick shell that will have to be thrown away. She knew that she would be able to harvest either 10,000 small cantaloupes or 7,000 of the large cantaloupes per acre of land. Use 3.14 for π.

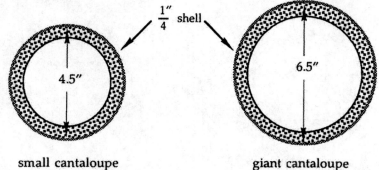

small cantaloupe   giant cantaloupe

51) How many cubic inches of fruit could she harvest per small cantaloupe that she grew?

52) How many cubic inches of fruit could she harvest per giant cantaloupe that she grew?

53) How many cubic inches of fruit could she harvest per acre if she grew the small cantaloupe?

54) How many cubic inches of fruit could she harvest per acre if she grew the giant cantaloupe?

55) Would Melinda earn more money growing the small or giant cantaloupes? How much more?

Skills Check

1. If the radius is 10, how many times larger than pi is the area of a half circle?

Use the shape below for questions 2 and 3:

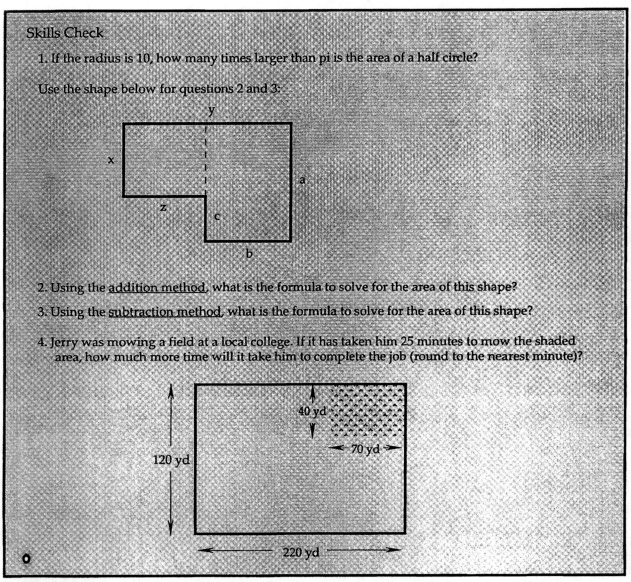

2. Using the <u>addition method</u>, what is the formula to solve for the area of this shape?

3. Using the <u>subtraction method</u>, what is the formula to solve for the area of this shape?

4. Jerry was mowing a field at a local college. If it has taken him 25 minutes to mow the shaded area, how much more time will it take him to complete the job (round to the nearest minute)?

Answers to Skills Check: 1) 50; 2) (x • z) + (a • b); 3) (y • a) - (z • c); 4) 211 minutes or 3 hours and 31 minutes.

Chapter 6   Algebraic Expressions

The first big mathematical transition in this book occurred when we introduced signed numbers in chapter 3. This was movement from arithmetic to prealgebra. We are now ready for our second major transition in mathematics—from prealgebra to pure algebra.

Algebra is an area of mathematics which uses symbols and variables (letters of the alphabet) instead of concrete numbers to problem solve. When we look at the equation of $4 + 3 = 7$, this is arithmetic. If we write the equation as $4 + x = 7$, we have algebra.

In fact, we have already been using variables and elements of algebra in our work—and we are still alive!! Algebra is a powerful problem-solving tool which generalizes all of the math truths we have studied! Remember, as we continue forward in math: **All arithmetic and prealgebra concepts and processes we have learned are still true.** Algebra demands that we apply these concepts and processes with unyielding faith.

Before we can take full advantage of algebra, in Section 6.1 we must learn some new vocabulary and concepts which are important to this new area of math.

Section 6.1   Algebraic Expressions: Monomials, Polynomials and Combining Like Terms

Objectives:

- To learn new vocabulary associated with algebraic expressions
- To recognize like and unlike terms
- To combine expressions
- To distribute a negative sign into a polynomial

Application:

At a family farm, two crates of fruit were brought to its roadside fruit stand for sale. The first crate had 20 apples and 30 bananas. The second crate had 30 apples and 15 cantaloupes. If a man stopped and bought 6 apples, 5 bananas, and 3 cantaloupes, how many of each kind of fruit was still left? Before solving this question, set up an expression that shows inside parentheses: (1) the amount of each kind of fruit in the first crate, (2) the amount of each kind of fruit in the second crate, and (3) the amount of each kind of fruit which the man bought.

Vocabulary:

> **Algebraic expression**—An **algebraic expression** is a mathematical phrase that includes a variable or variables. It does not have an equal sign. If it did, it would be an equation.
>
> Examples: $2x$ $-4y - 7$ $5x^2 - 3x + 2$ $3a^2b^3c + 2ab - c$

Monomial—A **monomial** (the same as a <u>term</u>) is an algebraic expression that is either a number, a variable, or a series of numbers and variables connected by multiplication and/or division.

Examples: 5   y $3x^2$ $\dfrac{2a}{5}$ $-12xyz$ $\dfrac{m}{6}$

Polynomial—A **polynomial** ("poly" means "many") is an algebraic expression that consists of 2 or more monomials (terms). <u>Terms are separated by</u> a combining operation, either <u>addition or subtraction</u>.

Binomial—A **binomial** ("bi" means "two") is a polynomial that consists **of 2 terms.**

Examples: $6x + 8$ is a binomial because it has two terms—the $6x$ and the 8. They are separated by the addition symbol.

$n - 3$ is a binomial because it consists of two terms—the n and the -3

Trinomial—A **trinomial** ("tri" means "three") is a polynomial that consists of 3 terms.

Examples: $5x + y - 5$ is a trinomial because it has three terms—the $5x$, the y, and the -5.

$r^4 - 3s^2 + rs$ is a trinomial because it consists of three terms—the r^4, the $-3s^2$, and the rs.

The Parts that make up a Monomial or a Term:

(1) **Coefficient**—A **coefficient** is a lone number or the number attached to the variable by multiplication.

(2) **Variable(s)**—A **variable** or variables are the letter(s) of the alphabet.

(3) **Degree**—The **degree** of a term is the sum of the exponents raised above the variables. If there is only one variable, the degree is the exponent above that variable.

*** Every term has a coefficient and a degree, but some do not have a variable. Let's look at the examples that follow.

Example #1: $3x^2$

where: **3** is the coefficient.
        x is the variable.
        2 is the degree.

Example #2:   y

where: 1 is the coefficient.

The coefficient here is an "invisible" <u>1</u>. There is no doubt that there is <u>one</u> "y" before us. When there is no written coefficient, it is always <u>1</u>.

y is the variable.

1 is the degree.

Unless otherwise written, every value has an <u>exponent of one</u> raised above it.

Example #3: $-2z$

where: **-2** is the coefficient.

The sign of the term belongs to the coefficient.

z is the variable.

1 is the degree.

Example #4: $\dfrac{2a^5}{3}$

where: $\dfrac{2}{3}$ is the coefficient.

We want to take note here that $\dfrac{2a^5}{3}$ is exactly the same as $\dfrac{2}{3}a^5$. Remember that the coefficient can be a whole number, a decimal, or a fraction.

a is the variable.

5 is the degree.

Example #5:   -b

where: **-1** is the coefficient.

Here is another example with the "invisible" coefficient of <u>1</u>. The coefficient is -1 because the sign belongs to the coefficient.

b is the variable.

1 is the degree.

Example #6: 7

where: 7 is the coefficient.

There is no variable.

0 is the degree.

How can a term without a variable have a degree of zero? We have to look at this theoretically. If there was a variable, what would the degree have to be for the expression to equal 7?

Theoretical example: $7 = 7x^?$ The only way that this statement can be true is if $x^?$ equals 1 (that is only $7 \cdot 1 = 7$). As a generalized rule, no matter what the value is for x, $x^?$ is always equal to one if the degree is 0. This is of course true because any non-zero value to the zero power equals 1.

Example #7: $8.4x^2y$

where: 8.4 is the coefficient.

x and y are the variables

3 is the degree.

3 is the sum of the exponents of both the variables in the term.

***Identifying the degree of a polynomial:** The degree of a polynomial is the highest degree of any single monomial in the expression.

Example: $7x^4 - 2x^3 + 4xy - 5$

To find the degree of a polynomial, we must identify the degree of each monomial or term. There are four terms.

$7x^4$ has a degree of 4. $-2x^3$ has a degree of 3.

$4xy$ has a degree of 2. -5 has a degree of 0.

The highest degree of any term is 4. Therefore, 4 is the degree of the polynomial.

Like terms—Terms that have the same variable or variables, with each variable raised to the same exponent, are called **like terms.** If terms are not like terms, they are called **unlike terms.**

Example #1: $3xy^2$ and $0.75xy^2$

These are like terms because they meet the two requirements. **They both have: (1) the same variables**—in this case they both have an x and a y, and **(2) each variable is raised to the same exponent**—in this case, the x variables are both raised to the power of 1 and the y variables are both raised to the power of 2.

***Remember: When identifying like terms, it <u>does</u> <u>not</u> matter what the coefficients are!

Example #2: $\dfrac{2y}{3}$ and $-6y$

These are **like terms**. They both have the same variables—in this case they both have a <u>y</u>, and both variables of y are raised to the same power of 1.

Example #3: 3.5 and 2

These are **like terms**. In a peculiar way, they both have the same variables— that is, in this case they both lack any variables. Because they both have no variables, they both have degrees of 0.

Example #4 3a and 3ab

These are **unlike terms**. They <u>do not</u> have the same variables. The first term has an <u>a</u> variable, but the second term has both an <u>a</u> and a <u>b</u> variable.

Example #5: $2x^4y^2z$ and $-5x^4yz^2$

These are **unlike terms**. These terms do meet the first requirement of like terms—they do have the same variables of <u>x</u>, <u>y</u>, and <u>z</u>. However, they <u>do not</u> meet the second requirement of like terms—they do not have the same exponents raised above each variable. In the first term the <u>y</u> variable has an exponent of 2 while the second term has an exponent of 1 above its <u>y</u> variable.

That alone is enough to prove that these are unlike terms. We should also take note, however, that the exponents above the <u>z</u> variables are also different. In the first term the exponent above the <u>z</u> variable is a 1 while in the second term there is an exponent of 2 above its <u>z</u> variable.

***Why is it important that we can identify <u>like terms</u>?** It is vital because we can combine (add/ subtract) <u>only</u> like terms. If the terms are unlike, they cannot be combined.

***Writing a polynomial:** When we write in a language, we agree upon a standard procedure— correct grammar and syntax (order of presentation). For polynomials, the standard writing syntax is to write our terms in the following order:

(1) **Write the terms alphabetically by their variables.** For example, a term with an <u>a</u> variable would be written before a term with a <u>b</u> variable, etc.

(2) **(If the variables are the same): Write the terms in descending (highest to lowest) order of degree.** For example, an x term with a degree of 3 would be written before an x term with a degree of 2.

Don't worry too much about this syntax for polynomials, but keep it in mind as you solve problems and write answers.

***Distributing a Negative Sign into a Parenthesis that Contains a Polynomial:** We already know that the negative sign in front of a parenthesis means "take the opposite sign of" whatever value is inside the parenthesis. We know that $-(6) = -6$ and that $-(-4) = 4$.

We will now expand upon this foundation. When we have a polynomial with unlike terms inside a parenthesis, we can't combine them. Therefore, when we distribute the subtraction (negative) sign into the parenthesis, it means that we "<u>take the opposite sign</u>" of <u>every term</u> inside the parenthesis.

Example #1: $-(3m - 5)$ The subtraction sign in front of the parenthesis is telling us to take the "opposite sign" of both $3m$ and -5.

After distributing the sign, we get: $-3m + 5$

Example #2: $-(-4xy + 3y + 7)$ The subtraction sign in front of the parenthesis is telling us to take the "opposite sign" of $-4xy$, $+3y$, and $+7$

After distributing the sign, we get: $4xy - 3y - 7$

***Remember that a Plus or Positive Sign is weak!!** Distributing a <u>Plus or Positive Sign</u> into a parenthesis <u>**NEVER** changes any signs</u> inside the parenthesis.

How to:

Combine Terms in a Polynomial:

1. Identify any like terms.

2. Combine the like terms by combining the coefficients. The variable(s) and degree of the like terms stay the same.

Example #1: $6x^3 - 2x^3$

Step #1: Identify any like terms in a polynomial.

$6x^3$ and $-2x^3$ are like terms.

Step #2: Combine the like terms by combining the coefficients.

$6x^3 - 2x^3$ is the same as $(6 - 2)(x^3)$ $\Rightarrow$ There are 4 x^3's

Answer: $4x^3$

Example #2: $\frac{2}{3} y^2 + \frac{1}{4} y - \frac{5}{6} y$

Step #1: Identify any like terms in a polynomial.

$\frac{2}{3} y^2$ is the only term with y^2

$\frac{1}{4} y$ and $-\frac{5}{6} y$ are like terms.

Step #2: Combine the like terms by combining the coefficients.

For the fractional coefficients, we find the common denominator of 12.

$\frac{1}{4} y - \frac{5}{6} y$ becomes $\frac{3}{12} y - \frac{10}{12} y$ which equals: $-\frac{7}{12} y$

Answer: $\frac{2}{3} y^2 - \frac{7}{12} y$

Notice that the answer is written in descending order of the degrees.

Here is a visual progression of the above problem without the written explanation:

$$\frac{2}{3} y^2 + \frac{1}{4} y - \frac{5}{6} y$$

$$\frac{2}{3} y^2 + \frac{3}{12} y - \frac{10}{12} y$$

$$\frac{2}{3} y^2 - \frac{7}{12} y$$

How to:

Simplify Polynomials:

1. Distribute the addition or subtraction symbol into the polynomial(s).

***Remember that a <u>plus sign</u> in front of a parenthesis <u>never changes anything</u>. However, the <u>minus sign</u> distributes into the parenthesis and <u>changes the sign</u> ("opposite of") <u>of every term inside the parenthesis</u>.

2. Reorder the terms so like terms are next to each other.

3. Combine the like terms by combining the coefficients. The variable(s) and degree of the like terms stay the same.

Example #3: Simplify the expression: $(4x - 6) + (x + 4)$

    Step #1: Distribute the addition or subtraction symbol into the polynomial(s).

        The first polynomial of $(4x - 6)$ has no sign in front of it. It stays the same.

        The second polynomial of $(x + 4)$ has a plus sign in front of it. It technically distributes into the parenthesis, <u>but a plus sign never changes anything</u>. Therefore this second polynomial also stays the same.

$$(4x - 6) + (x + 4) \quad \text{becomes} \quad (4x - 6) + x + 4$$

        The problem is the same now whether the parenthesis are there or not.

    Step #2: Reorder the terms so like terms are next to each other.

        The 4x and x are like terms. So are –6 and 4

$$(4x - 6) + x + 4 \quad \text{becomes} \quad 4x + x - 6 + 4$$

    Step #3: Combine the like terms by combining the coefficients.

$$4x + x - 6 + 4$$

Answer: **5x – 2** ***Notice that 4x + x equals 5x because the x term has an "invisible" coefficient of one.

    Here is a visual progression of the above problem without the written explanation:

$$(4x - 6) + (x + 4)$$
$$(4x - 6) + x + 4$$
$$4x + x - 6 + 4$$
$$\mathbf{5x - 2}$$

Example #4: Simplify the expression: $(8a + 3) - (-5a + 2)$

    Step #1: Distribute the addition or subtraction symbol into the polynomial(s).

        The first polynomial of $(8a + 3)$ has no sign in front of it. It stays the same.

        The second polynomial of $(-5a + 2)$ has a subtraction sign in front of it. The minus sign distributes into the parenthesis, meaning that we "take the opposite sign" of <u>every term</u> inside the parenthesis.

        We rewrite the problem: $(8a + 3) + 5a - 2$

Step #2: Reorder the terms so like terms are next to each other.

The 8a and 5a are like terms. So are the 3 and -2

Rewrite the problem: $8a + 5a + 3 - 2$

Step #3: Combine the like terms by combining the coefficients.

$$\underbrace{8a + 5a} + \underbrace{3 - 2}$$

Answer: $13a + 1$

Here is a visual progression of the above problem without the written explanation:

$$(8a + 3) \underbrace{- (-5a + 2)}$$

$$(8a + 3) + 5a - 2$$

$$\underbrace{8a + 5a} + \underbrace{3 - 2}$$

$$13a + 1$$

Sample #1:   Simplify: $7y^2 + 2y - 4 - 3y^2 - 2y - 3$

First we identify this as a combining problem.

We find like terms: $7y^2$ and $-3y^2$

$2y$ and $-2y$

-4 and -3

Reorder the terms to put like terms next to each other.

$$7y^2 + 2y - 4 - 3y^2 - 2y - 3$$

becomes $7y^2 - 3y^2 + 2y - 2y - 4 - 3$

Combine like terms:

$$\underbrace{7y^2 - 3y^2} \underbrace{+ 2y - 2y} \underbrace{- 4 - 3}$$
$$4y^2 \ + \ 0y \ - 7$$

$0y$ has a value of zero (any value multiplied by zero equals zero), so we don't write it in the answer.

Answer: $4y^2 - 7$

You try it now:

a) $-3m^3 + 5m^2 - 2 - 3m^3 - 2m^2 + 2$

b) $2a^2b - 2ab - 7 - 4a^2b - 5ab + 4$

Sample #2:   Simplify: $-(5x - 3) + (3x - 8)$

First we identify this as a combining of polynomials problem.

We have to distribute the signs into the parentheses.

The negative sign in front of the first polynomial of $(5x - 3)$ means to take the opposite sign of $5x$ and -3.

The positive sign in front of the second polynomial of $(3x - 8)$ does not change the signs of $3x$ and -8.

$$-(5x - 3) + (3x - 8)$$

becomes $-5x + 3 + 3x - 8$

Reorder the terms to put like terms next to each other.

$$-5x + 3 + 3x - 8$$

becomes $-5x + 3x + 3 - 8$

Combine like terms:

$$\underbrace{-5x + 3x}\ \underbrace{+ 3 - 8}$$

Answer: **$-2x - 5$**

▪ **You try it now:**

c) $-(m - 4) - (m + 3)$

d) $(6x^2 - 4x - 3) - (6x^2 - 4x + 3)$

Sample #3:   Simplify: Subtract $5r - 4$ from $r - 8$

First we have to translate this statement into pure math. The English states that we are subtracting the first polynomial from the second polynomial.

Translation: $(r - 8) - (5r - 4)$

***Notice that each polynomial has been put inside a parenthesis because each one is acting as a single unit or a quantity.

***Also, as always: the value that comes after the word "from" in this translation is what we start with.

Now this simply becomes a combining of polynomials problem.

We have to distribute the negative sign into the second parenthesis.

$$(r - 8) - (5r - 4)$$

becomes $(r - 8) - 5r + 4$

Reorder the terms to put like terms next to each other.

$$(r - 8) - 5r + 4$$

becomes $r - 5r - 8 + 4$

Combine like terms:

Answer: $-4r - 4$

You try it now:

e) Subtract $3r^2 - 2r - 1$ from $r^2 - 2r - 3$

f) Find the difference of $-8xy - 4x$ and $5xy - x$

Answers to You try it now: a) $-6m^3 + 3m^2$; b) $-2a^2b - 7ab - 3$; c) $-2m + 1$; d) -6; e) $-2r^2 - 2$; f) $-13xy - 3x$

Answer to Application: To approach this problem in a way which will help us gain algebraic skills, first set up a "math picture" of what exists here. Each crate and the fruit sold to the man will each be put inside a parenthesis. The set up is:

(20 apples + 30 bananas) + (30 apples + 15 cantaloupes) − (6 apples + 5 bananas + 3 cantaloupes)

The first thing we have to do is distribute the negative or subtraction sign into the last parenthesis to give the true value of each type of fruit. The negative sign means the "opposite sign" of every term inside the parenthesis.

− (6 apples + 5 bananas + 3 cantaloupes) becomes − 6 apples − 5 bananas − 3 cantaloupes

Rewrite the set up:

(20 apples + 30 bananas) + (30 apples + 15 cantaloupes) − 6 apples − 5 bananas − 3 cantaloupes

Now bring together like types of fruit and rewrite the problem:

20 apples + 30 apples − 6 apples + 30 bananas − 5 bananas + 15 cantaloupes − 3 cantaloupes

Now combine like types of fruit:

20 apples + 30 apples − 6 apples + 30 bananas − 5 bananas + 15 cantaloupes − 3 cantaloupes

Answer: 44 apples + 25 bananas + 12 cantaloupes

Of course in algebra we could write: $44a + 25b + 12c$ where a, b, and c are not apples, bananas, and cantaloupes, but unknown numbers.

6.1 Problems on Monomials, Polynomials & Combining Like Terms

In exercises #1-8, identify whether each of the given algebraic expressions is a monomial, a binomial, a trinomial, or none of these.

1) $2m + 4$

2) $4x^2y^2z$

3) $7x^2 - 6x + 4$

4) $5r^2 - 3r$

5) $3x^2 - \dfrac{x}{4} - 2y + 2$

6) $-7m + 3.2n - 1$

7) 5

8) $9x^3 - 3x + y + z$

In exercises #9-13, decide whether the following statements are True or False.

9) A binomial is a polynomial.

10) The degree of a polynomial is the highest degree of any monomial in the expression.

11) Like terms must have the same variable(s).

12) Like terms must have the same coefficients.

13) Like terms must have the same exponents above each common variable.

In exercises #14-20, answer the following questions.

14) What are the three parts that can make up a term?

15) The sign in front of a term belongs to what part of that term?

16) When combining like terms, what is the only part of the terms to change?

17) The negative sign in front of the following parenthesis changes the sign of how many terms? $-(2x + y)$

18) The negative sign in front of the following parenthesis changes the sign of how many terms?
$-(x - y) + z$

19) The negative sign in front of the following parenthesis changes the sign of how many terms? $-(x) + y$

20) The negative sign in front of the parenthesis below changes the sign of how many terms?
$-(-4x^2 + 2x - y) + 2$

In exercises #21-36, identify the coefficient, the variable(s), and the degree of each term. If there is no variable(s), state that.

21) $3x^4$

22) $-3y^5$

23) $-8a$

24) $2y$

25) $-7.6r$

26) $\dfrac{3}{5}x^4$

27) $\dfrac{2}{7}a^3$

28) $\dfrac{-9x^2}{5}$

29) $\dfrac{2m}{3}$

30) $\dfrac{x}{8}$

31) $-\dfrac{m}{6}$

32) $-r$

33) 11

34) -5

35) $-mn$

36) $4.2x^2y$

In exercises #37-42, state the degree of the given polynomial.

37) $3x^3 - 2x^2 + x - 5$ 38) $4x^2y^4 - 9$ 39) $7y - 2$

40) $12mno^2 - 4mn + 6$ 41) $18x^5y^2z$ 42) $-m^3n - m^2 + n^2$

In exercises #43-54, state whether the given terms are like or unlike.

43) $4x$ and $-\frac{1}{5}x$ 44) $7y$ and $0.62y$ 45) $5mn^2$ and $-mn^2$

46) $\frac{x}{5}$ and $\frac{z}{5}$ 47) $-3r$ and $-3s$ 48) $6x^2yz$ and $-2x^2y$

49) $3ab^2c$ and $3abc$ 50) $2m^3n^2$ and $4m^2n^3$ 51) $2.1rs$ and $4rst$

52) $\frac{3}{4}x^2$ and $-\frac{2x^2}{3}$ 53) $-3x$ and 4 54) 0.23 and $\frac{1}{10}$

In exercises #55-80, simplify the following expressions.

55) $3y + 2y$ 56) $6r - 4r$ 57) $-2m - 4m$ 58) $-3x + 7x$

59) $\frac{2}{5}rs + \frac{1}{10}rs$ 60) $\frac{1}{3}x^3 - \frac{2}{9}x^3$ 61) $4x - 3y$ 62) $-7m + 7n$

63) $4x - 4x$ 64) $-3y + 3y$ 65) $-y + 3y$ 66) $r + r$

67) $-x + 3x - x$ 68) $4m^2 - 6m^2 - 2m$ 69) $-m^3 - 3m^3 - 3$ 70) $8x^2 - 4xy + 4xy$

71) $-6x - \frac{4y}{3} + y$ 72) $\frac{m^2}{5} + \frac{m}{5} - \frac{m}{20}$ 73) $3xy^2 - xy^2 - 4x - 2$ 74) $r^3s^2t + 2r^3st - 3rst$

75) $5m^2 - 2m^2 + 2m - 5m$ 76) $-11xy - 3xy + z^2 - 3z^2$ 77) $\left(3ab - 2\right) + \left(2ab + 4\right)$

78) $\left(-7a^2 - a\right) + \left(-4a^2 - 3a\right)$ 79) $\left(x + y - z\right) + \left(x + y + z\right)$ 80) $\left(5m^2 + 3m - 4\right) + \left(-3m^2 - 3m + 2\right)$

In exercises #81-86, simplify the following expressions by distributing the negative sign into the parenthesis.

81) $-\left(2x - 6\right)$ 82) $-\left(3m^2 - 2mn - 4\right)$ 83) $-\left(-5x^2y + 7x + 1\right)$

84) $-\left(-2x^2 - 2x + 60\right)$ 85) $-\left(3r^2\right) - \left(5r - 2\right)$ 86) $-\left(-5m^2 + 5m\right) - \left(2n^2 - n\right)$

In exercises #87-100, simplify the following expressions.

87) $\left(-3xy - 4\right) - \left(2xy + 3\right)$ 88) $\left(4a - 6\right) - \left(2a - 4\right)$

89) $\left(5r^2s^2 + 3rs\right) - \left(-2r^2s^2 + 3rs\right)$ 90) $-\left(8m - 3\right) + \left(8m + 2\right)$

91) $-(-x + 3) + (3x - 5)$

92) $-(3y - 11) - (10y + 7)$

93) $-(m - 4) - (m + 4)$

94) $-3x^2 - 2x^2 + 4x - 2x - 3 + 8$

95) $x^3y + x^3y - 2x^2 - x^2 + 4 - 3$

96) $-2ab - 3ab - 6a - a + b - b$

97) $2m^2 - 5m + n^2 - n + 3 - 7$

98) $4x^2y - x^2y - 5x - 5y - 2$

99) $(6r^2 - r - 4) - (-2r^2 + 3r + 3)$

100) $(-3y^2 + 2y + 10) - (4y^2 - y - 1)$

In exercises #101-108: a) translate the following words into math expressions, and then b) simplify the expressions.

101) Find the sum of $3x - 8$ and $-3x + 8$.

102) Find the sum of $3m^2 + m - 3$ and $2m^2 + m - 3$.

103) Find the difference of $-4a + 7$ and $8a - 4$.

104) Find the difference of $a^2 - 3a$ and $3a^2 - a$.

105) Find the difference of $2ab - 2a - b$ and $5ab + 3a - 2b$.

106) Subtract $7x - 3$ from $-3x - 5$.

107) Subtract $-3r^2 + 2$ from $-r^2 + 1$

108) Subtract $-2x^2 + 3x - 6$ from $-2x^2 - 3x - 6$

Skills Check

1. What is the volume of a cube that has a height of 8 inches?

2. What is the volume of a cone with a radius of 7 feet and a height of 20 feet (use 3.14 for π)? Round answer to the nearest whole foot.

3. Change $\dfrac{2673}{56}$ to a mixed number.

4. What is the volume of a sphere with a diameter of $4\dfrac{1}{2}$ inches (use $\dfrac{22}{7}$ for π)? Give the answer as a mixed number.

Answers to Skills Check: 1) 512 cubic inches; 2) 1026 cubic feet; 3) $47\dfrac{41}{56}$; 4) $47\dfrac{41}{56}$ cubic inches

Section 6.2   Simplifying Algebraic Expressions Involving Multiplication & Division

Objectives:

• To multiply terms

• To divide terms

• To distribute a term into a polynomial

Application:

Three bins of fruit were delivered to the store in the morning. Each bin contained 30 apples, 50 bananas, and 15 cantaloupes. How many of each kind of fruit did the store receive? Before solving this question, set up an algebraic expression that shows the number of bins being multiplied by the amount of each type of fruit in one bin.

Vocabulary:

Distributive Property—In math, **distribution** means multiplying into a parenthesis. We have already distributed a negative sign into a parenthesis in the last section. Now we will distribute an entire term.

Example #1: $2(4 + 7)$ The $(4 + 7)$ in the parenthesis is being multiplied by the 2. We have already learned to follow order of operations and solve inside the parenthesis first.

This would give us: $2(11)$ which of course equals 22.

The distribution process can solve this problem by separately multiplying the 2 by each of the values inside the parenthesis.

In other words: $2(4 + 7)$ is the same as $2(4) + 2(7)$.

$\underline{2(4)} + \underline{2(7)} = 8 + 14$ which gives us the same answer of 22.

Although we could solve this problem by using the distribution property, we usually reserve its use for a polynomial inside a parenthesis where the terms are unlike and cannot be combined.

Example #2: $-3(8x^2 - 2x + 5)$ Here the $(8x^2 - 2x + 5)$ is being multiplied by the -3.

The three terms inside the parenthesis are all unlike terms so we can only simplify this expression by using the distribution process—that is, multiplying each term inside the parenthesis by the -3.

$-3(8x^2 - 2x + 5)$ means $-3(8x^2) + (-3)(-2x) + (-3)(5)$

$$\underbrace{-3\left(8x^2\right)}_{} + \underbrace{(-3)(-2x)}_{} + \underbrace{(-3)(5)}_{}$$

$-24x^2 + 6x - 15$ This is the simplified answer.

***Taking a Second Look at the Division of Exponential Expressions with Same Bases: We have already learned that when we identify the division of same bases, we subtract the exponents.

Let's look at how we simplified a problem like this in Chapter 4.

Example #1: $\left(\dfrac{5^2}{5^5}\right) = 5^{(2-5)} = 5^{-3} = \dfrac{1}{5^3}$

This is good math. When we have same bases, we can always subtract the exponent in the numerator by the exponent in the denominator. <u>This will always be good math</u>. We can always use this method and get the correct answer. But now that we have a solid foundation on how this process works, we can use another method to solve this problem quickly.

We can in fact simplify a "division of same bases" problem by always subtracting the exponent of less value from the exponent of the greater value. It doesn't matter which exponent is in the numerator and which exponent is in the denominator. The benefit of this process is that we will always get an answer with a positive exponent immediately.

Same Example #1: $\left(\dfrac{5^2}{5^5}\right)$

We identify that the exponent in the numerator is of less value than the exponent in the denominator. Therefore we can subtract the exponent of 2 from the exponent of 5.

$\left(\dfrac{5^2}{5^5}\right)$ becomes $\dfrac{1}{5^{(5-2)}}$ which is $\dfrac{1}{5^3}$

Does this "short cut" make sense? Well, let's look at $\left(\dfrac{5^2}{5^5}\right)$ in the factored form of

$\dfrac{5 \cdot 5}{5 \cdot 5 \cdot 5 \cdot 5 \cdot 5}$. By canceling common factors $\left(\dfrac{{}^1 5 \cdot {}^1 5}{{}^1 5 \cdot {}^1 5 \cdot 5 \cdot 5 \cdot 5}\right)$, we can see that there is still 5^3 in the denominator. This visualization also helps us see why there is still a 1 in the numerator.

Example #2: $\dfrac{a^3 b^{-2}}{ab^4}$

We identify two "division of same bases."

For the "a" bases, the exponent in the denominator is of less value than the exponent in the numerator. Therefore we can subtract the exponent of 1 from the exponent of 3.

For the "b" bases, the exponent in the numerator is of less value than the exponent in the denominator. Therefore we can subtract the exponent of −2 from the exponent of 4.

Visualizing the process, this is what we get: $\dfrac{a^{(3-1)}}{b^{[4-(-2)]}}$

The simplified answer is: $\dfrac{a^2}{b^6}$

We discover that this method makes sense. In a division of same bases problem, the base ends up wherever (the numerator or the denominator) the exponent of the greatest value is located.

How to:

Multiply Terms:

1. Look at the given terms. Identify the coefficient and the variable part (variable(s) and its exponent(s)) of each term.

2. Multiply the coefficients.

3. Multiply the variable(s) (remember to follow the rule of exponents for multiplication of same bases—add the exponents!).

Example #1: $3x^2 \cdot (-x)$

Step #1: Identify the coefficient and the variable part of each term.

$3x^2$ has a coefficient of 3 and a variable part of x^2.

$(-x)$ has a coefficient of -1 and a variable part of x.

Step #2: Multiply the coefficients.

$3(-1) = -3$

Step #3: Multiply the variable(s).

$x^2 \cdot x = x^3$ because with multiplication of same bases, we add the exponents.

Answer: $-3x^3$

Example #2: $4a^3bc \cdot 2ac$

Step #1: Identify the coefficient and the variable part of each term.

$4a^3bc$ has a coefficient of 4 and a variable part of a^3bc.

$2ac$ has a coefficient of 2 and a variable part of ac.

Step #2: Multiply the coefficients.

$4(2) = 8$

Step #3: Multiply the variable(s).

$a^3bc \cdot ac = a^4bc^2$ To see this, understand that the like variables are multiplied by each other.

$a^3 \cdot a = a^4$ because with multiplication of same bases, we add the exponents.

Only the first term has a b variable. Don't discard it. It is part of the multiplication problem and must be a part of the answer.

$c \cdot c = c^2$ because with multiplication of same bases, we add the exponents.

Answer: $8a^4bc^2$

How to:

Distribute a term into a parenthesis:

1. Multiply the term outside the parenthesis by <u>every</u> term inside the parenthesis, one multiplication problem at a time.

2. After distribution, write a combining expression where the product of each multiplication problem is connected by the sign of its answer.

***Remember: After distribution, the parenthesis is gone.

Example #3: $7a\left(2a^2b - 3a + 4\right)$

Step #1: Multiply the term outside the parenthesis by <u>every</u> term inside the parenthesis, one multiplication problem at a time.

The term outside the parenthesis, the "7a" must be multiplied individually with the terms inside the parenthesis, the "$2a^2b$," the "$-3a$," and the "4."

$7a \cdot 2a^2b = \mathbf{14a^3b}$

$7a \cdot (-3a) = \mathbf{-21a^2}$

$7a \cdot 4 = \mathbf{28a}$

Step #2: Write a combining expression where the product of each multiplication problem is connected by the sign of its answer.

$14a^3b - 21a^2 + 28a$

Answer: $14a^3b - 21a^2 + 28a$

***Another way to visualize distribution is written below:

$7a\left(2a^2b - 3a + 4\right)$ is the same as $\underline{7a\left(2a^2b\right)} + \underline{7a\left(-3a\right)} + \underline{7a\left(4\right)}$

Distribute and we get the same answer: **$14a^3b - 21a^2 + 28a$**

Example #4: $\dfrac{7x^4y^{-2}}{21x^3y^{-5}}$

Step #1: Identify the coefficient and the variable part of each term.

The coefficient of the numerator is 7.

The coefficient of the denominator is 21.

The variable part in the numerator is x^4y^{-2}.

The variable part in the denominator is x^3y^{-5}.

Step #2: Simplify the coefficients.

The common factor for 7 and 21 is 7; $\dfrac{7}{21}$ reduces to $\dfrac{1}{3}$

Step #3: Divide the variables.

$\dfrac{x^4}{x^3} = x$ After identifying that the exponent in the denominator has less value than the exponent in the numerator, we subtract the smaller exponent of 3 from the exponent of 4 in the numerator $\left(\dfrac{x^{(4-3)}}{1} \right)$. This leaves us with the base of x raised to the power of 1 in the numerator.

$\dfrac{y^{-2}}{y^{-5}} = y^3$ After identifying that the exponent in the denominator has less value than the exponent in the numerator, we subtract the smaller exponent of –5 from the exponent of –2 in the numerator $\left(\dfrac{y^{[-2-(-5)]}}{1} \right)$. This leaves us with the base of y raised to the power of 3 in the numerator.

***Notice that the –5 has less value than the –2 because it resides farther to the left on the number line.

Answer: $\dfrac{1}{3}xy^3$ or $\dfrac{xy^3}{3}$

Sample #1: Simplify: $\left(-3m^2\right)\left(\dfrac{1}{5}\,mn\right)\left(\dfrac{5}{6}\,mn^2\right)$

We have a multiplication problem—multiplying 3 terms together.

Multiply the coefficients. $\left(-\dfrac{3}{1}\right) \bullet \dfrac{1}{5} \bullet \dfrac{5}{6} = -\dfrac{1}{2}$

Multiply the like variables: $m^2 \bullet m \bullet m = m^4$

$$n \bullet n^2 = n^3$$

Answer: $-\dfrac{1}{2}\,m^4n^3$ or $-\dfrac{m^4n^3}{2}$

You try it now:

a) Simplify: $(7x)\left(-2x^2y^2\right)(-3x)$

b) Simplify: $\left(\dfrac{3r}{4}\right)\left(\dfrac{2s^2}{3}\right)(5r)$

Sample #2: Simplify: $2r^2s\left(-4r + rs - 2s\right)$

We have a distribution or a multiplication problem. The term outside the parenthesis, the "$2r^2s$" needs to be multiplied by each of three terms inside the parenthesis.

$$2r^2s \bullet (-4r) = -8r^3s$$

$$2r^2s \bullet rs = 2r^3s^2$$

$$2r^2s \bullet (-2s) = -4r^2s^2$$

Now write these products in a combining expression.

Answer: $-8r^3s + 2r^3s^2 - 4r^2s^2$

***Remember that here is another way to visualize distribution:

$2r^2s\left(-4r + rs - 2s\right)$ is the same as $\underline{2r^2s\left(-4r\right)} + \underline{2r^2s\left(rs\right)} + \underline{2r^2s\left(-2s\right)}$

Distribute and we get the same answer: $-8r^3s + 2r^3s^2 - 4r^2s^2$

You try it now:

c) Simplify: $-3m\left(2m^2 - 4m - 2\right)$

d) Simplify: $4xy^2\left(-2x - 2y + 1\right)$

Sample #3: Simplify: $\dfrac{40x^3y}{8x^5y^2}$

Reduce the coefficient (by the common factor of 8): $\dfrac{40}{8} = \dfrac{5}{1}$

Divide the "x" variables: $\dfrac{x^3}{x^5} = \dfrac{1}{x^2}$

Divide the "y" variables: $\dfrac{y}{y^2} = \dfrac{1}{y}$

Answer: $\dfrac{5}{x^2y}$

■ **You try it now:**

e) Simplify: $\dfrac{-8a}{2a^3b^2}$

f) Simplify: $\dfrac{5x^4y^3z}{20x^2z}$

Sample #4: Simplify: $\dfrac{8x^3y^{-2}}{12x^{-2}y}$

Reduce the coefficient (by the common factor of 4): $\dfrac{8}{12} = \dfrac{2}{3}$

Divide the "x" variables: $\dfrac{x^3}{x^{-2}} = \dfrac{x^5}{1}$

Divide the "y" variables: $\dfrac{y^{-2}}{y} = \dfrac{1}{y^3}$

Answer: $\dfrac{2x^5}{3y^3}$

■ **You try it now:**

g) Simplify: $\dfrac{-12rs^{-1}}{15r^{-2}s^4}$

h) Simplify: $\dfrac{18a^2bc}{20a}$

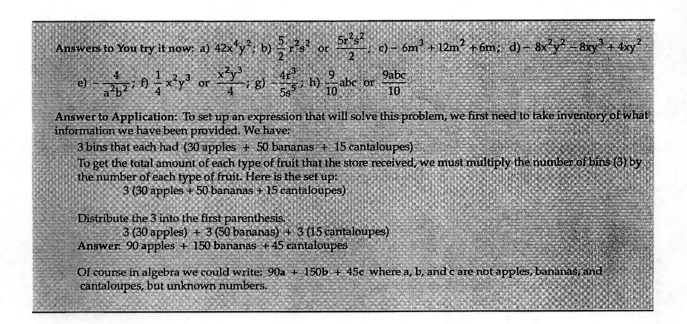

Answers to You try it now: a) $42x^4y^2$; b) $\frac{5}{2}r^2s^2$ or $\frac{5r^2s^2}{2}$; c) $-6m^3 + 12m^2 + 6m$; d) $-8x^2y^2 - 8xy^3 + 4xy^2$

e) $-\frac{4}{a^2b^2}$; f) $\frac{1}{4}x^2y^3$ or $\frac{x^2y^3}{4}$; g) $-\frac{4r^3}{5s^5}$; h) $\frac{9}{10}abc$ or $\frac{9abc}{10}$

Answer to Application: To set up an expression that will solve this problem, we first need to take inventory of what information we have been provided. We have:

3 bins that each had (30 apples + 50 bananas + 15 cantaloupes)

To get the total amount of each type of fruit that the store received, we must multiply the number of bins (3) by the number of each type of fruit. Here is the set up:

3 (30 apples + 50 bananas + 15 cantaloupes)

Distribute the 3 into the first parenthesis.

3 (30 apples) + 3 (50 bananas) + 3 (15 cantaloupes)

Answer: 90 apples + 150 bananas + 45 cantaloupes

Of course in algebra we could write: 90a + 150b + 45c where a, b, and c are not apples, bananas, and cantaloupes, but unknown numbers.

Exercise 6.2:   Problems with Simplifying Algebraic Expressions Involving Multiplication and Division

In exercises #1-4, answer the following questions.

1) In math, distribution refers to what operation?

2) The 5y in the expression of $5y\left(2y^2 - y + 3\right)$ affects how many terms?

3) The -2 in the expression of $-2\left(m - 4\right) + 7n$ affects how many terms?

4) The $4rs^2$ in the expression of $4rs^2\left(r^2 + 2rs - s^2\right) - 8$ affects how many terms?

In exercises #5-16, decide the outcome of the "x" variable in the simplified answer. Will the "x" variable: (1) be gone, (2) be in the numerator, or (3) be in the denominator? If the answer has "no denominator," that is the same as saying the answer is in the numerator because every value has a denominator of 1.

5) $\frac{4x^2}{2x^5}$

6) $\frac{4xy}{5x^2y}$

7) $\frac{3x^3}{2x^{-6}}$

8) $\frac{x^{-4}}{x}$

9) $\frac{2x^{-3}}{2x^{-2}}$

10) $\frac{-7x^{-1}}{5x^{-2}}$

11) $-6x^3\left(4x^{-2}\right)$

12) $xy^{-2} \bullet x^{-1}y$

13) $-x\left(x^4\right)$

14) $4x^2y\left(3x^{-4}\right)\left(x^{-1}y^3\right)$

15) $\frac{x^3}{y} \bullet \frac{x^5}{x^8}$

16) $x^{-3} \bullet x^{-5}$

In exercises #17–20, decide whether each group of expressions all have the same value. Answer yes or no. If your answer is no, identify the letter of the one expression that does not equal the others.

17) a) $\dfrac{7}{3}x^2y$ b) $\dfrac{7x^2y}{3}$ c) $\dfrac{7}{3} \cdot \dfrac{x^2}{1} \cdot \dfrac{y}{1}$ d) $\dfrac{(7 \cdot x \cdot x \cdot y)}{3}$

18) a) $5a^2b^{-3}$ b) $5a^2 \cdot b^{-3}$ c) $5a^2 \cdot \dfrac{1}{b^3}$ d) $\dfrac{5a^2}{b^3}$

19) a) $-7m^2n^{-1}$ b) $\dfrac{-7}{1} \cdot \dfrac{m^2}{1} \cdot \dfrac{n^{-1}}{1}$ c) $\dfrac{m^2}{7n^1}$ d) $\dfrac{-7m^2}{n}$

20) a) $\dfrac{4x^{-3}y^2}{5x^2}$ b) $\dfrac{4}{5} \cdot \dfrac{x^{-3}}{x^2} \cdot \dfrac{y^2}{1}$ c) $\dfrac{4}{5} \cdot \dfrac{x^{-5}}{1} \cdot \dfrac{y^2}{1}$ d) $\dfrac{4y^2}{5x^5}$

In exercises #21–36, simplify these multiplication of monomials problems.

21) $-4a^2 \bullet -2a$ 22) $6x \bullet -4x^3$ 23) $5r^2s \bullet rs^2$ 24) $2mn^5(-2)$

25) $4 \bullet \left(-7x^2y^2z\right)$ 26) $2a^2b^3c^4 \bullet 5a^3b^2c$ 27) $-m^2 \bullet n$ 28) $-a \bullet (-b)$

29) $\left(-3x^2\right)\left(4xy\right)$ 30) $(11rs)\left(2st^2\right)$ 31) $\left(\dfrac{3}{4}r^2\right)\left(\dfrac{1}{4}rs\right)$ 32) $\left(\dfrac{3}{5}x^2y\right)\left(\dfrac{5}{3}x^2\right)$

33) $\left(\dfrac{7x^{-2}y}{8}\right)\left(\dfrac{4x^2y^2}{3}\right)$ 34) $\left(\dfrac{5a^{-1}b^3}{6}\right)\left(\dfrac{8ab^{-3}}{5c}\right)$ 35) $(-4x)(-3xy)(-xz)$ 36) $(3m)\left(m^2n\right)(-n)$

In exercises #37-48, simplify the following expressions by distributing the term outside the parenthesis to <u>every</u> term inside the parenthesis.

37) $4(2x - 5)$ 38) $3\left(-4y^2 - 7\right)$ 39) $6a(-5ab - 5)$

40) $-2m(-3m - 4)$ 41) $-3x\left(2x^2 - 3x + 5\right)$ 42) $-2ab(a - 3b - 1)$

43) $2x^2y\left(-4x^2 - 2xy + 1\right)$ 44) $7xy^2(-3x - 2y + 7)$ 45) $-x(-2x + y - 1)$

46) $\dfrac{2}{3}r^2(-9r - 3)$ 47) $\dfrac{3}{4}mn(8m - 4n)$ 48) $-\dfrac{3}{5}\left(15r^3 + 2r^2\right)$

In exercises #49-60, simplify these division of monomials problems.

49) $\dfrac{12x^2y}{4x}$ 50) $\dfrac{4xyz^2}{10xy}$ 51) $\dfrac{-3a^2}{9b^3c}$ 52) $\dfrac{-6ab}{15ab^4}$

53) $\dfrac{27xy^3z^5}{18x^4yz^3}$

54) $\dfrac{50x^5y^2z}{35x^3y^2z^4}$

55) $\dfrac{10rs^{-2}}{100r^{-1}s^3}$

56) $\dfrac{5r^2s^4}{20r^{-1}s^{-2}}$

57) $\dfrac{-2a^3bc}{8a^{-1}c}$

58) $\dfrac{-3a^2b^2c^{-1}}{27a^3b^4c^3}$

59) $-\dfrac{x^5y^{-3}z^{-1}}{2x^{-4}y^{-2}z^{-5}}$

60) $-\dfrac{6x^{-1}y^2z}{2x^{-1}y^2z}$

In exercises #61–68, simplify the following problems.

61) Find the length of Side 1 (s_1).

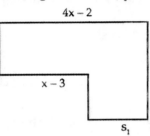

62) Find the length of Side "a."

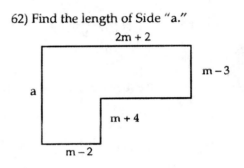

63–64) Use the figure below:

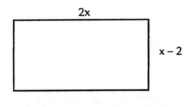

63) What is the perimeter of the rectangle?

64) What is the area of the rectangle?

65–66) Use the figure below:

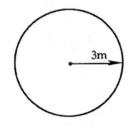

65) What is the diameter of the circle?

66) What is the circumference of the circle (use 3.14 for π)?

67–68) Use the figure below:

67) What expression would represent the area of the triangle if its area was doubled?

68) Find the area of the unshaded region of the figure below if the area of the square is $16m^2 - 16m + 4$ and the area of the shaded region is $4m^2 - 2m - 8$.

In exercises #69–74: a) translate the following words into math expressions, and b) simplify the expressions.

69) Find the product of $3m$ and the binomial of $-2mn + 3$.

70) Find the product of $-5rs$ and the binomial of $-r + s$.

71) Find the quotient of $10x^3y$ and $4xy^2$

72) Find the quotient of $12x^2y^2$ and $6x^4y$

73) Distribute $7m$ into the expression of $\left(-8m^2 - 3m + 2\right)$.

74) Distribute $-2n$ into the expression of $\left(-4m^2 + 4mn - 1\right)$.

Skills Check

1. Simplify: $-\left(2x^2 - 3xy + 4\right)$

2. Like terms have what in common?

3. Find the difference of $3rs - 7$ and $-2rs + 5$

4. Subtract $4xy - 8x$ from $-2xy - 3$

Answers to Skills Check: 1) $-2x^2 + 3xy - 4$; 2) Like terms have the same variable(s) and the same exponents raised above each variable; 3) set up: $\left(3rs - 7\right) - \left(-2rs + 5\right)$; answer: $5rs - 12$; 4) set up: $\left(-2xy - 3\right) - \left(4xy - 8x\right)$; answer: $-6xy + 8x - 3$

Section 6.3 Terms Raised to a Power and Simplifying More Complex Algebraic Expressions

Objectives:

• To apply the power to a power exponent rule to terms

• To simplify algebraic expressions following the order of operations

Application:

The store manager took a quick inventory of the fruit which a local farmer had brought to him that morning. There were four bins that were labeled as follows: 45 apples, 60 bananas, and 20 cantaloupes. Another 2 bins were labeled as follows: 50 apples and 30 cantaloupes. Finally, there was a hand-written note that said that the three families who had harvested the fruit had each taken 10 apples, 10 bananas, and 5 cantaloupes. How many of each kind of fruit did the store receive? Before solving this question, set up an algebraic expression that shows: (1) the amount of each type of fruit in the first four bins, (2) the amount of each type of fruit inside the next two bins, and (3) the amount of each type of fruit which the families took.

Vocabulary:

Remember the Order of Operations—**We must remind ourselves again that the one overarching process to <u>always</u> follow when solving mathematical expressions is the** order of operations—PEMDAS. We <u>first</u> **do what is inside the parenthesis,** <u>second</u> **we solve the exponent(s),** <u>third</u> **we work out any multiplication and division (left to right) and** <u>last</u> **we work out any addition and subtraction (<u>combining</u> is always done last).**

Let's look at the following problem: $8 \div (-2) + 5 \cdot 3^2$

We can agree that this expression has 4 operations—division, addition, multiplication, and an exponent. To solve this we follow PEMDAS.

Evaluate the exponent:	$8 \div (-2) + 5 \cdot \underset{\smile}{3^2}$
Evaluate the division:	$\underset{\smile}{8 \div (-2)} + 5 \cdot 9$
Evaluate the multiplication:	$-4 + \underset{\smile}{5 \cdot 9}$
Evaluate the addition (combining):	$\underset{\smile}{-4 + 45}$
Answer:	**41**

Simplify Algebraic Expressions **by following** the Order of Operations. **If we understand the example problem above, then we already know how to solve the more complex algebraic expressions in this section.**

Example and sample problems will of course follow, but look at the example problem below and recognize that you already know the framework under which we will solve these problems. The only difference here is that we are simplifying, not evaluating.

$$\text{Example:} \quad \frac{-8a^3b}{2a} + 5b \cdot (3a)^2$$

We can see here that we have 4 operations—division $(-8a^3b \div 2a)$, addition $(+5b)$, multiplication $\left(5b \cdot (3a)^2\right)$, and an exponent raised above a term $\left[(3a)^2\right]$. To simplify we follow PEMDAS.

Simplify the exponent $\left[(3a)^2 \text{ means } 3a \cdot 3a\right]$: $\qquad \dfrac{-8a^3b}{2a} + 5b \cdot \underline{(3a)^2}$

Simplify the division: $\qquad\qquad\qquad\qquad \dfrac{-8a^3b}{2a} + 5b \cdot 9a^2$

Simplify the multiplication: $\qquad\qquad\qquad -4a^2b + \underline{5b \cdot 9a^2}$

Simplify the addition (combining like terms): $\qquad -4a^2b + 45a^2b$

$$\text{Answer:} \qquad 41a^2b$$

How to:

Simplify a Term with a Power raised above it:

1. Apply the exponent rule of "power to a power" to the coefficient. Always evaluate the coefficient.

2. Apply the exponent rule of "power to a power" to the variable(s) (remember to follow the rule of exponents for power to a power—multiply the exponents!).

Example #1: $\left(4a^2b\right)^3$

Step #1: Apply the exponent rule of "power to a power" to the coefficient.

The exponent of 3 affects all parts of the term inside the parenthesis. It first affects the coefficient of 4.

This means we have: $\left(4^1\right)^3$. Power to a power gives us 4^3.

Always evaluate the coefficient: $4^3 = 64$

Step #2: Apply the exponent rule of "power to a power" to the variable(s).

The exponent of 3 affects a^2. $\left(a^2\right)^3 = a^6$

The exponent of 3 affects b^1. $\left(b^1\right)^3 = b^3$

Answer: $64a^6b^3$

How to:

Simplify an Algebraic Expression with Multiple-Operations:

1. Follow the Order of Operations (PEMDAS).

    (a) Simplify any work inside a Parenthesis first.

    (b) Simplify any Exponent work (the power to a power rule).

    (c) Simplify any Multiplication and Division (working left to right).

    (d) Simplify any combining (Addition and Subtraction).

Example #2: $2x\left(5x^2 - 4xy - 3\right) + \left(-3x^3 - x^2y + 4\right)$

Step #1: (a) Simplify any work inside a parenthesis first.

Inside each parenthesis there are only unlike terms. We can't do anything here.

Step #2: (b) Simplify any exponent work (the power to a power rule).

The only exponents are individually raised above "x" variables. There are no exponents raised above a parenthesis to create a "power to a power" expression. There is nothing to do here.

Step #3: (c) Simplify any multiplication and division (working left to right).

We do have multiplication. The polynomial of $\left(5x^2 - 4xy - 3\right)$ is being multiplied by the 2x term. We must distribute (multiply) the 2x to every term inside the parenthesis.

$2x\left(5x^2 - 4xy - 3\right)$ is the same as $2x\left(5x^2\right) + 2x\left(-4xy\right) + 2x\left(-3\right)$

The problem of: $\underline{2x\left(5x^2 - 4xy - 3\right)} + \left(-3x^3 - x^2y + 4\right)$

becomes: $10x^3 - 8x^2y - 6x + \left(-3x^3 - x^2y + 4\right)$

Now the problem is all combining.

Step #4: (d) Simplify any combining (addition and subtraction).

First we need to distribute the plus sign into the second parenthesis. Of course the plus sign never changes any other signs. $+ \left(-3x^3 - x^2y + 4\right)$ is the same as $-3x^3 - x^2y + 4$

The problem now looks like: $10x^3 - 8x^2y - 6x - 3x^3 - x^2y + 4$

Reorder/put like terms next to each other. We can combine <u>only</u> like terms. Remember to write the terms in the proper syntax: (1) alphabetically, and then, (2) by order of degree.

The problem now looks like: $\underbrace{10x^3 - 3x^3}\ \underbrace{-8x^2y - x^2y}\ -6x + 4$

Combine like terms: $7x^3 - 9x^2y - 6x + 4$

We are done. **Answer:** $7x^3 - 9x^2y - 6x + 4$

Example #3: $\dfrac{-9r^2s^2}{3r} \cdot \left(-8r^2 + 3s + 2\right) - \left(r^3s^2 - rs^3 - 6rs^2\right)$

Step #1: (a) Simplify any work inside a parenthesis first.

Inside each parenthesis there are only unlike terms. We can't do anything here.

Step #2: (b) Simplify any exponent work (the power to a power rule).

The only exponents are individually raised above "r" and "s" variables. There are no exponents raised above a parenthesis to create a "power to a power" expression. There is nothing to do here.

Step #3: (c) Simplify any multiplication and division (working left to right).

We do have multiplication and division. We must work left to right, so we will solve the division problem of $\dfrac{-9r^2s^2}{3r}$ first.

Divide the coefficients: $\dfrac{-9}{3} = -\dfrac{3}{1}$.

Divide the variables: $\dfrac{r^2}{r} = \dfrac{r}{1}$. $\dfrac{s^2}{1}$ stays as $\dfrac{s^2}{1}$

$\dfrac{-9r^2s^2}{3r}$ becomes $-\dfrac{3}{1} \cdot \dfrac{r}{1} \cdot \dfrac{s^2}{1}$ which is $-3rs^2$

The problem of: $\underbrace{\dfrac{-9r^2s^2}{3r}} \cdot \left(-8r^2 + 3s + 2\right) - \left(r^3s^2 - rs^3 - 6rs^2\right)$

becomes: $-3rs^2 \cdot \left(-8r^2 + 3s + 2\right) - \left(r^3s^2 - rs^3 - 6rs^2\right)$

Now we must solve the multiplication.

The polynomial of $\left(-8r^2 + 3s + 2\right)$ is being multiplied by the $-3rs^2$ term. We must distribute (multiply) the $-3rs^2$ to every term inside the parenthesis.

$-3rs^2 \cdot \left(-8r^2 + 3s + 2\right)$ is the same as $-3rs^2\left(-8r^2\right) + \left(-3rs^2\right)(3s) + \left(-3rs^2\right)(2)$

The problem of: $\underbrace{-3rs^2 \cdot \left(-8r^2 + 3s + 2\right)} - \left(r^3s^2 - rs^3 - 6rs^2\right)$

becomes: $24r^3s^2 - 9rs^3 - 6rs^2 - \left(r^3s^2 - rs^3 - 6rs^2\right)$

Now the problem is all combining.

Step #4: (d) Simplify any combining (addition and subtraction).

First we need to distribute the subtraction sign info the second parenthesis. The subtraction (negative) sign changes the sign of every term inside the parenthesis.

$-\left(r^3s^2 - rs^3 - 6rs^2\right)$ is the same as $-r^3s^2 + rs^3 + 6rs^2$

The problem now looks like: $24r^3s^2 - 9rs^3 - 6rs^2 - r^3s^2 + rs^3 + 6rs^2$

Reorder/put like terms next to each other. Here, we need to look very closely at the terms, identifying both the variables and the exponents above them. At first glance some of these may appear to be like terms, but upon closer inspection we see that they are in fact unlike terms.

Like terms: $24r^3s^2$ and $-r^3s^2$

$-9rs^3$ and $+rs^3$

$-6rs^2$ and $+6rs^2$

Remember to write the terms in the proper syntax: (1) alphabetically, and then, (2) by order of degree.

The problem now looks like: $\underbrace{24r^3s^2 - r^3s^2} \underbrace{-9rs^3 + rs^3} \underbrace{-6rs^2 + 6rs^2}$

Combine like terms: $23r^3s^2 - 8rs^3 + 0rs^2$

We don't write the $0rs^2$.   **Answer: $23r^3s^2 - 8rs^3$**

Sample #1: Simplify: $\left(\dfrac{4}{3} m^{-1} n^3\right)^2$

We see the exponent of 2 raised above a parenthesis; we identify a "power to a power" operation where the exponent affects the entire term.

First, the exponent affects the coefficient: $\left(\dfrac{4}{3}\right)^2 = \dfrac{16}{9}$

Second, the exponent affects the "m^{-1}" variable: $\left(m^{-1}\right)^2 = m^{-2}$

Third, the exponent affects the "n^3" variable: $\left(n^3\right)^2 = n^6$

The problem now looks like: $\dfrac{16}{9} m^{-2}n^6$

Get rid of the negative exponent above the "m" variable by taking the reciprocal of m^{-2}.

Answer: $\dfrac{16n^6}{9m^2}$

You try it now:

a) $\left(-\dfrac{2}{5} x^2y^4z\right)^3$

b) $\left(\dfrac{3a^{-2}b^2}{7a}\right)^4$

Sample #2: Simplify: $\left(-4xy^2\right)^3 \left(\dfrac{3}{8} x^2\right)$

Looking at order of operations, we have two operations—the exponent of 3 above $\left(-4xy^2\right)$ and multiplication of the two terms of $\left(-4xy^2\right)^3$ and $\left(\dfrac{3}{8} x^2\right)$.

We do the exponent (power to a power) first: $\left(-4xy^2\right)^3 = -64x^3y^6$

The problem now looks like: $-64x^3y^6 \left(\dfrac{3}{8} x^2\right)$

Multiply the terms (the coefficients together, and then the variables).

Answer: $-24x^5y^6$

You try it now:

c) $\left(-5x^2yz^3\right)^2 (-3y)$

d) $\left(\dfrac{3mn}{2m^2}\right)^3 \left(16m^{-2}\right)$

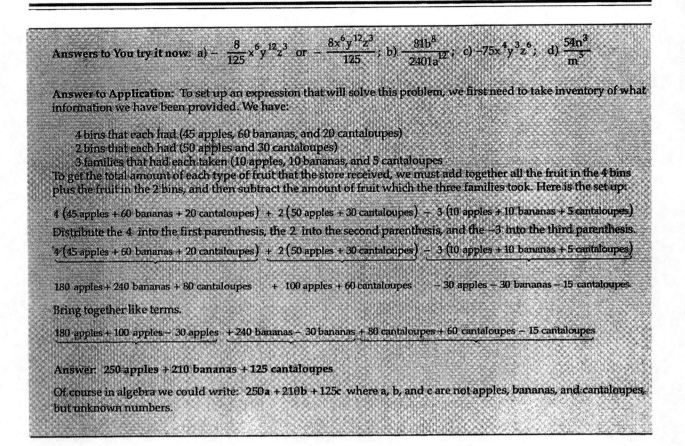

Answers to You try it now: a) $-\dfrac{8}{125}x^6y^{12}z^3$ or $-\dfrac{8x^6y^{12}z^3}{125}$; b) $\dfrac{81b^8}{2401a^{12}}$; c) $-75x^4y^3z^6$; d) $\dfrac{54n^3}{m^5}$

Answer to Application: To set up an expression that will solve this problem, we first need to take inventory of what information we have been provided. We have:

    4 bins that each had (45 apples, 60 bananas, and 20 cantaloupes)
    2 bins that each had (50 apples and 30 cantaloupes)
    3 families that had each taken (10 apples, 10 bananas, and 5 cantaloupes

To get the total amount of each type of fruit that the store received, we must add together all the fruit in the 4 bins plus the fruit in the 2 bins, and then subtract the amount of fruit which the three families took. Here is the set up:

4 (45 apples + 60 bananas + 20 cantaloupes) + 2 (50 apples + 30 cantaloupes) − 3 (10 apples + 10 bananas + 5 cantaloupes)

Distribute the 4 into the first parenthesis, the 2 into the second parenthesis, and the −3 into the third parenthesis.

4 (45 apples + 60 bananas + 20 cantaloupes) + 2 (50 apples + 30 cantaloupes) − 3 (10 apples + 10 bananas + 5 cantaloupes)

180 apples + 240 bananas + 80 cantaloupes   + 100 apples + 60 cantaloupes   − 30 apples − 30 bananas − 15 cantaloupes

Bring together like terms.

180 apples + 100 apples − 30 apples + 240 bananas − 30 bananas + 80 cantaloupes + 60 cantaloupes − 15 cantaloupes

Answer: 250 apples + 210 bananas + 125 cantaloupes

Of course in algebra we could write: $250a + 210b + 125c$ where a, b, and c are not apples, bananas, and cantaloupes, but unknown numbers.

Exercise 6.3:   Terms Raised to a Power and Simplifying More Complex Algebraic Expressions

In exercises #1–8, identify which rule of exponents still needs to be done to simplify the expression. Your answer is either: (1) power to a power, (2) multiplication of same bases, (3) division of same bases, or (4) eliminating the negative exponent.

1) $\left(2m^3n\right)^2$ 2) $\left(\dfrac{3}{5}xy\right)^5$ 3) $\dfrac{3x^3yz^2}{xz^2}$ 4) $-7m^3\,(4mn)$

5) $2x^2 \bullet y^{-3}$ 6) $\dfrac{(-m)^3}{(-m)^2}$ 7) $ab\left(-2a^2-b\right)$ 8) $\dfrac{3x}{4z^{-2}}+4y$

In exercises #9–20, decide whether each group of expressions all have the same value. Answer yes or no. If your answer is no, identify the letter of the one expression that does not equal the others.

9) a) $5r\left(6rs^{-2}-r\right)+r^2$ b) $30r^2s^{-2}-5r^2+r^2$ c) $30r^2s^{-2}-4r^2$ d) $\dfrac{30r^2}{s^2}-4r^2$

10) a) $-3r\left(-2r^2s+s^{-2}\right)-s^{-2}$ b) $-3r\left(-2r^2s\right)$ c) $6r^3s-3rs^{-2}-s^{-2}$ d) $6r^3s-\dfrac{3r}{s^2}-\dfrac{1}{s^2}$

11) a) $3x^3$ b) $3 \cdot x^3$ c) $3 \cdot (x)^3$ d) $(3x)^3$

12) a) $-5m^2$ b) $(-5)^2 \cdot (m)^2$ c) $-5 \cdot m^2$ d) $(-5) \cdot (m^2)$

13) a) $(4a)^3$ b) $(4)^3 \cdot (a)^3$ c) $4a \cdot 4a \cdot 4a$ d) $(4 \cdot 4 \cdot 4) \cdot (a \cdot a \cdot a)$

14) a) $(-3x)^2$ b) $(-3)^2 \cdot (x)^2$ c) $(-3x) \cdot (-3x)$ d) $(-3 \cdot -3) \cdot (x^2 \cdot x^2)$

15) a) $(-2rs^2)^3$ b) $(-2)^3 \cdot (r)^3 \cdot (s^2)^3$ c) $-8r^3s^6$ d) $\dfrac{r^3s^6}{8}$

16) a) $(-5mn^{-1}o^4)^2$ b) $(-5)^2 (m)^2 (n^{-1})^2 (o^4)^2$ c) $25m^2n^{-2}o^8$ d) $\dfrac{25m^2o^8}{n^2}$

17) a) $\dfrac{9y^6}{x^4}$ b) $9x^{-4}y^6$ c) $(3)^2 \cdot (x^{-2})^2 \cdot (y^3)^2$ d) $(3x^{-2}y^3)^2$

18) a) $\left(-\dfrac{2}{3}x\right)^3$ b) $\left(\dfrac{-2x}{3}\right)^3$ c) $\dfrac{(-2x)^3}{(3)^3}$ d) $\dfrac{(-2)^3(x)^3}{(3)^3}$

19) a) $\left(\dfrac{2m^2}{5}\right)^2$ b) $\left(\dfrac{2}{5}m^2\right)^2$ c) $\dfrac{(2)^2(m^2)^2}{(5)}$ d) $\dfrac{(2m^2)^2}{(5)^2}$

20) a) $5\left(\dfrac{3a}{4b^{-3}}\right)^2$ b) $\dfrac{5}{1} \cdot \dfrac{(3a)^2}{(4b^{-3})^2}$ c) $\dfrac{5}{1} \cdot \dfrac{9a^2}{16b^{-6}}$ d) $\dfrac{45a^2b^6}{16}$

In exercises #21–32, simplify these power to a power problems. Remember to get rid of any negative exponents at the end of the problem.

21) $(2x^3y)^4$ 22) $(3xy^4z^3)^3$ 23) $(-5m^2n)^3$ 24) $(-4mn^3)^2$

25) $\left(\dfrac{2}{3}rs^2\right)^3$ 26) $\left(\dfrac{7}{5}r^5s^3t^2\right)^3$ 27) $(x^{-2}y^3)^2$ 28) $(m^{-1}n^2)^2$

29) $(2m^{-2}n^{-3})^5$ 30) $(3x^{-2}y^{-4})^4$ 31) $\left(-\dfrac{3}{4}x^3y^{-2}\right)^2$ 32) $\left(-\dfrac{1}{2}x^{-1}y^{-2}\right)^3$

In exercises #33–44, follow the order of operations by first distributing any outside term into a parenthesis, and then combining any like terms.

33) $3(2x^2 - 3x + 2) + (x^2 - 2x - 2)$ 34) $5(-4y^3 + 3y - 7) + (3y^3 - 6y + 10)$

35) $6a(-5ab - 2) + 4b(3a^2 - 4a)$ 36) $-2ab(a - b) + 3a(2ab - 3b^2)$

37) $3m\left(6m^3 + 6m - 3\right) - \left(-2m^4 - 4m^2 + m\right)$

38) $4m\left(-3m^2 - 2m + 4\right) - \left(-3m^3 + m^2 - 4m\right)$

39) $2x^2y\left(4x^2 - 3xy\right) + 3x\left(x^3y - x^2y^2\right)$

40) $5xy^2\left(-2x - 3y\right) + x\left(-2xy^2 + 4y^3\right)$

41) $-x\left(2x - y + 1\right) - y\left(x - 3\right)$

42) $-m\left(-3m + n - 4\right) - n\left(5m - 2\right)$

43) $\frac{2}{3}r^2\left(-6r - 2\right) + \frac{3}{5}\left(10r^3 + r^2\right)$

44) $\frac{3}{4}mn\left(8m - n\right) + \frac{1}{3}m\left(12mn - n^2\right)$

In exercises #45–56, simplify the following expressions. Remember to always follow the order of operations.

45) $\left(3a^2b\right)^2\left(4ab^3\right)$

46) $\left(-2a^3b\right)^3\left(2a\right)$

47) $\left(\frac{4}{3}x^2y\right)^2 - \frac{5}{18}x^4y^2$

48) $\left(\frac{3}{5}xy\right)^2 + \frac{4}{5}xy$

49) $\left(\frac{15m^2n}{5n}\right) + \left(\frac{3m}{m^{-1}}\right)$

50) $\left(\frac{-8m^2n^3}{2n}\right) - \left(\frac{14mn^2}{2m^{-1}}\right)$

51) $\left(\frac{-4r^2s}{2rs}\right) \bullet \left(3r + s^2\right) - \left(4r^2 - s^2\right)$

52) $\left(\frac{21rs}{7s}\right) \bullet \left(4r - rst\right) - \left(2r^2 - 3r^2st\right)$

53) $\left(\frac{8rs^3}{10rs}\right) - \left(\frac{2rs^3}{5rs}\right) \bullet \left(2r\right)$

54) $\left(\frac{-3m^2}{12mn^{-2}}\right) - \left(\frac{2m^2}{6mn^{-2}}\right) \bullet \left(-3mn\right)$

55) $-3x\left(-2x^2 - 4xy - 1\right) - 6\left(x^2 + 2x^2y + x\right)$

56) $2xy^2z\left(-2x + 3y - z\right) - 2xy\left(-2xyz + 3y^2z + 5yz^2\right)$

In exercises #57–62, simplify the following expressions.

57–58) Use the figure below:

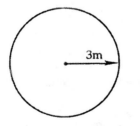

57) What is the area of the circle (use 3.14 for π)?

58) If the radius was increased by 2m, what would the area of this new circle be?

59) Take the expression of $-3m^2n$ and cube it.

60) Take the expression of $-5ab^3$ and cube it.

61) If a sphere had a radius of $\frac{3x}{2}$ inches, what would the volume of the sphere be ($V = \frac{4}{3}\pi r^3$)? Use $\frac{22}{7}$ for π.

62) If a rectangle has a length of $(5rs^2)^3 + 2$ and a width of $3r$, what is the area of this rectangle ($A = L \bullet W$)?

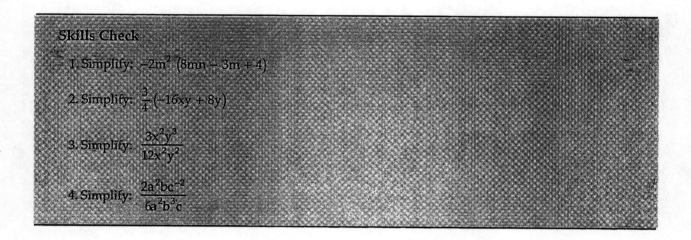

Skills Check

1. Simplify: $-2m^2(8mn - 3m + 4)$

2. Simplify: $\frac{3}{4}(-16xy + 8y)$

3. Simplify: $\frac{3x^2y^3}{12x^2y^2}$

4. Simplify: $\frac{2a^2bc^{-2}}{6a^2b^3c}$

Answers to Skills Check: 1) $-16m^3n + 6m^3 - 8m^2$; 2) $-12xy + 6y$; 3) $\frac{y}{4}$; 4) $\frac{1}{3b^2c^3}$

Section 6.4 Factoring and Evaluating Polynomials

Objectives:

• To find the GCF of monomials

• To factor a polynomial

• To evaluate an algebraic expression

Application:

At a beginner's detective training school, an instructor had 3 men walk into the classroom and then quickly leave. Five minutes later she asked her students to recall the 3 men—detailing whether each man wore a hat or not, whether his shoes were athletic or dress shoes, whether he wore socks or not, whether his pants were brown or green, and whether his shirt was long-sleeved or short-sleeved.

Andrew recalled the following. Man #1 wore a hat, had athletic shoes and socks, brown shorts, and a short-sleeved shirt. Man #2 wore a hat, had brown shorts and a short-sleeved shirt. He also wore athletic shoes, but had no socks. Man #3 had no hat. He wore athletic shoes and socks, green shorts and a short-sleeved shirt. If Andrew's recollection is correct, what clothing items did all three men have in common?

Vocabulary:

Greatest Common Factor (for numbers)—The **greatest common factor** (GCF) for numbers, as defined in section 2.3, is the greatest or highest whole number that can divide evenly into two or more given numbers. It is the same as the greatest common divisor (GCD).

Example: Find the GCF of 24 and 30

When we prime factor 24 $(2 \bullet 2 \bullet 2 \bullet 3)$ and 30 $(2 \bullet 3 \bullet 5)$, we can see that both numbers have "$2 \bullet 3$" or 6 in common.

Answer: 6 is the GCF of 24 and 30.

Greatest Common Factor (for terms)—The **greatest common factor for terms** is the greatest or highest term that can divide evenly into two or more given terms.

Finding the GCF of terms has two parts: (1) finding the GCF of the coefficients, and (2) finding the GCF of each variable held in common.

Example: Find the GCF of $7x^2y^2$ and $14x^3yz$

We first find the GCF of the coefficients of 7 $(1 \bullet 7)$ and 14 $(2 \bullet 7)$. 7 is the greatest number that divides evenly into both 7 and 14.

Second, we look at what variables the terms have in common. They both have "x" and "y" variables. Only one of the terms has a "z" variable, so the "z" variable is <u>not</u> a part of the GCF.

The first term has x^2 and the second term has x^3. What they have in common is the highest degree that they share. Both are raised to at least the degree of 2. Therefore, they both have x^2.

The first term has y^2 and the second term has y^1. What they have in common is the highest degree that they share. Both are raised to at least the degree of 1. Therefore, they both have y.

Put these factors together: $7 \cdot x^2 \cdot y$ and we get the GCF of the term: **$7x^2y$**

How to:

Find the Greatest Common Factor (for terms):

1. Identify and find the GCF of the coefficients.

2. Identify the variables that the terms have in common and find the GCF for each variable. Remember that the GCF for each variable is the highest degree which they both have. This is actually the smallest exponent number.

3. Write the common factors together as a product (remember that factoring is a multiplicative function).

Example #1: Find the GCF of $42m^2n$ and $63m^3$

Step #1: Identify and find the GCF of the coefficients.

The coefficient of the first term is 42.

The coefficient of the second term is 63.

Prime factor the terms: $42 = 2 \cdot 3 \cdot 7$

$63 = 3 \cdot 3 \cdot 7$

Both terms have "3 • 7" or 21. The GCF of the coefficients is 21.

Step #2: Identify the variables and find the GCF for each variable.

The first term has "m" and "n" variables.

The second term has an "m" variable.

The terms both have <u>only</u> the "m" variable. The first term has m^2 and the second term has m^3. They both have at least a degree of two.

The GCF of the variables is m^2.

Step #3: Write the common factors together as a product.

The common factors are $21 \cdot m^2$.

Answer: $21m^2$

Example #2: Find the GCF of $12a^2b$ and $40c$

Step #1: Identify and find the GCF of the coefficients.

The coefficient of the first term is 12.

The coefficient of the second term is 40.

Prime factor the terms: $12 = 2 \cdot 2 \cdot 3$

$40 = 2 \cdot 2 \cdot 2 \cdot 5$

Both terms have "$2 \cdot 2$" or 4. The GCF of the coefficients is 4.

Step #2: Identify the variables and find the GCF for each variable.

The first term has "a" and "b" variables.

The second term has a "c" variable.

The terms have no variables in common. A variable cannot be a part of the GCF.

Step #3: Write the common factors together as a product.

There is only one common factor—the 4.

Answer: 4

How to:

Factor a Polynomial:

1. Identify the GCF of the terms.

2. Factor out the GCF of each term. Do this by dividing each term by the GCF to get a quotient (parts of each term leftover).

3. Rewrite the polynomial in factored form. This means that the GCF is in front of a parenthesis and thus being multiplied by the combined "leftovers" of each term inside a parenthesis.

The final factored form of a polynomial with three terms will look like this:

GCF (leftovers of 1st term + leftovers of 2nd term + leftovers of 3rd term)

Example #3: Factor the polynomial: $10x^3y^2 + 15xy^2z$

Step #1: Identify the GCF of the terms.

The factors of the first term are: $(2 \bullet 5) \bullet x^3 \bullet y^2$

The factors of the second term are: $(3 \bullet 5) \bullet x \bullet y^2 \bullet z$

The GCF is: $5xy^2$

Step #2: Factor out the GCF of each term.

We divide each term by the GCF of $5xy^2$.

First term: $\dfrac{10x^3y^2}{5xy^2} = 2x^2$

The quotient or "leftovers" of the first term is $2x^2$.

Second term: $\dfrac{15xy^2z}{5xy^2} = 3z$

The quotient or "leftovers" of the second term is $3z$.

Step #3: Rewrite the polynomial in factored form.

The factored form needs to fit the model of:

GCF (leftovers of 1st term + leftovers of 2nd term)

Substitute $5xy^2$ for the GCF, $2x^2$ for the "leftovers" of the 1st term, and $3z$ for the "leftovers" of the 2nd term.

Answer: $5xy^2\left(2x^2 + 3z\right)$

*** Check our answer. Until we have done factoring for a while, we may find this process very challenging. Therefore, always check the answer. We do this by distributing the GCF to each of the "leftover" terms inside the parenthesis.

In other words, our answer is correct if in fact $5xy^2\left(2x^2 + 3z\right)$ is equal to the original expression of $10x^3y^2 + 15xy^2z$.

Using the distributive property, we know that $5xy^2\left(2x^2 + 3z\right)$ is the same as $5xy^2\left(2x^2\right) + 5xy^2(3z)$. After multiplying, we get $10x^3y^2 + 15xy^2z$.

Yes, this answer is proven to be true! The circle has been completed!

Example #4: Factor the polynomial: $12r^3s - 7rs^2t^3$

Step #1: Identify the GCF of the terms.

The factors of the first term are: $(2 \cdot 2 \cdot 3) \cdot r^3 \cdot s$

The factors of the second term are: $(1 \cdot 7) \cdot r \cdot s^2 \cdot t^3$

**Take note: The GCF of the coefficients here is 1. If it looks like there is no GCF for the coefficients, it is always "1." It is "invisible" in the GCF written below.

The GCF is: rs

Step #2: Factor out the GCF of each term.

We divide each term by the GCF of rs.

First term: $\dfrac{12r^3s}{rs} = 12r^2$

The quotient or "leftovers" of the first term is $12r^2$.

Second term: $\dfrac{-7rs^2t^3}{rs} = -7st^3$

The quotient or "leftovers" of the second term is $-7st^3$.

Step #3: Rewrite the polynomial in factored form.

The factored form needs to fit the model of:

GCF (leftovers of 1st term + leftovers of 2nd term)

Substitute rs for the GCF, $12r^2$ for the "leftovers" of the 1st term, and $-7st^3$ for the "leftovers" of the 2nd term.

Answer: $rs\left(12r^2 - 7st^3\right)$

*** Check our answer.

Using the distributive property, we know that $rs\left(12r^2 - 7st^3\right)$ is the same as $rs\left(12r^2\right) + rs\left(-7st^3\right)$. After multiplying, we get $12r^3s - 7rs^2t^3$.

Yes, this answer is proven to be true! The circle has been completed!

How to:

Evaluate a Polynomial:

1. Write the polynomial.

2. Substitute the given value for each variable. Place a parenthesis around each substituted value.

3. Solve by following the order of operations.

Example #5: Evaluate: $3x - y$ where $x = -3$ and $y = -2$

Step #1: Write the polynomial.

$3x - y$

Step #2: Substitute the given value for each variable.

$3(-3) - (-2)$ Notice that the substituted values are in parenthesis. This makes it easy to maintain order of operations.

Step #3: Solve by following the order of operations.

Multiplication: $\underbrace{3(-3)} - (-2)$

Combining: $-9 - (-2)$

Answer: -7

Example #6: Evaluate: $-x^2 + 2y^2 - y$ where $x = -5$ and $y = -3$

Step #1: Write the polynomial.

$-x^2 + 2y^2 - y$

Step #2: Substitute the given value for each variable.

$-(-5)^2 + 2(-3)^2 - (-3)$

Step #3: Solve by following the order of operations.

Exponents: $-\underbrace{(-5)^2} + 2\underbrace{(-3)^2} - (-3)$

Multiplication: $-(25) + \underbrace{2(9)} - (-3)$

Combining: $-(25) + 18 - (-3)$

Answer: -4

Sample #1: Find the GCF of $-28x^2yz^3$, $-14xyz$, and $-70x^5y^4z^2$.

    Look at the coefficients.   28 factors into $(2 \bullet 2 \bullet 7)$

                                 14 factors into $(2 \bullet 7)$

                                 70 factors into $(2 \bullet 5 \bullet 7)$

The coefficients all have factors of $(2 \bullet 7)$. The coefficients are also all negative, so <u>they have a negative sign in common too</u>. The GCF of the coefficients is **−14**.

Look at the variables.

All three terms have an "x" variable $\left(x^2, x, \text{ and } x^5\right)$. The highest degree they all have is the first degree. The GCF for the "x" variable is **x**.

All three terms have a "y" variable $\left(y, y, \text{ and } y^4\right)$. The highest degree they all have is the first degree. The GCF for the "y" variable is **y**.

All three terms have a "z" variable $\left(z^3, z, \text{ and } z^2\right)$. The highest degree they all have is the first degree. The GCF for the "z" variable is **z**.

Answer: **−14xyz** is the GCF of the terms.

■ **You try it now:**

    a) Find the GCF of $2m^2$, $7mn$, and $20m^2n^2$

    b) Find the GCF of $-4a^3bc$, $-10a^3b^2c$, and $-8a^2c$

Sample #2: Factor the polynomial: $20a^4b^3 - 50a^3b^2 + 10a^2b$

    Find the GCF of the three terms. The GCF of the coefficients is: 10

        The GCF of the "a" variable is: a^2

        The GCF of the "b" variable is: b

    The GCF is: **$10a^2b$**

    Divide each term by the GCF of **$10a^2b$** to solve for the quotient (the "leftovers") of each division problem.

    First term: $\dfrac{20a^4b^3}{10a^2b} = 2a^2b^2$

Second term:　$\dfrac{-50a^3b^2}{10a^2b} = -5ab$

Third term:　$\dfrac{10a^2b}{10a^2b} = 1$

Write this information in its factored form of:

GCF (leftovers of 1st term + leftovers of 2nd term + leftovers of 3rd term)

Answer: $10a^2b\left(2a^2b^2 - 5ab + 1\right)$

Check our answer by distributing $10a^2b$ to all the terms inside the parenthesis. This is correct, but notice how <u>we must include the leftover of 1 for the third term</u>!!

You try it now:

c) Factor the polynomial:　$6r^3s - 15rst - 3$

d) Factor the polynomial:　$-16m^2n^2 - 35m^2n - 40m^2$

Sample #3: Fill in the blank with the missing term that will complete the following equation:

$12xy^3 = -2y \bullet \left(\ \ \right)$

This, of course, is still a factoring problem. We are asking ourselves: $12xy^3$ equals $-2y$ multiplied by what term?

One way to solve this problem is to talk through it. Solve for one part of the missing term at a time. Start first with the coefficients.

$12 = -2 \bullet \left(\ \ \right)$　　The coefficient answer is -6.

$x = \left(\ \ \right)$　　　　　The answer here is 'x." The variable of "x" to the first degree is needed in the blank to make this equation true.

$y^3 = y \bullet \left(\ \ \right)$　　　The answer here is y^2.

Answer: $-6xy^2$

We check our answer by multiplying $-2y$ by $-6xy^2$, which does in fact equal $12xy^3$. This is the correct answer.

***Another way to find the missing term (and what may be visually more welcoming for us) is to divide $12xy^3$ by $-2y$.

$\dfrac{12xy^3}{-2y} = -6xy^2$

You try it now:

e) $30m^2n = 5mn \bullet (\quad)$

f) $-8x^2y = xy \bullet (\quad)$

Sample #4: Evaluate $-c^3 - 2b^2 - a$ where $a = -5$; $b = -4$; $c = -3$

Write the polynomial.	$-c^3 - 2b^2 - a$
Substitute number values.	$-(-3)^3 - 2(-4)^2 - (-5)$
Follow order of operations.	
Evaluate the exponents.	$-\underbrace{(-3)^3} - 2\underbrace{(-4)^2} - (-5)$
Evaluate the multiplication.	$-(-27) - \underbrace{2(16)} - (-5)$
Evaluate the combining.	$\underbrace{-(-27)} - 32 \underbrace{- (-5)}$
	$27 - 32 + 5$
Answer: 0	

You try it now:

g) Evaluate $-a^2 - b^2 + 4b$ where $a = 3$ and $b = -2$

h) Evaluate $\dfrac{x^5 \bullet y^3}{-y - x^2}$ where $x = -1$ and $y = -2$

Answers to You try it now: a) m; b) $-2a^2c$; c) $3(2r^3s - 5rst - 1)$; d) $-m^2(16n^2 + 35n + 40)$; e) 6m; f) $-8x$;

g) -21; h) 8

Answer to Application: To discover what all three men had in common, we take a separate inventory of the clothing items each man wore or did not wear. The chart below shows this information.

	Hat	Shoes	Socks	Shorts	Shirt
Man #1	Yes	Athletic	Yes	Brown	Short-sleeve
Man #2	Yes	Athletic	No	Brown	Short-sleeve
Man #3	No	Athletic	Yes	Green	Short-sleeve

Looking down each column, we see that all three of the men wore **athletic shoes and a short-sleeve shirt**.

Exercise 6.4: Problems Factoring and Evaluating Polynomials

In exercises #1-6, state the highest degree that each of the terms have in common.

1) $7m^4, -2m^3, m^6,$ and $3m^2$

2) $4x, 3x, 2x^5,$ and x^3

3) $-y^2, 3y^3, y^5,$ and $4y^3$

4) $3r^2, -r^4, 2r^4,$ and $-5r^8$

5) $5, 2x^2, 10x^3,$ and $-x^4$

6) $-2m^3, 4m^2, 5m,$ and 3

In exercises #7-12, state what variable(s) each of the terms have in common. If they have no variables in common, write "none."

7) $3rs, 4s^3t^2, -rst,$ and $5r^2s^2t$

8) $5abc, -3a^2c, 2ab,$ and $7a^3bc^2$

9) $2ax^5yz, -4bx^3y, 3a^2bx^2y,$ and $2a^2bxy$

10) $-a^2bxy^2z^2, 2ab^3y^3z, 5a^5bxz,$ and $-3b^2xy^2z^3$

11) $m^2n^2r^3st^3, mnos^2t^4, mo^3rs,$ and $-2no^5r^2t$

12) $3m^4nos^2t, -m^2n^2rs^2t^5, 4mnor^3st,$ and $m^2no^3r^3s$

In exercises #13-18, decide whether each group of expressions all have the same value. Answer yes or no. If your answer is no, identify the letter of the one expression that does not equal the others.

13) a) $4a^2b \div 2a$
b) $\dfrac{4a^2b}{2a}$
c) $\dfrac{2a^2b}{a}$
d) $2ab$

14) a) $-9xy^2 \div 3xy$
b) $\dfrac{-9xy^2}{3xy}$
c) $\dfrac{-3xy^2}{xy}$
d) $-3y$

15) a) $10mn^2 \div (-4mn)$
b) $\dfrac{10mn^2}{-4mn}$
c) $\dfrac{-5mn^2}{2mn}$
d) $-\dfrac{5n}{2}$

16) a) $-15a^3bc \div \left(-6a^3bc\right)$
b) $\dfrac{-15a^3bc}{-6a^3bc}$
c) $\dfrac{5a^3bc}{2a^3bc}$
d) $\dfrac{5}{2}$

17) a) $8x^3y^2z^3 \div 8x^2y^2z^2$
b) $\dfrac{x^3y^2z^3}{x^2y^2z^2}$
c) $\dfrac{xy^2z^3}{y^2z^2}$
d) z

18) a) $3mn^2o \div (-3mn)$
b) $\dfrac{3mn^2o}{-3mn}$
c) $-\dfrac{mn^2o}{mn}$
d) $-mno$

In exercises #19-26, prime factor the given numbers. If the number is prime, simply write the word "prime" for the answer.

19) 40   20) 54   21) 84   22) 117

23) 69   24) 154   25) 47   26) 161

In exercises #27-46, Find the GCF of the given terms.

27) 18 and 24   28) 28 and 42   29) 15, 30, and 45   30) $-4, -10,$ and 20

31) x^2yz and x^3y^2 32) ab^4c^2 and a^2c 33) m^3no^2 and $-mn^3o$

34) $-xy^5z^2$ and $-x^2y^2z$ 35) $2x^2y$ and $6xz$ 36) $12xy^2z^3$ and $4xy$

37) $7m^4n^5$ and $21o^3$ 38) $3a^2bc^4$ and 33   39) $-2ab^3$ and $-10b^2c$

40) $4x^2y$ and $17z$ 41) $-3rs^2$ and $-7t^5$ 42) $6a^2b, -24ab^2c,$ and $36a^3c$

43) $5x^3y^2z, -20xy^2z,$ and $-35xz^3$ 44) $60rs^3t^2, -30r^3s^2t,$ and $42r^2st^3$

45) $-7s, -14r,$ and $-r^2s^2$ 46) $-11x^2y, -22y^2,$ and $-45xy^3$

In exercises #47-65, factor the given polynomial.

47) $8x + 4y$ 48) $2r - 10s$ 49) $5m^2n - 7m$ 50) $3ab + 4b^2$

51) $10a^3bc - 20ab$ 52) $15x^2y^2 - 25x$ 53) $-63xy^3z^2 - 21xyz$

54) $-36r^2s - 90r$ 55) $3x^2y^3 + x^2y$ 56) $-4mn - 2m$

57) $-7a^2b^3 + 21a^3b^4$ 58) $-9a^5bc^2 + 21ab^3c$ 59) $13x^2yz - 3xy - 7xz$

60) $11rs^2 - 8rt + 5rst$ 61) $5m^2 - 5mn - 10$ 62) $4x^2y + 6xy + 2$

63) $-3x^3y - 9x^2y^2 - 3xy^2$ 64) $6a^2b^3c - 18ab^2c + 22ab^2$ 65) $12mn^2o + 3mn^2o^2 - 15mo$

In exercises #66-74, fill in each blank with the term that will complete the given equation.

66) $15xy^2 = 3xy \cdot \left(\ \ \right)$ 67) $10x^2y = 2x \cdot \left(\ \ \right)$ 68) $14r^3s^4t^2 = 7r \cdot \left(\ \ \right)$

69) $20r^2st^2 = 4rs \cdot \left(\ \ \right)$ 70) $-24a^3b^2 = 8 \cdot \left(\ \ \right)$ 71) $-50x^3y^2z = x^3y \cdot \left(\ \ \right)$

72) $33xy^5z^3 = xy \cdot \left(\ \ \right)$ 73) $40a^4b^5c^8 = 8a^2b^2c^2 \cdot \left(\ \ \right)$ 74) $-28a^3bc^2 = 28a^3bc \cdot \left(\ \ \right)$

In exercises #75-80, state whether the given equations are true or false.

75) $8a\left(-2ab + 3\right) = -16ab + 24a$ 76) $-3ab\left(3a - 2b\right) = -9a^2b - 6ab^2$

77) $2x^2\left(3xy - 2y + 2\right) = 6x^3y - 4x^2y + 4x^2$ 78) $4m\left(2m - n - 3\right) = 8m^2 - 4mn - 12m$

79) $3x^2y^3z(-x + y - z) = -3x^3y^3z + 3x^2y^4z - 3x^2y^3z^2$

80) $-2xy^3z^2(-2x + 3y - 4z) = 4x^2y^3z^2 - 6xy^2z^2 + 8xy^3z^4$

In exercises #81-88, evaluate the following expressions where $x = -2$ and $y = -5$.

81) $-x$

82) $-y$

83) $-x + y$

84) $x - y$

85) $-3x(4y)$

86) $-2x - (4 - y)$

87) $5y - (y - x)$

88) $-4y(-2x)$

In exercises #89-100, evaluate the following expressions where $a = 2$, $b = -1$, and $c = -3$.

89) $a^2 + b^2 - c^2$

90) $-a^2 - b$

91) $-c^2 + b$

92) $c^2 - b^2 - a$

93) $(ab)^2$

94) $(bc)^2$

95) $-c^3 - c^2$

96) $-b^3 - c - a^3$

97) c^2ab^2

98) ab^2c^3

99) $a^b - \dfrac{c}{6}$

100) $c^a - \dfrac{1}{\left(c^a\right)^b}$

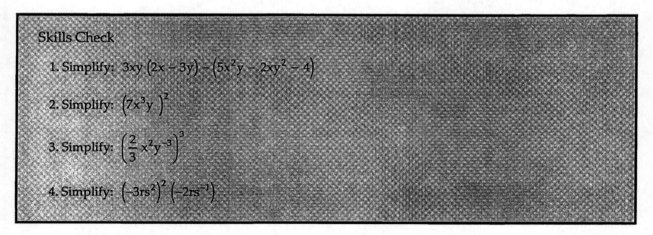

Skills Check

1. Simplify: $3xy(2x - 3y) - (5x^2y - 2xy^2 - 4)$

2. Simplify: $\left(7x^3y\right)^2$

3. Simplify: $\left(\dfrac{2}{3}x^2y^{-3}\right)^3$

4. Simplify: $\left(-3rs^2\right)^2\left(-2rs^{-1}\right)$

Answers to Skills Check: 1) $x^2y - 7xy^2 + 4$; 2) $49x^6y^2$; 3) $\dfrac{8x^6}{27y^9}$; 4) $-18r^3s^3$

Chapter 7 Algebraic Equations

Section 7.1 Solving Linear Equations that Have Variables on One Side of the Equation

Objectives:

- To solve one-step equations
- To solve multi-step equations
- To solve an equation with a fractional coefficient

Application:

An entrance exam was provided for workers in the Department of Defense who were interested in cryptography, the art of writing and interpreting messages in code. The workers were presented with a simple line of code and told that a hidden message, telling the hour of a secret meeting, could be found by deciphering the information provided by the characters that were located in the sequence by multiples of 5. What is the hour of the meeting?

Here is the line of encrypted code: xa3=25-3+x2=01-/80-46/=a=-2/a1-3+x0=48

Vocabulary:

> **equation**—An **equation** is a mathematical statement that consists of one expression equal to a second expression. In algebra we set up and use equations to solve for the value(s) of a variable or variables.
>
> Equation example: $5x = 10$ where the:
>
> > $5x$ is the expression on the left side of the equation
> > (that is the left side of the equal sign) and
> >
> > 10 is the expression on the right side of the equation
> > (that is the right side of the equal sign)
>
> In this book we will be solving what are called linear equations, called this because the degree of all our variables will be one. The processes we will learn in this unit will be the same processes we will use to solve equations throughout our future math advancement.
>
> Equations were introduced on pages viii and x at the beginning of this book. Before continuing in this section, we need to **reread pages viii through x** and make sure we know the answers to the questions below.
>
> **What operations are opposites of each other?**
>
> **How do we get rid of any number or value in an equation?**
>
> **When working with an equation, it only stays true if we do what to both sides of the equation?**

The Equation Goal—The <u>goal</u> of any equation <u>is to isolate the variable</u>, that is <u>get the variable alone on one side of the equation</u>. Whatever operation we choose to do, it should make the equation easier or more simple to work and should lead to the variable being isolated.

Simplify—When we are solving equations, the concept of **simplifying** means to do any distribution and/or combining. **We can only simplify the same side of any equation.**

How to:

Solve Linear Equations:

1. Simplify (distribute and combine any like terms) each side of the equation.

2. Get rid of any values on the same side of the equation as the variable by doing the <u>opposite operation</u>.

3) Get rid of the coefficient of the variable last by doing the <u>opposite operation</u>.

*** For steps #2 and #3 we must remember <u>the equation truth</u>: What we do to one side of the equation, we must do to the other side!!

Example #1: Solve: $x + 8 + 3 = 20$

Step #1: Simplify each side of the equation.

On the left side of the equation, we have the like terms of 8 and 3.

We combine them to get 11.

The equation of $x + 8 + 3 = 20$ becomes $x + 11 = 20$

Remember our goal—to get the variable isolated (by itself). In this case, to get "x" by itself, **we need to get rid of one value—the "plus 11."**

Step #2: Get rid of any values (not the coefficient of the variable) on the same side of the equation as the variable.

We get rid of $+11$ by doing the opposite operation: -11.

We must do the same thing to both sides of the equation.

$$x + 11 = 20 \text{ becomes } x + 11 - 11 = 20 - 11$$

This leaves us with: $x = 9$

We have successfully reached our goal of isolating the variable.

Answer: $x = 9$

Here is a visual progression of the above problem without the written explanation:

$x + \underbrace{8 + 3} = 20$

$x + 11 = 20$

$x + 11 \underbrace{- 11} = 20 \underbrace{- 11}$

$x = 9$

***Check our answer!** We check our answer by substituting the value of 9 for the "x" variable into the given equation.

Original equation:	$x + 8 + 3 \ = \ 20$
Substitute:	$(9) + 8 + 3 \ = \ 20$

Evaluate both sides of the equation: $20 \ = \ 20$ True!

The solution is correct.

Example #2: $\dfrac{x}{6} - 4 \ = \ -8$

Step #1: Simplify each side of the equation.

There is nothing to simplify. The terms on the left side of the equation are unlike terms.

Remember our goal—to get the variable isolated (by itself). In this case, to get "x" by itself, **we need to get rid of two values**—the "divide by 6" and the "subtract 4."

Step #2: Get rid of any values (not the coefficient of the variable) on the same side of the equation as the variable.

The "divide by 6" is a part of the coefficient of the x term, so we don't get rid of that yet.

We must get rid of **- 4** by doing the opposite operation: **+ 4**.

We must do the same thing to both sides of the equation.

$\dfrac{x}{6} - 4 \ = \ -8$ becomes

This leaves us with: $\dfrac{x}{6} \ = \ -4$

Step #3: Get rid of the coefficient of the variable last.

The coefficient of the x term is $\dfrac{1}{6}$. We need to get rid of the "divide by six" by doing the opposite operation: "multiply by 6."

We must do the same thing to both sides of the equation.

$$\frac{x}{6} = -4 \text{ becomes } \frac{x}{6}(6) = -4(6)$$

The sixes on the left side of the equation cancel out each other.

This leaves us with: $x = -24$

Answer: $x = -24$

Here is a visual progression of the above problem without the written explanation:

$$\frac{x}{6} - 4 = -8$$

$$\frac{x}{6} - 4 + 4 = -8 + 4$$

$$\frac{x}{6} = -4$$

$$\frac{x}{6}(6) = -4(6)$$

$$x = -24$$

***Check our answer.** We check our answer by substituting the value of -24 for the "x" variable into the given equation.

Original equation: $\quad \frac{x}{6} - 4 = -8$

Substitute: $\quad \frac{(-24)}{6} - 4 = -8$

Evaluate both sides of the equation: $\quad -8 = -8 \quad\quad$ True!

The solution is correct.

Example #3: Solve: $5(a - 2) = -8 + 13$

Step #1: Simplify each side of the equation.

On the left side of the equation, we have distribution.

The left side of the equation of $5(a - 2)$ becomes $5a - 10$.

On the right side of the equation, we have combining.

The right side of the equation of $-8 + 13$ becomes 5.

The equation of $5(a - 2) = -8 + 13$ becomes $5a - 10 = 5$

Remember our goal—to get the variable isolated (by itself). In this case, to get "a" by itself, we need to get rid of two values—the "subtract 10" and "multiply by 5."

Step #2: Get rid of any values (not the coefficient of the variable) on the same side of the equation as the variable.

We get rid of **−10** by doing the opposite operation: **+ 10**.

We must do the same thing to both sides of the equation.

$$5a - 10 = 5 \text{ becomes } 5a \underbrace{- 10 + 10} = \underbrace{5 + 10}$$

This leaves us with: $5a = 15$

Step #3: Get rid of the coefficient of the variable last.

The coefficient of the "a" term is 5. We need to get rid of the "multiply by 5" by doing the opposite operation: "divide by 5."

We must do the same thing to both sides of the equation.

$$5a = 15 \text{ becomes } \frac{5a}{5} = \frac{15}{5}$$

The fives on the left side of the equation cancel out each other. On the right side of the equation we get 3.

This leaves us with: $a = 3$

We have successfully reached our goal of isolating the variable.

Answer: a = 3

Here is a visual progression of the above problem without the written explanation:

$$\underbrace{5\left(a - 2\right)} = \underbrace{-8 + 13}$$

$$5a - 10 = 5$$

$$5a \underbrace{- 10 + 10} = \underbrace{5 + 10}$$

$$5a = 15$$

$$\underbrace{\frac{5a}{5}} = \underbrace{\frac{15}{5}}$$

$$a = 3$$

***Check our answer.** We check our answer by substituting the value of 3 for the "a" variable into the given equation.

Original equation: $5\left(a - 2\right) = -8 + 13$

Substitute: $5\left[(3) - 2\right] = -8 + 13$

Evaluate both sides of the equation: $5 = 5$ True!

The solution is correct.

Example #4: $\frac{3}{4}m - 5 = 4$

Step #1: Simplify each side of the equation.

There is nothing to simplify. The terms on the left side of the equation are unlike terms.

Remember our goal—to get the variable isolated (by itself). In this case, to get "m" by itself, **we need to get rid of two values**—the "multiply by $\frac{3}{4}$" and the "subtract 5."

Step #2: Get rid of any values (not the coefficient of the variable) on the same side of the equation as the variable.

The "multiply by $\frac{3}{4}$" is the coefficient of the "m" term, so we don't get rid of that yet.

We must get rid of -5 by doing the opposite operation: $+5$.

We must do the same thing to both sides of the equation.

$$\frac{3}{4}m - 5 = 4 \quad \text{becomes} \quad \frac{3}{4}m - 5 \underline{+5} = 4 \underline{+5}$$

This leaves us with: $\frac{3}{4}m = 9$

Step #3: Get rid of the coefficient of the variable last.

The coefficient of the m term is $\frac{3}{4}$. We need to get rid of the "multiply by $\frac{3}{4}$" by doing the opposite operation: "divide by $\frac{3}{4}$."

***Because we know that dividing by a fraction is the same as multiplying by its reciprocal, we deduce that we will actually "multiply by $\frac{4}{3}$."

***The easiest way to <u>get rid of a fractional coefficient is to multiply it by its reciprocal</u>. We do this because any number multiplied by its reciprocal equals 1 (the coefficient we want!).

We must do the same thing to both sides of the equation.

$$\frac{3}{4}m = 9 \quad \text{becomes} \quad \frac{3}{4}m\left(\frac{4}{3}\right) = 9\left(\frac{4}{3}\right)$$

The fractions on the left side of the equation cancel out each other.

This leaves us with: $m = 12$

Answer: $m = 12$

Here is a visual progression of the above problem without the written explanation:

$$\frac{3}{4}m - 5 = 4$$

$$\frac{3}{4}m - 5 + 5 = 4 + 5$$

$$\frac{3}{4}m = 9$$

$$\left(\frac{4}{3}\right)\frac{3}{4}m = 9\left(\frac{4}{3}\right)$$

$$m = 12$$

***Check our answer**. We check our answer by substituting the value of **12** for the "m" variable into the given equation.

Original equation: $\quad \frac{3}{4}m - 5 = 4$

Substitute: $\quad \frac{3}{4}(12) - 5 = 4$

Evaluate both sides of the equation: $\quad 4 = 4 \quad$ True!

The solution is correct.

***We should also note** that when we got to the equation of $\frac{3}{4}m = 9$, we could have solved this problem in two steps.

If we had viewed $\frac{3}{4}m$ as $\frac{3m}{4}$, we could have decided to get rid of only "divide by 4" first. We get rid of "divide by 4" by "multipling by 4."

$\frac{3}{4}m = 9$ would have become $\frac{3}{4}m(4) = 9(4)$.

The fours on the left side of the equation cancel out each other.

This leaves us with: $3m = 36$

Now we get rid of "multiply by 3" by "dividing by 3."

$3m = 36$ would have become $\frac{3m}{3} = \frac{36}{3}$

The threes on the left side of the equation cancel out each other.

The answer would still be: $m = 12$

If solving this in two steps is easier for you right now, feel free to use this method.

Sample #1: $4 + 2 = 3a - a + 6$

Simplify both sides of the equation:

$$\underbrace{4 + 2} = \underbrace{3a - a} + 6$$

$$\Downarrow \qquad \Downarrow$$

Get rid of the "plus 6" (on the same side of
the equation as the variable term) by doing
the opposite operation.

$$6 = 2a + 6$$

"Subtract 6" from both sides of the equation.

$$6 \underbrace{\;- 6\;} = 2a + 6 \underbrace{\;- 6\;}$$

Get rid of the "multiply by 2" (the coefficient)
by doing the opposite operation.

$$0 = 2a$$

Divide both sides of the equation by 2.

$$\frac{0}{2} = \frac{2a}{2}$$

Zero divided by any number is zero.

$$0 = a$$

Answer: $a = 0$

***Remember to check our answer.

You try it now:

a) $-11 + 5 = -4a + a + 3$

b) $3x - 5 - x = -8$

Sample #2: $2x - (3x - 4) = 7$

Simplify both sides of the equation. Distribute
the negative sign into the parenthesis.

$$2x \underbrace{- (3x - 4)} = 7$$

Combine the like terms.

$$\underline{2x - 3x + 4} = 7$$

Get rid of the "plus 4" (on the same side of
the equation as the variable term) by doing
the opposite operation.

$$-x + 4 = 7$$

"Subtract 4" from both sides of the equation.

$$-x + 4 \underbrace{\;- 4\;} = 7 \underbrace{\;- 4\;}$$

We are still <u>not</u> done. We don't want to know
what negative "x" is. We want to know what
a positive "x" equals.

$$-x = 3$$

We need to get rid of "multiply by -1." We do
this by doing the opposite operation.

Divide both sides of the equation by -1.

$$\frac{-x}{-1} = \frac{3}{-1}$$

The negatives cancel out on the left side of the equation.

$$x = -3$$

Answer: $x = -3$

***Remember to check our answer.

■ **You try it now:**

c) $m - (2m + 6) = 8$

d) $10 = 1 - 2y + y + 5$

Sample #3: $-\frac{3}{5}a + \frac{1}{3}a = -2$

Simplify both sides of the equation. Combine like terms on the left side of the equation.

$$-\frac{3}{5}a + \frac{1}{3}a = -2$$

Find the common denominator of 15 and rewrite the fractions.

$$\frac{-9 + 5}{15}a = -2$$

The equation now looks like this:

$$-\frac{4}{15}a = -2$$

The "a" variable is now isolated except for the coefficient. We can get rid of the fractional coefficient by multiplying by its reciprocal.

$$-\frac{4}{15}a\left(-\frac{15}{4}\right) = -2\left(-\frac{15}{4}\right)$$

The fractions on the left side of the equation cancel out each other.

$$a = \frac{15}{2}$$

Answer: $a = \frac{15}{2}$

***Remember to check our answer.

■ **You try it now:**

e) $\frac{2}{5}x + \frac{1}{2}x = 4$

f) $\frac{4}{7}b - \frac{2}{3}b = -6$

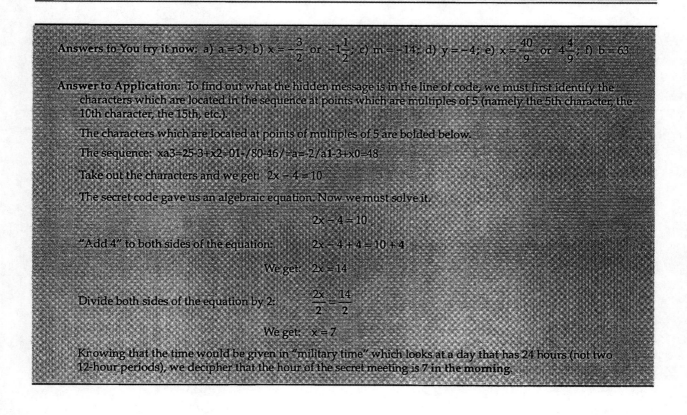

Answers to You try it now: a) $a = 3$; b) $x = -\frac{3}{2}$ or $-1\frac{1}{2}$; c) $m = -14$; d) $y = -4$; e) $x = \frac{40}{9}$ or $4\frac{4}{9}$; f) $b = 63$

Answer to Application: To find out what the hidden message is in the line of code, we must first identify the characters which are located in the sequence at points which are multiples of 5 (namely the 5th character, the 10th character, the 15th, etc.).

The characters which are located at points of multiples of 5 are bolded below.

The sequence: xa3=25-3+x2=01+/80-46/=a=-2/a1-3+x0=48

Take out the characters and we get: $2x - 4 = 10$

The secret code gave us an algebraic equation. Now we must solve it.

$$2x - 4 = 10$$

"Add 4" to both sides of the equation: $\qquad 2x - 4 + 4 = 10 + 4$

We get: $2x = 14$

Divide both sides of the equation by 2: $\qquad \frac{2x}{2} = \frac{14}{2}$

We get: $x = 7$

Knowing that the time would be given in "military time" which looks at a day that has 24 hours (not two 12-hour periods), we decipher that the hour of the secret meeting is 7 in the morning.

Exercise 7.1: Linear Equation Problems

In exercises #1-16, answer the following questions.

1) How do we get rid of a value in an equation?

2) If we added 6 to one side of an equation, what would we have to do to the other side of the equation so that the equation would still be true?

3) If we subtracted 5 on one side of an equation, what would we have to do on the other side of the equation so that the equation would still be true?

4) If we multiplied one side of an equation by −5, what would we have to do to the other side of the equation so that the equation would still be true?

5) If we divided one side of an equation by 7, what would we have to do on the other side of the equation so that the equation would still be true?

6) How do we get rid of "plus 4?"

7) How do we get rid of "plus 10?"

8) How do we get rid of "subtract 7?"

9) How do we get rid of "subtract 2?"

10) How do we get rid of "divide by 3?"

11) How do we get rid of "divide by −6?"

12) How do we get rid of "multiply by −2?"

13) How do we get rid of "multiply by 8?"

14) In one step how can we get rid of a fractional coefficient?

15) In one step how can we get rid of the coefficient of $-\frac{2}{3}$ in the term $-\frac{2}{3}x$?

16) In one step how can we get rid of the coefficient of $\frac{3}{5}$ in the term $\frac{3}{5}x$?

In exercises #17-24, answer the following questions.

17) How many values do we need to get rid of to solve the equation of $4x = 8$?

18) How many values do we need to get rid of to solve the equation of $-3x = 6$?

19) How many values do we need to get rid of to solve the equation of $\frac{x}{4} = 2$?

20) How many values do we need to get rid of to solve the equation of $\frac{y}{-10} = -5$?

21) How many values do we need to get rid of to solve the equation of $2a + 5 = 7$?

22) How many values do we need to get rid of to solve the equation of $4m - 7 = 10$?

23) How many values do we need to get rid of to solve the equation of $\frac{4}{5}x - 4 = 12$?

24) How many values do we need to get rid of to solve the equation of $-\frac{7}{8}x = 56$?

In exercises #25-90, solve the following equations.

25) $x - 6 = -3$

26) $x - 4 = 1$

27) $7 + a = -10$

28) $m + 6 = 2$

29) $x + \frac{2}{5} = \frac{1}{4}$

30) $-\frac{3}{5} + x = -\frac{1}{3}$

31) $7.5 = y - 2.4$

32) $y + 6.25 = -1.4$

33) $5x = 25$

34) $-7x = 28$

35) $-3a = -21$

36) $-80 = -4a$

37) $\frac{m}{5} = -30$

38) $\frac{x}{-2} = -6$

39) $-8 = \frac{y}{-8}$

40) $\frac{y}{-3} = 18$

41) $-x = -4$

42) $-n = 5$

43) $2x + x = -6$

44) $12 = 5x - x$

45) $10 + x - 4 = 5$

46) $-7 + y - 11 = -4$

47) $3x - 5x = -10 - 8$

48) $-6 + 8 = -x + 2x$

49) $-\dfrac{1}{4} + \dfrac{3}{8} = 2n$

50) $3n = \dfrac{2}{5} - \dfrac{5}{8}$

51) $2x - 5 = 7$

52) $4y - 8 = -20$

53) $15 = -2y - 3$

54) $-11 = -3y + 4$

55) $-x - 4 = -7 - 3$

56) $-a + 7 = -2 - 5$

57) $23 = \dfrac{a}{7} - 5$

58) $\dfrac{a}{4} - 6 = -22$

59) $\dfrac{x}{3} - 3 = 9$

60) $\dfrac{x}{-5} + 8 = -7$

61) $-4 + 5 = -3 + \dfrac{m}{-4}$

62) $-7 + 9 = -10 + \dfrac{m}{-3}$

63) $-4 = x - 4$

64) $y + 7 = 7$

65) $3r = -7$

66) $-5 = 11r$

67) $\dfrac{x}{3} = \dfrac{1}{17}$

68) $\dfrac{x}{-2} = \dfrac{4}{15}$

69) $\dfrac{a}{3} = 0$

70) $0 = \dfrac{x}{-8}$

71) $3(x - 4) = -3$

72) $2(x + 2) = 6$

73) $-2(m - 3) = 8$

74) $-10(x - 1) = 20$

75) $-(x + 2) = 2$

76) $-4 = -(y - 5)$

77) $0 = 4(2 - x)$

78) $3(-3 - y) = 6$

79) $-5(-x - 3) + x = 2$

80) $4 = -2x - 3(x + 2)$

81) $\dfrac{2}{3}m = \dfrac{1}{5}$

82) $\dfrac{3}{4}r = \dfrac{3}{5}$

83) $-\dfrac{1}{2}n = 8$

84) $-\dfrac{1}{5}x = 6$

85) $\dfrac{2}{5}x - 3 = 5$

86) $\dfrac{1}{3}x + 4 = 7$

87) $-\dfrac{3}{7}a - 2 = -5$

88) $-\dfrac{4}{3}a + 5 = -10$

89) $-\dfrac{2}{3}x - x + 2 = 4$

90) $\dfrac{3}{4}x + 2x = -6$

Skills Check

1. Find the GCF of $-6x^2y$, $-3xyz$, and $-9yz^2$

2. Fill in the blank: $-2r^2 \bullet () = -8r^3s$

3. Factor the polynomial: $4m^2n - 12mn^2 + 2n$

4. Evaluate the expression of $-x^2 - y^3$ where $x = -3$ and $y = -2$

Answers to Skills Check: 1) $-3y$; 2) $4rs$; 3) $2n(2m^2 - 6mn + 1)$; 4) -1

Section 7.2 Solving More Linear Equations: Variables on Both Sides of the Equation and Eliminating Fractions and Decimals

Objectives:

• To solve equations with variables on both sides of an equation

• To solve certain equations by eliminating fractional and decimal numbers

Application:

Sue earned the same amount of money in two different weeks. During the first week she worked 40 hours. In the second week she worked 30 hours and received a holiday bonus of $125. What was her hourly wage?

Vocabulary:

The Equation-solving process—As we move forward toward more complex equations, it is important to remind ourselves that the process which we learned in the last section is always the process to follow.

There are simply a few added twists to still look at. For instance, in the process to solve equations with variable terms on both sides of the equation there is only one difference—Step #2 below—to get rid of one of the variable terms.

No solution—Sometimes equations cannot be solved because there is no real number that can be substituted for the variable to make it true. For example: $x = x + 4$. This is impossible. There is no number that equals that number itself plus 4. The answer to this equation would be: **no solution**. See Example #3 in this section for an example of an equation without a solution.

How to:

Solve Linear Equations (with variable terms on both sides of the equation):

1. Simplify (distribute and combine any like terms) each side of the equation.

2. Get rid of one of the variable terms (so the only remaining variable term is on one side of the equation) by doing the opposite operation.

3) Get rid of any values (not the coefficient of the variable) on the same side of the equation as the variable by doing the opposite operation.

4) Get rid of the coefficient of the variable last by doing the opposite operation.

***For steps #2-#4 we must remember the equation truth: What we do to one side of the equation, we must do to the other side!!

Example #1: $5x + 4 = 3x - 8$

Step #1: Simplify (distribute and combine any like terms) each side of the equation.

There is nothing to simplify. There is no distribution nor combining to be done.

Step #2: Get rid of <u>one</u> of the variable terms.

Mathematically we could decide to get rid of either the $5x$ term or the $3x$ term and still eventually get the correct answer. For this problem, let's get rid of the $3x$ term.

The $3x$ is positive or a plus. We get rid of "plus $3x$" by "subtracting $3x$." Remember, <u>we are getting rid of the entire term</u> here (not just the coefficient of a term as we did in the last section).

The equation of $5x + 4 = 3x - 8$ becomes $5x - 3x + 4 = 3x - 3x - 8$

We know this equation is still true
because we have done the same thing
to both sides of the equation.

Combine the like terms: $5x - 3x + 4 = 3x - 3x - 8$

Notice that we have successfully rid $2x + 4 = -8$
the problem of having variable terms
on both sides of the equation.

Step #3: Get rid of any values (not the coefficient of the variable) on the same side of the equation as the variable.

We get rid of "plus 4" by "subtracting 4." $2x + 4 = -8$

$2x + 4 - 4 = -8 - 4$

This leaves us with: $2x = -12$

Step #4: Get rid of the coefficient of the variable last. $\dfrac{2x}{2} = \dfrac{-12}{2}$
We get rid of "multiply by 2" by "dividing
by 2."

Answer: $x = -6$

***Check our answer.

Example #2: $-4\left(m + 2\right) + 1 = 3m$

Step #1: Simplify (distribute and combine any like terms) each side of the equation.

On the left side of the equation we must distribute the -4 into the parenthesis.

$-4\,(m + 2) + 1 = 3m$ becomes $-4m - 8 + 1 = 3m$

On the left side of the equation we must combine the like terms of -8 + 1. The result is: $-4m - 7 = 3m$

Step #2: Get rid of <u>one</u> of the variable terms.

Mathematically we could decide to get rid of either the -4m or the 3m term and still eventually get the correct answer. For this problem let's get rid of the -4m term.

The -4m is negative or a subtract. We get rid of "subtract 4m" by "adding 4m." Remember, <u>we are getting rid of the entire term</u> here (not just the coefficient of a term as we did in the last section).

The equation of $-4m - 7 = 3m$ becomes $-4m \underbrace{+\, 4m}\ - 7 = 3m \underbrace{+\, 4m}$

We know this equation is still true because we have done the same thing to both sides of the equation.

Combine the like terms: $\underbrace{-4m + 4m}\ - 7 = \underbrace{3m + 4m}$

Notice that we have successfully rid the problem of having variable terms on both sides of the equation. $-7 = 7m$

Step #3: Get rid of any values (not the coefficient of the variable) on the same side of the equation as the variable.

There are no other terms on the same side of the equation as our variable term.

Step #4: Get rid of the coefficient of the variable last.

We get rid of "multiply by 7" by "dividing by 7." $\dfrac{-7}{7} = \dfrac{7m}{7}$

           Answer: $m = -1$

***Check our answer.

Example #3: $8x - 4 = 8x$

Step #1: Simplify (distribute and combine any like terms) each side of the equation.

There is nothing to simplify. There is no distribution nor combining to be done.

Step #2: Get rid of <u>one</u> of the variable terms.

For this problem. Let's get rid of the 8x term on the left side of the equation.

The 8x is positive or a plus. We get rid of "plus 8x" by "subtracting 8x." Remember, <u>we are getting rid of the entire term</u> here (not just the coefficient of a term as we did in the last section).

The equation of $8x - 4 = 8x$ becomes We know this equation is still true because we have done the same thing to both sides of the equation.

$$8x \underbrace{- 8x} - 4 = 8x \underbrace{- 8x}$$

Combine the like terms:

$$\underbrace{8x - 8x} - 4 = \underbrace{8x - 8x}$$

We have successfully rid the problem of having variable terms on both sides of the equation, but in fact we now have no variables left. **The remaining equation is <u>false</u>!**

$$-4 = 0$$

Whenever we are left with a false equation at the end of our manipulations, it means that the equation has <u>no solution</u>.

Answer: no solution

How to:

Solve Linear Equations (by eliminating fractions and decimals):

1. Find the LCD (Lowest Common Denominator) for <u>all</u> the terms.

2. Multiply both sides of the equation by the LCD. This means that <u>every</u> term on both sides of the equation must be multiplied by the LCD.

3) Solve the equation by following the established process.

***Remember <u>the equation truth</u>: What we do to one side of the equation, we must do to the other side!!

Example #4: $\dfrac{3}{5}x - \dfrac{1}{2} = \dfrac{3}{4}$

Step #1: Find the LCD (Lowest Common Denominator) for <u>all</u> the terms.

We identify the denominators of all the terms. They are 5, 2, and 4. The LCD for these three numbers is **20**.

Step #2: Multiply both sides of the equation by the LCD.

The best way to approach this process is to put all the terms on each side of the equation within a parenthesis.

We can rewrite $\dfrac{3}{5}x - \dfrac{1}{2} = \dfrac{3}{4}$ as $\left(\dfrac{3}{5}x - \dfrac{1}{2}\right) = \left(\dfrac{3}{4}\right)$

Now we multiply our LCD of 20 into both parenthesis. This allows us to recognize that on the left side of the equation we will have **distribution** as the 20 will be multiplied by two terms—the $\dfrac{3}{5}x$ and the $-\dfrac{1}{2}$.

The problem now looks like: $\qquad (20)\left(\dfrac{3}{5}x - \dfrac{1}{2}\right) = (20)\left(\dfrac{3}{4}\right)$

Distribute the LCD of 20 to each term and we get: $12x - 10 = 15$
We have successfully eliminated the fractions.

Step #3: Solve the equation by following the established process.

Get rid of −10 by doing the opposite operation: + 10. Combine like terms. $\qquad 12x - 10 + 10 = 15 + 10$

Our equation now looks like: $\qquad\qquad\qquad\qquad 12x = 25$

We now get rid of "multiply by 12" by doing the opposite operation—"dividing by 12." $\qquad \dfrac{12x}{12} = \dfrac{25}{12}$

$$\text{Answer:} \quad x = \dfrac{25}{12} \ \text{ or } \ 2\dfrac{1}{12}$$

***Check our answer.

Example #5: $0.5x = 0.25x + 5$

Step #1: Find the LCD (Lowest Common Denominator) for <u>all</u> the terms.

We identify the denominators of all the terms. The first term of $0.5x$ is the same as $\frac{5}{10}x$, so it has a denominator of 10. The second term of $0.25x$ is the same as $\frac{25}{100}x$, so it has a denominator of 100. The third term of 5 is a whole number, so it has a denominator or 1.

The LCD for 10, 100, and 1 is **100**.

Step #2: Multiply both sides of the equation by the LCD.

The best way to approach this process is to put all the terms on each side of the equation within a parenthesis.

We can rewrite $0.5x = 0.25x + 5$ as $(0.5x) = (0.25x + 5)$

Now we multiply our LCD of 100 into both parenthesis. This allows us to recognize that on the right side of the equation we will have **distribution** as the 100 will be multiplied by two terms—the $0.25x$ and the $+5$.

The problem now looks like: $(100)(0.5x) = (100)(0.25x + 5)$

Distribute the LCD of 100 to each term and we get: $50x = 25x + 500$

We have successfully eliminated the decimals.

Step #3: Solve the equation by following the established process.

We have variable terms on both sides of the equation, so <u>we must get rid of an entire term</u>- either $50x$ or $25x$. Let's get rid of the positive or "plus $25x$" by "subtracting by $25x$."

Do the same thing to both sides of the

equation. Then combine the like terms. $\underbrace{50x - 25x}_{} = \underbrace{25x - 25x}_{} + 500$

Our equation now looks like: $25x = 500$

We now get rid of "multiply by 25" by doing the opposite operation—"dividing by 25." $\frac{25x}{25} = \frac{500}{25}$

Answer: $x = 20$

***Check our answer.

Sample #1: $-\dfrac{1}{3}x - 4 = -\dfrac{1}{2}$

One way to solve this problem is to eliminate the fractions. We will do this by multiplying every term by the LCD.

The denominator for $-\dfrac{1}{3}x$ is 3; for -4 it is 1; and for $-\dfrac{1}{2}$ it is 2. The LCD of 3, 1, and 2 is 6.

Show that we need to multiply both sides of the equation by **6.**

$$-\frac{1}{3}x - 4 = -\frac{1}{2} \quad \text{becomes} \quad (6)\left(-\frac{1}{3}x - 4\right) = (6)\left(-\frac{1}{2}\right)$$

Distribute the **6** and we get: $-2x - 24 = -3$
We have eliminated the fractions.

Now isolate the variable. $-2x - 24 \underbrace{+\ 24} = -3 \underbrace{+\ 24}$

$-2x = 21$

$\dfrac{-2x}{-2} = \dfrac{21}{-2}$

Answer: $x = -\dfrac{21}{2}$ or $-10\dfrac{1}{2}$

You try it now:

a) $-\dfrac{1}{4}m + 2 = \dfrac{1}{2}$

b) $\dfrac{3}{5} = \dfrac{1}{2}m - 2$

Sample #2: $\dfrac{1}{2}y = -\dfrac{1}{4}y - \dfrac{2}{3}$

One way to solve this problem is to eliminate the fractions. We will do this by multiplying every term by the LCD.

The denominators for three terms are 2, 4, and 3. The LCD is **12.**

Show that we need to multiply both sides of the equation by **12.**

$$\frac{1}{2}y = -\frac{1}{4}y - \frac{2}{3} \quad \text{becomes} \quad (12)\left(\frac{1}{2}y\right) = (12)\left(-\frac{1}{4}y - \frac{2}{3}\right)$$

Distribute the **12** and we get: $6y = -3y - 8$
We have eliminated the fractions.

We have variable terms on both sides of the equation. We need to get rid of one entire variable term. Let's get rid of the $-3y$ by "adding $3y$."

Add $3y$ to both sides of the equation:

$$6y + 3y = -3y + 3y - 8$$

$$9y = -8$$

Now isolate the variable.

$$\frac{9y}{9} = \frac{-8}{9}$$

Answer: $y = -\dfrac{8}{9}$

You try it now:

c) $\dfrac{1}{6}m - \dfrac{2}{3}m + \dfrac{1}{2} = -\dfrac{1}{2}m$

d) $\dfrac{1}{2}x = \dfrac{2}{3}x - \dfrac{1}{5}$

Sample #3: $0.4x = 0.2x + 10$

One way to solve this problem is to eliminate the decimals. We will do this by multiplying every term by the LCD.

The first term of $0.4x$ is the same as $\dfrac{4}{10}x$, so it has a denominator of 10. The second term of $0.2x$ is the same as $\dfrac{2}{10}x$, so it has a denominator of 10. The third term of 10 is a whole number, so it has a denominator or 1.

The denominators for three terms are 10, 10, and 1. The LCD is 10.

Show that we need to multiply both sides of the equation by 10.

$$0.4x = 0.2x + 10 \quad \text{becomes} \quad (10)(0.4x) = (10)(0.2x + 10)$$

Distribute the 10 and we get: $\qquad 4x = 2x + 100$
We have eliminated the decimals.

We have variable terms on both sides of the equation. We need to get rid of one entire variable term. Let's get rid of the positive $2x$ by "subtracting $2x$."

Subtract $2x$ to both sides of the equation:

$$4x - 2x = 2x - 2x + 100$$

$$2x = 100$$

Now isolate the variable.

$$\frac{2x}{2} = \frac{100}{2}$$

Answer: $x = 50$

■
■   **You try it now:**
■
■   e) $0.15x - 0.2 = 0.35x$
■
■   f) $5r - 0.2r = -9 + 0.3r$
■

Answers to You try it now: a) $m = 6$; b) $m = \dfrac{26}{5}$ or $5\dfrac{1}{5}$; c) no solution; d) $x = \dfrac{6}{5}$ or $1\dfrac{1}{5}$; e) $x = -1$; f) $r = -2$

Answer to Application: To find out what Sue's hourly wage was, we have to recognize what information was supplied to us. We know she worked 40 hours the first week; the second week she worked 30 hours and received a bonus of $125. Most important, we are told that the amounts of money she earned for each week were the same—were EQUAL!

This gives us an equation: (Earnings for week #1) = (Earnings for week #2)

          or more specifically:

                    (40 hours times her hourly wage) = (30 hours times her hourly wage) + ($125 bonus)

We don't know Sue's hourly wage so we will represent this wage with a variable—"x."
Now we can set up an algebraic equation.

$$40x = 30x + 125$$

Get rid of the positive 30x term by subtracting 30x
from both sides of the equation.

$$40x - 30x = 30x - 30x + 125$$

Combine like terms to get:

$$10x = 125$$

Divide both sides of the equation by 10 to get "x" isolated:

$$\frac{10x}{10} = \frac{125}{10}$$

$$x = 12.5$$

Answer: Sue's wage was $12.50 per hour

Exercise 7.2: More Linear Equation Problems

In exercises #1-12, answer the following questions.

1) What is the value of "x" in the equation: $-x = -3$?

2) What is the value of "x" in the equation: $-x = 5$?

3) What is the answer to the equation: $x + 4 = x$?

4) What is the answer to the equation: $a = a - 6$?

5) What is the answer to the equation: $3m = 2m$?

6) What is the answer to the equation: $4x = 0$?

7) What is the answer to the equation: $0 = 3r$?

8) What is the answer to the equation: $y = 2y$?

9) If we added $2x$ to both sides of the equation of $4x = -2x + 6$, would there still be "x" terms on both sides of the equation?

10) If we divided both sides of the equation of $2m = m + 5$ by 2, would there still be "m" terms on both sides of the equation?

11) If we divided both sides of the equation of $y - 4 = 3y$ by 3, would there still be "y" terms on both sides of the equation?

12) If we subtracted $5r$ from both sides of the equation of $2r = 5r - 1$, would there still be "r" terms on both sides of the equation?

In exercises #13-80, solve the following equations.

13) $3x - 1 = 4x$

14) $6y = 5y + 4$

15) $-4m = -5m - 5$

16) $-3y + 2 = -2y$

17) $4a = 8 + 2a$

18) $-3a + 10 = -5a$

19) $-2x = 6x + 40$

20) $7x = -3x + 20$

21) $3r + 6 - 5r = 4r$

22) $5x + 2 = 3x - 8$

23) $3m - 5 = -m - 1$

24) $2r + 2 = -4r - 4$

25) $x + 10 = -2x - 2$

26) $-2y + y - 6 = 4$

27) $7 - 11 = 4x - 5x - 2$

28) $m + 3m - 16 = m - 1$

29) $-2m + m = m + 10$

30) $3x = 4x$

31) $7a = -5a$

32) $4a = 6a + 1$

33) $-3x - 3 = -6x + 15$

34) $4(x - 6) = 5x$

35) $-3(x + 5) = -2x$

36) $2(m - 3) = 5m$

37) $6(a - 2) = 2a$

38) $10x = -7(x + 2)$

39) $2w = -2(w - 3)$

40) $5n = 3(n + 2)$

41) $n - 4(n - 3) = 3n$

42) $4x = x - 5(x + 4)$

43) $3a + 7 = 3a$

44) $5x - 3 = 5x - 8$

45) $-4y - 6 = 2(3y + 7)$

46) $-3(3y - 4) = -4y + 6$

47) $5(2 - x) = 3x - 14$

48) $-1 - 2x + 3(-x - 2) = -2x + 8$

49) $12 - 3m - (3m + 2) = 4m + 100$

50) $5(r - 6) = 5r$

51) $2(m - 3) = -6$

52) $-m = m$

53) $\dfrac{2}{3}x - \dfrac{1}{3} = -3$

54) $\dfrac{1}{5}x + \dfrac{1}{5} = 5$

55) $-4 = \dfrac{3}{4}m + \dfrac{1}{2}$

56) $-6 = \dfrac{4}{9}x - \dfrac{2}{3}$

57) $\dfrac{1}{4}x + \dfrac{2}{5} = 12$

58) $5 = \dfrac{1}{6}x + \dfrac{3}{4}$

59) $-1 = -\dfrac{1}{2}r + \dfrac{3}{5}$

60) $-\dfrac{3}{10}a + \dfrac{1}{3} = -2$

61) $\dfrac{1}{10} - \dfrac{3}{5}x = -\dfrac{1}{2}$

62) $-\dfrac{7}{8} = \dfrac{3}{8} - \dfrac{1}{4}y$

63) $\dfrac{5}{2}x - \dfrac{3}{8} = \dfrac{17}{8}$

64) $\dfrac{2}{3}m - \dfrac{1}{3} = \dfrac{2}{7}$

65) $\dfrac{1}{3} = \dfrac{4}{3}r + \dfrac{1}{5}$

66) $\dfrac{4}{5}w - \dfrac{4}{5} = \dfrac{4}{5}w$

67) $0.1x - 0.2 = 0.5$

68) $0.2x - 0.15 = 0.45$

69) $3 = 0.4 + 0.02a$

70) $-0.6 = 0.3 - 0.3y$

71) $7.75 = 1.5x + 0.25$

72) $0.404x + 0.002 = 0.81$

73) $0.4x = 0.5x - 3$

74) $1.25x = 0.5x + 1.5$

75) $0.42x = 0.27x - 0.3$

76) $-2.2y = 1.8y - 0.4$

77) $-0.5m - 2.7m = 2(0.4m - 4)$

78) $3(0.5 + 0.05m) = 0.02m + 0.2$

79) $4(0.2x - 1) = 0.3x - 4$

80) $1.8x = 1.8x - 10$

In exercise #81 – 84: (a) set up an equation that will solve for the value of x, and (b) give the solution.

81)

82)

83) The areas of the rectangle and triangle below are the same.

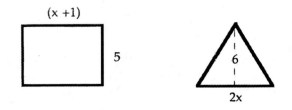

84) The areas of the two rectangles below are the same.

(a + 4)

3

(a − 2)

5

Skills Check

1. $-\dfrac{4}{5} m = -8$　　　2. $\dfrac{a}{-5} = 25$　　　3. $-r = -3 - 4$　　　4. $\dfrac{x}{-4} - 8 = 12$

Answers to Skills Check: 1) m = 10; 2) a = −125; 3) r = 7; 4) x = −80

Section 7.3 Solving Percent Equations & Geometry Equations

Objectives:

- To translate words into an equation
- To solve percent equations
- To solve geometry equations

Application:

The first side of a triangle is 2 inches shorter than the second side. The third side is 5 inches longer than the second side. If the perimeter of this triangle is 33 inches, how long is each side?

Vocabulary:

is—In math **is** means equals.

what— In math **what** means the unknown, which is represented by a variable. It is common to use the variable of "x."

of—In the form of "a value **of** another value," **of** means multiply.

Look at the following examples translating words to math:

"Three-fifths <u>of what</u> number <u>is</u> twelve" becomes: $\frac{3}{5}x = 12$

"The radius <u>is</u> half (<u>of</u>) the diameter" becomes: $r = \frac{1}{2}d$

"Five more than <u>what</u> number is three" becomes: $x + 5 = 3$

"Twice <u>a number</u>, minus 4 <u>is</u> <u>that number</u>" becomes: $2x - 4 = x$

In this last example the word "what" is not used, but we can still see that "a number" and "that number" here are unknowns that need to be represented by a variable.

Percentages—By definition **percent (%) means "out of 100."** Therefore 20% means "20 out of every 100." This can be expressed in the fractional form of $\frac{20}{100}$.

We know that every fraction is a division problem, so we can also see that a **percent means "divide by 100."**

What other equivalencies do we know? We know that divide by 100 in a fractional form looks like $\div \frac{100}{1}$. In turn, we divide fractions by multiplying by the reciprocal of the divisor. So, divide by $\frac{100}{1}$ is the same as multiplying by $\frac{1}{100}$. In fact, we can say that **percent means "multiply by $\frac{1}{100}$."**

Finally, we know that any fraction can also be written in a decimal form. Multiply by $\frac{1}{100}$ is the same as multiplying by .01; we can say that **percent means "multiply by 0.01."**

Let's look at the example of 20%. We can represent this value many different ways by getting rid of the percent symbol. Make sure you can see why each value below is the same as the others.

$$20\% = \frac{20}{100} = 20 \div \frac{100}{1} = 20 \bullet \frac{1}{100} = 20 \bullet (0.01) = 0.20$$

If we were asked to translate the words "what percent," we would first recognize that the word "what" represents an unknown value. It would be translated into a variable. We will use "x."

"What percent" translates into "x %." It also equals the following:

$$x\% = \frac{x}{100} = x \div \frac{100}{1} = x \bullet \frac{1}{100} = x \bullet (0.01) = 0.01x$$

Commutative Property—We first mentioned the commutative property back in section 1.6. The **Commutative Property** (for addition and multiplication) recognizes the fact that the answer will be the same when we <u>change the order</u> of the given values when the problem is either <u>all</u> addition or <u>all</u> multiplication.

In this section we will take advantage of the Commutative Property of multiplication. It is a handy tool. Here are two examples of the commutative property:

2 • 3 • 4 is the same as 4 • 3 • 2

a • b • c is the same as c • a • b

We can also use the commutative property with percents. Look at the translations/manipulations below to see how we can translate words into a visually appealing mathematical expression.

Example: "what percent of 40"

Left to right, this literally translates into: x% (40)

The commutative property allows us to
reorder of the values and rewrite this as: 40%x

By changing the percent to a decimal we
get the expression of: 0.4x

Here are two more examples:

"what percent of 5.4" literally translates into: x% (5.4)

The commutative property allows me to rewrite this as: 5.4%x

By changing the percent to a decimal we get the expression of: 0.054x

"what percent of $3\frac{1}{2}$" literally translates into: $x\% \left(3\frac{1}{2}\right)$

The commutative property allows us to rewrite this as: $\left(3\frac{1}{2}\right)\%x$

By changing the percent to a fraction $\left(\dfrac{7}{2} \bullet \dfrac{1}{100}\right)$
we get the expression of: $\dfrac{7}{200}x$

Here are two examples of literal translations from <u>words to an equation</u> (that is translations that include an equal sign).

"25 is 8% of what number" becomes $25 = 8\%x$

"30 is what percent of 80" becomes $30 = x\% (80)$

***Identifying the Three Parts of a Percent Equation Problem**: The three parts of an equa-
tion are: (1) the **percent**; (2) the **whole or total quantity** (sometimes called the Base); and
(3) the **part quantity** (sometimes called the Amount).

Let's look at the given examples:

(1) 10% of 80 is what?

The **percent** is the given percent—10%.

The **whole or total quantity** is 80. The <u>whole quantity always comes after the word "of."</u>

The **part quantity** is "what." In this case, the part quantity is the unknown value; it
would be represented by the variable "x" in a translation.

(2) 4 is 30% of what number

The **percent** is the given percent—30%.

The **whole or total quantity** is "what number." This is what follows the word "**of**." The whole quantity is the unknown value; it would be represented by the variable "x" in a translation.

The **part quantity** is the 4.

(3) 7 is what percent of 21

The **percent** is "what." The percent is the unknown value; it would be represented as "x%" in a translation.

The **whole or total quantity** is 21—the value that comes after the word "**of**."

The **part quantity** is 7.

***The Percent Equation Model:** After identifying the 3 parts of a percent word problem, we can always set up this equation:

(Part Quantity) = (Percent) • (Whole Quantity)

To solve any percent problem, we must know the values of two of the three concepts above. Only one of them can be the unknown (the "x").

***The concept of a whole or total quantity can sometimes be the original or normal amount. It is <u>not</u> always the largest number.

How to:

Solve Percent Problems Using Equations

1. Translate words into a math statement (Utilize the commutative property if this helps).

2. Change the percent to a decimal (or a fraction).

3. Solve by following the equation-solving process already learned.

Example #1: 10% of 80 is what?

Step #1: Translate words into a math statement.

| 10% of 80 is what? | becomes | $10\%(80) = x$ |

Step #2: Change the percent to a decimal (or a fraction).

| $10\%(80) = x$ | becomes | $0.1(80) = x$ |

Step #3: Solve by following the equation-solving process.

Multiply the 0.1 by 80 $8 = x$

Answer: $x = 8$

Example #2: 4 is 30% of what number

Step #1: Translate words into a math statement.

4 is 30% of what number   becomes $4 = 30\%(x)$

Step #2: Change the percent to a decimal (or a fraction).

$4 = 30\%(x)$ becomes $4 = 0.3x$

Step #3: Solve by following the equation-solving process.

Divide both sides of the equation by 0.3 $\dfrac{4}{0.3} = \dfrac{0.3x}{0.3}$

$13.\overline{3} = x$

Answer: $x = 13\dfrac{1}{3}$ **or** $13.\overline{3}$

Example #3: 7 is what percent of 28

Step #1: Translate words into a math statement.

7 is what percent of 28   becomes $7 = x\%\,(28)$

Use the commutative property to reorder the values: $7 = 28\%(x)$

Step #2: Change the percent to a decimal (or a fraction).

$7 = 28\%(x)$ becomes $7 = 0.28x$

Step #3: Solve by following the equation-solving process.

Divide both sides of the equation by 0.28 $\dfrac{7}{0.28} = \dfrac{0.28x}{0.28}$

$25 = x$

Remember that our unknown is the percent, so
our answer must include the percent symbol.

Answer: $x = 25\%$

How to:

Solve Geometry Problems Using Equations

1. Identify the geometric formula (in our case, for perimeter, area, or volume) we must use to solve for the unknown(s).

2. Identify the algebraic expressions that represent each part of this geometric formula.

3. Substitute the algebraic expressions for the variables in the formula.

4. Solve by following the equation-solving process already learned.

5. Check to see if we need to do any more calculations to answer the question(s).

6. Check to see if the solution(s) are correct by plugging them back into the equation.

Example #4: If the circumference of a circle is 70.336 cm., what is the radius (use 3.14 for)?

Step #1: Identify the geometric formula we must use to solve for the unknown(s).

The formula to be used is for the circumference: $C = \pi d$

Step #2: Identify the algebraic expressions that represent each part of this geometric formula.

The **circumference** is given as **70.336 cm.**

For , the directions have told us to use **3.14.**

The diameter is unknown, so we will let it remain as the variable of "d."

Step #3: Substitute the algebraic expressions for the variables in the formula.

$C = \pi d$ becomes $70.336 = 3.14d$

Step #4: Solve by following the equation-solving process.

Divide both sides of the equation by 3.14. $\dfrac{70.336}{3.14} = \dfrac{3.14d}{3.14}$

$22.4 = d$

Step #5: Check to see if we need to do any more calculations.

Yes, we need to make another calculation. We have solved for the diameter, but the question asks for the radius.

We need to divide the diameter by 2 to get the radius. $r = \dfrac{d}{2}$

Substitute: $r = \dfrac{22.4}{2}$

Answer: **The radius equals 11.2 cm.**

Step #6: Check to see if the solution(s) are correct.

The formula: $C = 2\pi r$

Substitute: $70.336 = 2\,(3.14)\,(11.2)$ This statement is true so the answer is correct!

Example #5: The area of a rectangle is 25.5 inches. The width of the rectangle is 3 inches and the length is $2x - 6$ inches. Solve for the actual length of the rectangle.

Step #1: Identify the geometric formula we must use to solve for the unknown(s).

The formula to solve for the area of a rectangle is: $Area = L \bullet W$

Step #2: Identify the algebraic expressions that represent each part of this geometric formula.

We can identify the following: $Area = 25.5$

$Width = 3$

$Length = (2x - 6)$

Step #3: Substitute the algebraic expressions for the variables in the formula.

$Area = L \bullet W$ becomes $25.5 = 3\,(2x - 6)$

Step #4: Solve by following the equation-solving process.

Distribute the <u>3</u> into the parenthesis: $25.5 = 6x - 18$

Add <u>18</u> to both sides of the equation: $25.5 + 18 = 6x - 18 + 18$

$43.5 = 6x$

Divide both sides of the equation by <u>6</u>: $\dfrac{43.5}{6} = \dfrac{6x}{6}$

$7.25 = x$

Step #5: Check to see if we need to do any more calculations.

Yes, we need to make another calculation. We have solved for the value of "x", but the question asks for the distance of the length of the rectangle.

The length of the rectangle is the algebraic expression: $(2x - 6)$.

To find the actual length, substitute 7.25 for "x": $[2(7.25) - 6]$

Answer: The length of the rectangle is **8.5 inches**

Step #6: Check to see if the solution(s) are correct.

Formula for area of a rectangle: Area = L • W

Substitute: 25.5 = 8.5 • 3   The answer is correct.

Sample #1: A dinner bill came to $25. If Carol decided to leave a 15% tip, how much money did she pay the restaurant, including the tip?

First identify the parts that make up a percent problem.

The **percent** is **15%**.

The **whole quantity** is the **$25**, the total dinner bill.

The **part quantity** is the tip (the part extra that Carol will pay). It is unknown and therefore is represented by the variable of "x."

Now set up the Percent Equation Model [**(Part Quantity) = (Percent) • (Whole Quantity)**]; substitute the value for each of the equation parts.

Equation translation. $x = 15\%(25)$

Change the percent to a decimal. $x = 0.15(25)$

Solve. $x = 3.75$

Now the "x" represents the amount of the tip, but it does not answer the question asked— how much did Carol pay the restaurant?

She paid the sum of the dinner + tip: $25 + $3.75

Answer: Carol paid **$28.75**

■ **You try it now:**
■
■
■ a) Marcus decided to buy some electronic equipment priced at $185. Because the sales tax rate was
■   7.5%, how much money did Marcus pay the store (round to the nearest cent)?
■
■ b) Michelle worked as a sales clerk in a local department store. She earned $7 per hour, plus a commis-
■   sion rate of 2% on everything she sold. Last week she worked 40 hours and sold $11,500 worth of
■   clothing. How much money did she earn?
■

Sample #2: After exports increased 50% for Company A last year, the Company gave all its employees a 12% salary increase. If Aricella's salary increased by $3,500 a year, what was her salary before the increase?

First identify the parts that make up a percent problem.

The **percent** is **12%** (that is the amount of the salary increase). The 50% is the increase in exports, not salary.

The **whole quantity** (that is the original salary before the increase) is unknown and therefore is represented by the variable of "x."

The **part quantity** is Aricella's salary increase—**$3,500**.

Now set up the Percent Equation Model [(Part Quantity) = (Percent) • (Whole Quantity)]; substitute the value for each of the equation parts.

Equation translation.	$3,500 = 12\%\,(x)$
Change the percent to a decimal.	$3,500 = 0.12x$
Solve.	$\dfrac{3,500}{0.12} = \dfrac{0.12x}{0.12}$
	$29,166.\overline{6} = x$

Round the answer to the nearest cent.

Answer: Aricella's original salary was **$29,166.67**

■ **You try it now:**

c) A company's sales for this year increased by $300,000 over last year's sales. If this represented a 25% increase in all sales for last year, what were the company's sales the last year?

d) Andrew earned $600 in commissions last month. If his commission rate is 3.5%, what were his total sales last month (round to the nearest cent)?

Sample #3: A gallon of milk that sold for $2.50 a year ago now sells for $3.20. What is the percent increase in the price for a gallon of milk?

First identify the parts that make up a percent problem.

The **percent** is unknown and therefore is represented by the variable phrase of "x%."

The **whole quantity** (that is the original price for a gallon of milk) is **$2.50** per gallon.

The **part quantity**, that is the amount of the increase for a gallon milk, is derived by finding the difference between the new price and the original price. $3.20 subtract $2.50 gives us the increase of **$0.70** per gallon.

Now set up the Percent Equation Model [(Part Quantity) = (Percent) • (Whole Quantity)]; substitute the value for each of the equation parts.

Equation translation.	$\$.70 = x\% \, (2.50)$
Use the commutative property to reorder the values.	$.70 = 2.50\% \, (x)$
Change the percent to a decimal.	$.70 = .025x$
Solve.	$28 = x$

Remember that our unknown is the percent, so our answer must include the percent symbol.

Answer: The price of milk increased by 28%

You try it now:

e) Ming's salary increased from $34,000 a year to $38,000 a year. What was the percent increase of her salary (round to the nearest whole percent)?

f) Lupe had seen a painting with a price tag of $130. She told a friend she would buy the painting if the price dropped by at least 25%. Two weeks later the painting was on sale for $95. If Lupe kept her word, would she buy the painting now?

Sample #4: The second side of a triangle is 5 feet longer than the first side. The third side is twice as long as the second side. If the perimeter of this triangle is 43 feet, how long is each side?

The formula to solve for the perimeter of a triangle is

$$S_1 + S_2 + S_3 \; = \; \text{Perimeter}$$

When we identify the different sides of this triangle, we face a "relational" situation between the sides. Notice how the distance of the second side is given in relation to the first side; also, the distance of the third side is given in relation to the second side.

The most important thing is to find the "simplest" unknown—the one side that we can label as just "x." In fact this would be side one.

So we know the expression that represents the length of the first side of the triangle: $S_1 = x$

Now look at side two. It is "5 feet longer than the first side." This means it is the same length as the first side plus five.

We now know the expression that represents the length of the second side: $S_2 = (x + 5)$

Finally, the third side is given as "twice as long as the second side." The third side is twice (multiply by two!) the second side.

The expression that represents the length of the third side must be:

$$S_3 = 2(x + 5)$$

We also know that the perimeter is 43.

We write the perimeter formula for a triangle:

$$S_1 + S_2 + S_3 = \text{Perimeter}$$

Substitute the algebraic expressions that represent the three sides:

$$x + (x + 5) + 2(x + 5) = 43$$

Solve. First distribute the 2 into the parenthesis to get:

$$x + (x + 5) + 2x + 10 = 44$$

Simplify the left side of the equation to get:

$$4x + 15 = 43$$

Finish solving the equation:

$$4x + 15 - 15 = 43 - 15$$

$$4x = 28$$

$$\frac{4x}{4} = \frac{28}{4}$$

$$x = 7$$

We have solved for "x," but we have not yet answered the question that was asked—**What is the length of each side?**

Substitute the value of "x" into the algebraic expressions that represent the length of each side.

First side: $S_1 = x$

Substitute: $S_1 = 7$ The length of **side one is 7 ft.**

Second side: $S_2 = (x + 5)$

Substitute: $S_2 = (7 + 5)$ The length of **side two is 12 ft.**

Third side: $S_3 = 2(x + 5)$

Substitute: $S_3 = 2(7 + 5)$ The length of **side three is 24 ft.**

Check: $7 + 12 + 24$ does equal 43.

Answer: The lengths of the three sides are 7, 12, and 24 feet.

■
■
■ **You try it now:**
■
■   g) The perimeter of a rectangle is 34 meters. It's length is 6 meters more than a number; the width is 2
■   times that number minus 4. What is the length and width of this rectangle?
■
■   h) The perimeter of a triangle is 180 yards. The base is twice as long as each of the other two sides. What
■   are the lengths of the three sides of the triangle?

Answers to You try it now: a) $198.88;   b) $510;   c) $1,200,000;   d) $17,142.86;   e) 12%;   f) Yes (27% drop in the price); g) algebraic expressions that identify the sides: the length: $x + 6$; the width: $2x - 4$; substitution: $34 = 2(x + 6) + 2(2x - 4)$; solution: length = 11 meters; width = 6 meters; g) algebraic expressions that identify the three sides: 2x, x, and x; substitution: $180 = 2x + x + x$; solution: The three sides are 90 yards, 45 yards, and 45 yards in length.

Answer to Application: This problem deals with the perimeter of a triangle.

The formula is: $P = s_1 + s_2 + s_3$ We already know the perimeter is 33 inches.

We first must identify the algebraic expressions that represent the length for each of the sides. The sides are "relational" to each other. We can see that the first side is described as 2 inches shorter than the second side.

We can identify the second side as our "simplest" unknown and call it "x."

The first side is the same as the second side, but 2 inches shorter.

     The first side can be written as: $(x - 2)$

     The third side is 5 inches longer than the second side. The third side can be written as: $(x + 5)$

     Write the formula: $P = s_1 + s_2 + s_3$

     Substitute the expressions: $33 = (x - 2) + x + (x + 5)$
     Solve: $33 = 3x + 3$
                              $33 - 3 = 3x + 3 - 3$
                              $30 = 3x$
                              $x = 10$

We have solved for the value of "x" but this doesn't answer the question asked yet. To find the length of each of the three sides, substitute the value of 10 for each "x" in the expressions that make up the length of each side.

     side one: $s_1 = (x - 2)$ side two: $s_2 = x$ side three: $s_3 = (x + 5)$
     Substitute: $s_1 = [(10) - 2]$ Substitute: $s_2 = (10)$ Substitute: $s_3 = [(10) + 5]$
               $s_1 = 8$ $s_2 = 10$ $s_3 = 15$

     Check answers by substitution: $P = s_1 + s_2 + s_3$
                                    $33 = 8 + 10 + 15$ Yes, the answers are correct.

Answers: The lengths of the three sides are 8 inches, 10 inches, and 15 inches.

7.3 Percent and Geometry Equation Problems

In exercises #1-8, change the given percent to a: (a) decimal, and (b) fraction.

1) 8%   2) 15%   3) 8.75%   4) 2.3%

5) $7\frac{3}{4}$%   6) $12\frac{1}{2}$%   7) 100%   8) 225%

In exercises #9-20: (a) translate the following words of each sentence into an algebraic equation (use "x" for the unknown value), and (b) give the solution for the value of "x."

9) Five more than a number is negative two.

10) Four less than a number is six.

11) Two less than triple a number is thirty-one.

12) Three times a number, then added to five is eleven.

13) $\frac{2}{3}$ of what is 18

14) $\frac{1}{8}$ of what is 10

15) Four more than double a number is sixteen.

16) Four is the same as 5 plus double a number.

17) Eight minus a number is -4

18) Six subtract a number is 12

19) Double a number is six more than that number.

20) Triple a number is two less than that number.

In exercises #21-32, translate the following statements into algebraic expressions or equations. This translation should show the percent changed into its decimal or fractional form (example: for 25%x = 50, the answer for the equation set up would be 0.25x = 50). Do not solve.

21) 20% of a number

22) 4.5% of a number

23) 40% of 30

24) 12% of 20

25) What percent

26) What percent of 50

27) 30% of 70 is what number

28) 8% of 10 is what number

29) 25% of a number is eleven

30) 35% of a number is 70

31) What percent of 12 is eight?

32) What percent of 4 is 5?

In exercises #33-43, decide whether each group of expressions is identical. Answer yes or no. If your answer is no, identify the letter of the one expression that does not equal the others.

33) a) 15%   b) $\dfrac{15}{100}$ c) $15 \div 100$ d) $15 \cdot \dfrac{1}{100}$ e) 15 (.01)

34) a) $\dfrac{8}{100}$ b) $8 \div 100$ c) 8%   d) $8 \cdot \dfrac{1}{100}$ e) 8 (.01)

35) a) 25%   b) $25 \cdot 100$ c) $25 \div 100$ d) $\dfrac{25}{100}$ e) 0.25

36) a) 11%   b) 0.11   c) $11 \cdot \dfrac{1}{100}$ d) $\dfrac{11}{100}$ e) 11

37) a) .026   b) $2.6 \div 100$ c) 2.6%   d) $2.6 \cdot \dfrac{1}{100}$ e) $2.6 \cdot (.01)$

38) a) 40%x   b) $\dfrac{40}{100} x$ c) $40 \cdot \dfrac{1}{100} \cdot x$ d) 0.4x

39) a) 75%x   b) 0.75x   c) 75 (.01)x   d) $\dfrac{75}{100} x$

40) a) x% of 30   b) $x \cdot \% \cdot 30$ c) 30%x   d) 0.3x

41) a) x% of 500   b) $x \cdot \dfrac{1}{100} \cdot 500$ c) 5x   d) 5%x

42) a) x% of 7   b) 7%x   c) $7 \cdot \dfrac{1}{100} \cdot x$ d) 0.07x

43) a) what % of 56   b) x%56   c) 56%x   d) 0.56x

In exercises #44-53, identify the unknown part of a percent equation problem. The answer will be either: (1) the percent, (2) the part quantity, or (3) the whole quantity.

44) What is 50% of 80?

45) Eleven is 12% of what number?

46) 7 is what percent of 12?

47) Four is what percent of 4?

48) 6 is 30 percent of what?

49) $12\dfrac{1}{2}$% of 64 is what?

50) What percent of 8 is 5?

51) 2.4 is 10% of what?

52) 6 percent of 20 is what?

53) What is 30 percent of 1000?

In exercises #54-65: (a) write an equation (using "x" for the unknown value) that will solve the problem [this set up should have the percent changed into its decimal or fractional form (example: for 25%x = 50, the equation set up would be 0.25x = 50)], and (b) give the solution.

54) 10% of 80 is what?

55) 4 is 30% of what number?

56) 7 is what percent of 28?

57) 7% of 40 is what?

58) 15 is what percent of 40?

59) 20 is what percent of 160?

60) 5 is 20% of what number?

61) 12% of 70 is what number?

62) What percent of 40 is 60?

63) 8% of what number is 10?

64) Four out of five is what percent?

65) Seven out of eight is what percent?

In exercises #66-77, solve the following problems.

66) If forty percent of the adults in Santa Rosa were born in Sonoma County and there are 90,000 adults in Santa Rosa, how many of these adults were born in the county?

67-68) In Texas the Perez family had an average monthly winter utility bill of $80. When they moved to Minnesota, their average monthly winter utility bill increased by 85%.

67) What was the average increase for each monthly winter payment for the Perez family in Minnesota?

68) What was an average monthly winter utility bill for the Perez family in Minnesota?

69) At a local horseshoe throwing contest, Mr. Mann scored 8 "ringers" in 15 tosses. What percent of his tosses were "ringers" (round to the nearest whole percent)?

70) At Hal's "blowout" sale, Brianna bought an antique oak table that was marked down 25% from its original price (the whole). If her discount for the table was $108, what was its original price?

71) The basketball team from Regent High School made forty percent of the sixty shots they attempted. If each shot they made was worth two points, how many points did Regent High score?

72) After a truck brought part of the apple crop from the fields to the storehouse, inspectors looked over the fruit. They identified 30 bruised apples out of a batch of 570. What percent of the apples were bruised (round answer to the nearest tenth of a percent)?

73) Barry gets a 5.25% commission on the amount of merchandise he sells. What is the value of the merchandise he must sell to earn $100 (round answer to the nearest cent)?

74) Gretta put $900 in a special savings account that earned her 6% interest. How much money did she have in her account after a year?

75) Two years ago the BT model of The Big Computer company sold for $2,500. Today its sells for $2,075. What is the percent decrease in the price of the computer from two years ago to today?

76) In 1997 the population of the city of Hillview was 18,000. The population today is 22,500 people. What is the percent increase in the population of Hillview?

77) On a contractor's blueprint, the levee which was to be built was $8\frac{1}{3}$ inches long. Maribel could see that her crew has completed about $\frac{1}{2}$ inch out of this total. What percent of the levee had been built so far?

In exercises #78-90: (a) write the geometric formula (showing substitutions) which will solve the problem and, (b) give the solution.

78) If the length of a rectangle is 9 feet and the perimeter is 80 feet, what is its width?

79) If the length of a rectangle is 7.5 meters and the perimeter is 26 meters, what is its width?

80) A trapezoid with an area of 78 sq. ft. has two parallel sides of 10 and 16 feet long respectively. What is the height of the figure?

81) A triangle has a base of 14 inches and an area of 56 sq. inches. What is the height of the triangle?

82) A circle has a circumference of 88 feet. What is the diameter of the circle (use $\frac{22}{7}$ for)?

83) A circle has a circumference of 33 yards. What is the radius of the circle (use $\frac{22}{7}$ for)?

84) A circle has a diameter that is three times the length of . What is the cir cumference of the circle (use 3.14 for)? Round answer to the near est tenth of an inch.

85) The area of a rectangle is 60 sq. in. The width of the rectangle is 5 inches and the length is $x + 2$ inches. Solve for the actual length of the rectangle.

86) The area of a rectangle is 72 sq. meters. The length of the rectangle is 12 meters and the width is 3 less than a number. Solve for the actual width of the rectangle.

87) In a triangle, the second side is 2 inches longer than the first side. The third side is 1 inch shorter than the first side. If the perimeter is 25 inches, what is the length of each side of the triangle?

88) In a triangle, the first side is twice as many inches long as the second side. The third side is 4 inches longer than the first side. If the perimeter of the triangle is 214 inches, what is the length of each side of the triangle?

89) The length of a rectangle is 8 inches more than the width. If the perimeter of the rectangle is 80 inches, what is the length and width of the rectangle?

90) The length of a rectangle is double its width. If the perimeter of the rectangle is 48.6 centimeters, what is its length and width?

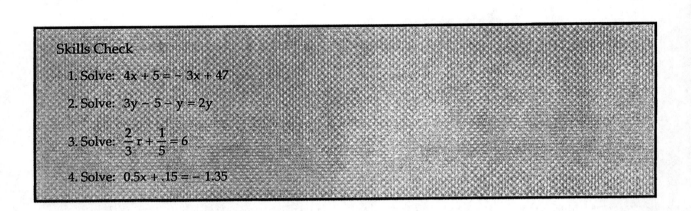

Skills Check

1. Solve: $4x + 5 = -3x + 47$

2. Solve: $3y - 5 - y = 2y$

3. Solve: $\dfrac{2}{3}r + \dfrac{1}{5} = 6$

4. Solve: $0.5x + .15 = -1.35$

Answers to Skills Check: 1) x = 6; 2) no solution; 3) r = $\dfrac{87}{10}$ or $8\dfrac{7}{10}$; 4) x = -3

Appendix A: Conversions & Comparisons Among Percents, Decimals, and Fractions

Objectives:

• To find equivalencies for decimal, percent, and fractional forms of a value

• To compare values given in decimal, percent, and fractional forms

• To solve basic percent problems

Application:

When Malcolm joined a salmon-fishing crew for one month, he was given two options for payment. His first option guaranteed him $100 a day for each of 30 working days plus 5% of the profit. His second option gave him no salary, but 12% of the profit. If the fishing expedition made a profit of $50,000, would Malcolm have made more money from the first or second option?

Vocabulary:

Percent—Percent (%) means "out of 100." 100% represents the whole or the total amount. Any value less than 100% means less than the whole or total amount; any value more than 100% means more than the whole or the total.

The mathematical concept of a percent is the same as that of a fraction—**a part out of a whole**. Unlike a fraction where the whole is always represented by the denominator—which could be any number,—**the whole percent is <u>always</u> 100**. This never changes.

$$5\% \text{ means "five out of 100" or } \frac{5}{100}.$$

$$90\% \text{ means "90 out of 100" or } \frac{90}{100}.$$

$$250\% \text{ means "250 out of 100" or } \frac{250}{100}.$$

Percents are not always whole numbers; they can be written in decimal form or fractional form, but they are still percents.

Here are some **decimal percents:**

8.25% means "8.25 out of 100" or $\dfrac{8.25}{100}$

0.5% means "0.5 out of 100" or $\dfrac{0.5}{100}$

Here are some **fractional percents:**

$12\dfrac{1}{2}$ % means "$12\dfrac{1}{2}$ out of 100" or $\dfrac{12\frac{1}{2}}{100}$

$5\dfrac{1}{4}$ % means $5\dfrac{1}{4}$ out of 100" or $\dfrac{5\frac{1}{4}}{100}$

Equivalencies for Decimals, Fractions, and Percents: In section 2.8 we learned how to find the equal values for fractions and decimals (example: $\dfrac{2}{5}$ is the same as 0.4). We will now expand our knowledge of equivalent values to include percentages. We will learn that $\dfrac{2}{5}$ and 0.4 have a percent equivalency of 40%.

Though more explanations will follow we really only need to remember the following to correctly make conversions between percents and fractions/decimals:

When we convert **<u>from</u>** a decimal or a fraction <u>TO</u> a percent: MULTIPLY by 100!

When we convert <u>FROM</u> a percent **<u>to</u>** a decimal or a fraction: DIVIDE by 100!

How to:

Convert a Decimal to a Percent:

1. Multiply by 100 (remember that when we multiply by 100, all we have to do is move the decimal point <u>2</u> places to the right).
2. Add the percent symbol.

Example #1: Change 0.3 to a percent.

Step #1: Multiply by 100.

Take the decimal number of 0.3 and move the decimal point 2 places to the right. We get 30.

Step #2: Add the percent symbol.

Answer: 30%

How to:

Convert a Percent to a Decimal:

1. Divide by 100 (remember that when we divide by 100, all we have to do is move the decimal point 2 places to the left). When we divide by 100 the percent symbol disappears.

Example #2: Change 85% to a decimal.

Step #1: Divide by 100.

Take the number of 85% and move the decimal point 2 places to the left. We get 0.85

Answer: 0.85

How to:

Convert a Fraction to a Percent:

1. Multiplying by 100 (which is the same as multiplying by $\frac{100}{1}$). Now solve this multiplication of fractions problem. Remember to cancel.

2. Add the percent symbol.

Example #3: Change $\frac{3}{8}$ to a percent.

Step #1: Multiply by 100 (which is the same as multiplying by $\frac{100}{1}$).

$$\frac{3}{8} \cdot \frac{100}{1}$$

4 is the common factor for 8 and 100. 4 divides into 8 two times and into 100 twenty-five times. After canceling the problem looks like:

$$\frac{3}{\underset{2}{8}} \cdot \frac{\overset{25}{\cancel{100}}}{1}$$

Multiply straight across to get: $\frac{75}{2}$

We change $\frac{75}{2}$ to a mixed number to get: $37\frac{1}{2}$ or 37.5

Step #2: Add the percent symbol.

Answer: $37\frac{1}{2}\%$ or 37.5%

How to:

Convert a Percent to a Fraction:

1. Divide by 100 (which is the same as dividing by $\frac{100}{1}$). Now solve this division of fractions problem. When we divide by 100 the percent symbol disappears.

Example #4: Change $7\frac{1}{2}$ % to a fraction.

Step #1: Divide by 100 (which is the same as dividing by $\frac{100}{1}$).

$$7\frac{1}{2} \div \frac{100}{1}$$

To do this division problem we need to turn the mixed number of $7\frac{1}{2}$ into an improper fraction. The problem becomes:

$$\frac{15}{2} \div \frac{100}{1}$$

Now we need to take the reciprocal of the divisor of $\frac{100}{1}$ and multiply. The problem becomes:

$$\frac{15}{2} \cdot \frac{1}{100}$$

5 is the common factor for 15 and 100. 5 divides into 15 three times and into 100 twenty times. After canceling the problem looks like:

$$\frac{\overset{3}{\cancel{15}}}{2} \cdot \frac{1}{\underset{20}{\cancel{100}}}$$

Multiply straight across to get: $\frac{3}{40}$

Answer: $\frac{3}{40}$

> **How to:**
>
> Compare Decimals, Fractions, and Percents:
>
> 1. Put all number values into the same form—either <u>all</u> decimals, <u>all</u> fractions, or <u>all</u> percents.
>
> 2. (As it is most often easiest to change all the values into decimal form, this is what we will do in the example below). Line up the decimal points to compare the values.

Example #5: Put the following values in order from the smallest to the largest: $\frac{1}{3}$, 0.3, and 35%

Step #1: Put all number values into the same form (in this case into decimal form).

$\frac{1}{3}$ becomes $0.\overline{3}$ 0.3 stays 0.3   35% becomes 0.35

Step #2: Line up the decimal points to compare the values.

<u>Values in decimal form</u> $\Downarrow$	$\Rightarrow$	Represent all values to the same place value (in this case: the hundredths)
$\frac{1}{3}$ = $0.\overline{3}$	$\Rightarrow$	becomes: $0.3\overline{3}$
0.3 = 0.3	$\Rightarrow$	becomes: 0.30
35% = 0.35	$\Rightarrow$	becomes: 0.35

We can now see that 0.3 (represented as thirty-hundredths) is the smallest value.

The value of $\frac{1}{3}$ (represented as thirty-three [repeating] hundredths) is the middle value.

35% (represented as thirty-five hundredths) is the largest value.

**Answer: 0.3 , $\frac{1}{3}$, 35%

**When we give the answer for a comparison problem, we always use the original given forms of the number values.

How to:

Solve for the Percent of a Number:

1. Change the percent into a decimal or a fraction.
2. Multiply the values.

Example #6: What is 6.5% of $260?

Step #1: Change the percent into a decimal or a fraction.

6.5% becomes 0.065

Step #2: Multiply the values.

$(0.065) \bullet (260)$

```
      260
   x 0.065
     1300
     1560
     000
   16.900
```

Answer: $16.90

In the first four Example problems of this section, we looked at four isolated conversions. Now let's look at the Conversion Triangle illustrated in next page to see the interrelated nature of all six conversions—fraction to a decimal, decimal to a fraction, decimal to a percent, percent to a decimal, fraction to a percent, and percent to a fraction.

Consider the outline of the triangle as a road upon which we can drive—from one equivalency to another. We can drive in any direction we want, but we must follow the given directions (the conversion processes).

Fraction/Decimal/Percent Conversion Triangle

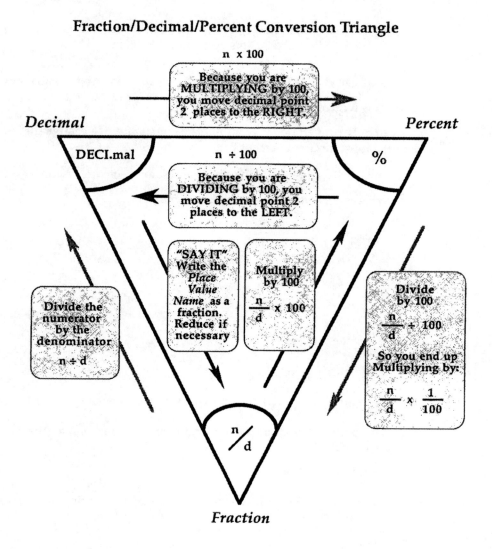

Sample #1: Change $\frac{3}{4}$ % to a fraction.

Utilizing the Conversion Triangle, let's solve this two different ways.

First Method: One conversion: change a percent to a fraction.

We change a percent to a fraction by dividing by 100.

Set up: $\dfrac{\frac{3}{4}}{100}$ or $\dfrac{3}{4} \div \dfrac{100}{1}$

Solve: $\dfrac{3}{4} \cdot \dfrac{1}{100}$

Answer: $\dfrac{3}{400}$

<u>Second Method</u>: Two conversions: (1) change the percent to a decimal;
(2) then change this decimal to a fraction.

Before we can change $\frac{3}{4}$% into a decimal, we need to recognize that our percent is written in a fractional form.

We can <u>only</u> convert this percent into a decimal <u>after</u> we change the fractional percent into a decimal percent.

To do this, we <u>keep the percent symbol</u> and simply convert $\frac{3}{4}$ into a decimal form (process: the numerator ÷ the denominator).

$$3 \div 4 \;\Rightarrow\; 4\overline{)\begin{array}{r} 0.75 \\ 3.00 \\ -2\,8 \\ \hline 20 \\ -20 \\ \hline 0 \end{array}}$$

$\frac{3}{4}$ is the same as 0.75

Therefore, $\frac{3}{4}$% is the same as 0.75%

Now our percent is written in its decimal form; we are ready for our first conversion.

Change a percent to a decimal by dividing by 100 (which moves the decimal point two places to the left).

0.75% becomes 0.0075

Now, **change this decimal to a fraction** by "saying it" (placing the number value over the place value).

0.0075 becomes $\frac{75}{10000}$

Reduce (ALWAYS!) this fraction to get the **answer:** $\frac{3}{400}$

It is important to notice that we arrived at the same answer whichever way we decided to move around the Conversion Triangle.

You try it now:

a) Change $\frac{2}{5}$% to a fraction

b) Change $\frac{1}{2}$% to a fraction.

Sample #2: Change 6.3% to a fraction.

Utilizing the Conversion Triangle, let's solve this two different ways.

<u>First Method</u>: One conversion: change a percent to a fraction.

Before we can change 6.3% into a fraction, we need to recognize that our percent is written in a decimal form.

We can <u>only</u> convert this percent into a fraction <u>after</u> we change the decimal percent into a fractional percent.

To do this, we <u>keep the percent symbol</u> and simply convert the decimal number of 6.3 into a fractional (or mixed number) form.

6.3 is the same as $6\frac{3}{10}$

Therefore, 6.3% is the same as $6\frac{3}{10}$ %

Now our percent is written in its fractional form; we are ready for our conversion.

Change a percent to a fraction by dividing by 100.

Set up: $\dfrac{6\frac{3}{10}}{100}$ or $6\frac{3}{10} \div \dfrac{100}{1}$

Solve: $6\frac{3}{10} \cdot \dfrac{1}{100}$

$\dfrac{63}{10} \cdot \dfrac{1}{100}$

Answer: $\dfrac{63}{1000}$

<u>Second Method</u>: Two conversions: (1) change the percent to a decimal; (2) then change this decimal to a fraction.

Change a percent to a decimal by dividing by 100 (which moves the decimal point two places to the left).

6.3% becomes 0.063

Now, **change this decimal to a fraction** by "saying it" (placing the number value over the place value).

0.063 becomes $\dfrac{63}{1000}$

Answer: $\dfrac{63}{1000}$

Again, notice that we arrived at the same answer whichever way we decided to move around the Conversion Triangle.

▪ **You try it now:**

▪   c) Change 10.5% to a fraction.

▪   d) Change 4.8% to a fraction.

Sample #3: Change $\dfrac{5}{16}$ to a percent.

Utilizing the Conversion Triangle, let's solve this two different ways.

First Method: One conversion: change a fraction to a percent.
          Change a fraction to a percent by multiplying by 100.

Set up: $\dfrac{5}{16} \cdot \dfrac{100}{1}$

Solve: ⇒ Cancel: $\dfrac{5}{\overset{}{\underset{4}{16}}} \cdot \dfrac{\overset{25}{\cancel{100}}}{1}$

     $= \dfrac{125}{4}\%$

Change to a mixed number: **Answer:** $31\dfrac{1}{4}\%$

Second Method: Two conversions: (1) change the fraction to a decimal; (2) then change this
          decimal to a percent.

Change a fraction to a decimal by dividing the numerator by the denominator).

$$5 \div 16 \;\Rightarrow\; 16\overline{)\begin{array}{l} 0.3125 \\ 5.0000 \end{array}}$$
$$\begin{array}{r} -\;4\,8 \\ \hline 2\,0 \\ -\,1\,6 \\ \hline 4\,0 \\ -\,3\,2 \\ \hline 8\,0 \\ -\,8\,0 \\ \hline 0 \end{array}$$

The fraction $\dfrac{5}{16}$ is the same as the decimal of 0.3125

Now **change this decimal to a percent** by multiplying by 100 (which moves the decimal point two places to the right).

0.3125 becomes 31.25%

Answer: 31.25% which is the same as $31\dfrac{1}{4}\%$

You try it now:

e) Change $\frac{5}{8}$ to a percent.

f) Change $1\frac{2}{3}$ to a percent.

Sample #4: Which has a greater value: $\frac{2}{5}$ of \$700 or 45% of \$600?

We are asked to compare two values here, so we must solve each value independently.

***We know now that in the form of "a number of another number" that the word "of" means multiply.

Look at our two values:

$\frac{2}{5}$ <u>of</u> \$700 means $\frac{2}{5} \cdot \frac{700}{1}$ 45% <u>of</u> \$600 means $0.45 \cdot 600$

$\Downarrow$ $\Downarrow$

Solve: $\frac{2}{5} \cdot \frac{\overset{140}{\cancel{700}}}{1} = \$280$ Solve: **\$270**

Answer: $\frac{2}{5}$ of 700 is the greater value

You try it now:

g) Which has a greater value: $\frac{2}{3}$ of \$810 or 60% of \$880?

h) Which has a greater value: $\frac{1}{8}$ of \$100 or 25% of \$55?

Sample #5: A store owner bought a sofa from a wholesaler for \$270. If the owner increased this price by 35%, for what price did he sell the sofa to his customers?

Concept: (Wholesale cost) + (markup by owner)

$\Downarrow$ $\Downarrow$

(Original Price)   + (35% <u>of</u> the original cost)

Set up: $\Rightarrow$ $370 + \left(35\% \cdot 370\right)$

Solve: $\Rightarrow$ Change the % to a decimal: $370 + \left(0.35 \cdot 370\right)$

Work inside the parenthesis: $370 + (129.50)$

Answer: **\$499.50**

You try it now:

i) Anna had a salary of 40,000 a year. If she received a salary increase of 8%, what is her new annual salary?

j) Bob invested $3500 in a new medical company last year. This year he earned back all of his original investment plus 40% more. How much income did he get this year from his investment?

Answers to You try it now: a) $\frac{1}{250}$; b) $\frac{1}{200}$; c) $\frac{21}{200}$; d) $\frac{6}{125}$; e) 62.5% or $62\frac{1}{2}$%; f) $166.\overline{6}$% or $166\frac{2}{3}$%;

g) $\frac{2}{3}$ of 810 = $540; 60% of 880 = $528; solution: $\frac{2}{3}$ of 810 has a greater value;

h) $\frac{1}{8}$ of 100 = $12.50; 25% of 55 = $13.75; solution: 25% of 55 has a greater value;

i) Set up: 40,000 + 8% (40,000); solution: $43,200; j) Set up: $3500 + 40% (3500); solution: $4900.

Answer to Application: We can recognize that this is a comparison problem between two options. First we need to solve for the result of each option separately.

First option: Malcolm get $100 a day for 30 days plus 5% of the profit.

We are given the profit as $50,000; Malcolm will get 5% of this amount.

Set up: 100 (30) + 5% (50,000)

Solve: Change the percent to a decimal and get: 100 (30) + 0.05 (50,000)

Multiply to get: 3000 + 2500

Malcolm would earn $5500 with the first option.

Second option: Malcolm gets no salary, but 12% of the profits.

Set up: 12% (50,000)

Solve: Change the percent to a decimal and get: 0.12 (50,000)

Malcolm would earn $6,000 with the second option.

Answer: Malcolm would have made more money if he had chosen the second option.

Appendix A: Conversion and Comparison Problems

In exercises #1-12, change any given decimals into percents and any given percents into decimals.

1) 15%	2) 28%	3) 0.85	4) 0.7	5) 3%	6) 9.5%
7) 0.675	8) 0.01	9) 2	10) 125%	11) 0.4%	12) 0.25%

In exercises #13-36, change any given fractions into percents and any given percents into fractions.

13) 39% 14) 7% 15) $\frac{4}{5}$ 16) $\frac{1}{4}$ 17) 15% 18) 30%

19) $\frac{3}{4}$ 20) $\frac{1}{5}$ 21) 100% 22) 150% 23) $\frac{5}{4}$ 24) $\frac{7}{2}$

25) $5\frac{1}{2}$% 26) $20\frac{1}{4}$% 27) $\frac{3}{8}$ 28) $\frac{5}{8}$ 29) $\frac{1}{12}$ 30) $\frac{3}{16}$

31) $8\frac{1}{3}$% 32) $14\frac{2}{7}$% 33) $112\frac{1}{2}$% 34) $\frac{1}{3}$ 35) $\frac{4}{3}$ 36) $\frac{5}{6}$

In exercises #37-47, decide whether each group of expressions all have the same value. Answer yes or no. If your answer is no, identify the letter of the one expression that does not equal the others.

37) a) 8% b) $\frac{8}{100}$ c) $8 \div 100$ d) $\frac{8}{1} \cdot \frac{1}{100}$

38) a) $3\frac{1}{2}$% b) $\frac{3\frac{1}{2}}{100}$ c) $3\frac{1}{2} \div 100$ d) $\frac{7}{2} \cdot \frac{1}{100}$

39) a) 7.5% b) $7\frac{1}{2}$% c) 0.075 d) $\frac{7\frac{1}{2}}{100}$

40) a) 20.8% b) $20\frac{4}{5}$% c) 20.8 d) 0.208

41) a) $8\frac{2}{3}$% b) $8.\overline{6}$ c) $\frac{8\frac{2}{3}}{100}$ d) $8.\overline{6}$%

42) a) 0.306 b) 30.6% c) $\frac{306}{1000}$ d) $30\frac{3}{5} \div 100$

43) a) 0.25% b) 0.0025 c) $\frac{25}{100}$ d) $\frac{25}{10000}$

44) a) $\frac{3}{1000}$ b) 0.003 c) 0.3% d) $\frac{3}{10}$%

45) a) $9\frac{1}{5}\%$ b) 9.2%   c) 0.092   d) $\frac{92}{1000}$

46) a) $\frac{5}{12}$ b) $5 \div 12$ c) $\left(\frac{5}{12} \bullet \frac{100}{1}\right)\%$ d) $\left(\frac{5}{12} \div \frac{100}{1}\right)\%$

47) a) $\frac{2}{11}$ b) $\left(\frac{2}{11} \bullet \frac{100}{1}\right)\%$ c) $2 \div 11$ d) $\left[(2 \div 11) \bullet 100\right]\%$

In exercises #48-55, for each given percent find its equivalent value as a: (a) fraction, and as a (b) decimal. If necessary, round your decimal answer to the nearest ten-thousandths place.

48) 5.2%   49) 0.2%   50) $\frac{7}{10}\%$ 51) $2\frac{3}{5}\%$

52) $16.\overline{3}\%$ 53) 6.25%   54) $42\frac{6}{7}\%$ 55) $7\frac{3}{4}\%$

In exercises #56-67, for each given fraction or decimal find its equivalent as a percent. Write the non-integer percent in its: (a) fractional or mixed number form, and its (b) decimal form. Use the repeater bar as necessary.

56) 0.037   57) 1.455   58) $\frac{1}{8}$ 59) $\frac{2}{3}$

60) 0.086   61) 0.00015   62) $\frac{1}{6}$ 63) $\frac{1}{22}$

64) $\frac{7}{6}$ 65) $2\frac{1}{3}$ 66) $\frac{11}{16}$ 67) $0.25\overline{3}$

In exercises #68-77, write the following values in order from smallest to largest.

68) $\frac{1}{4}$, 0.251, and 0.28   69) $\frac{1}{2}$, 0.531, and 53%   70) $\frac{3}{8}$, $\frac{2}{5}$, and 38.5%

71) 0.052, $\frac{1}{20}$, and 5.5%   72) 2.6, $\frac{8}{3}$, and 26%   73) $\frac{7}{21}$, 3.5, and 35%

74) 7.62, 0.7621, 7.6, and 7.6%   75) $\frac{4}{9}$, 60%, $\frac{2}{3}$, and $\frac{7}{15}$ 76) 0.3, $\frac{301}{100}$, $\frac{1}{3}$, and 33%

77) 1.1, 1, $\frac{6}{5}$, and 101%

In exercises #78-89, solve the following expressions.

78) 6% of 50

79) 30% of 80

80) 11% of 250

81) 120% of 60

82) 500 + 8% of 500

83) 40 + 75% of 120

84) 70 + 70% (70)

85) 200 + 35% (200)

86) 800 - 15% of 800

87) 12 - 7.5% (12)

88) 40% (300) - $\frac{1}{3}$ of 93

89) $\frac{4}{5}$ of 80 - 10% (640)

In exercises #90-95: (a) write a mathematical expression that will solve the problem, and (b) give the solution.

90) A car dealer bought a second-hand car for $2200. If the dealer increased this price by 40%, for what price did she sell the car to a customer?

91) Derrick earned $12 an hour before last month's 15% raise. How much money is he making per hour now?

92) Charles had a painting assessed at a value of $1500. Unfortunately, only two days later one corner of the canvas was slightly scratched. An assessor told him that the painting had lost 60% of its value. What is the value of the painting now?

93) Helena worked in a retail store, earning money from both a salary and a commission (a percentage earned from her total sales). Last week she earned $250 in salary and received a 3% commission on her total sales of $4000 dollars worth of goods. How much money did Helena earn last week?

94) Nalishma invested $2000 dollars in an organic farm. One year later she had earned back all the money she invested plus another 25%. What was her income from this investment during the past year?

95) Kurt earned $38,000 last year before taxes. If all his taxes cost him 32% of his income, how much money did Kurt actually take home last year?

In exercises #96-102, solve the problems.

96) Which has a greater value: $\frac{3}{8}$ of $400 or 20% of $600?

97) Which has a greater value: $\frac{3}{5}$ of $275 or 7% of $2000?

98) Which has a greater value: $\frac{1}{2}$ of $50,000 or 51% of $50,000

99-100) In a television game show, the winner of a contest had one minute to pick her winning prize. The first prize offered her $200 plus $\frac{2}{7}$ of $2100. The second prize offered her 16% of $12,000.

99) Which prize was worth more money, the first or the second?

100) What was the dollar difference between the two prizes?

101-102) Eleanor was offered a sales contract with two different options. The first option offered to pay her a salary of $400 a week plus 4% of her total sales. The second option offered no salary, but a 15% commission on her total sales.

101) If Eleanor's sales for a week averaged $4,000, would she have earned more money with the first or second option?

102) What would be the weekly difference in income between the two options?

Chapter 1: Whole Numbers & Decimals

1.1 Place Value and Comparisons

1) tens 3) hundreds 5) thousands 7) ten millions 9) billions 11) hundredths 13) thousandths

15) hundred thousandths 17) hundredths 19) thousandths 21) ten thousands 23) thousandths

25) seventy-five 27) forty-three hundredths 29) thirty-two and seven hundred two thousandths

31) three thousand, three hundred dollars and three cents 33) eight thousand five dollars and ninety-two cents

35) 764 37) 1.6 39) 3,530,722 41) 40,000,000.00009 43) 0.0012 45) true 47) true 49) false 51) true

53) true 55) false 57) true 59) 306 61) 8 63) 88 < 89 65) 800.3 < 800.5 67) 5.063 < 5.1 69) 4.25 > 4.2

71) a) 0.81, 3.057, 3.57, 7.92, 8; b) 2.4, 2.428, 2.43, 24, 24.2

73) a) 0.145 < 1.44 < 14 < 14.04 < 14.4; b) 8.58 < 8.6 < 8.608 < 8.68 < 8.7;

75) 400,000 77) 5 79) 0 81) 0.05 83) part of a whole 85) 14 oz. package 87) 12 doughnuts for $2.59

89) Mount Holontite.

1.2 Add and Subtract Whole Numbers and Decimals

1) 11,512 3) 101.615 5) 1005.95 7) 479.45 9) 4,283.7809 11) 6,879.25 13) 0.784 15) 107.81 17) 357.64

19) 35.35 21) translation: 3.06 + 18; solution: 21.06 23) translation: 12 + 11.3; solution: 23.3

25) translation: 214.25 - 84.17 solution: 130.08 27) translation: 67.14 - 29.8; solution: 37.34

29) translation: 52 - 15.736; solution: 36.264 31) x + 7 33) 18 - x 35) x - 3 37) 10 - x 39) x + 40

41) true 43) true 45) false 47) true 49) 12 = 19 - 7 or 7 = 19 - 12 51) x = 15 + 8

53) x = 12 - 7 or 7 = 12 - x 55) x = 20 - 4 or 4 = 20 - x 57) x = 3.8 59) x = 11 61) x = 57.17

63) x = 10.4 65) Set up: 2184 + 928 + 1370; solution: 4482 people 67) Set up: 52 − (16 + 9 + 12) solution: 15 women 69) Set up: 74 - 28; solution: 46 degrees

71) Set up: 74 - 67; solution: 7 degrees 73) Set up: 700 + 350 + 300; solution: $1,350

75) Set up: (700 + 350) - (500 + 200 + 110 + 200); solution: $40

77) Set up (the difference between the amount spent on his sister and his 2 brothers):
85 - (38.79 + 43.05); solution: Spent $3.16 more on his sister

79) Set up: 250 - (38.79 + 43.05 + 82.55 + 40); solution: $45.61 81) Set up: 12 - 8.6; solution: 3.4 miles

83) Set up (the difference between the amount he ran on Tuesday and Thursday and the amount he ran on Monday, Wednesday, and Friday): (12 • 2) - (8.6 + 4.5 + 6.25); solution: Ran 4.65 miles more on Tuesday and Thursday.

1.3 Multiply Whole Numbers and Decimals

1) 234,918 3) 180,140 5) 168.02 7) 0.0203 9) 0.004844 11) 240,000 13) 96 15) 25.8 feet 17) 168 hours

19) 285 minutes 21) 1344 hours 23) 15,840 feet 25) 234 inches 27) 3 • 12 + 11 29) 20 • 10 - 150

31) 3 • 20 - 47 33) (8 • 8) - (6 • 5) 35) 10 • x 37) x • y - 6 39) 2 • x - 5

41) Set up: 800 (5.6); solution: 4480 people 43) Set up: 35 (11.50); solution: $402.50

45) Set up: [(3 • 12) + (2 • 6.5) + 20] (12); solution: 828 miles 47) Set up: 100 • 8 • 4; solution: $3200

49) Set up (the difference between the amount Serena earned and the amount Rohan earned):

[(25 • 6) (4) + 125 (2)] - [(3 • 6) (6 + 5) (4)]; solution: Serena earned $58 more than Rohan in the 4 weeks.

51) Set up: [seeing how many <u>inches</u> long the line of ants is] 16,200 (0.02)(12); solution: Yes (the line of ants in 3888 inches long);

53) Set up: 23,072.5 (0.02)(12); solution: 5537.4 inches;

55) Set up: (0.9)(30); solution: no, the grass hopper only 25 inches (not the necessary 27 inches);

57) Set up: (0.9)(40) – 1(3)(12); solution: the distances are the same.

1.4 Divide Whole Numbers and Decimals

1) 31 3) 7 5) 24 7) 6 9) 263 11) 3500 13) 2.55 15) 75 17) 220 19) 605 21) 0.025 23) undefined

25) 0.0305 27) translation: (15 ÷ 3) + 6; solution: 11 29) translation: (26 ÷ 2) - 11; solution: 2

31) translation: (11 • 20) - 1.2; solution: 218.8 33) translation: (5 ÷ 25) - 0.15; solution: 0.05

35) 3 ÷ x 37) x ÷ y 39) (x ÷ x) + 3 41) (y ÷ x) - y 43) true 45) true 47) false 49) true

51) 20 = 4 • 5 53) x = 70 ÷ 10 or 10 = 70 ÷ x 55) x = 3.5 (18) 57) 11 = x ÷ 7 or 7 = x ÷ 11

59) x = 10 61) x = 4 63) x = 120 65) x = 10 67) x = 5.75 69) Set up: 200,000 ÷ 80; solution: $2500

71) Set up: 9000 ÷ 2.5; solution: 3600 gallons 73) Set up: 50 ÷ 800; solution: 0.0625 gallons

75) Set up: 25,219,200 ÷ 240; solution: $105,080 77) Set up: 0.24 ÷ 12; solution: 0.02 feet

79) Set up: (2400 ÷ 0.02) (50); solution: 6,000,000 ants 81) Set up: 8000 ÷ (1000 • 100); solution: $0.08 or 8¢

1.5 Rounding and Estimation

1) 708 3) 30 5) 0 7) 60 9) 46,800 11) 16,300 13) 100 15) 408,000 17) 7000 19) 1000 21) 48.3 23) 406.9

25) 64.5 27) 99.95 29) 99.99 31) whole: 21; tenths: 20.7; hundredths: 20.73; thousandths: 20.730

33) whole: 280; tenths: 279.9; hundredths: 279.89; thousandths: 279.889;

35) whole: 7; tenths: 7.3; hundredths: 7.33; thousandths: 7.333

37) whole: 630; tenths: 629.9; hundredths: 629.90; thousandths: 629.899

39) cent: $.91 or 91¢; tenth of a cent: $.910 or 91.0¢

41) cent: $.67 or 67¢; tenth of a cent: $.667 or 66.7¢ 43) $10 45) $0 47) d 49) b

51) translation: 9 + 4.4; solution: 13.4   53) translation: 1100 - 850; solution: 250

55) translation: 5400 - 2500; solution: 2900   57) translation: 810 • 56.7; solution: 45,927

59) translation: 11.2 ÷ 4; solution: 2.8   61) Set up: 38,686.34 - 34,257.88; solution: $4400

63) Set up: 3.10 ÷ 12; solution: $0.26 or 26¢   65) Set up: no set up; solution: $0.20 or 20¢

67) Set up: (0.195) (25); solution: $4.88;   69) Set up (the difference between the price of the 2 smaller
boxes and the price of the jumbo box): [(0.195 • 25) (2)] - (0.1575 • 50); solution: $1.88

71) Set up: 14,135 ÷ 144; solution: 98 viruses   73) 1300   75) 300   77) 600   79) 800   81) $400   83) 20

85) 120   87) 6   89) 5   91) translation: 9 - 5; solution: 4   93) translation: 8 • 12; solution: 96

95) translation: 0 • 0; solution: 0   97) translation: 4 ÷ 5; solution: 0.8

99) Set up: 500 + 400 + 500; solution: $1400   101) Set up: 900 - (600 + 0); solution: $300

103) Set up: 865.38 - (565 + 46); solution: $254.38   105) Set up: $1.82 ÷ 6; solution: $0.30 or 30¢

1.6 A Certain Order of Operations

1) 8   3) 1   5) 28   7) 19   9) 12   11) 12   13) 13   15) 58   17) 2   19) b   21) a   23) c   25) b

27) Set up: [(300 + 400 + 820 + 480) ($1.50)] ÷ 4 solution: $750

29) Set up: (4 min 32 sec + 4 min 46 sec + 5 min + 5 min 14 sec) ÷ 4 solution: 4 min 53 sec or
293 sec

31) Set up: [20 (.019) + 30 (.018) + 50 (.017)] ÷ 100 solution: .0177 inches

33) Set up: { [(18 + 12) (2)] (3)} ÷ 12 solution: 15 feet

35) Set up: [6 (35,000) – 45,000] ÷ 5 solution: $33,000   37) commutative and associative properties

39) associative property   41) 36   43) 69   45) 100   47) 120   49) true   51) false   53) true

55) true   57) true   59) true

1.7 Mental Math: Expanded Notation and Powers of 10

1) 400 + 50 + 2   3) 4000 + 600 + 20 + 3   5) 7000 + 40 + 2   7) 10,000 + 5,000 + 600 + 40

9) 200,000 + 10,000 + 50   11) 3,000,000 + 70,000 + 5,000 + 200   13) $9 + \frac{3}{10} + \frac{5}{100}$

15) $70 + 1 + \frac{2}{10} + \frac{4}{100}$ 17) $\frac{6}{10} + \frac{3}{10,000}$ 19) a) (50 + 2) • 7; b) 350 + 14; c) 364

21) a) (70 + 9) • 4; b) 280 + 36; c) 316   23) a) (80 + 5) • 6; b) 480 + 30; c) 510

25) a) (90 + 6) • 2; b) 180 + 12; c) 192   27) a) (30 + 4) • 7; b) 210 + 28; c) 238   29) 84   31) 368

33) 684   35) 920   37) 3060   39) 2310   41) 864   43) 5600   45) 4800   47) 0.1   49) 1000 and 10,000

51) 0.001 and 0.01   53) 10   55) 0.1   57) 10   59) 0.01   61) true. One example: 6 • 10 = 60 while 6 • 0.1
equals only 0.6   63) 76.5   65) 1.2   67) 0.0343   69) 60   71) 86   73) 7,000,000   75) 6400

77) 0.5   79) false. One example: 6 ÷ 10 = 0.6 while 6 ÷ 0.1 = 60   81) 100   83) 0.1   85) 1,000

87) 100   89) 0.0004   91) 750   93) 86   95) 6125   97) 10,500   99) 4,000

101) Set up: (110) (5) or (110 ÷ 4) (20) solution: $550

103) Set up: 49,754 (10) solution: No. Only $497,540

105) Set up: 250,000 ÷ 1000 solution: 250

107) Set up: 14,864 − 14 (1000) − 6 (100) solution: $84

109) Set up: [835,600 − 80 (10,000)] ÷ 100 solution: 35 medium-sized cans

111) Set up: 827,000 ÷ 1 solution: 827,000 cans   113) Set up: 3 ÷ 10,000 solution: 0.0003 inches

115) Set up: 18 • 100 solution: $1800.

Chapter 2: Fraction

2.1 The Meanings of Fractions

1) $\frac{5}{9}$ 3) $\frac{7}{16}$ 5) $\frac{4}{7}$ 7) division 9) the whole 11) 1 whole 13) 3 15) 8 17) yes 19) y 21) the part

23) $\frac{14}{11}$ 25) $\frac{5}{6}$ 27) $\frac{3}{4}$ 29) $\frac{5}{9}$ 31) $\frac{y}{x}$ 33) $\frac{y}{x}$ 35) $\frac{1}{10}$ 37) $\frac{329}{700}$ 39) $\frac{43}{500}$ 41) $\frac{333}{757}$ 43) $\frac{97}{757}$ 45) $\frac{7}{22}$

47) $\frac{7}{25}$ 49) $\frac{9}{23}$ 51) $\frac{120}{397}$ 53) $\frac{7\ shaded}{11\ unshaded}$ 55) $\frac{5\ shaded}{1\ unshaded}$ 57) $\frac{5\ shaded}{7\ unshaded}$ 59) $\frac{8\ classes}{5\ days}$ 61) $\frac{200\ plums}{1\ tree}$

63) $\frac{7\ men}{10\ women}$ 65) $\frac{4\ people\ under\ 21}{7\ people\ over\ 21}$ 67) $\frac{x\ classes}{y\ days}$ 69) $\frac{a\ dogs}{b\ cats}$ 71) $\frac{4\ incorrect\ answers}{11\ correct\ answers}$

73) Set up: $\frac{265}{700-(371+265)}$ solution: $\frac{265\ votes\ for\ Sergio}{64\ votes\ for\ two\ other\ candidates}$

75) Set up: $\frac{8}{15+10}$ solution: $\frac{8\ blue\ shirts}{25\ red\ \&\ white\ shirts}$

77) Set up: $\frac{4}{8+5}$ solution: $\frac{\$4\ spent\ on\ food}{\$13\ spent\ on\ rent\ \&\ various\ bills}$

79) Set up: $\frac{3(10)+2(7)}{5(15)}$ solution: $\frac{44\ swordfish\ \&\ angel\ fish}{75\ guppies}$

81) Set up: $\frac{2(7)+3}{3(10)+5(15)+6}$ solution: $\frac{17\ angel\ fish\ \&\ catfish}{111\ other\ fish}$ 83) True 85) False 87) True 89) False

91) True 93) True 95) True 97) 14 99) 90 101) 10 acres 103) 135,00 people

105) Set up: $\frac{3}{8}=\frac{x}{18,000}$ solution: 6750 people

107) Set up: $\frac{2}{5}=\frac{x}{18,000}$ solution: 7200 residents 109) Set up: $\frac{1}{4}=\frac{x}{200}$ solution: 50 worms

111) Set up: $\frac{15}{800}=\frac{x}{160}$ solution: 3 winners 113) Set up: $\frac{5}{\$18}=\frac{30}{x}$ solution: $108

115) Set up: $\frac{3}{\$10}=\frac{x}{\$25}$ solution: 7 books.

2.2 Divisibility & Prime Factorization

1) 2 only   3) 2, 3, and 5   5) 5 only   7) 5 only   9) 2 and 3   11) True   13) True   15) False   17) True

19) prime   21) composite   23) composite   25) composite   27) prime   29) 2 factors   31) 11

33) 2 factors   35) 4 factors (1 • 35, 5 • 7)   37) 4 factors (1 • 57, 3 • 19)

39) 8 factors (1 • 70, 2 • 35, 5 • 14, 7 • 10)   41) 1 and x   43) $x = 37$ 45) composite   47) $2^3 \cdot 3$

49) $3^2 \cdot 5$ 51) $3^2 \cdot 11$ 53) $3 \cdot 7^2$ 55) $2 \cdot 3^2 \cdot 7$ 57) prime   59) 11 • 19   61) 11^3

63) 10 columns of 10 chairs <u>or</u> 20 columns of 5 chairs

65) 4 piles of 50 chips <u>or</u> 5 piles of 40 chips <u>or</u> 8 piles of 25 chips

67) 2 rows of 10 candles <u>or</u> 4 rows of 5 candles <u>or</u> 5 rows of 4 candles <u>or</u> 10 rows of 2 candles

69) 3 shelves with 14 dolls each <u>or</u> 6 shelves with 7 dolls each <u>or</u> 7 shelves with 6 dolls each

2.3 Greatest Common Factor (GCF), Reducing Fractions, and Improper Fractions & Mixed Numbers

1) 2 plums, and 1 banana   3) 1 quarter and 3 pennies   5) 4   7) 1   9) 15   11) 6   13) 11   15) 28   17) $\frac{1}{7}$

19) $\frac{2}{3}$ 21) $\frac{5}{2}$ 23) $\frac{8}{15}$ 25) $\frac{13}{9}$ 27) $\frac{29}{34}$ 29) $5\frac{1}{3}$ 31) $\frac{21}{8}$ 33) $7\frac{1}{2}$ 35) $\frac{19}{8}$ 37) $51\frac{2}{3}$ 39) $\frac{75}{11}$ 41) 22

43) $\frac{302}{15}$ 45) $\frac{41}{18}$ 47) proper because there are fewer parts than make one whole   49) $\frac{3}{4}$ 51) $\frac{4}{9}$

53) $\frac{2}{3}$ 55) yes   57) True   59) False   61) False   63) $\frac{11}{25}$ of a packaging box   65) $\frac{5}{12}$ of a crate

67) 10 baskets   69) 3 displays   71) 13 piles

2.4 Multiply and Divide Fractions

1) 1   3) 3   5) 12   7) 3   9) 0   11) 6   13) $\frac{3}{20}$ 15) $\frac{12}{5}$ and $2\frac{2}{5}$ 17) $\frac{7}{15}$ 19) $\frac{1}{8}$ 21) 1   23) $\frac{8}{17}$

25) $\frac{84}{5}$ and $16\frac{4}{5}$ 27) $\frac{1}{4}$ 29) $\frac{7}{6}$ and $1\frac{1}{6}$ 31) translation: $\frac{3}{7} \cdot \frac{4}{5}$ solution: $\frac{12}{35}$

33) translation: $11 \div \frac{1}{9}$ solution: 99   35) translation: $\frac{5}{8} \cdot \frac{320}{1}$ solution: 200

37) translation: $\left(\frac{1}{5} \div \frac{2}{3}\right) \div 4$ solution: $\frac{3}{40}$ 39) translation: $(11-3) \div \left(\frac{3}{8} \cdot \frac{2}{1}\right)$ solution: $\frac{32}{3}$ or $10\frac{2}{3}$

41) $\frac{3}{13} \cdot x$ or $\frac{3}{13}x$ 43) $x \div \frac{5}{6}$ or $\frac{x}{\frac{5}{6}}$ 45) $\left(\frac{8}{3} \div \frac{4}{1}\right) - 14$ 47) $\frac{3}{4}x \div \frac{4}{7}$ 49) $\left(2 \cdot \frac{5}{8}\right) + 11$ 51) True   53) False

55) False   57) True   59) True   61) no; <u>d</u> is different   63) no; <u>b</u> is different   65) yes

67) no; <u>a</u> is different   69) no; <u>d</u> is different   71) Set up: $\frac{3}{5} \cdot \frac{200,000}{1}$ solution: 120,000 gallons

73) Set up: $200,000 - \left(\dfrac{3}{5} \cdot \dfrac{200,000}{1} \right)$ or $\left(1 - \dfrac{3}{5} \right) \cdot 200,000$; solution: 80,000 gallons

75) Set up: $240 \div \dfrac{3}{16}$ solution: 1280 parcels 77) Set up: $\dfrac{1}{8} \div \dfrac{5}{1}$; solution: $\dfrac{1}{40}$ of the original size

79) Set up: $\dfrac{1}{50} \cdot \dfrac{40,000,000}{1}$ or $\dfrac{1}{50} \cdot \dfrac{40\,million}{1}$; solution: \$800,000 or $\dfrac{4}{5}$ of a million dollars

81) Set up: $140 - \left(\dfrac{1}{10} \cdot \dfrac{140}{1} \right)$ or $\left(1 - \dfrac{1}{10} \right) \cdot 140$; solution: 126 grams

83) Set up: $1 - \left(\dfrac{1}{10} + \dfrac{2}{7} \right)$; solution: $\dfrac{43}{70}$

2.5 Multiply and Divide Mixed Numbers and Fractions

1) $\dfrac{44}{5}$ and $8\dfrac{4}{5}$ 3) 36 5) 243 7) $\dfrac{18}{35}$ 9) $\dfrac{23}{31}$ 11) $\dfrac{25}{7}$ and $3\dfrac{4}{7}$ 13) $\dfrac{5}{32}$ 15) $\dfrac{1600}{7}$ and $228\dfrac{4}{7}$ 17) $\dfrac{55}{2}$ and $27\dfrac{1}{2}$

19) True 21) False 23) False 25) False 27) True 29) True 31) no; b is different 33) no; d is different

35) no; c is different 37) no; b is different 39) no; d is different 41) True 43) True 45) False

47) True 49) $\dfrac{3}{5} = 4\dfrac{1}{2} \div \dfrac{15}{2}$ or $\dfrac{15}{2} = 4\dfrac{1}{2} \div \dfrac{3}{5}$ 51) $4 = 6 \cdot \dfrac{2}{3}$ 53) $\dfrac{3}{8} = \dfrac{1}{2} \div x$ or $x = \dfrac{1}{2} \div 3$

55) $y = 1\dfrac{2}{3} \cdot \dfrac{3}{8}$ 57) $x = \dfrac{10}{21}$ 59) $x = 4$ 61) $x = \dfrac{7}{5}$ 63) $x = 1\dfrac{2}{5}$ 65) $x = \dfrac{9}{8}$ 67) $x = \dfrac{20}{3}$

69) Set up: $7\dfrac{1}{2} \cdot 250$ solution: 1875 people   71) Set up: $55\dfrac{1}{2} \div 12$ solution: $4\dfrac{5}{8}$ acres per month

73) Set up: $(400 \cdot 12) \div \dfrac{5}{8}$ solution: 7680 ants   75) Set up: $(100 \cdot 3) \div 2\dfrac{2}{5}$ solution: 125 steps

77) Set up: $\dfrac{2\frac{2}{5}}{3}$ or $2\dfrac{2}{5} \div 3$ solution: $\dfrac{4}{5}$ of a yard 79) Set up: $\dfrac{19}{100,000} \cdot \dfrac{10,000}{1}$ solution: $1\dfrac{9}{10}$ miles

81) Set up: $500 \div (30 \div 5\dfrac{1}{2})$ *where the answer to this division problem inside the parenthesis is lowered to just the whole number* solution: 100 30-foot boards would be needed

2.6 Find Lowest Common Multiples (LCM), Build Fractions, and Add Fractions & Mixed Numbers

1) True because 25 ends in a 5 or true because 5 multiplied by 5 equals 25

3) true because the digits 8 and 7 add up to 15, which is divisible by 3 or true because 3 multiplied by 29 equals 87

5) True because $5 \cdot 6 = 30$ 7) 16, 28, and 62 9) 40 and 200 11) 3, 57, and 381 13) 11 and 121 15) 21

17) 2 19) 84 21) 36 23) 16 25) 168 27) 120 29) 90 31) 40 33) 42 35) $\dfrac{5}{6}$ 37) $\dfrac{13}{6}$ and $2\dfrac{1}{6}$

39) $\frac{37}{24}$ and $1\frac{13}{24}$ 41) $\frac{73}{36}$ and $2\frac{1}{36}$ 43) $\frac{187}{126}$ and $1\frac{61}{126}$ 45) 6   47) $\frac{35}{16}$ and $2\frac{3}{16}$ 49) $\frac{271}{22}$ and $12\frac{7}{22}$

51) $\frac{3899}{1000}$ and $3\frac{899}{1000}$ 53) 16   55) $\frac{3}{4}+1\frac{1}{5}$ 57) $\left(\frac{4}{5}\cdot1\frac{1}{2}\right)-\frac{1}{3}$ 59) $\left(5\cdot2\frac{3}{5}\right)+\frac{2}{7}$ 61) $\left(\frac{2}{7}\cdot2\frac{3}{5}\right)+x$

63) $\frac{1}{4}\cdot x+\left(\frac{x}{y}\div2\right)$ 65) Set up: $\frac{1}{2}+\frac{1}{12}+\frac{2}{5}$ solution: $\frac{59}{60}$ of an inch

67) Set up: $\left(3\frac{1}{4}+4+2\frac{5}{6}+7\frac{1}{2}\right)\div4$ solution: $4\frac{19}{48}$ hours

69) Set up: $1\frac{1}{8}+\frac{1}{4}$ solution: $1\frac{3}{8}$ million people

71) Set up: $12+3\frac{2}{5}+\frac{1}{2}$ solution: $15\frac{9}{10}$ million dollars   73) Set up: $2\frac{2}{5}+\frac{3}{4}$ solution: \$3,150,000

75) Set up: $\frac{1}{8}+2\frac{1}{3}+1\frac{3}{8}$ solution: $3\frac{5}{6}$ inches   77) 12 pieces   79) $25\frac{1}{3}$ 81) $\frac{3}{5}$ 83) $\frac{7}{8}$ 85) $1\frac{1}{2}$

87) no; <u>c</u> is different   89) no; <u>b</u> is different   91) yes   93) yes

2.7 Subtract Fractions & Mixed Numbers

1) $\frac{1}{8}$ 3) $\frac{1}{18}$ 5) $\frac{2}{15}$ 7) $\frac{46}{21}$ and $2\frac{4}{21}$ 9) $\frac{29}{24}$ and $1\frac{5}{24}$ 11) 0   13) $\frac{16}{15}$ and $1\frac{1}{15}$ 15) $\frac{33}{20}$ and $1\frac{13}{20}$

17) $\frac{80}{21}$ and $3\frac{17}{21}$ 19) $\frac{253}{16}$ and $15\frac{13}{16}$ 21) $\frac{9}{7}$ and $1\frac{2}{7}$ 23) $\frac{48}{13}$ and $3\frac{9}{13}$ 25) $\frac{1}{3}$ 27) $\frac{3937}{40}$ and $93\frac{17}{40}$

29) $\frac{3}{20}$ 31) $\frac{21}{10}$ and $2\frac{1}{10}$ 33) $\frac{1}{4}$ 35) 0   37) translation: $5\frac{3}{10}+3\frac{3}{100}$ solution: $8\frac{33}{100}$

39) translation: $1+\frac{2}{3}$ solution: $1\frac{2}{3}$ 41) translation: $\frac{1}{7}-\frac{1}{14}$ solution: $\frac{1}{14}$

43) translation: $7\frac{1}{4}-7$ solution: $\frac{1}{4}$ 45) translation: $2-\frac{2}{3}$ solution: $1\frac{1}{3}$ 47) $\frac{9}{10}-x$ 49) $x-2\frac{3}{7}$

51) $4\frac{1}{5}-x$ 53) $4\frac{1}{3}-x$ 55) $x+1\frac{5}{6}$ 57) $\frac{1}{2}x-\frac{3}{x}$ 59) True   61) True   63) False   65) True

67) $8=7\frac{7}{8}+\frac{1}{8}$ 69) $\frac{7}{10}=\frac{2}{5}+x$ 71) $x=5\frac{3}{7}-2\frac{1}{3}$ 73) $\frac{9}{10}=\frac{1}{4}+x$ 75) $x=\frac{2}{5}$ 77) $x=\frac{5}{28}$

79) $x=\frac{7}{12}$ 81) Set up: $30-22\frac{23}{100}$ solution: $7\frac{77}{100}$ inches   83) Set up: $\frac{76}{100}-\frac{61}{100}$ solution: $\frac{3}{20}$ of the exam

85) Set up: $25-\left(6\frac{1}{4}+5\frac{1}{2}+7\right)$; solution: $6\frac{1}{4}$ hours

87) Set up: $(110\div30)-(70\div30)$ or $(110-70)\div30$; solution: $1\frac{1}{3}$ packages

89) Set up: $\left(2\frac{1}{4}\cdot60\right)-\left(1\frac{3}{5}\cdot60\right)$ or $\left(2\frac{1}{4}-1\frac{3}{5}\right)\cdot60$; solution: 39 minutes

91) Set up: $\left(\frac{1}{4}\cdot\frac{200}{1}\right)-\left(\frac{1}{10}\cdot\frac{200}{1}\right)$ or $\left(\frac{1}{4}-\frac{1}{10}\right)\cdot200$; solution: 30 more acres

93) $\frac{8}{y}$ 95) $\frac{5}{a}$ 97) $\frac{3}{v}$ 99) 1   101) $3\frac{1}{5}b$ 103) 1

2.8 Conversions and Comparisons between Fractions & Decimals

1) $\frac{3}{4}$ 3) $\frac{1}{2}$ 5) $\frac{7}{9}$ 7) 2.8 9) 124.1 11) 3.0271 13) 5.76 15) $\frac{27}{100}$ 17) $\frac{63}{500}$ 19) $2\frac{7}{10}$ and $\frac{27}{10}$

21) $4\frac{4}{25}$ and $\frac{104}{25}$ 23) $2\frac{1}{250}$ and $\frac{501}{250}$ 25) $4\frac{1}{3}$ and $\frac{13}{3}$ 27) 0.75 29) 2.2 31) $0.\overline{6}$ 33) 0.175 35) 0.06

37) 0.015 39) $3.\overline{4}$ 41) 20.125 43) $5.41\overline{6}$ 45) 0.43 47) 0.7 49) $5\frac{1}{4}$ 51) $\frac{2}{3}$ 53) $0.\overline{3}$ 55) $\frac{67}{100}$

57) $4\frac{1}{12}$ 59) $\frac{51}{20}$ 61) 0.3, $\frac{3}{8}$, 0.38, 0.7, $\frac{3}{4}$ 63) 0.0801, $\frac{7}{9}$, 0.78, $\frac{4}{5}$, 0.81 65) $2\frac{1}{40}$, 2.03, $2\frac{1}{5}$, 2.25, $2\frac{3}{10}$

67) 15.0084, 15.084, $\frac{46}{3}$, 15.8, $15\frac{5}{6}$ 69) False 71) True 73) True 75) True 77) False 79) False

81) True 83) False 85) False 87) True

89) Set up: $\left(500 + 1\frac{1}{3} \text{ thousand}\right) - \left(\frac{5}{8} \text{ thousand} + 1.1 \text{ thousand}\right)$ solution: $108\frac{1}{3}$ feet

91) Set up: $10\frac{1}{4} \div 0.45$; solution: 22 pieces   93) Set up: $5\frac{3}{16} + 0.5 + 1\frac{5}{8}$; solution: $7\frac{5}{16}$

95) Set up: $\left[50 \bullet \left(5\frac{3}{16} + 0.5 + 1\frac{5}{8}\right)\right] - \left(50 \bullet 5\frac{3}{16}\right)$ or $\left(0.5 + 1\frac{5}{8}\right)(50)$; solution: $106.25

97) Set up: $\frac{15 + 25 + 40}{50}$ solution: $1\frac{3}{5}$ or 1.6 laps   99) Set up: $4.5 - \left(\frac{15}{50} + \frac{25}{50} + \frac{40}{50} + 1 + 1\frac{1}{4}\right)$

solution: Rafeal swam $\frac{13}{20}$ or 0.65 laps more one month later

101) Set up: $\left(2500 + \frac{1}{4} \bullet \frac{2500}{1}\right) - \left[800\,(0.75) + 2250\right]$ solution: Ringo earned $275 more

103) Set up: $\left[\left(\frac{1}{10} \bullet \frac{2850}{1}\right) + 375\right] - \left(\frac{1}{5} \bullet \frac{3125}{1}\right)$ solution: Ringo would have given $35 more to charity

105) $\frac{x+3}{x}$ 107) $x + 0.23$ 109) $0.\overline{7} \bullet x$ 111) $\frac{a}{0.2}$ 113) $\frac{b}{b-1}$ 115) $\frac{3}{2}$

Chapter 3: Signed Numbers

3.1 The Number Line & the Meaning of Signed Numbers

1) D 3) No 5) three 7) $-1\frac{1}{2}$ and -1.5 9) two 11) none 13) yes 15) $1\frac{1}{2}$ and 1.5 17) $-\frac{3}{5}$ 19) No

21) $\frac{7}{10}$ 23) $|Pt.D|$ 25) -5 27) 2.3 29) -3 31) 4 33) -7 35) $\frac{1}{5}$ 37) -2 39) 4 41) 28

43) 3 45) -5 47) $-\frac{2}{3}$ 49) -4 51) -15 53) 1 55) 8 57) 3 59) -10 61) 1 63) $-\frac{1}{3}$

65) True   67) False   69) False   71) True   73) $1,000,000   75) Cooperative B showed the least gain in earnings ($1,000,000)

77) The NGO assistance was a tremendous success. Other cooperatives only gained $50,000 a year in annual profits while Cooperative A earned $2,000,000 more, Cooperative B earned $1,000,000 more, Cooperative C earned $3,000,000 more.

79) 12 noon   81) 2 hours   83) 7 p.m.   85) 46 feet   87) -14 feet   89) 36 feet   91) $-(7 - 2)$

93) $-(-2 + 7 \cdot 3)$ 95) last week: ($70 $\cdot$ 3); second week: $-($70 $\cdot$ 3)$ 97) negative   99) positive

101) positive

3.2 Combining Integers and Decimals

1) addition & subtraction 3) two negative signs next to each other: $-(-)$ 5) Yes   7) No   9) Add

11) True 13) False 15) True 17) False 19) False 21) d 23) b 25) d 27) (a) same signs, (b) add

29) (a) different signs, (b) subtract   31) (a) different signs, (b) subtract   33) (a) same signs, (b) add

35) -3   37) 5   39) -10   41) -7   43) 0   45) 11   47) -400   49) 400   51) 90   53) -13   55) -5.2

57) 2.25   59) -3.2   61) 10.34   63) -62.2   65) -10.175   67) -23   69) 15   71) -50   73) -13.15

75) -18.125   77) (a) c (b) $1355   79) (a) a (b) $14.95 per share   81) (a) b (b) -$350

83) set up: 30,000 - 18,000 + 6,000 - 11,000; solution: 7,000 feet

85) set up: 1.25 - (1.60 + 0.45 + 1.05); solution: -$1.85   87) set up: 75 - 81; solution: -6°

89) set up: 5,000,000 + (-15,000,000); solution: -$10,000,000

91) set up: 20,000,000 - 0; solution: $20,000,000   93) graph is not shown

95) set up: 3 + 1.25 - 0.75 - 2.50 - 2 + 1.25; solution: $0.25

3.3 Multiply and Divide Integers and Decimals

1) by the number of negative signs   3) negative   5) positive because there are an even number of negative signs   7) positive   9) negative   11) negative 13) positive   15) positive   17) d   19) a

21) a   23) b   25) 35   27) 10   29) -4   31) 4   33) 5   35) 0.8   37) 24   39) 0   41) -30   43) 0

45) undefined   47) 2   49) 1   51) -6.24   53) -80   55) 0.2   57) -78   59) -200   61) 0.182   63) 7

65) -13   67) 7   69) 2   71) 11   73) -3   75) $-\dfrac{25}{6}$ or $-4\dfrac{1}{6}$ 77) 2.45   79) -4   81) 7   83) 1

85) translation: -8 $\cdot$ -4; solution: 32   87) translation: (6 $\cdot$ -2) + (40 ÷ -8); solution: -17

89) translation: (-4 $\cdot$ -10) + (-44 ÷ 4); solution: 29   91) translation: $\dfrac{(-4 + -5)}{(1 - (-2))}$; solution: -3

93) set up: 8(-600); solution: -4800 feet   95) set up: 4 + (3 $\cdot$ -5); solution: -11°

97) set up: -2.10 + (-5.20) + (-0.60) + (-1.10); solution: -$9

99) set up: 4 $\cdot$ (-75); solution: -300 lira   101) positive   103) negative   105) negative

107) positive   109) True   111) True   113) True   115) False   117) True

3.4 Multiply and Divide Signed Mixed Numbers & Fractions

1) positive 3) positive 5) positive 7) negative 9) positive 11) No, d is different 13) No, c is different

15) No, b is different 17) Yes 19) $\frac{4}{3}$ 21) $-\frac{3}{4}$ 23) $-\frac{14}{9}$ 25) $-\frac{87}{109}$ 27) $\frac{5}{11}$ 29) $-6\frac{2}{3}$ 31) $-\frac{22}{7}$

33) $-8\frac{1}{2}$ 35) $-\frac{27}{4}$ 37) 19 39) $\frac{92}{5}$ 41) $-\frac{3}{20}$ 43) $-\frac{1}{21}$ 45) $-\frac{32}{105}$ 47) $\frac{5}{24}$ 49) -32

51) $\frac{37}{8}$ or $4\frac{5}{8}$ 53) $-\frac{7}{12}$ 55) $-\frac{10}{3}$ or $-1\frac{1}{3}$ 57) $-\frac{12}{11}$ or $-1\frac{1}{11}$ 59) $-\frac{15}{136}$ 61) $\frac{17}{2}$ or $8\frac{1}{2}$

63) $\frac{27}{10}$ or $2\frac{7}{10}$ 65) $-\frac{9}{2}$ or $-4\frac{1}{2}$ 67) -8 69) 0.002 71) $\frac{28}{9}$ or $3\frac{1}{9}$ 73) $\frac{1}{2}$ 75) 7

77) translation: $\frac{4}{9} \cdot \frac{-5}{-3}$; solution: $\frac{20}{27}$

79) translation: $\frac{2}{3} \cdot \frac{-14}{30}$; solution: $-\frac{14}{45}$ 81) translation: $\left(4 \div \frac{-1}{4}\right) - 5$ solution: -21

83) translation: $\left(4 + -7\right) \div -2\frac{3}{4}$; solution: $\frac{12}{11}$ or $1\frac{1}{11}$

85) set up: $-3\frac{5}{8} \div 4$; solution: $-\$\frac{29}{32}$ million 87) set up: $\left(1 - \frac{1}{5}\right) \cdot 40,000$; solution: 32,000 hours

89) set up: $20\frac{1}{2} \div \frac{1}{6}$; solution: 123 homes 91) set up: $25 \cdot \left(-\frac{3}{4}\right)$; solution: $-\$18\frac{3}{4}$ million

93) set up: $12 \cdot \left(-8\frac{3}{10}\right)$; solution: $\$99\frac{3}{5}$

95) set up: $20\,(12) - \left[\left(200 - 20\right) \cdot \left(5\frac{1}{5}\right)\right]$; solution: -$696 97) set up: $6 \cdot \left(-6\frac{2}{3}\right)$; solution: -40 lbs.

99) set up: $\dfrac{-5\frac{7}{10}}{4} = \dfrac{x}{50}$ solution: $-71\frac{1}{4}$ pounds

3.5 Combining Signed Mixed Numbers & Fractions

1) Yes, a double negative 3) No, not a double negative 5) Yes 7) False 9) True 11) False 13) True

15) negative 17) negative 19) negative 21) positive 23) negative 25) negative 27) c 29) b 31) b

33) d 35) d 37) c 39) -1 41) $\frac{1}{6}$ 43) $-\frac{37}{55}$ 45) $\frac{13}{21}$ 47) $\frac{1}{3}$ 49) $-\frac{49}{20}$ or $-2\frac{9}{20}$ 51) $-\frac{39}{50}$

53) $-\frac{41}{24}$ or $-1\frac{17}{24}$ 55) $\frac{9}{20}$ 57) $-\frac{89}{1000}$ 59) $-\frac{1}{15}$ 61) $-\frac{253}{30}$ or $-8\frac{13}{30}$ 63) $\frac{97}{14}$ or $6\frac{13}{14}$

65) $-\frac{25}{9}$ or $-2\frac{7}{9}$ 67) $\frac{52}{15}$ or $3\frac{7}{15}$ 69) $\frac{70}{9}$ or $7\frac{7}{9}$ 71) $\frac{11}{20}$

73) translation: $\frac{3}{8} + \left(-\frac{1}{3}\right)$; solution: $\frac{1}{24}$ 75) translation: $-1\frac{1}{5} + \frac{3}{4}$; solution: $-\frac{9}{20}$

77) translation: $-\frac{5}{4} + \frac{2}{3}$; solution: $-\frac{7}{12}$ 79) translation: $-\frac{1}{10} - \left(-\frac{2}{5}\right)$; solution: $\frac{3}{10}$

81) translation: $-\frac{3}{5} - \frac{3}{5}$; solution: $-\frac{6}{5}$ or $-1\frac{1}{5}$ 83) translation: $-8\frac{1}{3} + 2\frac{2}{3}$; solution: $-\frac{17}{3}$ or $-5\frac{2}{3}$

85) set up: $2\frac{3}{4} + 2 - \frac{4}{5}$; solution: $3\frac{19}{20}$ degrees

87) set up: $2\frac{1}{4}$ thousand $- \frac{1}{2}$ thousand $- 1\frac{1}{3}$ thousand; solution: $\frac{5}{12}$ thousand feet

89) Company A's balance was $\$\frac{3}{4}$ million   91) Company C's balance was $-\$1\frac{1}{2}$ million

93) set up: $\frac{3}{4}$ million $+ \left(-\frac{1}{2}\text{million}\right)$; solution: $\$\frac{1}{4}$ million   95) $\$\frac{2}{5}$ thousand   97) $-\$\frac{3}{5}$ thousand

99) set up: $\frac{2}{5} + \left(-\frac{1}{5}\right) + \left(-\frac{3}{5}\right) + \frac{3}{5}$; solution: $\$\frac{1}{5}$ thousand   101) graph not shown

103) False   105) True   107) $-\frac{10}{21}$ 109) $-\frac{10}{3}$ or $-3\frac{1}{3}$ 111) $\frac{15}{28}$

3.6 Order of Operations and Review

1) -15   3) 22   5) 9   7) -252   9) 3   11) -12   13) -12.3   15) 4.6   17) $\frac{11}{24}$ 19) $-\frac{13}{14}$ 21) $\frac{25}{12}$ or $2\frac{1}{12}$

23) $\frac{1}{40}$ 25) $-\frac{24}{11}$ or $-2\frac{2}{11}$ 27) $-\frac{5}{6}$ 29) $-\frac{35}{12}$ or $-2\frac{11}{12}$ 31) $-24\frac{2}{3}$ 33) $\frac{9}{20}$ 35) -16   37) $\frac{3}{2}$ or $1\frac{1}{2}$

39) undefined   41) 0   43) $-\frac{17}{x}$ 45) $\frac{1}{x}$ 47) $\frac{7}{x}$ 49) $-13\frac{19}{20}$ 51) $7\frac{19}{24}$ 53) undefined   55) 0   57) 1.67

59) 29.25   61) set up: $\frac{\$18 \text{ billion on education}}{\$98 \text{ billion} - \$18 \text{ billion on the rest}}$; solution: $\frac{\$9 \text{ billion on education}}{\$40 \text{ billion on the rest}}$

63) set up: $\frac{3}{5} = \frac{x}{570}$; solution: 342 adults   65) set up: $\frac{4500}{20,000}$; solution: $\frac{9}{40}$

67) set up: $\frac{20,000 - (5000 + 4500 + 6800)}{6}$; solution: 617 votes   69) $2 \cdot 7 \cdot 11$ 71) $3^2 \cdot 23$ 73) 12

75) 3   77) 77   79) 210   81) 120   83) True   85) False   87) True   89) True   91) False

93) set up: $\left(1-\frac{1}{4}\right) \cdot \left\{(20 + 60) - \left[\frac{1}{5} \cdot (20 + 60)\right] + 3(100)\right\}$; solution: 273 points

95) set up: $-12,000,000 \div 8$; solution: -$1,500,000

97) set up: $\left(10 \bullet 15,000\right) - \left[\frac{3}{10} \bullet \left(10 \bullet 15,000\right)\right]$ or $\left(1-\frac{3}{10}\right)\bullet \left(10 \bullet 15,000\right)$; solution: \$105,000

99) set up: $[10,000 \bullet (0.55)] - \$550$; solution: He was undercharged by \$4950 (he was supposed to be charged \$5500)

101) set up: $-\frac{9}{10} \div 4$; solution: $-\$\frac{9}{40}$ million   103) 672 hours   105) $\frac{1}{1680}$ of a week

107) 438 days   109) a) 125 b) 125.4 c) 125.37 d) 125.374 e) 130 f) 0

111) True   113) True   115) True   117) True   119) True   121) True   123) True   125) True

Chapter 4: Exponents

4.1 Understand & Evaluate Exponential Expressions

1) 8   3) -5   5) 2   7) 3   9) 2.61   11) $\frac{3}{4}$ 13) $-\frac{1}{4}$ 15) 3   17) negative   19) positive

21) negative   23) negative   25) negative   27) positive   29) negative   31) $2^2 \bullet 5 \bullet 7^2$

33) $(-4)^2 \bullet (-5)^3$ 35) $\left(\frac{3}{8}\right)^2 \bullet \left(-\frac{4}{5}\right)^3$ 37) $x^3 \bullet y^2$ 39) $(-x)^4$ 41) $5 \bullet 5 \bullet 5 \bullet 5 \bullet 7 \bullet 7$

43) $-\left(3 \bullet 3 \bullet 3 \bullet 3\right)$ 45) $-2 \bullet - 2 \bullet - 2 \bullet 3 \bullet 3 \bullet - 7 \bullet - 7$ 47) $\frac{4}{5} \bullet \frac{4}{5} \bullet - \frac{1}{3} \bullet - \frac{1}{3}$ 49) 81

51) 636.056   53) 16   55) -100 57) $\frac{27}{64}$ 59) $-\frac{1}{1000}$ 61) No; b is different   63) No: c is different

65) yes   67) yes   69) 10^2 71) 10^4 73) $2^3 + 4$ 75) $2^3 - 3^5$ 77) $x^2 + y^3$ 79) $y^5 - x^3$ 81) 7

83) 491   85) -2 87) -65 89) -24 91) -21 93) -1201.25 95) 171   97) $-\frac{191}{64}$ or $-2\frac{63}{64}$

99) 5   101) translation: $5 \bullet 2^3$; solution: 40;   103) translation: $80 \bullet 3^4$; solution: 6480;

105) translation: $5,000 \bullet 2^4$; solution: \$80,000;   107) set up: $100 \bullet 2^8$; solution: 25,600 viruses

109) set up: $30,000 \bullet 2^3$; solution: \$240,000   111) set up: $5,000 \bullet 15$; solution: \$75,000

113) set up: $\frac{3}{4} \bullet \frac{1,000,000}{1}$; solution: 750,000 mosquitoes

4.2 Manipulate Exponential Expressions

1) multiplication of sames bases   3) division of same bases   5) division of same bases

7) eliminate the negative exponent   9) division of same bases   11) division of same bases   13) positive

15) positive   17) positive   19) positive   21) positive   23) negative   25) 7^7 27) $2^8 \bullet 5^2$ 29) 2^2 31) 7^2

33) $\frac{1}{2^3}$ 35) $\frac{1}{2}$ 37) $\frac{3^3}{10^2}$ 39) 7^2 41) 1   43) 1   45) $\frac{1}{4^7}$ 47) 2   49) 15^5 51) $2^8 \bullet 3^4$ 53) 5   55) $\frac{9^2}{3^6}$

57) $\frac{1}{3^3 \bullet 5^4}$ 59) $\frac{3^2 \bullet 7}{5^4 \bullet 11^3}$ 61) $\frac{1}{x^2}$ 63) x^4 65) a^5 67) $\frac{y^3}{x^5}$ 69) no: c is different   71) no: b is different

73) yes   75) yes   77) no; $\underline{d}$ is different   79) yes   81) no: $\underline{c}$ is different   83) a) 7^5; b) 16807

85) a) $\dfrac{1}{3^6}$; b) $\dfrac{1}{729}$ 87) a) $\dfrac{1}{11^3}$; b) $\dfrac{1}{1331}$ 89) a) $\dfrac{1}{3^4}$; b) $\dfrac{1}{81}$ 91) a) $\dfrac{3^5}{2^2}$; b) $\dfrac{243}{4}$

93) a) $\dfrac{1}{3^6 \bullet 7^2}$; b) $\dfrac{1}{35,721}$ 95) a) $\dfrac{2^4 \bullet 5}{3^3}$; b) $\dfrac{80}{27}$ 97) a) $(-2)^5$; b) -32

99) a) $\dfrac{2^5}{3^2 \bullet 5^3}$; b) $\dfrac{32}{1125}$ 101) a) $\dfrac{3^2 \bullet 5^3}{2^5}$; b) $\dfrac{1125}{32}$

103) set up: $\dfrac{\$3,000,000 \text{ output for Country X}}{\$2,000,000 \text{ output for Country Y}}$; solution: $\dfrac{\$3 \text{ output for Country X}}{\$2 \text{ output for Country Y}}$

105) set up: $\$2,000,000 \bullet 3^5$; solution: $\$486,000,000$

107) set up: $\dfrac{\$768 \text{ million}}{\$486 \text{ million}}$ or $\dfrac{\$768 \text{ million}}{\$486 \text{ million}} = \dfrac{x}{1}$; solution: $\$1.58$

109) set up: $6,000,000(3)$; solution: 18,000,000 people

111) set up: $\dfrac{5}{6} = \dfrac{100}{x}$ or $(100 \bullet 6) \div 5$; solution: 120 people

113) set up: $\dfrac{18,000,000}{20,000,000} \bullet \dfrac{100}{1}$ or $\dfrac{18,000,000}{20,000,000} = \dfrac{x}{100}$; solution: 90%

115) set up: $10,000,000 \bullet \left(\dfrac{9}{10}\right)^4$; solution: 6,600,000 mosquitoes

4.3 More Exponential Expression Manipulation

1) yes   3) no: $\underline{b}$ is different   5) yes   7) no: $\underline{b}$ is different   9) yes   11) yes   13) 3^{14} 15) $2^{10} \bullet 7^{20}$

17) 2^6 19) 5^{12} 21) $\dfrac{1}{3^{12}}$ 23) 1   25) $\dfrac{1}{3^{12}}$ 27) 2^9 29) $\dfrac{1}{5^4}$ 31) 7^9 33) $(-2)^4$ 35) $3 \bullet 11^2$

37) $2^{10} \bullet 3^{10}$ 39) $\dfrac{11^4}{7^2}$ 41) $\dfrac{1}{2^4 \bullet 5^2 \bullet 7^2}$ 43) 1   45) 13^3 47) $\dfrac{1}{a^3}$ 49) y^2 51) m^{14} 53) $\dfrac{1}{x^5 \bullet y}$

55) $\dfrac{1}{x^{30}}$ 57) 2^4 59) 3^6 61) 2^{18} 63) $2^2 \bullet 7^2$ 65) $2^3 \bullet 3^9$ 67) 3^4 69) 1   71) 1000   73) 1202

75) $\dfrac{1}{125}$ 77) -8 79) $\dfrac{64}{9}$ 81) $\dfrac{4}{81}$ 83) $\dfrac{1}{91,125}$ 85) $-\dfrac{1}{2}$ 87) $-\dfrac{1}{27}$

89) set up: 50^3; solution: 125,000 cubic nanometers

91) set up: $\left(50 \bullet 2^4\right)^3$; solution: 512,000,000 cubic nanometers

93) set up: $15 \bullet 2^5$; solution: 480 cows

95) $\left(3^2\right)^3$ 97) $\left(2^3\right)^2$ 99) $\left(x^2 + y\right)^5$ 101) True   103) False   105) True   107) True   109) $3^2 = 5 + 4$

111) $3^5 = 3^6 - 486$ or $486 = 3^6 - 3^5$ 113) $x^2 = z^2 + y^2$ 115) $-m = -p + n$ or $-n = -p + m$

4.4 Scientific Notation, Squares & Square Roots, and the Pythagorean Theorem

1) As a decimal, an irrational number: (1) does not terminate, and (2) does not repeat in a pattern

3) rational   5) rational   7) move the decimal point to the right   9) less than 10   11) one answer

13) yes   15) yes   17) no; $\underline{b}$ is different   19) no; $\underline{c}$ is different   21) no; $\underline{d}$ is different   23) 10^{-1}, 0.01, 0.001

25) $10^{1}, 10^{0}, 10^{-2}$ 27) $10, 1, \dfrac{1}{10}, 10^{-2}$ 29) $\dfrac{10}{1^{5}}, 1, \dfrac{1}{10^{2}}, 0.001$ 31) $\dfrac{10}{10^{-2}}, \left(10^{-2}\right)^{-1}, 10 \times 10^{-2}, \dfrac{1}{10^{2}}$

33) 2400   35) 40,000   37) 0.583   39) 0.006   41) 0.00082   43) 70   45) 1.8×10^{3} 47) 1.05×10^{4}

49) 8.4×10^{-1} 51) 4.05×10^{-3} 53) 1.5×10^{1} 55) 3×10^{0} 57) 6.25×10^{-7} 59) 7.205×10^{12}

61) 1×10^{-5} 63) 7×10^{4} 65) 1×10^{-5} 67) a) 3 and -3; b) 3   69) a) 13 and -13; b) 13

71) a) 30 and -30; b) 30   73) a) $\dfrac{5}{12}$ and $-\dfrac{5}{12}$; b) $\dfrac{5}{12}$ 75) a) no real number solution; b) no real number solution

77) a) $\dfrac{8}{3}$ and $-\dfrac{8}{3}$; b) $\dfrac{8}{3}$ 79) 5.2   81) 5.385   83) -2   85) 3   87) $\dfrac{1}{9}$ 89) $-\dfrac{7}{4}$ 91) 14   93) 1.367

95) set up: $186,000\,(60)\,(60)$; solution: 6.696×10^{8} miles and 669, 600, 000 miles

97) 30,900,000,000,000 kilometers

99) set up: $\dfrac{3.26 \text{ light years}}{4.3 \text{ light years}} = \dfrac{3.09 \times 10^{13} \text{ kilometers}}{x \text{ kilometers}}$ or $\left[\left(3.09 \times 10^{13}\right) \div 3.26\right] \bullet 4.3$;

solution: 4.076×10^{13} kilometers

101) Set up: $39.37 \bullet (0.000000001)$; Solution: 3.937×10^{-8} and 0.00000003937

103) set up: $7,900 \bullet (1.01)^{10}$ or $7,900 \times \left(\dfrac{101}{100}\right)^{10}$; solution: 8727 miles

105) set up: $7,900 \bullet (0.9)^{5}$ or $7,900 \times \left(\dfrac{9}{10}\right)^{5}$; solution: 4665 miles

107) set up: $(15)^{2} + (20)^{2} = c^{2}$; solution: 25 meters

109) set up: $(1)^{2} + \left(\dfrac{4}{3}\right)^{2} = c^{2}$; solution: $1\dfrac{2}{3}$ inches   111) set up: $(90)^{2} + (90)^{2} = c^{2}$; solution: 127 feet

Chapter 5: Geometry

5.1 Perimeter and Area of the Four Common Geometric Shapes

1) True 3) True 5) False 7) False 9) True

11) ⇐ the height   13) ⇐ the height   15)

17) the vertex opposite the base   19) circumference   21) radius   23) square units   25) 10 ft.

27) $3\frac{7}{8}$ meters 29) 10 sq. ft. 31) $\frac{7}{10}$ 33) $\frac{7 \text{ yards paved}}{3 \text{ yards unpaved}}$ 35) 35% 37) $51\frac{11}{18}$ 39) $61\frac{1}{3}$ 41) $70\frac{134}{259}$

43) 32 ft. 45) $24\frac{1}{2}$ m. 47) 32 in. 49) 22 m. 51) 36.424 ft. 53) $1\frac{5}{16}$ sq. in. 55) 49.5 sq. m.

57) 55.5 sq. in.   59) 154 sq. ft.   61) $254\frac{4}{7}$ sq. m.   63) a) 22 - 8 - 5 or 22 - (8 + 5); b) 9 in.

65) $20 \div 4$ or $\frac{1}{4} \cdot 20$; b) 5 meters   67) a) $30 \div 2$ or $\frac{1}{2} \cdot 30$; b) 15 ft.   69) $x \div 2$ or $\frac{1}{2} \cdot x$;

71) a) $6^2 + 8^2 = c^2$; b) 10 ft.   73) a) $\frac{80}{380}$ or $\frac{80}{2\,(110)\, +\, 2\,(80)}$; b) $\frac{4}{19}$

75) a) $\frac{80}{2\,(110)\, +\, 80}$; b) $\frac{4 \text{ ft. of red fence}}{15 \text{ ft. of white fence}}$

77) a) $\left(\frac{40}{600 + 40}\right) \cdot 100$ or $\frac{1}{16} \cdot 100$; b) 6.25% or $6\frac{1}{4}$%   79) a) $\frac{154}{616}$; b) $\frac{1}{4}$

81) a) $\frac{154}{616 - 154}$; b) $\frac{1 \text{ sq. ft. of 3 ft. depth}}{3 \text{ sq. ft. of 8 ft. depth}}$ 83) a) $\frac{20}{44} \cdot \frac{100}{1}$ or $\left(\frac{20}{2\,(12)\, +\, 20}\right) \cdot 100$; b) $45.\overline{45}$% or

$45\frac{5}{11}$%

85) a) $16 \div 9$; b) $1\frac{7}{9}$ sq. cm.   87) a) $(3600 \div 18) + 10\%\,(3600 \div 18)$; b) 220 rolls

89) a) $\frac{1}{5} \cdot 100.48$; b) 20 ft.   91) a) (240 - 200) (640) (2) or (240 - 40) (640) $\div \frac{1}{2}$; b) 51,200 homes

93) a) $\dfrac{\left(1 - \frac{3}{8}\right) 2,000,000}{43,560}$ (5) or $\dfrac{\frac{5}{8} \cdot 2,000,000}{43,560}$ (5); b) 143 homes.

5.2 Finding the Perimeters of Irregular Shapes

1) diameter   3) 27 meters   5) 44 inches   7) 5.625 feet   9) 22 cm.   11) b   13) c   15) a + e

17) $2(a) + 2(c)$ or $2(c) + a + (d - e)$ 19) $\frac{1}{2} \bullet \pi \bullet c$ or $\frac{\pi \bullet c}{2}$ or $\pi \bullet b$ 21) $\left(\frac{\pi \bullet c}{2}\right) + d + f + a$ or

$(\pi \bullet b) + d + f + a$

23) side 6   25) side 3   27) $s_2 + s_4$ 29) $s_6 - s_2$ 31) $P = \frac{\pi \bullet d}{2}$ 33) No   35) Yes   37) Yes   39) Yes

41) (a) $P = s_1 + s_2 + s_3 + s_4$; (b) $P = 8 + 4 + (8 + 3) + 5$; (c) $P = 28$ inches

43) (a) $P = 2(a) + 2(b)$; (b) $P = 2 (5.4) + 2 (6)$; (c) $P = 22.8$ meters

45) (a) $P = \frac{1}{2} \bullet \pi \bullet d$; (b) $P = \frac{1}{2} \bullet \frac{22}{7} \bullet \frac{7}{1}$; (c) $P = 11$ miles

47) (a) $P = \frac{1}{2} \bullet \pi \bullet d$; (b) $P = \frac{1}{2} \bullet \frac{22}{7} \bullet 3 \frac{1}{2}$; (c) $P = 5 \frac{1}{2}$ ft.

49) (a) $P = \left(\frac{1}{2} \bullet \pi \bullet d\right) + d$; (b) $P = \left(\frac{1}{2} \bullet \frac{22}{7} \bullet \frac{14}{1}\right) + 14$; (c) $P = 36$ cm.

51) (a) $P = \left(\frac{1}{2} \bullet \pi \bullet d\right) + d$; (b) $P = \left(\frac{1}{2} \bullet \frac{22}{7} \bullet 9 \frac{1}{3}\right) + 9 \frac{1}{3}$; (c) $P = 24$ inches

53) (a) $P = \left(\frac{1}{2} \bullet \pi \bullet d\right) + 2(l) + w$; (b) $P = \left(\frac{1}{2} \bullet \frac{22}{7} \bullet \frac{14}{1}\right) + 2(10) + 14$; (c) $P = 56$ ft.

55) (a) $P = 2\left(\frac{1}{2} \bullet \pi \bullet d\right) + 2(a)$; (b) $P = 2\left(\frac{1}{2} \bullet 3.14 \bullet 7.6\right) + 2(6.25)$; (c) $P = 36$ ft.

57) (a) $P = 2(a) + 2(b)$ or $P = a + b + c + d + e + f$;

(b) $P = 2 (8) + 2 (3 + 4)$ or $P = 8 + (3 + 4) + 5 + 4 + (8 - 5) + 3$;   (c) $P = 30$ ft.

59) (a) $P = 2 (s_1) + 2 (s_2)$ or $P = s_1 + s_2 + s_3 + s_4 + s_5 + s_6$; (b) $P = 2(6) + 2\left(1 \frac{2}{5} + 2 \frac{2}{3}\right)$ or

$P = 6 + 1 \frac{2}{5} + \left(6 - 4 \frac{1}{3}\right) + 2 \frac{2}{3} + 4 \frac{1}{3} + \left(1 \frac{2}{5} + 2 \frac{2}{3}\right)$;   (c) $P = 20 \frac{2}{15}$ inches

61) (a) $P = 2L + 2W$ (b) $P = 2(12.5 \div 2) + 2(6)$;   (c) $P = 24.5$ inches

63) (a) $P = S_1 + S_2 + S_3$ (b) $P = 8 + 5 + (8 - 3) + 4$;   (c) $P = 22$ ft.

65) (a) $P = \frac{1}{8} \bullet (\pi \bullet d) + r + r$ (b) $P = \left(\frac{1}{8} \bullet \frac{22}{7} \bullet \frac{16}{1}\right) + 2(8)$;   (c) $P = 22 \frac{2}{7}$ inches

67) (a) $P = \frac{1}{2} \bullet (\pi \bullet d) + S_1 + S_2 + S_3$ (b) $P = \left(\frac{1}{2} \bullet \frac{22}{7} \bullet \frac{14}{1}\right) + 18 \frac{2}{5} + 7.265 + 3.75$;

(c) $P = 51.415$ inches or $51 \frac{83}{200}$ inches

69) $2090   71) 94 ft.

5.3 Finding the Areas of Irregular Shapes

1) (a) $\dfrac{50}{50+80}$; (b) $\dfrac{5}{13}$ 3) (a) $\dfrac{50 \text{ acres of spinach}}{80 \text{ acres of broccoli}}$; (b) $\dfrac{5 \text{ acres of spinach}}{8 \text{ acres of broccoli}}$

5) (a) $\left[50\,(600) + 80\,(450)\right] \div (50+80)$; (b) \$507.69

7) 1 mile x 20 miles, 2 miles x 10 miles, and 4 miles x 5 miles

9) (a) $80,000 \div \left[20 - \left(\dfrac{1}{4} \cdot \dfrac{20}{1}\right)\right]$; (b) 5333 people

11) (a) $\left[80,000 + (0.2)\,(80,000)\right] \div \left[20\,(640)\right]$; (b) 7.5 people per acre   13) Yes   15) No   17) No

19) Yes   21) No   23) Yes   25) No   27) Yes   29) No   31) Yes   33) No   35) No   37) Yes

39) (a) $A = (s_1 \cdot s_2) + \left(\dfrac{1}{2} \cdot \pi \cdot r^2\right)$; (b) $A = (10 \cdot 7) + \left[\dfrac{1}{2} \cdot \dfrac{22}{7} \cdot \left(\dfrac{7}{2}\right)^2\right]$; (c) $A = 89\dfrac{1}{4}$ sq. ft.

41) (a) $A = (x \cdot y) + (2)\left(\dfrac{1}{2} \cdot \pi \cdot r^2\right)$ or $A = (x \cdot y) + \left(\pi \cdot r^2\right)$;

(b) $A = (22 \cdot 14) + (2)\left(\dfrac{1}{2} \cdot \dfrac{22}{7} \cdot (7)^2\right)$ or $A = (22 \cdot 14) + \left(\dfrac{22}{7} \cdot (7)^2\right)$; (c) $A = 462$ sq. meters

43) (a) $A = (s_1)^2 + 3\left(\dfrac{1}{2} \cdot \pi \cdot r^2\right)$; (b) $A = (4.3)^2 + 3\left[\dfrac{1}{2} \cdot 3.14 \cdot (2.15)^2\right]$; (c) $A = 40$ sq. inches

45) (a) $A = \dfrac{1}{2}\,(s_3 + s_1) \cdot s_2$; (b) $A = \dfrac{1}{2}\left(5 + 8\dfrac{3}{4}\right) \cdot 5$; (c) $A = 34\dfrac{3}{8}$ sq. inches

47) (a) $A = (r \cdot m) - (o \cdot p)$; (b) $A = \left[(0.0325) \cdot (0.04)\right] - \left[(0.019) \cdot (0.0325 - 0.0165)\right]$;
(c) $A = 0.000996$ sq. inches

49) Yes   51) Yes   53) No   55) No   57) Yes   59) No   61) No   63) Yes

65) (a) $A = \left[(l \cdot w) + \left(\dfrac{1}{2} \cdot \pi \cdot r^2\right)\right] - \left(\dfrac{1}{2} \cdot b \cdot h\right)$

(b) $A = \left[(15 \cdot 7) + \left(\dfrac{1}{2} \cdot \dfrac{22}{7} \cdot \left(3\dfrac{1}{2}\right)^2\right)\right] - \left(\dfrac{1}{2} \cdot \dfrac{8}{1} \cdot \dfrac{7}{1}\right)$; (c) $A = 96\dfrac{1}{4}$ sq. ft.

67) (a) $A = \left[\dfrac{1}{2} \cdot \pi \cdot r^2\right] - \left(\dfrac{1}{2} \cdot b \cdot h\right)$ (b) $A = \left[\dfrac{1}{2} \cdot 3.14 \cdot (6)^2\right] - \left(\dfrac{1}{2} \cdot \dfrac{12}{1} \cdot \dfrac{5}{1}\right)$; (c) $A = 26.52$ sq.ft.

69) (a) $A = (l \cdot w) + \left(\dfrac{1}{2} \cdot b \cdot h\right) - 5\,(s^2)$ (b) $A = (20 \cdot 12) + \left(\dfrac{1}{2} \cdot \dfrac{12}{1} \cdot \dfrac{8}{1}\right) - 5\,(2^2)$; (c) $A = 268$ sq.ft.

71) 82,916 sq. ft.   73) 50%   75) $93\dfrac{1}{2}$ sq. ft.   77) \$10.50 per sq. ft.   79) \$25,200   81) 192 acres

83) 448 acres   85) $58.\overline{3}\%$ 87) \$40,320   89) 10,920 sq. ft.

5.4 Finding Volumes of Three-Dimensional Shapes

1) $\frac{1}{3}$ 3) There are three dimensions, not two   5) rectangular box   7) Yes or True   9) No or False

11) 1 cub. ft.   13) 8 cub. ft.   15) $77\frac{11}{12}$ cub. ft.   17) 350 cub. meters   19) 211.2 cub. meters

21) $4957\frac{1}{3}$ cub. meters   23) $665\frac{1}{2}$ cub. yd.   25) 14,130 cub. in.   27) $381\frac{6}{7}$ cub. ft.

29) 256 cub. yd.   31) $3854.1\overline{6}$ cub. yd.   33) 158,400,000 cub. ft.   35) 3.5×10^{17} cub. miles

37) 115.5 cub. in.   39) 82,944,000 cub. ft.   41) 4.9×10^{17} and 490,000,000,000,000,000 viruses

43) 3.3 sharks per cub. mile   45) $25\frac{1}{7}$ cub. in.   47) 1.6 cub. in.   49) 3120 cub. in.

51) $33.49\overline{3}$ cub. in.   53) $334,933.\overline{3}$ cub. in. per acre   55) She would earn $27,380.80 more if she grew the giant cantaloupe.

Chapter 6: Algebraic Expressions

6.1 Algebraic Expressions: Monomials, Polynomials and Combining Like Terms

1) binomial   3) trinomial   5) none of these   7) monomial   9) True   11) True   13) True

15) the coefficient   17) two   19) one   21) coefficient: 3 variable(s): x degree: 4

23) coefficient: -8 variable(s): a degree: 1   25) coefficient: -7.6 variable(s): r degree: 1

27) coefficient: $\frac{2}{7}$ variable(s): a degree: 3   29) coefficient: $\frac{2}{3}$ variable(s): m degree: 1

31) coefficient: $-\frac{1}{6}$ variable(s): m degree: 1   33) coefficient: 11 variable(s): none degree: 0

35) coefficient: -1 variable(s): mn degree: 2   37) 3   39) 1   41) 8   43) like   45) like   47) unlike

49) unlike   51) unlike   53) unlike   55) 5y   57) -6m   59) $\frac{1}{2}$ rs or $\frac{rs}{2}$ 61) $4x - 3y$ 63) 0   65) 2y

67) x   69) $-4m^2 - 3$ 71) $-6x - \frac{1}{3}y$ or $-6x - \frac{y}{3}$ 73) $2xy^2 - 4x - 2$ 75) $3m^2 - 3m$ 77) $5ab + 2$

79) $2x + 2y$ 81) $-2x + 6$ 83) $5x^2y - 7x - 1$ 85) $-3r^2 - 5r + 2$ 87) $-5xy - 7$ 89) $7r^2s^2$ 91) $4x - 8$

93) $-2m$ 95) $2x^3y - 3x^2 + 1$ 97) $2m^2 - 5m + n^2 - n - 4$ 99) $8r^2 - 4r - 7$

101) a) translation: $(3x - 8) + (-3x + 8)$; b) 0   103) a) translation: $(-4a + 7) - (8a - 4)$; b) $-12a + 11$

105) translation: $(2ab - 2a - b) - (5ab + 3a - 2b)$; b) $-3ab - 5a + b$

107) translation: $(-r^2 + 1) - (-3r^2 + 2)$; b) $2r^2 - 1$

6.2 Simplifying Algebraic Expressions Involving Multiplication & Division

1) multiplication   3) two   5) be in the denominator   7) be in the numerator

9) be in the denominator   11) be in the numerator   13) be in the numerator   15) be gone

17) yes   19) no; c is different   21) $8a^3$ 23) $5r^3s^3$ 25) $-28x^2y^2z$ 27) $-m^2n$

29) $-12x^3y$ 31) $\frac{3}{16}r^3s$ or $\frac{3r^3s}{16}$ 33) $\frac{7}{6}y^3$ or $\frac{7y^3}{6}$ 35) $-12x^3yz$ 37) $8x - 20$

39) $-30a^2b - 30a$ 41) $-6x^3 + 9x^2 - 15x$ 43) $-8x^4y - 4x^3y^2 + 2x^2y$ 45) $2x^2 - xy + x$

45) $2x^2 - xy + x$ 47) $6m^2n - 3mn^2$ 49) $3xy$ 51) $-\frac{a^2}{3b^3c}$ 53) $\frac{3y^2z^2}{2x^3}$ 55) $\frac{r^2}{10s^5}$

57) $-\frac{a^4b}{4}$ 59) $-\frac{x^9z^4}{2y}$ 61) $3x + 1$ 63) $6x - 4$ 65) $6m$ 67) $8m^2 - 4m - 16$

69) a) translation: $3m(-2mn + 3)$; b) $-6m^2n + 9m$ 71) a) translation: $\frac{10x^3y}{4xy^2}$; b) $\frac{5x^2}{2y}$

73) a) translation: $7m(-8m^2 - 3m + 2)$; b) $-56m^3 - 21m^2 + 14m$

6.3 Terms Raised to a Power to a Power and Simplifying More Complex Algebraic Expressions

1) power to a power   3) division of same bases   5) eliminating the negative exponent

7) multiplication of same bases   9) yes   11) no; d is different   13) yes   15) no; d is different

17) yes   19) no; c is different   21) $16x^{12}y^4$ 23) $-125m^6n^3$ 25) $\frac{8}{27}r^3s^6$ or $\frac{8r^3s^6}{27}$

27) $\frac{y^6}{x^4}$ 29) $\frac{32}{m^{10}n^{15}}$ 31) $\frac{9x^6}{16y^4}$ 33) $7x^2 - 11x + 4$ 35) $-18a^2b - 16ab - 12a$

37) $20m^4 + 22m^2 - 10m$ 39) $11x^4y - 9x^3y^2$ 41) $-2x^2 - x + 3y$ 43) $2r^3 - \frac{11}{15}r^2$

45) $36a^5b^5$ 47) $\frac{3}{2}x^4y^2$ or $\frac{3x^4y^2}{2}$ 49) $6m^2$ 51) $-10r^2 - 2rs^2 + s^2$ 53) $\frac{4}{5}s^2 - \frac{4rs^2}{5}$

55) $6x^3 - 6x^2 - 3x$ 57) $28.26m^2$ 59) $-27m^6n^3$ 61) $\frac{99x^3}{7}$ or $\frac{99}{7}x^3$

6.4 Factoring and Evaluating Polynomials

1) two   3) two   5) zero   7) s   9) xy   11) None   13) yes   15) yes

17) No; d is different   19) $2^3 \cdot 5$ 21) $2^2 \cdot 3 \cdot 7$ 23) $3 \cdot 23$

25) prime   27) 6   29) 15   31) x^2y 33) mno   35) 2x   37) 7   39) $-2b^2$ 41) -1 43) 5xz   45) -1

47) $4(2x + y)$ 49) $m(5mn - 7)$ 51) $10ab(a^2c - 2)$ 53) $-21xyz(3y^2z + 1)$ 55) $x^2y(3y^2 + 1)$

57) $7a^2b^3(-1 + 3ab)$ 59) $x(13xyz - 3y - 7z)$ 61) $5(m^2 - mn - 2)$ 63) $-3xy(x^2 + 3xy + y)$

65) $3mo(4n^2 + n^2o - 5)$ 67) 5xy   69) $5rt^2$ 71) $-50yz$ 73) $5a^2b^3c^6$ 75) False   77) True   79) True

81) 2   83) -3 85) -120 87) -22 89) -4 91) -10 93) 4   95) 18   97) 18   99) 1

Chapter 7: Algebraic Equations

7.1 Solving Linear Equations that have Variables on One Side of the Equation

1) Do the opposite operation   3) subtract 5   5) divide by 7   7) subtract 10   9) add 2

11) multiply by -6   13) divide by 8   15) multiply by $-\frac{3}{2}$ or divide by $-\frac{2}{3}$ 17) one   19) one

21) two   23) two   25) $x = 3$ 27) $a = -17$ 29) $x = -\frac{3}{20}$ 31) $y = 9.9$ 33) $x = 5$ 35) $a = 7$

37) $m = -150$ 39) $y = 64$ 41) $x = 4$ 43) $x = -2$ 45) $x = -2$ 47) $x = 9$ 49) $n = \frac{1}{16}$ 51) $x = 6$

53) $y = -9$ 55) $x = 6$ 57) $a = 196$ 59) $x = 36$ 61) $m = -16$ 63) $x = 0$ 65) $r = -\frac{7}{3}$ or $-2\frac{1}{3}$

67) $x = \frac{3}{17}$ 69) $a = 0$ 71) $x = 3$ 73) $m = -1$ 75) $x = -4$ 77) $x = 2$ 79) $x = -\frac{13}{6}$ or $-2\frac{1}{6}$

81) $m = \frac{3}{10}$ 83) $n = -16$ 85) $x = 20$ 87) $a = 7$ 89) $x = -\frac{6}{5}$ or $-1\frac{1}{5}$

7.2 Solving More Linear Equations: Variables on Both Sides of the Equation and Eliminating Fractions and Decimals

1) $x = 3$ 3) no solution   5) $m = 0$ 7) $r = 0$ 9) No   11) Yes   13) $x = -1$ 15) $m = -5$ 17) $a = 4$

19) $x = -5$ 21) $r = 1$ 23) $m = 1$ 25) $x = -4$ 27) $x = 2$ 29) $m = -5$ 31) $a = 0$ 33) $x = 6$

35) $x = -15$ 37) $a = 3$ 39) $w = \frac{3}{2}$ or $1\frac{1}{2}$ 41) $n = 2$ 43) no solution   45) $y = -2$ 47) $x = 3$

49) $m = -9$ 51) $m = 0$ 53) $x = -4$ 55) $m = -6$ 57) $x = \frac{232}{5}$ or $46\frac{2}{5}$ 59) $r = \frac{16}{5}$ or $3\frac{1}{5}$

61) $x = 1$ 63) $x = 1$ 65) $r = \frac{1}{10}$ 67) $x = 7$ 69) $a = 130$ 71) $x = 5$ 73) $x = 30$ 75) $x = -2$

77) $m = 2$ 79) $x = 0$ 81) (a) $(x + 6) = 3x + x$; (b) $x = 2$ 83) (a) $5(x + 1) = \frac{1}{2} \cdot 2x \cdot 6$; (b) $x = 5$

7.3 Solving Percent Equations and Geometric Equations

1) (a) 0.08 (b) $\frac{2}{25}$ 3) (a) 0.0875 (b) $\frac{7}{80}$ 5) (a) 0.0775 (b) $\frac{31}{400}$ 7) (a) 1 (b) 1

9) (a) $x + 5 = -2$ (b) $x = -7$ 11) (a) $3x - 2 = 31$ (b) $x = 11$ 13) (a) $\frac{2}{3}x = 18$ (b) $x = 27$

15) (a) $2x + 4 = 16$ (b) $x = 6$ 17) (a) $8 - x = -4$ (b) $x = 12$ 19) (a) $2x = x + 6$ (b) $x = 6$

21) $0.20x$ 23) $(0.4)(30)$ 25) $0.01x$ or $\frac{1}{100}x$ 27) $(0.3)(70) = x$ 29) $0.25x = 11$ 31) $0.12x = 8$

33) Yes   35) No; b is different   37) Yes   39) Yes   41) No; d is different   43) Yes

45) whole quantity   47) percent   49) part quantity   51) whole quantity   53) part quantity

55) (a) $4 = 0.3x$ (b) $13.\overline{3}$ or $13\frac{1}{3}$ 57) (a) $(0.07)(40) = x$ (b) 2.8   59) (a) $20 = 1.6x$ (b) 12.5%

61) (a) $(0.12)(70) = x$ (b) 8.4   63) (a) $0.08x = 10$ (b) 125   65) (a) $\frac{7}{8} = 0.01x$ or $\frac{7}{8} = \frac{1}{100}x$

or $7 = 0.08x$ (b) 87.5%   67) \$68 69) 53%   71) 48 points 73) \$1904.76   75) 17%   77) 6%

79) (a) $26 = 2(7.5) + 2w$ (b) width = 5.5 meters   81) (a) $56 = \frac{1}{2} \cdot 14 \cdot h$ (b) height = 8″

83) (a) $33 = \frac{22}{7}d$ or $33 = 2 \cdot \frac{22}{7} \cdot r$ (b) radius = $5\frac{1}{4}$ yards   85) (a) $60 = (x+2)(5)$ (b) length = 12″

87) (a) $25 = (x) + (x+2) + (x-1)$ (b) $s_1 = 8″;\ s_2 = 10″;\ s_3 = 7″$

89) (a) $80 = 2(x+8) + 2x$ (b) width = 16″; length = 24″

Appendix A

1) 0.15   3) 85%   5) 0.03   7) 67.5%   9) 200%   11) 0.004 13) $\frac{39}{100}$ 15) 80%   17) $\frac{3}{20}$

19) 75%   21) 1   23) 125%   25) $\frac{11}{200}$ 27) 37.5% or $37\frac{1}{2}$%   29) $8.\overline{3}$% or $8\frac{1}{3}$%   31) $\frac{1}{12}$

33) $\frac{9}{8}$ or $1\frac{1}{8}$ 35) $133.\overline{3}$% or $133\frac{1}{3}$%   37) Yes   39) Yes   41) No: $\underline{b}$ is different

43) No; $\underline{c}$ is different 45) Yes 47) Yes   49) (a) $\frac{1}{500}$ (b) 0.002   51) (a) $\frac{13}{500}$ (b) 0.026

53) (a) $\frac{1}{16}$ (b) 0.0625   55) (a) $\frac{31}{400}$ (b) 0.0775   57) (a) $145\frac{1}{2}$% (b) 145.5%

59) (a) $66\frac{2}{3}$% (b) $66.\overline{6}$%   61) (a) $\frac{3}{200}$% (b) 0.015%   63) (a) $4\frac{6}{11}$% (b) $4.\overline{54}$%

65) (a) $233\frac{1}{3}$% (b) $233.\overline{3}$%   67) (a) $25\frac{1}{3}$% (b) $25.\overline{3}$%   69) $\frac{1}{2}$, 53%, 0.531   71) $\frac{1}{20}$, 0.052, 5.5%

73) $\frac{7}{21}$, 35%, 3.5   75) $\frac{4}{9}$, $\frac{7}{15}$, 60%, $\frac{2}{3}$ 77) 1, 101%, 1.1, $\frac{6}{5}$ 79) 24   81) 72   83) 130   85) 270

87) 11.1   89) 0   91) (a) $12 + 15\%(12)$ (b) \$13.80 per hour   93) (a) $250 + 3\%(4000)$ (b) \$370

95) (a) $38{,}000 - 32\%(38{,}000)$ (b) \$25,840   97) $\frac{3}{5}$ of \$275   99) the second prize

101) the second option

Index

Formulas for Common Geometric Shapes & Solids

Perimeter

Square	$P = 4(s)$	where: s = length of one side
Rectangle	$P = 2(L) + 2(W)$	where: L = length W = width
Triangle	$P = S_1 + S_2 + S_3$	where: S_1 = length of side 1 S_2 = length of side 2 S_3 = length of side 3
Circle	$C = \pi \cdot d$ or $C = 2 \cdot \pi \cdot r$	where: π = 22/7 or 3.14 d = diameter of the circle where: π = 22/7 or 3.14 r = radius of the circle

Area

Square	$A = s^2$	where: s = length of one side
Rectangle	$A = L \cdot W$	where: L = length W = width
Triangle	$A = \frac{1}{2} \cdot b \cdot h$	where: b = base of the triangle h = altitude or height
Circle	$A = \pi \cdot r^2$ or $A = \pi \cdot d^2 / 4$	where: π = 22/7 or 3.14 r = radius of the circle where: π = 22/7 or 3.14 d = diameter of the circle

Area / continued

Parallelogram		
	$A = b \cdot h$	where: b = base of the figure h = altitude or height

Trapezoid		
	$A = \frac{1}{2}(b_1 + b_2) \cdot h$	where: b_1 = base 1 of figure (parallel to b_2) b_2 = base 2 of figure (parallel to b_1) h = height (distance between bases)

Volume

Cube		
	$V = s^3$	where: s = length of one side

Rectangular Box		
	$V = l \cdot w \cdot d$	where: l = length w = width d = depth

Cylinder		
	$V = \pi \cdot r^2 \cdot h$	where: π = 22/7 or 3.14 r = radius of the circle h = height

Sphere		
	$V = \frac{4}{3} \cdot \pi \cdot r^3$	where: π = 22/7 or 3.14 r = radius of the sphere

Cone		
	$V = \frac{1}{3} \cdot \pi \cdot r^2 \cdot h$	where: π = 22/7 or 3.14 r = radius of the circle h = height of cone

Pyramid		
	$V = \frac{1}{3} \cdot B \cdot h$	where: B = area of the base h = height of pyramid

Triangular Prism		
	$V = B \cdot h$	where: B = area of the triangular base h = height of prism